Replacement copy
1/2/72

THE CRYSTALLINE STATE

VOL. III

THE DETERMINATION
OF CRYSTAL STRUCTURES

THE CRYSTALLINE STATE

Vol. I. (A General Survey). By Sir Lawrence Bragg, O.B.E., D.SC., F.R.S.

Vol. II. The Optical Principles of the Diffraction of X-Rays. By R. W. James, F.R.S.

Vol. III. The Determination of Crystal Structures. By H. Lipson, D.SC., F.R.S. and W. Cochran, PH.D., F.R.S.

Vol. IV. Crystal Structures of Minerals. By Sir Lawrence Bragg and G. F. Claringbull, PH.D., F.G.S.

LONDON: G. BELL AND SONS LTD

THE CRYSTALLINE STATE. VOL. III

Editor: SIR LAWRENCE BRAGG

THE DETERMINATION OF CRYSTAL STRUCTURES

By

H. LIPSON

D.Sc., M.A., F.Inst.P., F.R.S.

PROFESSOR OF PHYSICS, UNIVERSITY OF MANCHESTER INSTITUTE OF SCIENCE AND TECHNOLOGY

and

W. COCHRAN

M.A., Ph.D., F.R.S.

PROFESSOR OF PHYSICS IN THE UNIVERSITY OF EDINBURGH

REVISED AND ENLARGED EDITION

LONDON

G. BELL AND SONS LTD

1968

G. BELL AND SONS LTD
Portugal St. London, WC 2

First published 1953
Second edition 1957
Third, revised and enlarged, edition 1966
Reprinted 1968

PRINTED IN GREAT BRITAIN BY ROBERT MACLEHOSE AND CO. LTD
THE UNIVERSITY PRESS, GLASGOW

PREFACE

The scope of this book is quite simply defined; we have tried to cover the subject of crystal-structure determination from the stage at which a set of structure amplitudes has been obtained to the final accurate positioning of the atoms. Some of the steps—such as the calculation of structure factors and the summation of Fourier series—are routine ones, and are described first; Chapters 6–10 are then concerned with the more difficult problems of the derivation of atomic positions, and in these chapters we have attempted to preserve some degree of logical order in the treatment. Nevertheless, we have emphasized throughout the book that each problem requires individual treatment, and that no single sequence of methods is likely to prove universally successful.

Two main classes of reader have been kept in mind—the beginner who has to find his way through the various procedures that he is expected to carry out, and the more advanced worker who wishes to have a resumé of the possible approaches to his own problem. To assist both these classes of reader, we have, throughout the book, adopted the principle of giving practical examples of the processes described; often these examples consist of a simple one designed to bring out the essential points and a more complicated one from an actual research project. In this way, we hope that we have preserved a sense of reality in the subjects treated.

It has been found necessary to give a considerable number of cross references in the book, and in order to make these as straightforward as possible, some departures from normal practice have been introduced. In addition to the decimal classification of sections, all figures, tables and equations bear the number of the page on which they appear, so that, for example, equation 10.3 is the third equation on page 10 and fig. 25 (ii) is the second figure on page 25 (figures appearing as half-tone illustrations on Plates bear the number of the page which the Plate faces). The author index and bibliography are combined, so that the page on which a particular reference occurs can easily be found. Finally space groups are designated by their numbers in the 1952 International Tables together with their Hermann-Mauguin symbols. It is hoped that this will become standard practice.

We wish to acknowledge the help and advice we have received from many of our friends and colleagues. Professor Sir Lawrence Bragg, the editor of this series, has spent a great deal of effort and time in moulding the book into shape, and his patience and wisdom have left their mark on most of the contents. Professor Kathleen Lonsdale and Dr. Dorothy Hodgkin have also given us considerable advice, and Dr. C. A. Taylor has been extremely helpful in checking manuscripts and proofs. Finally, we wish to record our gratitude to our first mentor in this most fascinating subject—Dr. C. A. Beevers.

The acknowledgments would not be complete without reference to the helpful co-operation of the publishers, and particularly of Mr. A. W. Ready, who discussed with us so patiently some of our more unorthodox ideas.

H.L.
W.C.

June 1953

PREFACE TO THIRD EDITION

The subject of crystal-structure analysis has changed extensively since the publication of the first edition in 1953. At that time it was possible to give a fairly complete account of the subject within a single volume; since then books and monographs have appeared on a variety of special topics in crystal-structure analysis and we cannot hope to deal with everything in the same detail here. In revising the book therefore we have aimed at giving what must now be considered to be an introductory account of the subject, although it contains considerably more material than did the previous editions. We have kept the initial chapters more-or-less the same, but with extended accounts of the use of intensity statistics and direct methods (kindly written for us by Dr. Hargreaves and Professor Woolfson respectively). We think that students should still verify for themselves that calculations of structure factors and Fourier syntheses can be done by hand and head, even if ultimately they use a computer.

The computer has of course been the biggest single factor in revolutionizing the subject; without it the determination of structures such as vitamin B_{12} and haemoglobin would still be as distant as they seemed to be when we were writing the first edition. We have thought carefully about our policy with respect to the computer and have decided that any attempt to deal adequately with it here is out of the question; although crystallographers must know how to get their computing done, they must learn from special courses and by practical experience. We have therefore deliberately omitted any detailed description of computer methods and techniques.

The disappearance of the appendices is also deliberate. Users of the book have told us that the appendices were not of great use since the information is given in greater detail in the International Tables for X-ray Crystallography.

We are grateful to those people—too numerous to mention here—who have helped us with constructive and destructive criticism. Both types are necessary if the book is to be kept up-to-date and is to continue to perform a useful function.

H.L.
W.C.

September 1965

CONTENTS

ACKNOWLEDGEMENTS

The authors wish to acknowledge with thanks permission to reproduce diagrams from the following journals:

Acta Crystallographica (figs. 63 i, 63 ii, 75, 106, 108 ii, 108 iii, 115, 122, 127, 130, 135 i, 135 ii, 173, 174, 177 i, 177 ii, 191, 232, 246, 283, 285, 287, 288 i, 290, 291 i, 291 ii, 291 iii, 294a, 334, 338 i, 338 ii).
Comptes rendus (figs. 179, 180, 181).
Journal and Proceedings of the Royal Society of New South Wales (fig. 365 ii).
Journal de Physique (figs. 374a, 374b).
Journal of the American Chemical Society (figs. 184, 185, 187 i).
Journal of Applied Physics (fig. 376).
Journal of Chemical Physics (fig. 176).
Journal of the Chemical Society (figs. 136, 205).
Journal of Physical Chemistry (fig. 176).
Nature (figs. 108 i, 108 iv, 215).
Philosophical Magazine (fig. 210).
Physical Review (fig. 360).
Proceedings of the Physical Society (fig. 282).
Proceedings of the Royal Society (figs. 104, 171 i, 206, 207, 211, 227, 228, 229, 277, 366, 369, 372).
Research (fig. 128).
Zeitshrift fur Kristallographie (figs. 73, 77, 78, 79 i, 79 ii, 80, 124, 171 ii, 313a, 313b, 315 iia, 315 iib).
Zeitshrift fur Physicalische Chemie (fig. 331).

Acknowledgement to the authors is made in the figure legends or in the nearby text.

Thanks are similarly due to the following publishers and authors:

The Clarendon Press for permission to reproduce figs. 113 and 294 i from *Chemical Crystallography* by C. W. Bunn.
Messrs. Macmillan and Co. Ltd for permission to reproduce fig. 8 from *The Interpretation of X-Ray Diffraction Photographs* by N. F. M. Henry, H. Lipson and W. A. Wooster, and figs. 118 i and 118 ii from *Crystals and Practical Crystal Measurement* by A. E. H. Tutton.
The Pergamon Press for permission to reproduce fig. 377 from *Structure Analysis by Electron Diffraction* by B. K. Vainshtein, and figs. 203, 204, 223, 226, 391 from *Computing Methods* edited by Pepinsky, Robertson and Speakman.
The Princeton University Press for permission to reproduce figs. 137a, 137b, 199, 217 from *The X-Ray Crystallographic Investigation of the Structure of Penicillin* by D. Crowfoot, C. W. Bunn, B. W. Rogers-Low and A. Turner-Jones.
Friedr. Vieweg & Sohn Verlag, for permission to reproduce fig. 364 from *Advances in Structure Research by Diffraction Methods*, 1.
John Wiley & Sons, Ltd, for permission to reproduce fig. 379 from *Advances in Structure Research by Diffraction Methods*, 1.

CHAPTER 1

X-RAY OPTICS

1. Introduction

The principles used in the determination of crystal structures are essentially those of physical optics. The complexity of the various formulae that arise may tend to disguise this fact, but this complexity occurs only because interest has shifted from the study of objects of known structure, such as diffraction gratings, to that of objects of unknown structure, such as crystals. If we wished to know the structure of a diffraction grating in as much detail as we wish to know the structure of a crystal, most of the problems in crystal-structure determination would appear; the only complications missing would be those due to the three-dimensional nature of crystals.

The importance of a proper appreciation of these optical principles has been emphasized by the devotion of Volume II of this series to the subject; the fundamental equations of X-ray crystallography have been derived in this volume and definitions of all the important concepts have been given. In order that this present volume shall be complete in itself, it is proposed to give an outline of the theory in this chapter also, although for the more complete statement the reader is referred to Volume II.

The general aim of this chapter is the derivation of the fundamental relationships between X-ray diffraction patterns and atomic arrangements. Several approaches are used. The first—the most common one—is based upon the lattice of a crystal, the dimensions of this lattice deciding completely the conditions necessary for the production of diffracted beams; these conditions can be expressed either as Bragg's law, or, more generally, in terms of the reciprocal lattice.

These concepts, however, give no information about the intensity scattered in any one diffracted beam, as this depends upon the atomic arrangement. The theory must be modified for two reasons: first, atoms have finite sizes and also, because of their heat motion, are displaced, at any one instant, from their mean positions in the crystal; and secondly, in practically all crystals the atomic centres do not lie upon one set of lattice points. The former effect can be allowed for, leaving the latter as the particular interest of this book; the results are expressed as the structure-factor equation, which gives that factor in the expression for the intensity of a diffracted beam which depends upon the positions of the atomic centres.

The second approach is a modification of the first. A crystal is considered as a continuous distribution of electron density, reaching maxima at the atomic centres and falling off asymptotically to zero in the space between atoms. This distribution is triply periodic since it repeats in each unit cell, and we shall show that its Fourier components are the structure factors of the various orders of diffraction.

This approach has made possible the determination of structures with unit cells containing large numbers of atoms. It is not, however, self-sufficient because the structure factors cannot be observed experimentally; the phases of the scattered beams are involved, but knowledge of these phases is lost in the process of recording the intensities. To state the difficulty mathematically, we may regard each structure factor as a complex quantity of which we are able to observe only the amplitude. This quantity is called the structure amplitude.

The third approach makes use only of these structure amplitudes. If a Fourier series is summed with the squares of the structure amplitudes as coefficients, the function obtained is related in a simple way to the electron density. This function—the Patterson function—can therefore be used as an aid to structure determination, but unfortunately its relation to the electron density, while simple in principle, in practice becomes excessively complicated when the number of atoms in the unit cell is large; no complete success in interpreting the Patterson function of a crystal can therefore be guaranteed.

The final approach is radically different from the others; instead of considering first the periodicity of the crystal and then inserting real atoms, we consider the scattering by a group of atoms and introduce the periodicity by placing other groups of atoms periodically separated from the first. The function representing the amplitude and phase of the radiation scattered by a group of atoms in a particular direction is the Fourier transform of the group. The addition of other periodically arranged groups of atoms causes the transform to be observed only at the points of the reciprocal lattice.

The value of this approach is that it allows use to be made of knowledge of relative atomic positions in a molecule, even if the positions of the atoms in the unit cell are unknown. The Fourier transform of the molecule can be evaluated, and the orientation of the molecule in the unit cell can, in principle, be determined by orienting the transform with respect to the reciprocal lattice until a fit with the observed structure amplitudes is obtained.

The chapter concludes with a discussion of the relation between X-ray and light diffraction. This is included in order to emphasize the optical principles mentioned in the opening paragraph of this section; while these principles have been fully stated in the approaches already discussed, the optical approach may cause them to be more readily appreciated. In addition, it has played some part in suggesting new methods of determining crystal structures, and may well play a still larger part in the future.

2. Diffraction by a Crystal

2.1 *X-ray diffraction by a lattice of electrons.* Crystals are composed of groups of atoms repeated at regular intervals, with the same orientation, in three dimensions. For certain purposes it is sufficient to regard each group of atoms as replaced by a representative point, and the collection of points so formed is the *space lattice* or *lattice* of the crystal (Volume I, p. 3). The word 'lattice' thus has a very definite meaning and should not be used in any other way; in particular, it should not be used to signify the complete atomic arrangement.

The lattice is important because it provides a basis for the theory of X-ray diffraction by the complete crystal: in the same way as the angles of diffraction produced by a diffraction grating depend only upon the spacing, so the angles of diffraction produced by a crystal depend only upon the dimensions of the lattice; the finer details of construction are not involved.

In order to invest the lattice with the power to diffract X-rays it is necessary to give it some material existence. We shall therefore assume that each lattice point is the site of an electron. Then the positions of the electrons can be specified by the ends of vectors $\mathbf{r}$ such that

$$\mathbf{r} = u\mathbf{a} + v\mathbf{b} + w\mathbf{c} \tag{3}$$

where $\mathbf{a}$, $\mathbf{b}$ and $\mathbf{c}$ are the primitive translations of the lattice (the *lattice constants* or *lattice parameters*) and u, v and w are integers.

Consider a parallel beam of X-rays of wave-length λ falling on the lattice in a direction defined by the vector $\mathbf{s}_0$; in Volume II $\mathbf{s}_0$ is taken

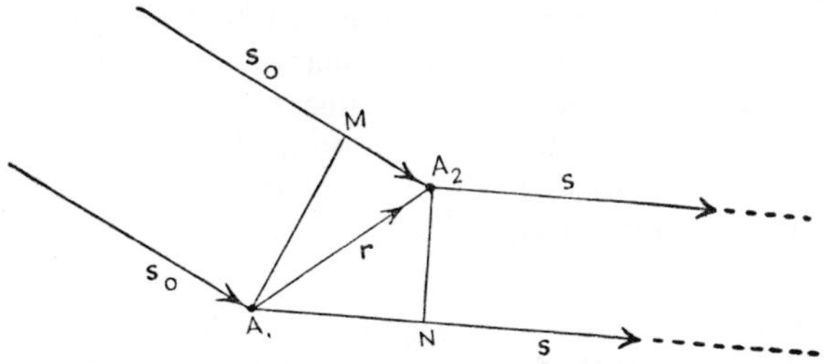

Fig. 3. Scattering from two lattice point; $\mathbf{s}$ is not necessarily in the same plane as $\mathbf{s}_0$ and $\mathbf{r}$

to be a unit vector, but some simplicity results if the magnitude of $\mathbf{s}_0$ is taken as $1/\lambda$. The electrons are set into vibration and so act as sources of secondary radiation, and in order to find the total effect of the combination of these secondary waves it is necessary to consider the phase differences between the waves scattered in any particular direction.

Suppose we choose a direction defined by the vector $\mathbf{s}$ which also has modulus $1/\lambda$. Let A_1 and A_2 (fig. 3) be two lattice points separated by a vector distance **r**, A_1M and A_2N being lines drawn in an incident and diffracted wave front respectively. Then the path difference between the two scattered waves is

$$A_1N - A_2M = \lambda(\mathbf{r}\cdot\mathbf{s} - \mathbf{r}\cdot\mathbf{s}_0)$$
$$= \lambda\mathbf{r}\cdot\mathbf{S} \qquad (4.1)$$

where $\mathbf{S} = \mathbf{s} - \mathbf{s}_0.$

S is called the scattering vector.

In order that the waves scattered by A_1 and A_2 shall be in phase, this path difference should be equal to a whole number of waves, and thus $\mathbf{r}\cdot\mathbf{S}$ must be equal to an integral number.

Thus $$(u\mathbf{a} + v\mathbf{b} + w\mathbf{c})\cdot\mathbf{S} = \text{integer}.$$

Since this equation must be true when u, v and w change by integral values, it follows that each of the products separately must be integral; that is, since u, v and w are already integral,

$$\left.\begin{aligned}\mathbf{a}\cdot\mathbf{S} &= h\\ \mathbf{b}\cdot\mathbf{S} &= k\\ \mathbf{c}\cdot\mathbf{S} &= l\end{aligned}\right\} \qquad (4.2)$$

where h, k and l are integers. These equations are known as Laue's equations.

When Laue's equations are simultaneously satisfied, a diffracted beam of maximum intensity will be produced. The numbers h, k and l specify the 'order' of diffraction, in the same way that single numbers specify the orders of diffraction from a one-dimensional grating.

The mathematical form of Laue's equations made them unsuitable at first for the interpretation of experimental results, and it was not until W. L. Bragg (1913) placed them on a physical basis that it was possible to make use of them, both to interpret X-ray spectra and to determine the structure of crystals.

2.2 *Bragg's Law.* Essentially, Bragg's contribution was to identify the integers h, k and l with the Miller indices (Volume I, p. 7) of the lattice planes. He was then able to reduce the problem to a one-dimensional one, and the method of attack so derived proved to be extremely fruitful. Its importance cannot be over-estimated, but as more difficult problems of crystal-structure determination have arisen, methods have had to become more general, and it is probably true to say that we are now back in the stage of direct use of Laue's equations. But whether this stage would have been reached had it not been for Bragg's equation is doubtful.

The connexion between Bragg's law and Laue's equations is brought out by rewriting the latter in the following form:

$$\frac{\mathbf{a}}{h}\cdot\mathbf{S}=1,$$

$$\frac{\mathbf{b}}{k}\cdot\mathbf{S}=1,$$

$$\frac{\mathbf{c}}{l}\cdot\mathbf{S}=1.$$

Subtraction of the first two equations gives

$$\left(\frac{\mathbf{a}}{h}-\frac{\mathbf{b}}{k}\right)\cdot\mathbf{S}=0,$$

which means that the vector **S** is perpendicular to the vector $\mathbf{a}/h-\mathbf{b}/k$. From fig. 5 (*a*) it can be seen that the latter is in the plane of Miller

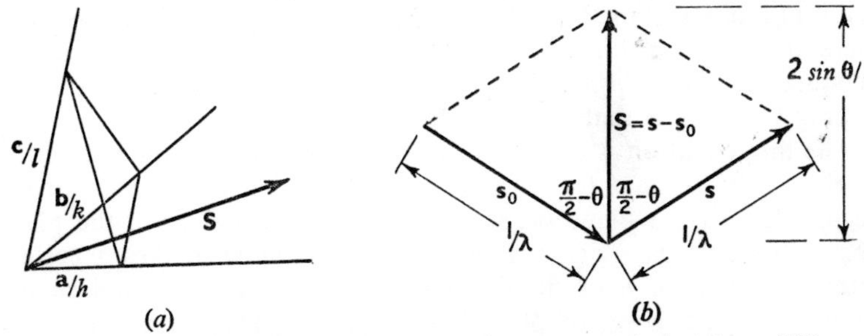

FIG. 5. (*a*) Relationship between the vector **S** and the plane (*hkl*). (*b*) Relationship between the vectors $\mathbf{s}_0$, **s**, and **S**

indices *hkl*. Similarly, it can be shown that **S** is perpendicular to the vector $\mathbf{a}/h-\mathbf{c}/l$, which is also a vector in the plane *hkl*. Thus **S** is perpendicular to this plane. But **S** is a vector in the direction of the bisector of the incident and diffracted beam, since the moduli of **s** and $\mathbf{s}_0$ are equal (fig. 5 (*b*)); thus this bisector is identified with the normal to the *hkl* plane—the first step in the proof of Bragg's law and the justification for the concept of each diffraction as a 'reflexion' of the rays from lattice planes.

To make the law quantitative we have to introduce the spacing *d* of the planes *hkl*; this is the perpendicular distance of the plane from the origin (fig. 5 (*a*)) and is the projection of $\mathbf{a}/h$, $\mathbf{b}/k$ or $\mathbf{c}/l$ on the vector **S**; that is

$$d=\frac{\frac{\mathbf{a}}{h}\cdot\mathbf{S}}{|\mathbf{S}|}$$

But $\frac{\mathbf{a}}{h}\cdot\mathbf{S}=1$ (equ. *4.2*) and $|\mathbf{S}|=\frac{2\sin\theta}{\lambda}$ (fig. 5 (*b*)).

Thus $$d = \lambda/2 \sin \theta$$
or $$\lambda = 2d \sin \theta. \qquad (6)$$

The quantity n that usually appears in Bragg's equation is now absorbed in the integers hkl. Indices of diffraction, unlike Miller indices of planes, can have a common factor; if n is this common factor the spacing corresponding to indices nh, nk, nl is regarded as $1/n$th of the spacing corresponding to indices hkl.

If it is thought that this proof of Bragg's law is rather tortuous it must be pointed out that the present chapter is not directed towards this proof but towards the formulae that are to be used in later chapters. Moreover, many of the so-called proofs of Bragg's law are deceptively simple and lack the completeness of the proof given by Bragg himself (Volume I, p. 13).

2.3. *Reciprocal lattice.* Bragg's equation may be regarded as the result of a physical method of solving Laue's equations. Mathematical methods lead to a different form of solution, and this is most neatly expressed by the *reciprocal lattice.* These methods are directed towards finding values of S that are solutions of the equations.

The first equation is equivalent to the statement that the projection of S on **a** is constant for a fixed value of h; that is, the ends of the vectors S lie on a plane perpendicular to **a**. If h is zero, the plane passes through the origin; if h is unity, the plane makes a certain intercept on **a**; if $h=2$, it makes double the intercept; and so on. In other words, a set of planes of constant spacing is set up, each plane of the set corresponding to a particular value of h. In a similar way a set of equidistant planes perpendicular to **b** will be set up, each plane corresponding to a particular value of k; and a further set of planes perpendicular to **c** will correspond to different values of l. The intersections of these planes represent the end points of vectors that satisfy the three Laue equations simultaneously, and so give the required solutions. These sets of planes define a lattice of points—the reciprocal lattice. The unit cell of this lattice is defined by three vectors, which are usually called **a***, **b*** and **c***, and each point in the lattice is defined by the three numbers h, k and l.

To find the reciprocal-lattice vectors, we make use of the fact that each is formed by the intersection of two planes perpendicular to two axes, and thus that **a***, for example, is perpendicular to **b** and **c**. Thus **a*** must be representable as $p(\mathbf{b} \times \mathbf{c})$, where p is a constant to be determined. We thus have the three equations

$$\mathbf{a}^* = p(\mathbf{b} \times \mathbf{c}),$$
$$\mathbf{b}^* = q(\mathbf{c} \times \mathbf{a}),$$
$$\mathbf{c}^* = r(\mathbf{a} \times \mathbf{b}),$$

where p, q and r are constants.

Then $\mathbf{S} = h\mathbf{a}^* + k\mathbf{b}^* + l\mathbf{c}^*$

$= hp(\mathbf{b} \times \mathbf{c}) + kq(\mathbf{c} \times \mathbf{a}) + lr(\mathbf{a} \times \mathbf{b})$.

But $h = \mathbf{a} \cdot \mathbf{S}$

$= \mathbf{a} \cdot \{hp(\mathbf{b} \times \mathbf{c}) + kq(\mathbf{c} \times \mathbf{a}) + lr(\mathbf{a} \times \mathbf{b})\}$

$= hp\mathbf{a} \cdot \mathbf{b} \times \mathbf{c}$

since $\mathbf{a} \cdot \mathbf{c} \times \mathbf{a}$ and $\mathbf{a} \cdot \mathbf{a} \times \mathbf{b} = 0$.

Therefore $1 = p\mathbf{a} \cdot \mathbf{b} \times \mathbf{c}$

or $p = \dfrac{1}{\mathbf{a} \cdot \mathbf{b} \times \mathbf{c}}$.

Similarly $q = \dfrac{1}{\mathbf{b} \cdot \mathbf{c} \times \mathbf{a}}$

and $r = \dfrac{1}{\mathbf{c} \cdot \mathbf{a} \times \mathbf{b}}$. (7.1)

It will be noted that p, q and r are all equal since $\mathbf{a} \cdot \mathbf{b} \times \mathbf{c}$, $\mathbf{b} \cdot \mathbf{c} \times \mathbf{a}$ and $\mathbf{c} \cdot \mathbf{a} \times \mathbf{b}$ are all representations of the volume V of the unit cell of the space lattice.

Thus $p = q = r = 1/V$,

and

$$\left.\begin{aligned} \mathbf{a}^* &= \mathbf{b} \times \mathbf{c}/V, \\ \mathbf{b}^* &= \mathbf{c} \times \mathbf{a}/V, \\ \mathbf{c}^* &= \mathbf{a} \times \mathbf{b}/V. \end{aligned}\right\} \quad (7.2)$$

These are the simplest expressions for the reciprocal-lattice vectors, but for purposes of computation they have to be expressed in terms of **a**, **b** and **c** and the interaxial angles α, β and γ; the required expressions can be found in the International Tables (1952). For some purposes, particularly when it is necessary to make use of the reciprocal lattice in the interpretation of X-ray photographs, it is usual to define the reciprocal-lattice vectors as, for example, $\mathbf{a}^* = \lambda\mathbf{b} \times \mathbf{c}/V$. It will be noted that this replacement does not affect the relative values of $\mathbf{a}^*$, $\mathbf{b}^*$ and $\mathbf{c}^*$, and produces quantities that are characteristic both of the crystal and of the process of diffraction.

The reciprocal lattice is important in almost all branches of X-ray diffraction; its use in the interpretation of X-ray photographs is particularly valuable. In this book its particular importance lies in the part it plays in the optics of X-ray diffraction, as described in section **1**.4.2. In this connexion the space between the reciprocal-lattice points becomes as important as the points themselves. It is customary to call the space in which the reciprocal lattice is plotted 'reciprocal space', and it may either be dimensionless, if λ is introduced into the expressions for the reciprocal-lattice constants, or of dimensions *length*$^{-1}$ if λ is not introduced.

2.4. *Atomic scattering factor.* In section **1**.2.1 the scattering units were assumed to be electrons in order that their linear dimensions could be neglected in comparison with the space-lattice dimensions, and, incidentally, in comparison with the wave-length of the X-rays; under these conditions the scattering by a single electron is independent of angle apart from any effects of polarization of the radiation. In atoms, however, the electrons occupy a finite volume and the phase differences between rays scattered from different points in this volume have to be taken into account.

For small angles of diffraction these phase differences are small and therefore the amplitude of scattering by an atom can be taken as the sum of the amplitudes of the scattering by its individual electrons. If, therefore, the electrons at the lattice points are replaced by an atom of atomic number Z, then the expression for the amplitude of the scattered beam must be multiplied by Z. As the angle of diffraction increases, however, the phase differences become larger, and thus the scattered beam becomes weaker; that is, the factor becomes less than Z. The factor is called the *atomic scattering factor*, *f*, and if the atom is assumed to have spherical symmetry the atomic scattering factor is constant for a given angle of diffraction. The curve of scattering factor against $(\sin\theta)/\lambda$ is called the scattering-factor curve or *f curve* (fig. 8). The calculation of these curves for the different atoms is described in Volume II, Chapter III.

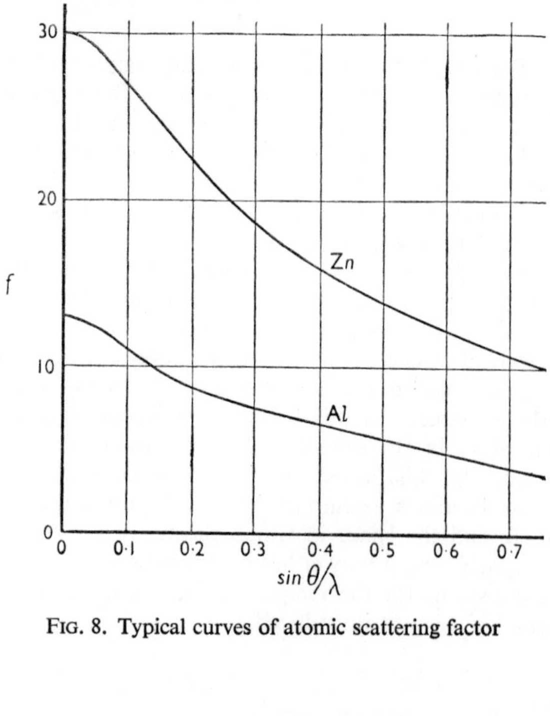

FIG. 8. Typical curves of atomic scattering factor

2.5 *Temperature factor.* The electron densities in atoms are independent of temperature for all ordinary temperatures, provided that there is no change in the state of ionisation; it might therefore be supposed that temperature should have no effect on the intensities of X-ray reflexions. This would be so if the atoms were scattering independently, as in a gas; but in a crystal the atoms are not scattering independently and it is necessary to see how this fact affects the total scattering.

At all temperatures, including absolute zero, atoms have a finite amplitude of oscillation. The frequency of this oscillation (about 10^{13} per second) is so much smaller than the frequency of X-rays (about 10^{18} per second) that, to a train of X-ray waves, the atoms would appear to be stationary, but displaced from their true positions in the lattice. Thus, in producing a given X-ray reflexion, atoms in neighbouring unit cells, which should scatter in phase, will scatter slightly out of phase, the total effect being apparently to reduce the scattering factor of the atom by an amount which increases with angle. Since displacements of neighbouring atoms are not disconnected, unusual diffraction effects are produced; these are the so-called 'diffuse reflexions'. But if the thermal waves have a random phase relationship, the form of the variation of scattering factor with angle can be worked out with certain assumptions about the nature of the atomic vibrations. The result is that, if the atomic scattering factor discussed in the previous section is called f_0, the factor f to be used in practice is $f_0 \exp(-\mathrm{B}\sin^2\theta/\lambda^2)$ where θ is the Bragg angle and B is a constant, if the mean square displacements $\overline{u^2}$ are the same for all atoms and are isotropic. The more general conditions are discussed in Chapter 11.

2.6. *Diffraction by a crystal with atoms in general positions.* We have now arrived at a stage at which the theory is physically significant; the crystal is one in which atoms of finite size are located with their mean positions at lattice points. Some crystals actually have this simple structure. But most crystals are much more complicated; they can be represented only by placing within each unit cell of the lattice a certain arrangement of atoms. We may still regard any one set of corresponding atoms in the different unit cells as lying upon a lattice, and thus a crystal with N atoms in the unit cell can be regarded as based upon N identical interpenetrating lattices. The equations already deduced are still obeyed by each separate lattice of atoms, and therefore by the complete crystal; but the rays scattered by the different lattices will differ in phase according to their separations. Thus, if there is a large number of atoms in the unit cell, complicated relationships may be expected between the intensities of the various orders of diffraction.

Suppose that the unit cell of a crystal contains N atoms, situated at points x_n, y_n, z_n. These quantities are best considered as co-ordinates with respect to the axes of the lattice, their magnitudes being equal to fractions of the lattice dimensions (fig. 10). (If the co-ordinates are taken as actual distances, as is sometimes preferable, quantities such as x/a appear in the formulae and result in rather cumbersome ex-

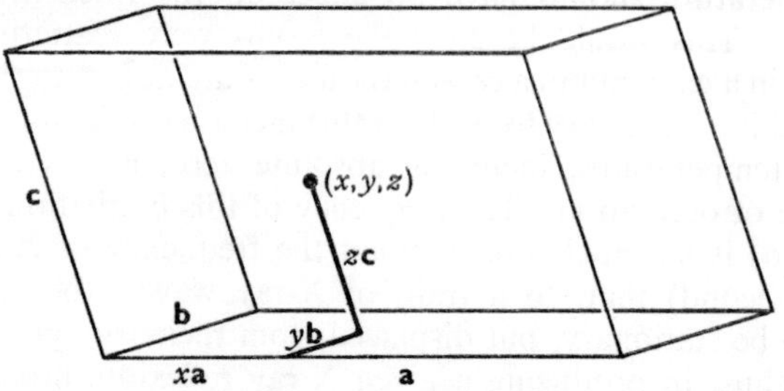

FIG. 10. Structural parameters x, y, z

pressions.) The position of the nth atom in the unit cell can thus be represented by the vector $\mathbf{r}_n$, where

$$\mathbf{r}_n = x_n\mathbf{a} + y_n\mathbf{b} + z_n\mathbf{c}. \qquad (10.1)$$

The path difference between the waves scattered by these atoms and those that would be scattered by a set of atoms at the points of the lattice that define the origins of the unit cells is, by analogy with equation *4.1*, $\lambda\mathbf{r}_n\cdot\mathbf{S}$. Thus the expression for the complete wave scattered by the nth lattice contains a term $f_n \exp \frac{2\pi i}{\lambda}\cdot\lambda\mathbf{r}_n\cdot\mathbf{S}$, or $f_n \exp 2\pi i\mathbf{r}_n\cdot\mathbf{S}$, where f_n is the scattering factor of the nth atom. Thus the expression for the complete wave scattered by the crystal would contain a term

$$\mathrm{F} = \sum_{n=1}^{N} f_n \exp 2\pi i\mathbf{r}_n\cdot\mathbf{S}. \qquad (10.2)$$

Substituting the value of $\mathbf{r}_n$ from equation *10.1*, we have

$$\begin{aligned}\mathrm{F} &= \sum_{n=1}^{N} f_n \exp 2\pi i(x_n\mathbf{a}\cdot\mathbf{S} + y_n\mathbf{b}\cdot\mathbf{S} + z_n\mathbf{c}\cdot\mathbf{S}) \\ &= \sum_{n=1}^{N} f_n \exp 2\pi i(hx_n + ky_n + lz_n) \qquad (10.3)\end{aligned}$$

(from Laue's equations *4.2*). This is the most important expression in crystal-structure determination. The quantity F is a function of h, k and l, and is called the *Structure Factor*; its modulus is called the *Structure Amplitude* and is defined as the ratio of the amplitude of the radiation scattered in the order h, k, l by the contents of one unit cell to that scattered by a single electron under the same conditions (Lonsdale, 1936). It will thus be seen that $|\mathrm{F}|$ is a pure number—a number of electrons.*

* It will be noted that the use of the expression 'Structure Amplitude' is the same as that in Volume I (p. 96) but not the same as that in Volume II (p. 28).

The complex form of the expression for the structure factor merely means that the phase of the scattered wave is not simply related to that of the incident wave. The phase, however, is not an observable quantity, the only observable quantity being the intensity, which is proportional to $|F|^2$. Then, if F be put equal to $A'+iB'$,

$$\left.\begin{aligned} A' &= \sum_n f_n \cos 2\pi(hx_n+ky_n+lz_n) \\ \text{and}\qquad B' &= \sum_n f_n \sin 2\pi(hx_n+ky_n+lz_n) \end{aligned}\right\} \quad (11.1)$$

and
$$F^2 = A'^2 + B'^2.$$

These are the equations that have to be used in practice. They will be discussed in more detail in Chapter 4.

A more fundamental interpretation of the structure-factor equation is possible, for the reduction of a structure to a set of point atoms with variable scattering factors is essentially artificial. This reduction is avoided by considering each element of volume of the unit cell separately. Thus if $\rho(x, y, z)$ is the electron density at the point (x, y, z), the amount of scattering matter in the volume element $Vdxdydz$ is $\rho Vdxdydz$, and the structure-factor equation is

$$F(hkl) = \int_{x=0}^{1}\int_{y=0}^{1}\int_{z=0}^{1} V\rho(x, y, z) \exp 2\pi i(hx+ky+lz)dxdydz \quad (11.2)$$

Although this equation is not used for calculating structure factors, it is necessary in the development of the theory which follows in the succeeding sections.

3. Applications of Fourier Series

3.1. *Representation of a crystal by a Fourier series.* Since a crystal is periodic in three dimensions, it can be represented by a three-dimensional Fourier series. This concept is most simply expressed by allotting to each Fourier coefficient C three integral indices h', k' and l', these symbols being chosen because they have a simple relation to the indices h, k, l of the X-ray reflexions. Thus we have

$$\rho(x, y, z) = \sum_{h'}\sum_{k'}\sum_{l'=-\infty}^{\infty} C(h', k', l') \exp 2\pi i(h'x+k'y+l'z).$$

This value for the electron density can be inserted in equation *11*.2, and thus

$$F(hkl) = \int_0^1\int_0^1\int_0^1 \sum\sum\sum_{-\infty}^{\infty} C(h', k', l') \exp 2\pi i(h'x+k'y+l'z) \exp 2\pi i(hx+ky+lz)Vdxdydz. \quad (11.3)$$

The exponential functions are both periodic and the integral of their product over a single complete period is zero in general; only if

$h=-h', k=-k', l=-l'$ is it not zero, since the periodicity disappears. Under these conditions

$$\mathrm{F}(hkl)=\int_0^1\int_0^1\int_0^1 \mathrm{C}(h'k'l')\mathrm{V}\,dx\,dy\,dz.$$

(The summations disappear since there is only one term to consider.)

Therefore $$\mathrm{F}(hkl)=\mathrm{C}(\bar{h}\bar{k}\bar{l})\mathrm{V}. \quad (12.1)$$

In other words, the Fourier coefficients C are directly related to the corresponding structure factors, and

$$\rho(x, y, z)=\frac{1}{\mathrm{V}}\sum_h\sum_k\sum_{l=-\infty}^{\infty}\mathrm{F}(hkl)\exp\{-2\pi i(hx+ky+lz)\}. \quad (12.2)$$

It may seem from this that the process of determining crystal structures is entirely straightforward: from experimental observation of intensities the values of the structure amplitudes are deduced; the Fourier coefficients are calculated; the series is summed; and the result is a representation of the crystal structure. It should not even be necessary to have absolute values of the structure amplitudes; relative values should give a recognizable representation.

That this is not possible appears when we consider the nature of the structure factor; as we have seen in section **1**.2.6, the structure factor is complex, and from the intensity we can derive only the modulus. But equations *12*.1 and *12*.2 are absolute; C and F are related in phase as well as in magnitude and so, in general, the process of crystal-structure determination cannot be carried out by direct means. If it could be, it would not be necessary to write the rest of this book, since it is entirely concerned with methods of overcoming the particular difficulty of lack of knowledge of the relative phases of the diffracted beams.

3.2 *Patterson's Fourier series.* An attempt to evade the difficulty mentioned in the last section was made by Patterson (1935*a*). Instead of the structure factors, he used the squares of the moduli as Fourier coefficients; these quantities are directly related to the observed intensities and so they can always be measured. He showed that the resulting synthesis was related in a simple way to the crystal structure, and could give direct evidence about atomic positions with no preliminary assumptions. It can rarely be used to work out complete structures, but in some projects it has played a major role in producing the final solution.

Patterson defines a function P(*u*, *v*, *w*) such that

$$\mathrm{P}(u, v, w)=\mathrm{V}\int_0^1\int_0^1\int_0^1 \rho(x, y, z)\rho(x+u, y+v, z+w)\,dx\,dy\,dz. \quad (12.3)$$

If we substitute in this expression the values for the electron densities given by equation *12.2* we arrive at the equation

$$P(u, v, w) = \frac{1}{V}\int_0^1\int_0^1\int_0^1 \sum_h \sum_k \sum_l \sum_{h'} \sum_{k'} \sum_{l'=-\infty}^{\infty} F(hkl) \exp\{-2\pi i(hx+ky+lz)\}$$
$$\times F(h'k'l') \exp\{-2\pi i(h'x+k'y+l'z)\} \exp\{-2\pi i(h'u+k'v+l'w)\} dxdydz.$$

For the reasons that apply to equation *11.3*, the right-hand side is zero unless $h=-h'$, $k=-k'$, $l=-l'$; when this condition applies,

$$P(u, v, w) = \frac{1}{V}\sum_h \sum_k \sum_{l=-\infty}^{\infty} F(hkl)F(\bar{h}\bar{k}\bar{l}) \exp\{-2\pi i(h'u+k'v+l'w)\}.$$

From equation *10.3* we note that $F(hkl)$ and $F(\bar{h}\bar{k}\bar{l})$ are complex conjugates and so

$$P(u, v, w) = \frac{1}{V}\sum_h \sum_k \sum_{l=-\infty}^{\infty} |F(hkl)|^2 \exp 2\pi i(hu+kv+lw). \qquad (13)$$

As stated above, the quantities $|F|^2$—the squares of the structure amplitudes—are directly derivable from the X-ray intensities, and so the series can be summed without ambiguity. What, then, is the physical significance of the summation?

Suppose that fig. 13 represents a crystal structure projected on to a plane, the electron density being finite within the circles and zero elsewhere. From any point (x, y) in the unit cell draw a vector with components u and v. In general, it is probable that the electron density is zero at each end of the line, and so the product will be zero. Even if we choose one end to lie within a circle, it is probable that the other end will not, and so the product will still be zero; thus it might be expected that there should be a high probability that the total summation for all points (x, y) will be zero.

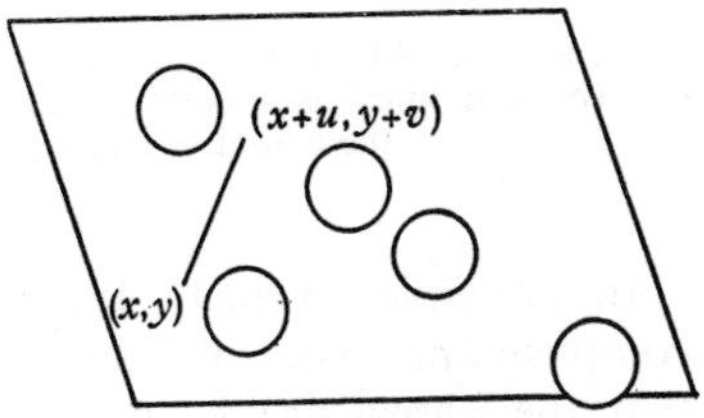

FIG. 13. Basis of theory of the Patterson synthesis

Under what conditions will the product not be zero? Obviously, when we deliberately choose u and v to be such that they represent the components of a vector whose ends lie within circles; in other words, the Patterson summation will be finite only for values of u and v that represent vectors joining two atoms. This is the importance of the Patterson series: it gives information about interatomic distances, but not about atomic positions.

It is improbable that a given vector, whatever its position in the unit cell, always has one end or the other at a point of zero electron density, and thus the Patterson summation rarely has zero value for a reasonably complicated crystal. This can be seen more clearly by regarding the Patterson summation, for given values of u and v, as the product of the structure with its counterpart displaced by components u and v. This process is known as convolution (Lipson and Taylor, 1958). This process is illustrated, for the same structure and vector displacement as in fig. 13; the regions where positive electron densities overlap are indicated. It can readily be visualized that, even for a structure as simple as this, it would be difficult to find values of u and v for which there was no overlapping at all.

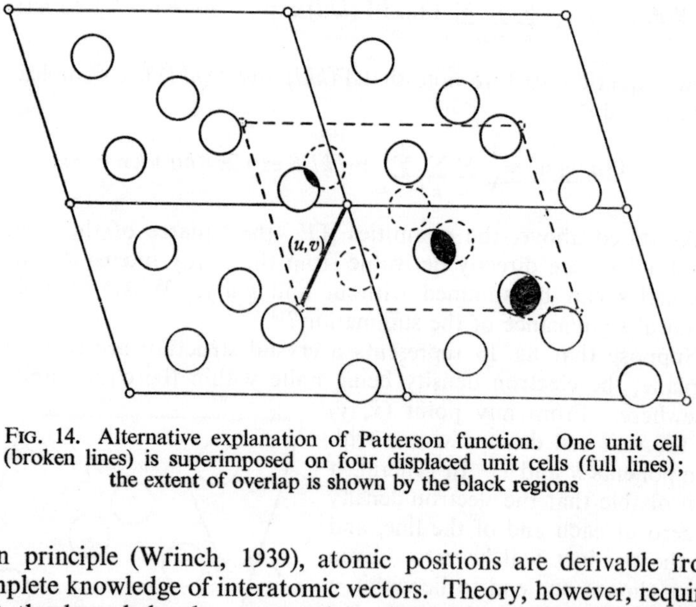

FIG. 14. Alternative explanation of Patterson function. One unit cell (broken lines) is superimposed on four displaced unit cells (full lines); the extent of overlap is shown by the black regions

In principle (Wrinch, 1939), atomic positions are derivable from complete knowledge of interatomic vectors. Theory, however, requires that the knowledge be presented in the form of distances between point atoms, whereas, in practice, one obtains only the information with respect to atoms of finite size. In other words, Patterson syntheses consist of collections of more-or-less broad and unresolved peaks, and no general method of deducing atomic positions has yet been put forward that will work in every possible circumstance. Nevertheless, the Patterson method has been extensively used to give information that could not be obtained in any other way, and its various uses will be described in Chapter 7.

That the quantity $P(u, v, w)$ is real for all values of u, v, w can be shown by collecting together the coefficients in pairs, hkl and $\bar{h}\bar{k}\bar{l}$. Then

$$P(u, v, w) = \frac{1}{2V}\sum\sum\sum_{-\infty}^{\infty} |F(hkl)|^2 \exp\{-2\pi i(hu+kv+lw)\} + |F(\bar{h}\bar{k}\bar{l})|^2 \exp\{2\pi i(hu+kv+lw)\}$$

$$= \frac{1}{2V} \sum\sum\sum_{-\infty}^{\infty} |F(hkl)|^2 [\exp\{-2\pi i(hu+kv+lw)\} + \exp\{2\pi i(hu+kv+lw)\}]$$

since $|F(\bar{h}\bar{k}\bar{l})| = |F(hkl)|$.

Thus $$P(u, v, w) = \frac{1}{V} \sum\sum\sum_{-\infty}^{\infty} |F(hkl)|^2 \cos 2\pi(hu+kv+lw) \qquad (15)$$

which is real for all values of u, v and w.

Equation *15* gives the form in which the Patterson summation is usually expressed.

3.3. *Fourier transforms.* There is another method of treating the problem of diffraction by a crystal: instead of starting with the lattice and then introducing atoms into the unit cell, we may consider the unit-cell contents first and then see how the diffraction pattern is affected by the juxtaposition of other unit cells in regular array. For simplicity we may still refer the positions of the atoms to the crystallographic axes, although obviously these axes have no particular significance when we are dealing with a non-periodic object.

The atoms in the unit cell are represented by co-ordinates (x_n, y_n, z_n) and by scattering factors f_n. The equation (*10*.2)

$$F = \sum_{n=1}^{N} f_n \exp 2\pi i \mathbf{r}_n \cdot \mathbf{S}$$

still applies, but now it represents the complete scattering from the set of atoms. The vector **S** may assume any value, not merely the discrete values given by Laue's equations (*4*.2); in other words, F can be evaluated at any point in reciprocal space. The function F is called the Fourier transform of the set of atoms; unlike F(hkl) it is continuous in reciprocal space, but the structure factors are the values, at the reciprocal-lattice points, of the Fourier transform of one unit cell (Lipson and Taylor, 1958).

The effect of placing two units at a distance apart of **a** is to multiply the Fourier transform by a set of sinusoidal fringes of separation $\mathbf{a}^{-1}$.† If a large number of units is placed regularly in line, then the fringes become extremely sharp, so that in effect the Fourier transform is observed only in planes given by $\mathbf{S}\cdot\mathbf{a} = h$, where h is an integer; this is the first Laue equation. The placing of the units in three-dimensional array causes the Fourier transform to be observed only in the intersections of the three sets of planes corresponding to the three Laue conditions. These intersections form the reciprocal lattice. We see then that the reciprocal lattice, with weights attached to each point proportional to the structure factor, is a complete representation of the diffraction pattern of the crystal.

† $\mathbf{a}^{-1}$ is a vector in the same direction as **a** and with modulus $1/|\mathbf{a}|$.

The simplest illustration of this idea is given by considering a crystal with only one atom per unit cell. The structure amplitude of any reflexion is then equal to the scattering factor of the atom at the corresponding angle, and hence it follows that the f-curve of an atom, regarded as spherically distributed in reciprocal space, is the Fourier transform of that atom.

For purposes of calculation, the Fourier transform of a set of atoms may be expressed as

$$F = \sum f_n \exp \{2\pi i(hx_n + ky_n + lz_n)\}$$

where h, k and l may have non-integral values. The details of the contents of the unit cell are contained in the Fourier transform, and we have seen that the process of stacking these unit cells in orderly array allows us to measure the amplitude of the Fourier transform at discrete points only; this is a considerable loss, for if we could observe the whole of the transform the work of the determination of crystal structures would be considerably simplified. On the other hand, if we had one unit only, the diffraction pattern would be too weak to be observed, and if we had a number in irregular array, unless the units were all parallel, the diffraction pattern would be almost a hopeless jumble. We have therefore to be satisfied that the crystalline regularity leads to certain advantages, and to counteract the disadvantages as best we may.

4. Comparison of X-ray and Light Diffraction

4.1. *Introduction.* The mathematical sections of this chapter are necessary in order to establish the formulae that are required in practice. Nevertheless, it is not intended to imply that a knowledge of the derivation of these formulae is a sufficient basis for one who is embarking upon the determination of crystal structures; X-ray diffraction is a physical phenomenon, and an understanding of the underlying physical principles is of value in following many of the developments in the subject.

The simplest way of appreciating these principles is to compare them with the known effects of light diffraction. It is, of course, not possible to produce a three-dimensional grating, but most of the general principles discussed in the preceding sections can be illustrated by effects that occur with one-dimensional and two-dimensional gratings.

4.2. *Theory of the diffraction grating.* The general equation for the diffraction grating is

$$n\lambda = d(\sin \phi + \sin \theta_n)$$

where ϕ is the angle of incidence and θ_n is the angle of diffraction. For normal incidence, $\phi = 0$, but if the grating is used in the position for

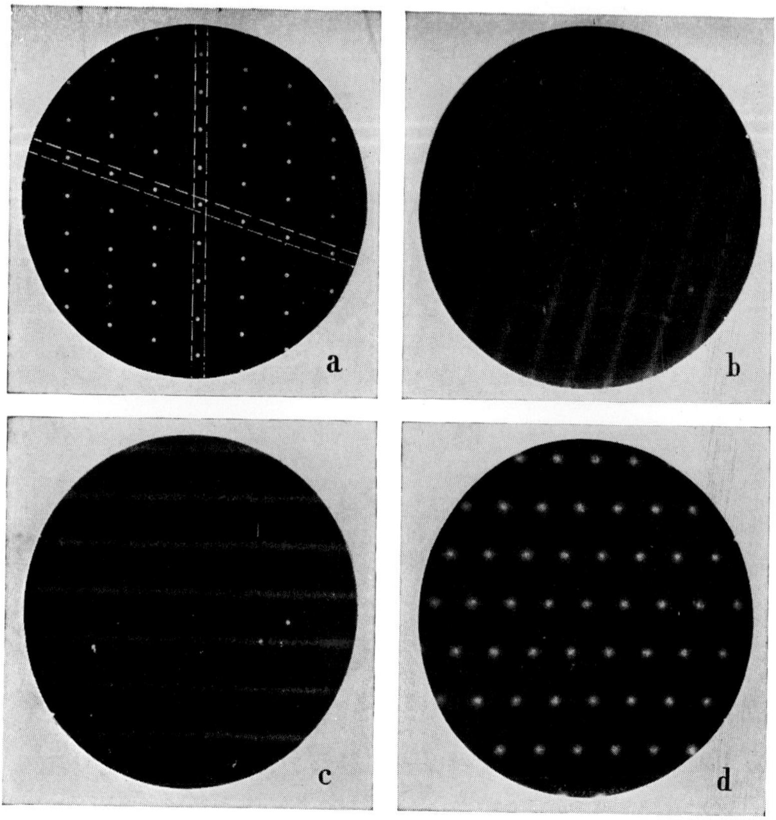

FIG. 17 (i)

(*a*) Two-dimensional array of holes, showing two basic linear elements between broken lines

(*b*) Fringes formed by one element, corresponding to first Laue equation

(*c*) Fringes formed by second element, corresponding to second Laue equation

(*d*) Diffraction pattern of (*a*), showing maxima only where fringes in (*b*) and (*c*) intersect minimum deviation of the nth order, $\phi=\theta_n$ and the equation reduces to

$$n\lambda=2d\sin\theta_n.$$

This is analogous to Bragg's equation (*6*).

For a one-dimensional diffraction grating, the order of diffraction is specified by a single number n, whereas for a two-dimensional grating two numbers are required. Such a grating can be made by first drilling a line of holes; this will behave as a diffraction grating producing orders of diffraction whose separation is inversely proportional to the spacing of the holes, as shown in Fig. 17 (i) (*b*). The two-dimensional grating may now be made by drilling similar sets of holes at equal distances apart; considering each set of holes as an element of a diffraction grating, we see that orders of diffraction are again formed perpendicular to the line of separation Fig. 17 (i) (*c*). Orders of diffraction from the two-dimensional grating are observed only where the two sets of orders intersect, and so we have a lattice of diffraction spots produced. This lattice of spots is analogous to the reciprocal lattice (section **1**.2.3).

If a grating is badly ruled various optical effects are produced, depending on the nature of the imperfection. If the error in the position of any one line is independent of the positions of neighbouring lines, the effect is, to a first approximation, equivalent to the effect of temperature on a crystal (section **1**.2.5); the grating can be considered as composed of broadened elements, and the orders of diffraction, particularly the higher ones, are reduced in intensity. If the displacements of the elements of the grating are not independent, then further diffraction effects occur that give rise to 'diffuse reflexions' (Vol. II, Chapter V).

The reason for the reduction in intensity can be seen by considering a diffraction grating of which the elements are narrow slits. As shown in textbooks on physical optics (e.g. Jenkins and White 1950, p. 327), the amplitude of a particular order of diffraction is governed by the amplitude diffracted in the same direction by the single element; the

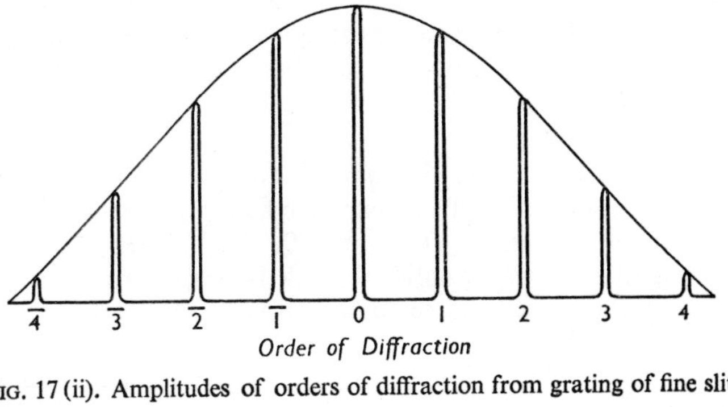

FIG. 17 (ii). Amplitudes of orders of diffraction from grating of fine slits

envelope of the ordinates representing the amplitude of the orders of diffraction is the curve representing the diffraction pattern of the single element. This curve is shown in fig. 17 (ii). If the spacing is large compared with the width of the slit, all the orders of diffraction are largely confined to a region near to the central maximum; otherwise they will be spaced farther out (fig. 18), and so will be reduced in intensity.

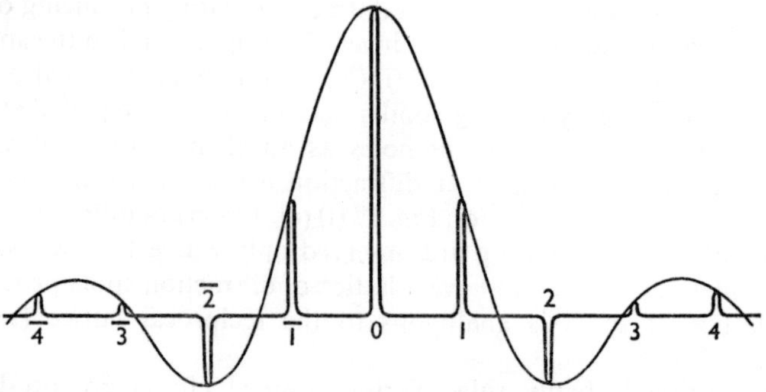

FIG. 18. Amplitudes of orders of diffraction from grating of coarse slits

This effect corresponds to the decrease in intensity due to the finite sizes of atoms (section **1**.2.4), and it will be noted that the central part of the curve in fig. 18 is similar in general outline to the curve in fig. 8; the lack of sharp outline of an atom, however, removes the negative regions shown in the former figure, but it will be noted that there is no *a priori* reason why the scattering factor of an atom should not be negative at certain angles.

The function showing the amplitude and phase of the beam diffracted in any direction by an object is the Fourier transform of the object; the Fourier transform of a crystal is the weighted reciprocal lattice, and the Fourier transform of the weighted reciprocal lattice is the crystal. Fig. 18 shows the Fourier transform of a single slit, and the superposition of the orders of diffraction on the diffraction pattern of the single slit is exactly analogous to the superposition of the reciprocal lattice on the Fourier transform of the unit-cell contents (section **1**.3.3.).

4.3. *Abbe's theory of image formation.* The process of Fourier synthesis of electron density can be explained simply in terms of Abbe's theory of image formation (Vol. I, p. 230, and Vol. II, p. 390). Abbe pointed out that image formation by a lens consisted of two parts—scattering by the object and re-combination of the scattered light by a lens.

If we choose a diffraction grating as an object and illuminate it normally by a narrow beam of light, then the scattered beams are confined to particular directions given by the grating equation

$$n\lambda = d \sin \theta_n. \qquad (19.1)$$

In fig. 19*a*, two orders of diffraction, $\pm n$, are shown as single lines,

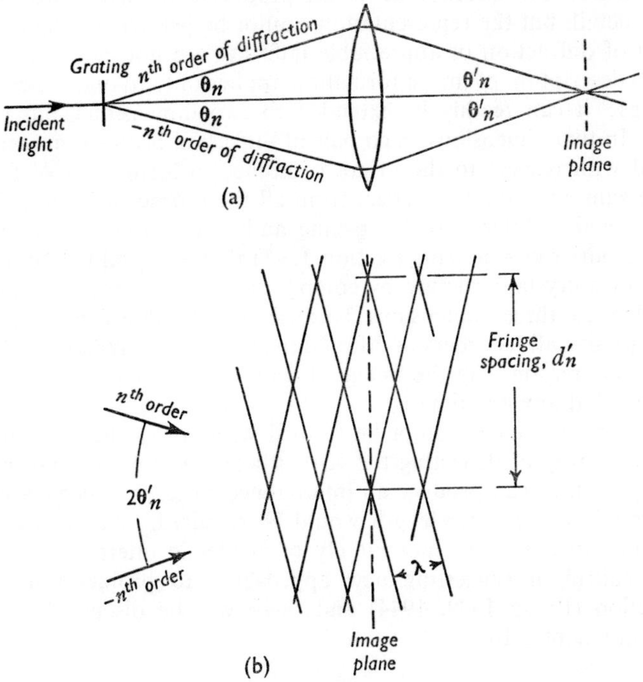

FIG. 19 (*a*, *b*). Production of one fringe component in the image of a diffraction grating

and these meet, after refraction by the lens, at an angle of $2\theta_n'$. If we represent these beams by the crests at any particular instant, as shown in fig. 19*b*, it will be seen that, in the image plane, diffraction fringes are formed with separation d_n' where

$$d_n' = \lambda / \sin \theta_n'. \qquad (19.2)$$

Now, to a first approximation, $\sin \theta_n / \sin \theta_n'$ is a constant and equal to the magnification m produced by the lens. Therefore

$$d_n' = m\lambda / \sin \theta_n$$
$$= md/n \qquad \text{(from equation 19.1).}$$

From this equation we can see how the image of the diffraction grating is built up. The zero order of diffraction gives an infinite value for d_0'; that is, there is no variation in intensity. The first orders give fringes of spacing *md*, that is, a true magnified image of the spacing, but with an intensity distribution independent of the shape of the grating element. The second orders produce fringes that modify the fringes formed by the first orders, and give a closer approximation to the truth. The addition of fringes produced by further orders adds to the detail, but the representation cannot be perfect so long as some orders of diffraction of appreciable intensity are not included.

This description of image formation applies only to one-dimensional gratings; it can readily be extended to two dimensions, but not to three. In two dimensions, each pair of diffracted beams symmetrically related with respect to the origin combines to form a set of fringes, whose sum gives the total effect from all the diffracted beams. These fringes, which differ both in spacing and orientation, are equivalent to the Fourier components (section **1**.3.1) that are used to produce an image of a crystal structure by computation. (The process cannot be extended to three dimensions because a three-dimensional grating does not give all its orders of diffraction simultaneously (section **1**.2.1); this is one reason why the image of only one plane of an object can be formed at any one time.)

An accurate image cannot be formed with X-rays because there is no known way of deflecting the X-rays scattered by a crystal in such a way that they can produce an interference pattern; a 'lens' accurate to a fraction of a wave-length would be required. Nevertheless, the ideas just discussed are not merely of academic interest; they have been fruitful in suggesting new approaches to problems in X-ray diffraction (Bragg 1939, 1944) and these will be discussed in more detail in Chapter 10.

CHAPTER 2

DETERMINATION AND USE OF SPACE GROUPS

1. Importance of Symmetry

In the theory outlined in Chapter 1, the unit cell of a crystal was supposed to contain N independent atoms, the positions of which were defined by 3N structural parameters. A crystal of such general type is, however, rare; most crystals show some symmetry, and, since this depends upon the way in which the atoms are arranged in the crystal, *a priori* knowledge of the symmetry of the atomic arrangement can be a very useful aid to structure determination. To begin with, when symmetry is present, the number of independent parameters is less than the value 3N, but frequently the information gained is much more helpful than this; certain sets of atoms in a crystal structure may be fixed by only one or two parameters, and, in extreme cases, some atoms can be precisely located from symmetry considerations alone.

Thus the determination of the full symmetry of a crystal structure is now regarded as a necessary preliminary to the determination of the atomic positions, and the present chapter is concerned with describing the accepted procedures for determining, as unequivocally as possible, the symmetry of a given crystal structure. The basic principles have been dealt with in Chapter V of Volume I. The present account, therefore, includes only a general review of these basic principles, and is chiefly concerned with describing in detail the various steps that may be taken in the deduction of the symmetry of a crystal structure.

2. External Symmetry of Crystals

2.1. *Types of symmetry.* A body is said to be symmetrical when it can be divided into parts that are related to each other in certain ways. The operation of transferring one part to the position of a symmetrically related part is termed a *symmetry operation*, the result of which is to leave the final state of the body indistinguishable from its original state. In general, successive application of the symmetry operation must ultimately bring the body actually into its original state again.

An infinite number of symmetry operations is possible. For example, a regular polygon of n sides will appear identical if turned through an angle of $2\pi/n$, and is said to have an *n-fold axis of rotation.* The possibilities in crystals are limited however, because the symmetry has to conform with that possible in an extended lattice, as can be seen by considering a two-dimensional lattice of dimensions a and b and angle γ (fig. 22 (i)). By making $a=b$ and ascribing various values to γ, lattices of different symmetry may be obtained; for example if $\gamma=\pi/2$, the lattice has four-fold symmetry and if $\gamma=\pi/3$ it has six-fold symmetry. Now, the angle of the general lattice may be taken as $\pi-\gamma$ instead of γ; the choice of one value or the other is arbitrary. Thus, in order that a lattice with higher than two-fold symmetry should be produced, both γ and $\pi-\gamma$ must be submultiples of 2π. That is

$$\gamma=2\pi/n$$

and

$$\pi-\gamma=2\pi/m$$

where n and m are integers. Thus

$$m=\frac{2\pi}{\pi-\dfrac{2\pi}{n}}$$

$$=\frac{2}{1-2/n}.$$

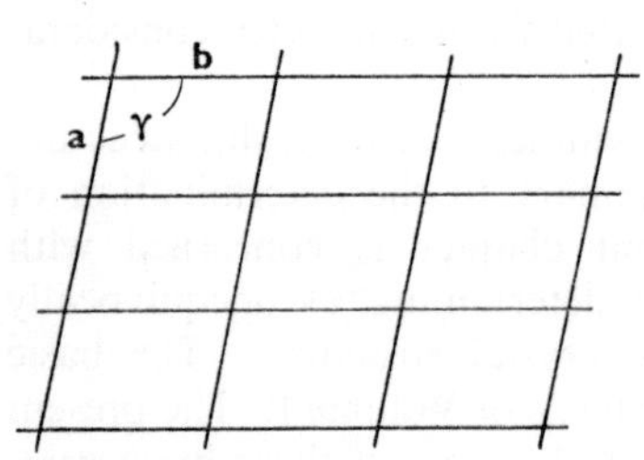

FIG. 22 (i). Two-dimensional lattice

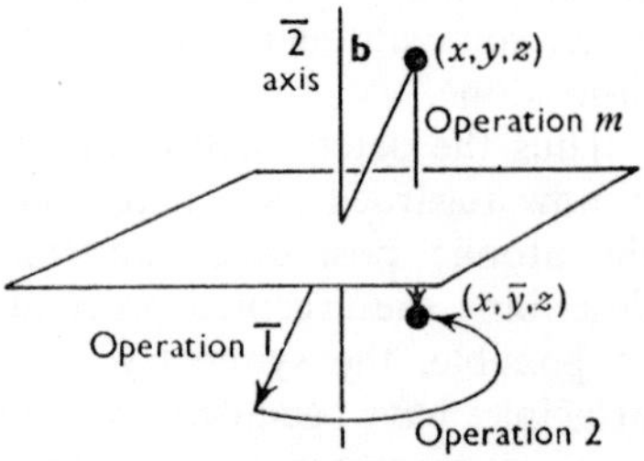

FIG. 22 (ii). Equivalence of $\bar{2}$ and m

By trial we find that the only values of n that satisfy this condition are 1, 2, 3, 4 and 6, and these numbers are used to represent the corresponding axes of rotation. The symbol 1 represents the *identical operation*, since it merely expresses the fact that a body turned through an angle of 2π will be coincident with itself.

The other important type of symmetry is that represented by inversion, and is possessed by a body which is such that any line drawn through a certain point within it intersects the surface at equal distances on either side of the point; the point is known as a *centre of inversion* or *centre of symmetry*. The operation of inversion combined with that of rotation produces a type of symmetry element known as an *inversion axis*; these axes are represented by the symbols $\bar{1}$, $\bar{2}$, $\bar{3}$, $\bar{4}$ and $\bar{6}$. Obviously $\bar{1}$ is the operation of inversion itself. From fig. 22 (ii) we see that $\bar{2}$ is equivalent to reflexion across a plane, and this is so important that it is given a special symbol, m.

The rotation axes and inversion axes are all the symmetries possible in the external form of a crystal.

2.2. *Lattice symmetry.* All lattices are centro-symmetrical, and thus the presence of a centre of symmetry does not introduce any relations between the lattice constants. A crystal with only this property is said to belong to the *triclinic system,* and such a crystal may have the symmetry represented by 1 or $\bar{1}$.

If a crystal has a two-fold axis, then a prominent row of lattice points will be associated with this direction; otherwise, if the points lay slightly off, the axis would produce another set of points at a slight angle to the first set. This axis is conventionally taken to be *b* (although occasionally it is taken to be *c*). Then it follows that the other two axes, *a* and *c*, must be perpendicular to *b*, since, by the same reasoning, if they were not perpendicular to *b*, two more axes would be produced. It can be shown in the same way that if a crystal has a reflexion plane, *m*, one of the axes can be taken perpendicular to the plane and the other two must then lie in the plane. Therefore if we find that the crystal lattice has one axis perpendicular to the other two we suspect that it has either a two-fold axis, a mirror plane, or a two-fold axis perpendicular to a mirror plane, denoted by the symbol $2/m$. Such crystals are said to belong to the *monoclinic system.*

The symmetry $2/m$ is the only one of the three possibilities in the monoclinic system which is centro-symmetrical. Thus, since all lattices are centro-symmetrical, the lattice of a monoclinic crystal must have symmetry $2/m$; nevertheless, the atomic arrangement in such a crystal may have symmetry 2, *m* or $2/m$, and these subdivisions of a crystal system are known as *point groups* (Phillips, 1946, p. 235). Each crystal system contains a number of point groups, lists being given in standard works such as the International Tables, Vol. I (1952).

2.3. *Analytical representation of symmetry elements.* The operation of a symmetry element can be represented by the position to which a point in the general position (x, y, z) (section **1**.2.6) would be moved by the operation. Thus from fig. 23 we see that the operation of a two-fold axis along *b* can be represented by the points (x, y, z) and $(\bar{x}, y, \bar{z})$, and from fig. 22 (ii) we see that reflexion in a mirror plane perpendicular to *b* can be represented by the points (x, y, z) and $(x, \bar{y}, z)$. Consequently, the symmetry $2/m$ can be expressed by the four points (x, y, z) $(\bar{x}, y, \bar{z})$ $(x, \bar{y}, z)$ and $(\bar{x}, \bar{y}, \bar{z})$. But this set of points has also a centre of symmetry and, amongst the many utilities of this representation, this property of showing the existence of further symmetry elements in a combination is particularly important.

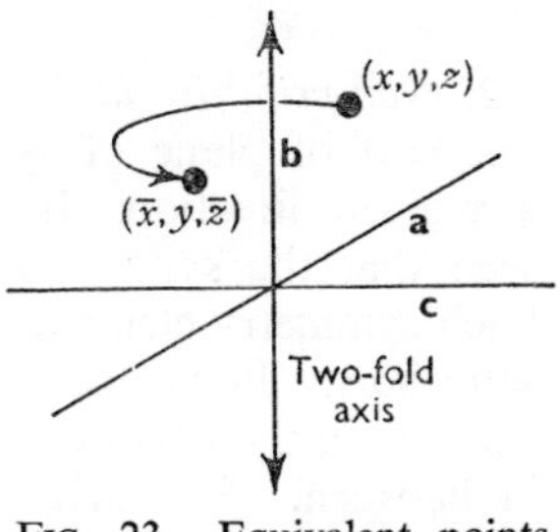

FIG. 23. Equivalent points produced by a two-fold axis

3. Symmetry of Crystal Structures

3.1. *Screw axes and glide planes.* In an extended array of atoms, types of symmetry are possible other than rotation and inversion axes: in addition to considering the relationship between atoms in the same unit cell, we can also consider the relationship between atoms in different unit cells. That is, we can consider symmetry operations whose continued application brings an atom not into self coincidence, but into coincidence with an atom in a neighbouring unit cell. For example, the following symmetry operation is possible—first, rotation of an angle π about an axis parallel to one of the crystallographic axes, followed by translation of half the length of the cell edge. This is called a *two-fold screw axis.* As shown in fig. 24, the repeated operation brings the point considered into coincidence with the corresponding one in the next unit cell, as contrasted with the two operations of a two-fold rotation axis which brings the point into coincidence with itself.

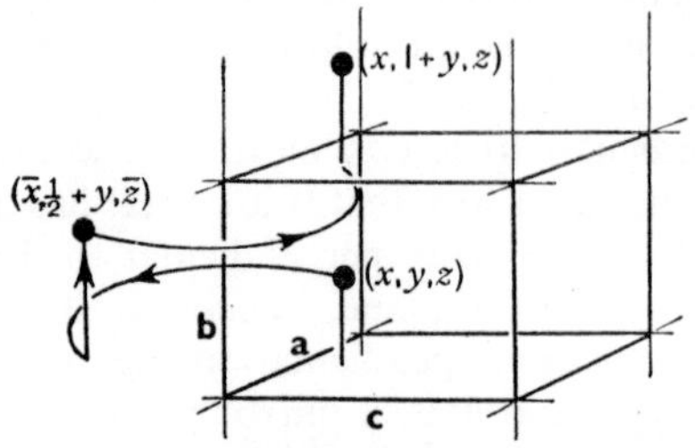

FIG. 24. Two successive operations of a screw axis. The points (x, y, z) and $(x, 1+y, z)$ are similar points in neighbouring unit cells

Many other such symmetry elements are possible; a complete list is given in the International Tables (1952). It will be noted that they can be classed as axes—screw axes—or planes—*glide planes.* Glide planes represent reflexion across the plane plus translation in a direction parallel to the plane. In the monoclinic system the plane of the glide is usually perpendicular to *b*, but in other systems the orientation of the plane is specified by the position of the symbol in the complete representation of the symmetry, as described in Vol. I (p. 87).

3.2. *Non-primitive lattices.* So far we have assumed that there is only one sort of plane of symmetry or one sort of axis of symmetry in any given direction. In the monoclinic system, for example, we have seen that the symmetry can be either 2, *m* or $2/m$ (section 2.2.2). Such symmetry elements will produce other symmetry elements of the same sort. For example, it can be seen from fig. 25 (i) that two-fold axes along the edges of the unit cell produce two-fold axes along lines in between. Similarly, mirror planes in opposite faces of the unit cell must be interleaved by other mirror planes.

It is therefore possible to introduce further symmetry elements, subject only to the rule that the operation of symmetry element upon symmetry element produces a self-consistent system. Thus, as shown in fig. 25 (ii), two-fold screw axes can be placed between two-fold rotation axes, and glide planes can be placed between mirror planes. The symmetry operations may then be expressed as $2+2_1$, and $m+a$,

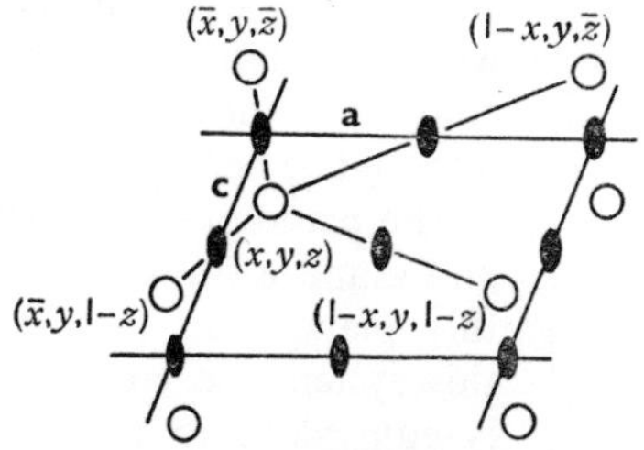

FIG. 25 (i). Two-fold axes lying half-way between two-fold axes along edges of unit cells

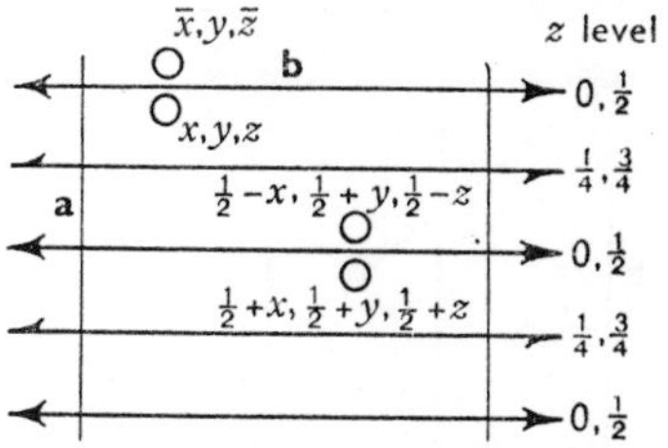

FIG. 25 (ii). Screw axes placed between rotation axes. The screw axes could also be placed at levels 0 and $\frac{1}{2}$

respectively. This process cannot be continued further for no type of symmetry operation can, for example, turn a screw axis into a rotation axis.

Where does this process lead? Consider the operations $2+2_1$, combined in the particular way shown in fig. 25 (ii). Operation 2 leads to equivalent points x, y, z and $\bar{x}$, y, $\bar{z}$, and the operation 2_1 leads to further points $\frac{1}{2}-x$, $\frac{1}{2}+y$, $\frac{1}{2}-z$, and $\frac{1}{2}+x$, $\frac{1}{2}+y$, $\frac{1}{2}+z$. The last one is important; it can be regarded as derived from the original point by a simple translation of $\frac{1}{2}(\mathbf{a}+\mathbf{b}+\mathbf{c})$. In other words, whatever set of atoms is placed around the origin, an exactly similar set of atoms, similarly oriented, is produced by the symmetry around the point $\frac{1}{2}$, $\frac{1}{2}$, $\frac{1}{2}$—the centre of the unit cell. Now from the definition of the lattice (section **1**.2.1), we see that all the lattice points are produced by simple translation. Therefore this process of combining symmetry elements has led to new lattice points in between the original ones.

This concept can, of course, be evaded by re-choosing the axes of the lattice, as shown in fig. 25 (iii), but such a choice no longer brings out clearly the relationship of the lattice to the symmetry. It is therefore customary to retain the original axes and to admit the possibility of non-primitive lattices—that is, lattices with points at positions other than the corners of the unit cells. The lattice produced by combining two-fold rotation and screw axes in this way is called a body-centred lattice, and is represented by the symbol I. The possible lattices are shown in fig. 48 of Volume I.

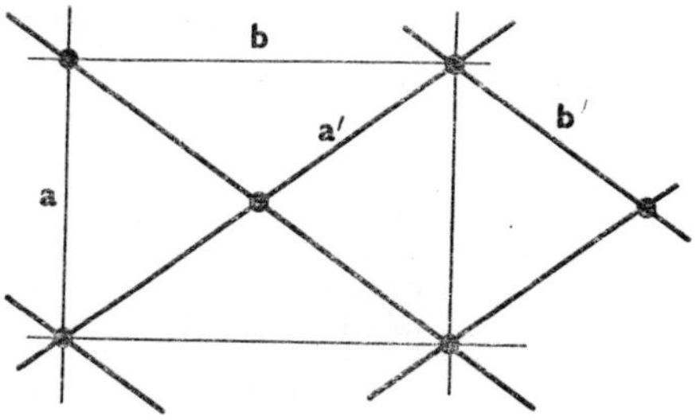

FIG. 25 (iii). Re-choice of axes to produce primitive cell from centred cell

Some of the lattices are not essentially different from each other. From fig. 26 we can see that in the monoclinic system the lattice I can be regarded as A, with the retention of the convention of axes—that **b** should be perpendicular to the plane of symmetry and **a** and **c** should lie in this plane. In fact, in this system the lattice A is equivalent to both C and F.

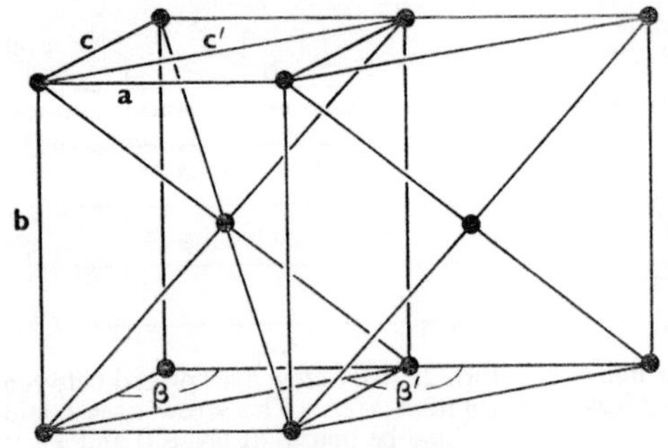

FIG. 26. Transformation of I lattice into A by re-choice of **c** axis

3.3. *Space groups.* A space group is an array of symmetry elements that is consistent with an infinitely extended, regularly repeating pattern. In specifying a space group it is not necessary to specify the complete collection of symmetry elements; those that can be derived from the others may be omitted. Thus the symbol 2 represents a space group, for we know (section **2**.3.2) that the placing of rotation axes along one set of parallel edges of a unit cell leads to other rotation axes.

On this basis, therefore, we should expect the scheme of derivation of the thirteen space groups of the monoclinic system to have some form such as that set out in table 26, in which the space groups are denoted both by their symmetry elements and by their Hermann-Mauguin symbols.

TABLE 26

The Monoclinic Space Groups

Point Group 2		Point Group *m*		Point Group 2/*m*	
2	P2	*m*	P*m*	2/*m*	P2/*m*
2_1	$P2_1$			$2_1/m$	$P2_1/m$
		c	P*c*	2/*c*	P2/*c*
		(*a*, *n*)	(P*a*, P*n*)	(2/*a*, 2/*n*)	(P2/*a*, P2/*n*)
				$2_1/c$	$P2_1/c$
				$(2_1/a, 2_1/n)$	$(P2_1/a, P2_1/n)$
$2+2_1$	C2	*m*+*a*	C*m*	2/*m*+*a*	C2/*m*
		(*m*+*c*, *m*+*n*)	(A*m*, I*m*)	(2/*m*+*c*, 2/*m*+*n*)	(A2/*m*, I2/*m*)
		c+*n*	C*c*	2/*c*+*n*	C2/*c*
		(*a*+*c*, *a*+*n*)	(I*a*, A*a*)	(2/*a*+*c*, 2/*a*+*n*)	(I2/*a*, A2/*a*)

Thus the symbol 2 is sufficient to describe the space group that has only two-fold rotation axes, but the Hermann-Mauguin notation gives also the lattice symbol P. The advantage of this notation can be seen by considering combinations of symmetry elements; thus if mirror planes *m* are interleaved with glide planes *a*, a C-face-centred lattice is produced, and the resulting space-group symbol C*m* is more informative than the symmetry notation $m+a$.

The number of combinations of the symmetry elements 2, 2_1, *m*, *a*, *c*, *n*, is much greater than thirteen, but several different combinations produce equivalent symmetries; some of the alternative space-group symbols are shown in brackets in table 26, the symmetry elements differing only in their orientations with respect to the chosen crystal axes. In particular, new space groups do not arise when the four symmetry elements, 2, 2_1, *m* and a glide plane, are combined.

Most space groups can be represented in several different ways, and, in dealing with an unknown crystal, it is possible that the original choice of axes will not result in a space-group symbol the same as one in the International Tables. For this reason, tables of space groups are usually accompanied by another table giving the symbols that are equivalent to each other (Volume I, Appendix VI).

This introduction to the theory of space groups has attempted no more than to lay the groundwork for a more complete study. It has dealt only with the triclinic and monoclinic systems, and the difficulties in the systems of higher symmetry, particularly in the cubic system, have not even been hinted at. A complete study could be attempted only in a book devoted solely to space-group theory, such as that written by Hilton (1906), which deals with the derivation of the 230 space groups.

4. Determination of Space Groups

4.1. *Determination of crystal system.* The classical method of finding the system to which a particular crystal belongs is to examine the arrangement of its faces (Phillips, 1946, Chapter 5). The normals to these faces are located with reference to arbitrary axes, and a stereographic projection is plotted; if the symmetry is not obvious from the projection, the orientation of the projection can be changed until symmetrical relationships are observed.

If this method is used, it is essential that several crystals should be measured, and they should have well-formed plane faces. This condition cannot always be obeyed, but effectively the same process can be carried through with X-rays. The more usual method, however, is to detect symmetry elements directly on X-ray photographs; if a fragment is found to be a single crystal, it is not difficult, by trial and error, to adjust it so that it gives straight layer lines, and then a plane of symmetry may make itself obvious. If there is no plane of symmetry, the crystal is triclinic; if a plane of symmetry is found, the crystal is at least monoclinic, and further examination with the crystal rotating about different axes should help to identify precisely the system to which a crystal belongs. Laue photographs may also be used to show more clearly symmetry elements that may be present.

If reasonably flat plates can be obtained, examination with the polarizing microscope should decide whether the crystal is cubic, uniaxial (hexagonal, trigonal or tetragonal) or biaxial (orthorhombic, monoclinic or triclinic) (Hartshorne and Stuart, 1950). A preliminary examination of this sort can be extremely useful as a guide to the application of the other methods.

4.2. *Determination of crystal class.* It is next necessary to allocate the crystal to the correct class within the system. The classical method of examination of the faces can be used, but it has an important limitation—faces of special form are not always sufficient to fix the true symmetry. For example, crystals of alum usually show only faces of the forms {100}, {110} and {111}, and these would indicate the highest symmetry of the cubic system, $m3m$. Nevertheless the symmetry is only $m3$, and this can be found from crystals that have faces of the form $\{hk0\}$; thus crystals with unusual faces are particularly important.

Because of this limitation, there is sometimes a tendency for too high a symmetry to be assigned to a crystal. For example, $BeSO_4.4H_2O$ was stated by Fricke and Havestadt (1928) to belong to the crystal class D_4^h or C_4^h ($4/mmm$ or $4/m$), but it was ultimately found that the only possible structure was based on a space group in the crystal class $D_2^d(\bar{4}2m)$ (Beevers and Lipson, 1932).

The data from the external form of the crystal should therefore be supplemented by the information obtained from other methods (Phillips, 1946, p. 151). For example, etch figures may give the true symmetry even if general faces are not developed on a crystal, and the presence of optical activity and piezo- and pyro-electricity will show the absence of a centre of symmetry. Such tests, however, are not always conclusive because the absence of these two effects does not necessarily indicate that centro-symmetry is present.

The symmetry of X-ray diffraction photographs is not, in itself, necessarily sufficient to establish the class of a crystal; it can place the crystal only into one of eleven groups, called *Laue groups.* This is so because all X-ray diffraction patterns must indicate a centre of symmetry, in that the reflexion hkl has the same intensity as the reflexion $\bar{h}\bar{k}\bar{l}$ (Friedel's law). All triclinic crystals therefore fall into the same Laue group $\bar{1}$, and all monoclinic crystals into the same Laue group $2/m$.

The X-ray diffraction pattern of a crystal does, however, contain other information about the true symmetry, and, if this information can be extracted, the space group, with a few exceptions, can be determined unequivocally. The methods of procedure are described in Chapter 3.

It will thus be seen that the determination of the class of a crystal presents certain difficulties which may not be resolvable. Fortunately, however, although logic would suggest that the crystal class should be determined as a prelude to the space group, it may happen that the step can be circumvented. As shown in the next section, the systematic absences of X-ray reflexions, necessary for space-group determination, may also fix the crystal class, and, even if this is not so, it is sometimes possible to show that certain crystal classes are not possible on structural grounds (Bradley and Thewlis, 1926). If this cannot be done, the class of highest symmetry may be tried first, and if no acceptable structure can be based upon it, lower symmetry may be tried (Bradley and Lu, 1937). Possibilities such as these should be considered, and certainly the X-ray investigator should not be discouraged from further effort by failure to fix a crystal class unambiguously.

4.3. *Systematic absence of X-ray reflexions.* The structure amplitude of a particular reflexion depends upon the atomic parameters, and, of course, it may be extremely small—so small that no reflexion corresponding to the particular indices can be observed. In general, such absent reflexions are randomly distributed amongst the possible indices, but sometimes they are systematically distributed, and are called *systematic absences* or *extinctions*.

We can see how this phenomenon arises by considering the expression for the structure factor

$$\mathrm{F}(hkl) = \sum_n f_n \exp 2\pi i(hx_n + ky_n + lz_n). \tag{29.1}$$

The summation has to be taken over all the atoms in the unit cell, and if there are no relations between the atomic co-ordinates the expression cannot be simplified. But, as we have seen in section **2**.1, there often *is* some relation between the atomic positions, and then equation *29*.1 can be simplified by collecting into a group those atoms that form a related set; the summation may then be made over the number of groups.

For example, consider a space group with the lattice C. We know that for each point xyz there must be another at $\frac{1}{2}+x, \frac{1}{2}+y, z$. Then if we sum over these pairs of atoms, we have

$$\begin{aligned}\mathrm{F}(hkl) &= \sum_{n=1}^{N/2} f_n[\exp\{2\pi i(hx_n + ky_n + lz_n)\} \\ &\qquad + \exp\{2\pi i(hx_n + ky_n + lz_n + \tfrac{1}{2}h + \tfrac{1}{2}k)\}] \\ &= \sum_{n=1}^{N/2} f_n\left[\exp\{2\pi i(hx_n + ky_n + lz_n)\}\left\{1 + \exp\left(2\pi i\,\frac{h+k}{2}\right)\right\}\right]. \end{aligned} \tag{29.2}$$

The last factor can have only two values; if $h+k$ is even it is two and if $h+k$ is odd it is zero. Thus if $h+k$ is odd the result must be zero whatever the values of x_n, y_n and z_n. Conversely, if we find that no reflexion is observed for which $h+k$ is odd, we may deduce that the lattice of the crystal investigated is C. Rules for the other lattices may be deduced in a similar way.

Suppose next that the crystal has a glide plane, *c*, passing through the origin and parallel to the plane (010). Then the atoms may be grouped in pairs with co-ordinates *xyz*, and $x, \bar{y}, \frac{1}{2}+z$. If we take the atoms in pairs, the expression for the structure factor becomes

$$F(hkl)=\sum_{n=1}^{N/2} f_n[\exp\{2\pi i(hx_n+ky_n+lz_n)\} + \exp\{2\pi i(hx_n-ky_n+lz_n+\tfrac{1}{2}l)\}]. \qquad (30.1)$$

This expression cannot be further simplified as equation *29.2* can, because the arguments of the exponentials are now dissimilar in that the sign of one term is different in the two. But if *k* were zero, the arguments would differ only by πl, and thus the expression would contain a factor, corresponding to the last factor in equation *29.2*,

$$1+\exp 2\pi il/2.$$

This expression is zero if *l* is odd, and therefore any reflexions that satisfy *both* the rules—that *k* should be zero and *l* should be odd—will be absent. This is the characteristic of the glide plane. General rules for other glide planes may be deduced in a similar way.

The final type of systematic absence is that which is connected with screw axes. If there is a two-fold screw axis along *b*, the equivalent points are *x*, *y*, *z* and $\bar{x}, \frac{1}{2}+y, \bar{z}$, and the expression for F is

$$F(hkl)=\sum_{n=1}^{N/2} f_n[\exp\{2\pi i(hx_n+ky_n+lz_n)\} + \exp\{2\pi i(-hx_n+ky_n-lz_n+\tfrac{1}{2}k)\}]. \qquad (30.2)$$

By comparing this with equation *30.1*, we see that if *both h* and *l* are zero, the expression will contain a factor

$$1+\exp 2\pi ik/2,$$

and this will be zero if *k* is odd. Therefore two-fold screw axes lead to the absence of reflexions for which two indices are zero and one is odd.

4.4. *An experimental difficulty—double reflexions.* Occasionally reflexions are observed on X-ray photographs which seem to be at variance with the symmetry indications of the other reflexions; for example, a reflexion 010 may be observed although all the others of type *hk*0 with *k* odd are absent. Such a reflexion should certainly be queried before arriving at the conclusion that the crystal has only an approximate glide plane.

One way in which spurious spots can arise has been pointed out by Renninger (1937): X-rays which have been reflected from one set of lattice planes may be reflected from another set of planes which happen, by chance, to be in the correct orientation; when this happens the resultant spot on the X-ray photograph will appear to have integral indices, and so to be a true reflexion. This may be seen by considering the conditions for reflexion as expressed by the sphere of reflexion (Ewald, 1921; Bernal, 1926); if AO (fig. 31) is the direction

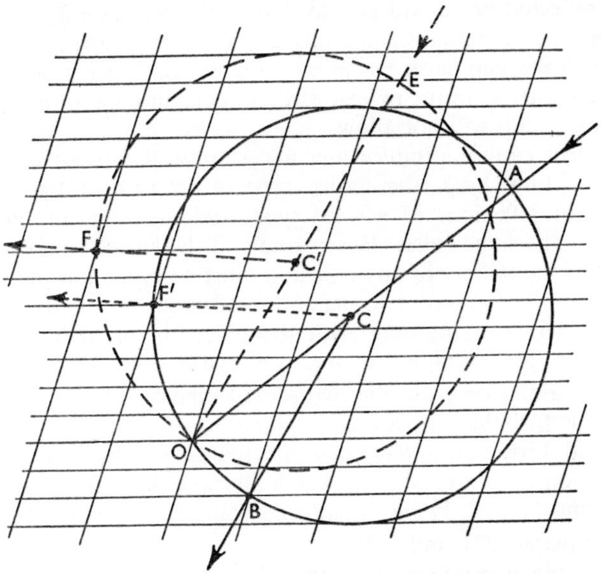

FIG. 31. Geometrical conditions for double reflexion of X-rays

of the incident beam, the reflexion $h_1k_1l_1$ in the direction CB will be produced when the sphere of reflexion, whose section in the diagram is ABO, passes through the reciprocal-lattice point B. To find the condition that the reflected ray CB should be reflected from another set of planes, we construct another sphere of reflexion on EO as diameter, where EO is parallel to CB; then if this sphere passes through a reciprocal-lattice point $h_2k_2l_2$, say F, the beam CB will be reflected to produce an emergent ray C′F.

This construction can, however, be simplified. Since we are concerned only with the direction of the emergent ray, we may draw a line CF′ from C equal and parallel to C′F, and simple geometry shows that F′ is also a reciprocal-lattice point. For if BC is equal and parallel to OC′, and F′C is equal and parallel to FC′, BF′ is equal and parallel to OF; but OF is a reciprocal-lattice vector, and therefore BF′ is also a reciprocal-lattice vector. Thus the doubly reflected ray CF′ will appear to be a singly reflected ray of indices hkl corresponding to the point F′, and will arise when the sphere of reflexion passes through two points simultaneously. The indices of the points B, F and F′ are related by the equations

$$h = h_1 + h_2, \quad k = k_1 + k_2, \quad l = l_1 + l_2.$$

With a reasonably complicated crystal this effect must occur quite frequently, but in general double reflexions are extremely weak, and so are inappreciable. Occasionally, however, the reflexions $h_1k_1l_1$ and $h_2k_2l_2$ may both be reasonably strong, and then the intensity of the doubly reflected beam will add to that of the reflexion h_1+h_2, k_1+k_2, l_1+l_2, producing perhaps some of the experimental errors that experience has shown can never be entirely eliminated. But here we are more concerned with spurious reflexions that occur in conditions which the true space group will not allow.

The effect cannot produce any uncertainty of lattice; as we have seen in section **2**.4.3, the lattice type is determined by systematic absences of reflexions of general type, and the sums of the indices must obey the same rules. For example, if the lattice is body-centred, the sum of the indices of any reflexion must be even, and therefore the sums of the indices of two separate reflexions must also be even. But the effect can interfere with the detection of glide planes and screw axes; for example, we may observe a spurious reflexion 010, formed by reflexion from the two sets of planes 111 and $\bar{1}0\bar{1}$, neither of which is forbidden by a b glide plane or a screw axis parallel to b. Collin and Lipscomb (1949) describe the observation of a spurious 302 reflexion from a crystal for which all the other reflexions indicated space group No. 62, *Pbnm*; this turned out to be the double reflexion from the planes 221 and $1\bar{2}1$.

A glide plane produces so many systematic absences that the presence of one non-conforming reflexion would be immediately suspect; the danger is much greater with screw axes, for which the number of systematic absences is fewer. The double reflexions can, however, be recognized by their shapes; since they are formed by the reflexion of truly parallel rays, they are much sharper than ordinary spots, and so cannot easily be mistaken for them. If an observed spot is suspected to be of this type, a check should be made to see if it could be formed by the simultaneous passage of the sphere of reflexion through two reciprocal-lattice points corresponding to strong reflexions; this check must, of course, be carried out in three dimensions. Another method of checking is to see if the suspected reflexion is still present if a different radiation is used.

4.5. *Summary.* The sequence of operations for determining space groups by means of the principles described in this chapter are as follows. First reflexions of general type *hkl* are considered; if any of these are systematically absent the lattice is non-primitive. Then reflexions with one zero index are considered; systematic absences amongst these give information about glide planes. Finally, reflexions with two zero indices give information about screw axes. For the uniaxial and cubic systems, other types of reflexions, as indicated in the International Tables, must be examined as well.

These rules must be used strictly in order, as systematic absences which are special cases of more general absences are not significant. For example, the absence of reflexions $0k0$ with k odd does not necessarily signify a screw axis if a glide plane is present which causes the absence of reflexions $hk0$ with $h+k$ odd.

Sometimes systematic absences allow a space group to be determined uniquely, because they are characteristic of only one space group in a crystal system; for instance, if a monoclinic crystal gives no reflexions $h0l$ with h odd, and no reflexions $0k0$ with k odd, the space group is No. 14, $P2_1/a$. If, however, the systematic absences are only $0k0$ with k odd, the space group may be either No. 4, $P2_1$ or No. 11, $P2_1/m$. Statistical methods as described in the following chapter should then be tried. If all these methods fail, or if they are inconclusive, the crystal-structure problem of course need not be abandoned; as stated in section **2**.4.2, structures have been solved without preliminary determination of the space group.

5. Space-group Representations

5.1. *General equivalent points.* A space group may be represented in two ways—as a collection of symmetry elements, each with its location in the unit cell precisely indicated, or as a collection of points arranged so that it possesses these symmetries. These points are obtained by applying the various symmetry operations to a point in a general position x, y, z in the unit cell; the collection of points, which is such that if any operation is applied to any point no new point is produced, is called a set of *general equivalent points.*

The representation of a symmetry element by a set of symmetrically related points (section **2**.2.3) is most simply illustrated by space group No. 2, $P\bar{1}$. If the centre of symmetry is taken to be at the origin (since the origin can be taken as any position it is preferable to place it at a centre of symmetry), the equivalent points are x, y, z and $\bar{x}, \bar{y}, \bar{z}$. It so happens that these are the general equivalent points in the space group, but this is not necessarily so; as shown in fig. 25 (i), a single symmetry element repeated by the lattice translations will produce other symmetry elements, and these may in turn produce further equivalent points in the same unit cell. In the space group $P\bar{1}$, the point $1-x, \bar{y}, \bar{z}$ is related to the point $\bar{x}, \bar{y}, \bar{z}$ by translation a. But it is also related to the point x, y, z by a centre of symmetry at $\frac{1}{2}, 0, 0$, and if we consider all the points related by lattice translations to the points xyz and $\bar{x}\bar{y}\bar{z}$ we find that there are centres of symmetry at the points $0\,0\,0$, $\frac{1}{2}\,0\,0$, $0\,\frac{1}{2}\,0$, $0\,0\,\frac{1}{2}$, $0\,\frac{1}{2}\,\frac{1}{2}$, $\frac{1}{2}\,0\,\frac{1}{2}$, $\frac{1}{2}\,\frac{1}{2}\,0$, $\frac{1}{2}\frac{1}{2}\frac{1}{2}$. These centres of symmetry are called *non-equivalent symmetry elements* because they are not themselves related by any symmetry elements in the unit cell.

They do not in this case lead to any further equivalent points and thus the points x, y, z and $\bar{x}$, $\bar{y}$, $\bar{z}$ form the complete set of general equivalent points for the space group P$\bar{1}$.

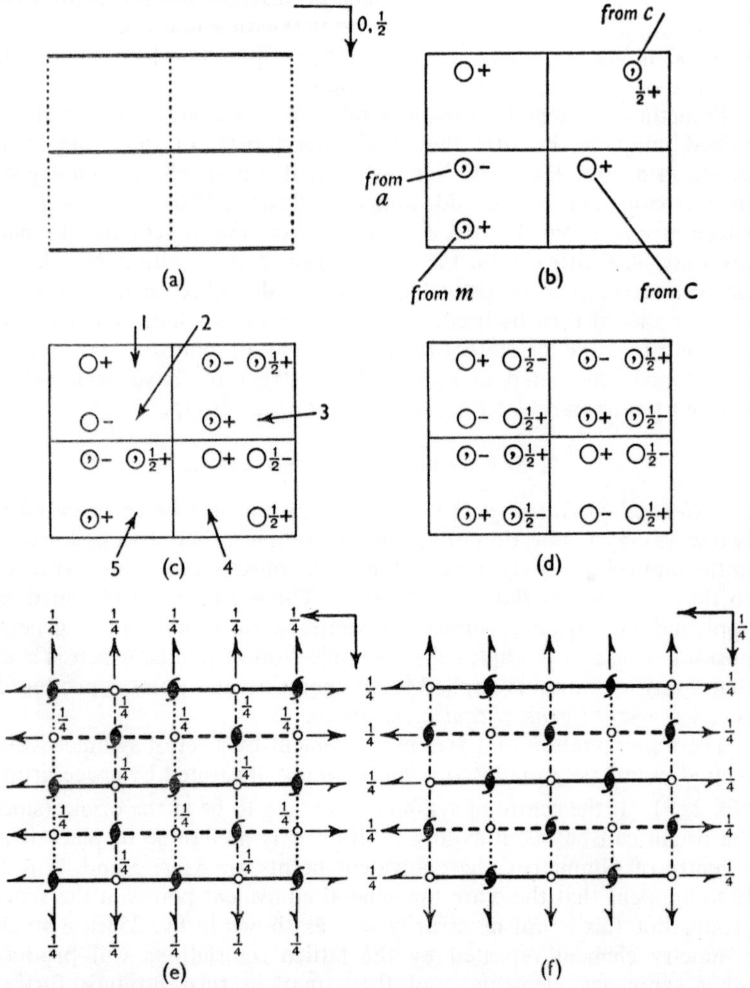

FIG. 34. Development of representation of space group No. 64 C*mca*. (*a*) Basic symmetry elements. (*b*) Points related by basic symmetry elements to point (x, y, z). (*c*) Points related by basic symmetry elements to points shown in (*b*). (*d*) Complete set of equivalent points. (*e*) Symmetry elements deduced from (*d*). (*f*) Diagram of symmetry elements from International Tables

Consider a more complicated space group, No. 64, C*mca*. The symbol tells us that this has a C-face-centred lattice, a mirror plane parallel to (100), a glide plane parallel to (010) with translation $\frac{1}{2}c$

and a glide plane parallel to (001) with translation $\frac{1}{2}a$. To find the complete set of symmetry elements, we first draw a diagram showing the elements given (fig. 34*a*) and another (fig. 34*b*) showing the four points that result from the operation of these elements on a general point *x*, *y*, *z*. The directions of the axes are drawn to agree with the International Tables—**a** downwards in the plane of the paper, **b** to the right, and **c** upwards from the plane of the paper. The origin is arbitrary, and it is simplest to place it at the point of intersection of the three planes of symmetry.

The points equivalent to (x, y, z) are then:

From operation C $\frac{1}{2}+x, \frac{1}{2}+y, z$;
From operation *m* $\bar{x}, y, z$;
From operation *c* $x, \bar{y}, \frac{1}{2}+z$;
From operation *a* $\frac{1}{2}+x, y, \bar{z}$.

The five points are shown in fig. 34*b*.

These points obviously do not satisfy the symmetry elements producing them, and the operations have to be repeated on each point in turn until no new points are produced. The next step is to apply each element in turn to each of the points in the list above except, of course, that produced by its own operation; thus:

C $(\frac{1}{2}-x, \frac{1}{2}+y, z), (\frac{1}{2}+x, \frac{1}{2}-y, \frac{1}{2}+z), (x, \frac{1}{2}+y, \bar{z})$;
m $(\frac{1}{2}-x, \frac{1}{2}+y, z), (\bar{x}, \bar{y}, \frac{1}{2}+z), (\frac{1}{2}-x, y, \bar{z})$;
c $(\frac{1}{2}+x, \frac{1}{2}-y, \frac{1}{2}+z), (\bar{x}, \bar{y}, \frac{1}{2}+z), (\frac{1}{2}+x, \bar{y}, \frac{1}{2}-z)$;
a $(x, \frac{1}{2}+y, \bar{z}), (\frac{1}{2}-x, y, \bar{z}), (\frac{1}{2}+x, \bar{y}, \frac{1}{2}-z)$.

It will be noted that these are not all different; they are equal in pairs, since the operations C and *m*, for example, must lead to the same point as the operations *m* and C.

Plotting these points together with the original five we obtain fig. 34*c*. This figure is still unsymmetrical, and the same operation should be repeated with the eleven points found. This process, although mechanical, is rather lengthy, and it can be avoided by guesswork. In fig. 34*c* gaps in the diagram are indicated by numbered arrows. Arrow (1) indicates that a point should occur at $(x, \frac{1}{2}-y, ?)$; such a point can be derived from the operation C on $(\frac{1}{2}+x, \bar{y}, \frac{1}{2}-z)$, which gives $(x, \frac{1}{2}-y, \frac{1}{2}-z)$. By similar reasoning, we arrive at the points

(2) $\frac{1}{2}-x, \frac{1}{2}-y, \frac{1}{2}+z$, by operation C from $(\bar{x}, \bar{y}, \frac{1}{2}+z)$;
(3) $(\frac{1}{2}-x, \bar{y}, \frac{1}{2}-z)$ by operation *m* from $(\frac{1}{2}+x, \bar{y}, \frac{1}{2}-z)$;
(4) $(\bar{x}, \frac{1}{2}+y, \bar{z})$ by operation C from $(\frac{1}{2}-x, y, \bar{z})$;
(5) $(\bar{x}, \frac{1}{2}-y, \frac{1}{2}-z)$ by operation *m* from $(x, \frac{1}{2}-y, \frac{1}{2}-z)$.

These points could have been derived from other points by means of other symmetry operations, but, in general, operations that do not involve translations are more easily visualized than screw axes and glide planes.

The complete set of equivalent points for the space group No. 64, C*mca*, is as follows:

$$(0, 0, 0;\ \tfrac{1}{2}, \tfrac{1}{2}, 0) +$$
$$x, y, z;\ \bar{x}, y, z;\ x, \bar{y}, \tfrac{1}{2}+z;\ \bar{x}, \bar{y}, \tfrac{1}{2}+z;$$
$$x, \tfrac{1}{2}+y, \bar{z};\ \bar{x}, \tfrac{1}{2}+y, \bar{z};\ x, \tfrac{1}{2}-y, \tfrac{1}{2}-z;\ \bar{x}, \tfrac{1}{2}-y, \tfrac{1}{2}-z.$$

The points thus found are shown in fig. 34*d*. (In accordance with the convention used in the International Tables those points which are enantiomorphous to the original point are marked with commas.) It does not follow that this collection is complete; this is proved by applying the symmetry elements to any point, when no further new points are produced. Moreover, the number of points—16—is that to be expected from the four symbols of the space group, each of which produces a doubling of the number of points. (This is not an invariable rule: in the space group No. 16, P222, for example, the three two-fold axes produce only four general equivalent points, not eight.)

5.2. *Symmetry representation.* From the general equivalent points it is possible to find further symmetry elements. It is difficult to do this systematically and experience of where to look for such elements is invaluable. For C*mca* the complete diagram of symmetry elements derived from the general equivalent positions is shown in fig. 34*e*. This figure differs from that given in the International Tables (fig. 34*f*); the difference will be discussed later (section **3**.1.1).

6. Application to Structure Determination

6.1. *Structural parameters.* The equivalent points are, from the crystal-structure point of view, the more important mode of representation of a space group, since a structure can be defined by placing atoms at various equivalent positions in the space group found; the problem of finding a crystal structure resolves itself, once the space group has been found, into the determination of the parameters, x_n, y_n, z_n, that define particular sets of atomic positions. Thus if a crystal with space group C*mca* contained 16 similar atoms, it would be probable that these atoms would be on a set of general equivalent positions, and they would be defined by three parameters—called *structural parameters*—instead of the 48 that would be required if each atom in the unit cell were considered separately. If there were 32 atoms, they could be divided into two sets of 16, and thus they would be defined by six structural parameters.

6.2. *Special equivalent positions.* Suppose however that the number of atoms is less than 16, or that it is not a multiple of 16; is it possible to fit such numbers of atoms into the unit cell? It *is* sometimes possible;

in addition to the general equivalent positions there are also special equivalent positions which are fewer in number, but which have the same space-group symmetry. These special positions arise when the co-ordinates chosen for the generation of equivalent points lie on certain types of symmetry element. For example, in the space group $P\bar{1}$, suppose we had started with the point $\frac{1}{2}, \frac{1}{2}, 0$ and had applied the symmetry operation to this; we should have found that no more points would have been produced in the unit cell. Thus it is possible to place an odd number of atoms in this unit cell provided that one atom is placed *at* a centre of symmetry.

Let us see what this implies in the more complicated space group No. 64, *Cmca*. In fig. 34*e* all the symmetry elements have been derived; which ones lead to special positions? The glide planes and screw axes cannot, because they involve a translation; the only symmetry elements that can lead to special positions are those that do not involve translations—the centre of symmetry, the mirror plane, the rotation axes and the inversion axes. The necessity for knowing whether such symmetry elements are present justifies the work involved in finding the complete symmetry representation of the space group; the Hermann-Mauguin symbol gives only a minimum of information and is sufficient only for classification. In the symbol *Cmca* the mirror plane appears directly but only the complete representation of the space group shows the other symmetry elements that lead to special positions—the centres of symmetry and the two-fold axes.

A method of finding the special positions is to consider a point on an appropriate symmetry element and to substitute the values of x, y and z in the expressions for the general equivalent points. We may first consider the mirror plane at $x=0$; that is, we take our original point as $(0, y, z)$. The sixteen equivalent points are then:

$$(0, 0, 0;\ \tfrac{1}{2}, \tfrac{1}{2}, 0)+$$

$$0, y, z;\ 0, y, z;\ 0, \bar{y}, \tfrac{1}{2}+z;\ 0, \bar{y}, \tfrac{1}{2}+z;$$

$$0, \tfrac{1}{2}+y, \bar{z};\ 0, \tfrac{1}{2}+y, \bar{z};\ 0, \tfrac{1}{2}-y, \tfrac{1}{2}-z;\ 0, \tfrac{1}{2}-y, \tfrac{1}{2}-z.$$

That the operation has been correctly performed is shown by the facts that the co-ordinates now appear in pairs and that there are only eight equivalent points, not sixteen.

In a similar way the other special positions may be found. *All* the symmetry elements must be considered; it is not sufficient to consider only one mirror plane, unless the special positions it produces include also those produced by the other at $x=\frac{1}{2}$. This is so in *Cmca*, because the special positions listed above include some with $x=\frac{1}{2}$. If we consider the two-fold axes, however, we find that they are in two sets: (i) at $x=\frac{1}{4}$, $z=0$; $x=\frac{3}{4}$, $z=0$; $x=\frac{1}{4}$, $z=\frac{1}{2}$; $x=\frac{3}{4}$, $z=\frac{1}{2}$; and (ii) at $y=\frac{1}{4}$, $z=\frac{1}{4}$; $y=\frac{3}{4}$, $z=\frac{3}{4}$; $y=\frac{1}{4}$, $z=\frac{3}{4}$; $y=\frac{3}{4}$, $z=\frac{3}{4}$. Substituting the first values, $x=\frac{1}{4}$, $z=0$, in the expressions for the general equivalent points gives the following set of equivalent positions:

$$\tfrac{1}{4}, y, 0, \quad \tfrac{3}{4}, \tfrac{1}{2}+y, 0, \quad \tfrac{3}{4}, y, 0, \quad \tfrac{1}{4}, \bar{y}, \tfrac{1}{2}$$
$$\tfrac{1}{4}, \tfrac{1}{2}+y, 0, \quad \tfrac{3}{4}, \tfrac{1}{2}-y, \tfrac{1}{2}, \quad \tfrac{3}{4}, \bar{y}, \tfrac{1}{2}, \quad \tfrac{1}{4}, \tfrac{1}{2}-y, \tfrac{1}{2}.$$

It will be noted that these include the positions on all the axes parallel to b, and so there is no need to consider these separately. In a similar way it can be shown that the two-fold axes parallel to a lead to only one set of special positions.

This is not so with the centres of symmetry. That at $\frac{1}{4}$, 0, 0 leads to the following special positions:

$$\tfrac{1}{4}, 0, 0, \quad \tfrac{3}{4}, \tfrac{1}{2}, 0, \quad \tfrac{3}{4}, 0, 0, \quad \tfrac{1}{4}, 0, \tfrac{1}{2}, \quad \tfrac{1}{4}, \tfrac{1}{2}, 0, \quad \tfrac{3}{4}, \tfrac{1}{2}, \tfrac{1}{2}, \quad 0, \tfrac{3}{4}, \tfrac{1}{2}, \quad \tfrac{1}{4}, \tfrac{1}{2}, \tfrac{1}{2};$$

these are half of the total number of centres. One of those not included is at 0, $\frac{1}{4}$, $\frac{1}{4}$. This produces the special positions:

$$0, \tfrac{1}{4}, \tfrac{1}{4}, \quad \tfrac{1}{2}, \tfrac{3}{4}, \tfrac{1}{4}, \quad 0, \tfrac{3}{4}, \tfrac{3}{4}, \quad \tfrac{1}{2}, \tfrac{1}{4}, \tfrac{3}{4}.$$

There are thus four still remaining, and these can be found to be another equivalent set:

$$\tfrac{1}{2}, \tfrac{1}{4}, \tfrac{1}{4}, \quad 0, \tfrac{3}{4}, \tfrac{1}{4}, \quad \tfrac{1}{2}, \tfrac{3}{4}, \tfrac{3}{4}, \quad 0, \tfrac{1}{4}, \tfrac{3}{4}.$$

That there should be two types of centres of symmetry is obvious, since eight lie on the intersections of mirror planes and two-fold axes and the others do not; but it is not obvious that the former divide into two non-equivalent sets of four each.

6.3. *The placing of atoms on general and special positions.* To summarize the results, we have found two sets of four equivalent points, on centres of symmetry; four sets of eight equivalent points, on centres of symmetry, on mirror planes, and on two sets of two-fold axes; and one set of sixteen equivalent points. By making use of the special positions it is possible to introduce numbers of atoms in multiples of four into the unit cell. For example, suppose there are 28 to be fixed; the simplest way of placing them is to put 16 in general positions, 8 in eight-fold special positions, and 4 on four equivalent centres of symmetry. In practice, it is better to apportion the atoms on the positions of smaller multiplicity first, in this case on the centres of symmetry. At first sight, it may seem that there are two possibilities, corresponding to the two sets of four special positions; this however is not so, as both sets have exactly the same environment of symmetry elements, and they differ only in choice of origin. Once a set of atoms has been placed, however, the origin of the structure is fixed, and further atoms must be placed on their correct symmetry elements even if there are others with similar environments. The choice cannot of course be made from space-group considerations only.

7. Practical Examples

7.1. *Alum, $KAl(SO_4)_2.12H_2O$.* Potassium aluminium alum is cubic, the unit cell containing $4\{KAl(SO_4)_2.12H_2O\}$; the only systematic absences are $0kl$ with k odd, $h0l$ with l odd, and $hk0$ with h odd, which show that the space group is No. 205, Pa3. The data for this space group are as follows.

24: (*d*) $xyz;\ zxy;\ yzx;$

$\tfrac{1}{2}+x, \tfrac{1}{2}-y, \bar{z};\ \tfrac{1}{2}+z, \tfrac{1}{2}-x, \bar{y};\ \tfrac{1}{2}+y, \tfrac{1}{2}-z, \bar{x};$

$\bar{x}, \tfrac{1}{2}+y, \tfrac{1}{2}-z;\ \bar{z}, \tfrac{1}{2}+x, \tfrac{1}{2}-y;\ \bar{y}, \tfrac{1}{2}+z, \tfrac{1}{2}-x;$

$\tfrac{1}{2}-x, \bar{y}, \tfrac{1}{2}+z;\ \tfrac{1}{2}-z, \bar{x}, \tfrac{1}{2}+y;\ \tfrac{1}{2}-y, \bar{z}, \tfrac{1}{2}+x;$

$\bar{x}\bar{y}\bar{z};\ \bar{z}\bar{x}\bar{y};\ \bar{y}\bar{z}\bar{x};$

$\tfrac{1}{2}-x, \tfrac{1}{2}+y, z;\ \tfrac{1}{2}-z, \tfrac{1}{2}+x, y;\ \tfrac{1}{2}-y, \tfrac{1}{2}+z, x;$

$x, \tfrac{1}{2}-y, \tfrac{1}{2}+z;\ z, \tfrac{1}{2}-x, \tfrac{1}{2}+y;\ y, \tfrac{1}{2}-z, \tfrac{1}{2}+x;$

$\tfrac{1}{2}+x, y, \tfrac{1}{2}-z;\ \tfrac{1}{2}+z, x, \tfrac{1}{2}-y;\ \tfrac{1}{2}+y, z, \tfrac{1}{2}-x.$

8: (*c*) $xxx;\ \tfrac{1}{2}+x, \tfrac{1}{2}-x, \bar{x};\ \bar{x}, \tfrac{1}{2}+x, \tfrac{1}{2}-x;\ \tfrac{1}{2}-x, \bar{x}, \tfrac{1}{2}+x;$

$\bar{x}\bar{x}\bar{x};\ \tfrac{1}{2}-x, \tfrac{1}{2}+x, x;\ x, \tfrac{1}{2}-x, \tfrac{1}{2}+x;\ \tfrac{1}{2}+x, x, \tfrac{1}{2}-x.$

4: (*a*) $000;\ 0\tfrac{1}{2}\tfrac{1}{2};\ \tfrac{1}{2}0\tfrac{1}{2};\ \tfrac{1}{2}\tfrac{1}{2}0.$ (*b*) $\tfrac{1}{2}\tfrac{1}{2}\tfrac{1}{2};\ \tfrac{1}{2}00;\ 0\tfrac{1}{2}0;\ 00\tfrac{1}{2}.$

The unit cell contains four potassium atoms, four aluminium atoms, eight sulphur atoms, thirty-two oxygen atoms and forty-eight water molecules. We attempt to locate the smaller numbers of atoms first, since the positions of these should be more definite. Thus the potassium atoms must occupy (*a*) or (*b*) positions. But there is no essential difference between one of the (*a*) positions (e.g. 0, 0, 0) and one of the (*b*) positions (e.g. $\tfrac{1}{2}$, 0, 0); they have the same environment of symmetry elements. Thus we may choose either to start with, but having made our choice we have not the same liberty of action for other atoms. We therefore choose to put the potassium atoms in the (*a*) positions.

The four aluminium atoms must occupy the other four-fold positions, (*b*). Thus both the sets of metal atoms are fixed solely by space-group considerations.

The eight sulphur atoms must occupy (*c*) positions—the only eight-fold ones—since all the four-fold positions are occupied. The sulphur atoms are not, however, definitely located in the unit cell, since their positions depend upon a parameter x about which we have so far no information.

The thirty-two oxygen atoms cannot all be equivalent since there is no set of thirty-two equivalent points; they must therefore be placed on twenty-four general positions (*d*) and eight special positions (*c*), or on four different sets of special positions (*c*). The fact that the (*c*) positions have already been chosen for the sulphur atoms is immaterial; any number of atoms can be placed upon the same set of positions provided that at least one variable parameter is involved. For the same reason, four sets of special positions could be chosen for the oxygen atoms, although this possibility is unlikely. Similarly, it is unlikely that the forty-eight water molecules will make use of the (*c*) positions; they probably lie on two sets of general positions (*d*).

The most probable arrangement of atoms is thus:

(i) K and Al on fixed special positions (*a*) and (*b*),
(ii) S on special positions (*c*) with one parameter,
(iii) O on one set of special positions (*c*) with one parameter and on one set of general positions (*d*) with three parameters,
(iv) H_2O on two sets of general positions (*d*) with six parameters.

Thus the position of the ninety-six atoms (excluding hydrogen) in the unit cell are determined by only eleven parameters—a striking instance of the usefulness of space-group theory. This of course is exceptional; for crystals of lower symmetry it is rare to have as great a gain in simplicity; but it is quite usual, even in monoclinic crystals, for space-group theory to lead immediately to important results.

7.2. *Potassium mercury chloride, $K_2HgCl_4.H_2O$.* An example of lack of definiteness in the space-group information is given by potassium mercury chloride, $K_2HgCl_4.H_2O$, which belongs to space group No. 55, *Pbam* (MacGillavry, de Wilde and Bijvoet, 1938). This space group has the following sets of equivalent points:

2: (*a*) 000; $\frac{1}{2}\frac{1}{2}0$. (*b*) $00\frac{1}{2}$; $\frac{1}{2}\frac{1}{2}\frac{1}{2}$. (*c*) $0\frac{1}{2}0$; $\frac{1}{2}00$. (*d*) $0\frac{1}{2}\frac{1}{2}$; $\frac{1}{2}0\frac{1}{2}$.
4: (*e*) $00z$; etc. (*f*) $0\frac{1}{2}z$; etc. (*g*) $xy0$; etc. (*h*) $xy\frac{1}{2}$; etc.
8: (*i*) xyz; etc.

Since the unit cell contains $K_8Hg_4Cl_{16}.4H_2O$, numerous possibilities arise for placing the atoms, and it is advisable to deal first with the smallest groups. Thus the mercury atoms may lie upon sets of positions (*e*) or (*g*), or upon any pairs of sets (*a*), (*b*), (*c*) and (*d*); there is no need to consider the sets (*f*) and (*h*) because these are equivalent to the sets (*e*) and (*g*) respectively, with a change of origin. Similar considerations apply to the water molecules, except that the four sets (*e*), (*f*), (*g*) and (*h*) must now be considered, since any arbitrariness in origin vanishes when some atoms have been fixed. Moreover, of course, the water molecules cannot occupy positions already occupied by the mercury atoms, but this fact does not preclude the placing of both on positions such as (*e*) which involve a variable parameter; this is permissible so long as the values of z are different.

The potassium atoms can be accommodated on the general positions (*i*) or upon combinations of special positions. Still more possibilities arise for the chlorine atoms. So many combinations are possible that the assignment cannot be considered systematically; methods of trial-and-error, as described in Chapter 6, have to be used, and the heaviness of the mercury atom (section **6**.5.2) makes the problem not too difficult. The structure actually contains atoms in the following positions:

Hg on (*e*),
H_2O on (*f*),
K on (*g*) + (*h*),
Cl on (*g*) + (*h*) + (*i*).

7.3. *Dibromo* p-*amino benzoic acid.* A good example of departure from the obvious is given by the crystal 3-5 dibromo *p*-amino benzoic acid. The space group is No. 53 P*man* and the unit cell contains eight molecules. Since there are eight general equivalent positions in the space group one would think that it is almost certain that the molecules lie in general positions. In fact (Pant, 1965) the molecules form two non-equivalent sets, one set lying on two-fold axes and the other on planes of symmetry.

7.4. *The Spinel structures.* That the theory of space groups applies to crystals is now taken as a matter of course. It is nevertheless remarkable that a theory worked out completely before the discovery of X-ray diffraction should apply so precisely in practice. That exceptions occur should not be regarded as remarkable—the remarkable fact is that exceptions are so rare! Rigid application of space-group theory should always be the first step in crystal-structure determination, but the fact should be borne in mind that there are crystals which to some extent disregard the theory or make use of it in unexpected ways.

The reason for this is that natural systems tend to disorder (the second law of thermodynamics), and the extreme degree of order found in crystals is exceptional; if possible some disorder will creep in. Normally this is negligible, but occasionally it may not be; cobalt (Edwards and Lipson, 1942) is so irregular that its structure is not even based on a lattice and this produces a broadening of some of the X-ray reflexions; but other crystals, such as some that are isomorphous with spinel, behave in a much more subtle manner.

Spinel is a mineral of composition $MgAl_2O_4$, and is isomorphous with a number of other compounds of similar formula, such as $MnCr_2O_4$ and $CuFe_2O_4$. The space group is No. 227, F*d*3*m*, and the unit cell contains $8(MgAl_2O_4)$.

In this space group there are 192 general equivalent positions; all the atoms are thus in special positions and we need not consider any sets of multiplicity higher than 32. The equivalent positions to be considered are as follows:

$$(000;\ 0\tfrac{1}{2}\tfrac{1}{2};\ \tfrac{1}{2}0\tfrac{1}{2};\ \tfrac{1}{2}\tfrac{1}{2}0)+$$

$$8\colon (a)\ 000;\ \tfrac{1}{4}\tfrac{1}{4}\tfrac{1}{4};\quad 8\colon (b)\ \tfrac{1}{2}\tfrac{1}{2}\tfrac{1}{2};\ \tfrac{3}{4}\tfrac{3}{4}\tfrac{3}{4}.$$

$$16\colon (c)\ \tfrac{1}{8}\tfrac{1}{8}\tfrac{1}{8};\ \tfrac{1}{8}\tfrac{3}{8}\tfrac{3}{8};\ \tfrac{3}{8}\tfrac{1}{8}\tfrac{3}{8};\ \tfrac{3}{8}\tfrac{3}{8}\tfrac{1}{8}.$$

$$16\colon (d)\ \tfrac{5}{8}\tfrac{5}{8}\tfrac{5}{8};\ \tfrac{5}{8}\tfrac{7}{8}\tfrac{7}{8};\ \tfrac{7}{8}\tfrac{5}{8}\tfrac{7}{8};\ \tfrac{7}{8}\tfrac{7}{8}\tfrac{5}{8}.$$

$$32\colon (e)\ xxx;\ x\bar{x}\bar{x};\ \tfrac{1}{4}-x,\tfrac{1}{4}-x,\tfrac{1}{4}-x;\ \tfrac{1}{4}-x,\tfrac{1}{4}+x,\tfrac{1}{4}+x;$$

$$\bar{x}x\bar{x};\ \bar{x}\bar{x}x;\ \tfrac{1}{4}+x,\tfrac{1}{4}-x,\tfrac{1}{4}+x;\ \tfrac{1}{4}+x,\tfrac{1}{4}+x,\tfrac{1}{4}-x.$$

The eight magnesium atoms should occupy either (*a*) or (*b*) positions; since the origin is arbitrary, it does not matter which are chosen and so we may put them on the (*a*) positions. The sixteen aluminium atoms can then occupy either the (*c*) or (*d*) positions; they cannot make use of the eight-fold positions since one of these sets is occupied by magnesium atoms. The oxygen atoms can occupy (*e*) positions with one variable parameter, to be determined.

These principles are obeyed, and the complete structure is defined in the following way:

8 Mg in (*a*),
16 Al in (*d*),
32 O in (*e*) with $x=\frac{3}{8}$ (approximately).

But certain compounds, such as $MgFe_2O_4$, do not fit into this scheme. They belong to the cubic system; X-ray photographs show that they have a face-centred lattice F; and the unit cell contains $8(MgFe_2O_4)$. Yet no structure based on the above principles will fit in with the X-ray data, and Barth and Posnjak (1932) have shown that the following sets of positions are occupied:

8 Fe on (*a*),
8 Fe + 8 Mg statistically distributed on (*d*),
32 O on (*e*) with $x = \cdot 390$.

Thus the structure is essentially similar to that of spinel, but the space-group rules are not obeyed except in a statistical way.

7.5. *Analcite*, $NaAlSi_2O_6.H_2O$. Analcite provides an instance of a much greater departure from space-group principles. It is cubic, the space group being No. 230, I*a*3*d*, and the unit cell containing $16(NaAlSi_2O_6.H_2O)$. The space group has the following sets of equivalent positions:

16: (*a*) 000; etc. (*b*) $\frac{1}{8}\frac{1}{8}\frac{1}{8}$; etc.
24: (*c*) $\frac{1}{8}0\frac{1}{4}$; etc. (*d*) $\frac{3}{8}0\frac{1}{4}$; etc.
32: (*e*) xxx; etc.
48: (*f*) $x0\frac{1}{4}$; etc. (*g*) $\frac{1}{8}, x, \frac{1}{4}-x$; etc.
96: (*h*) xyz; etc.

It will be noted that it is impossible to place the atoms in the unit cell in accordance with this scheme, because if the sodium and aluminium atoms occupy positions (*a*) and (*b*) there are no sixteen-fold positions left for the water molecules. There is, however, no difficulty in placing the silicon atoms in (*e*) and the oxygen atoms in (*h*).

In fact, the following structure is found (Taylor, 1930). The silicon and aluminium atoms together distribute themselves at random on the 48-fold positions (*g*); the water molecules occupy positions (*b*); the oxygen atoms occupy positions (*h*); and the sodium atoms, instead of occupying positions (*a*), distribute themselves so that on the average two-thirds of an atom occupies each of the 24-fold positions (*c*). The complete specification of the structure is:

48 (Si, Al) on (*g*) with $x=0{\cdot}661$.
16 Na statistically distributed on (*c*).
96 O on (*h*) with $x=0{\cdot}111$, $y=0{\cdot}131$, $z=0{\cdot}722$.
16 H_2O on (*b*).

This structure accounts adequately for all the X-ray intensities.

A way of evading this difficulty is suggested by Kästner (1931). The structure is regarded as merely pseudo-cubic, and lower symmetries are considered. The tetragonal space group No. 142, $I4_1/acd$, has most of the systematic absences of the cubic space group I*a*3*d* and so an attempt may be made to fit the structure into this space group. The following sets of equivalent positions exist:

8: (*a*) 000; etc. (*b*) $00\frac{1}{4}$; etc.
16: (*c*) $0\frac{1}{4}\frac{1}{8}$; etc. (*d*) $00z$; etc. (*e*) $\frac{1}{4}x\frac{1}{8}$; etc. (*f*) $xx\frac{1}{4}$; etc.
32: (*g*) xyz; etc.

There are thus many ways of placing the atoms in the unit cell, and Kästner states that the following specification gives a structure closely resembling the cubic one:

16 Na on (*e*) with $x=0{\cdot}625$.
16 A on (*f*) with $x=0{\cdot}339$.
32 Si on (*g*) with $x=0{\cdot}125$, $y=0{\cdot}411$, $z=0{\cdot}224$.
32 O on (*g*) with $x=0{\cdot}119$, $y=0{\cdot}111$, $z=0{\cdot}653$.
32 O on (*g*) with $x=0{\cdot}131$, $y=0{\cdot}472$, $z=0{\cdot}736$.
32 O on (*g*) with $x=0{\cdot}278$, $y=0{\cdot}139$, $z=0{\cdot}756$.
16 H_2O on (*f*) with $x=0{\cdot}125$.

If this is the true structure, space-group principles are not violated. Nevertheless, readiness to contemplate the possibility of violation led Taylor to essentially the correct structure whereas a more pedantic approach might have been less fruitful.

Problems of this sort are rare. Space-group theory works very well for almost all crystals, but, if difficulties are met with in its application, the possibilities of an unorthodox approach—such as the placing of two-thirds of a sodium atom on each of 24 equivalent positions—should not be ignored.

8. Plane Groups

8.1. *Two-dimensional symmetry operations.* Although crystals are three-dimensional, it is often necessary to consider projections of crystal structures on planes, and then only symmetry elements operating in two dimensions arise. The arrangements of these symmetry elements that produce a regularly repeating pattern are called plane groups, by analogy with the term space group.

The symmetry operations must necessarily be those that do not require the movement of the representative point out of the plane considered; thus only rotation axes, mirror planes and glide planes, all perpendicular to the plane, are possible. These may be represented by the symbols 1, 2, 3, 4, 6, *m* and *g*. Two-dimensional lattices are denoted by small letters, and only two need be considered—*p* and *c*.

8.2. *Two-dimensional systems.* The presence of these various symmetry elements leads to relationships between the two axes, which we may call *a* and *b*, and so provides a means of classification of projections of crystal structures into systems. These relationships are tabulated below:

Relationships		System	Plane groups
$a \neq b$	$\gamma \neq 90°$	Oblique	1 & 2; *p*1 & *p*2.
$a \neq b$	$\gamma = 90°$	Rectangular	3–9; *pm*; *pg*; *cm*; *pmm*; *pmg*; *pgg* & *cmm*.
$a = b$	$\gamma = 90°$	Square	10–12; *p*4; *p*4*m* & *p*4*g*.
$a = b$	$\gamma = 120°$	Hexagonal	13–17; *p*3; *p*3*m*1; *p*31*m*; *p*6 & *p*6*m*.

It will be noted that the number of systems is only four; projections of monoclinic crystals fall into one or other of the first two systems, the distinction between the trigonal and hexagonal systems—never a clear one even in three dimensions—disappears completely, and there is no system corresponding to the cubic. This last fact follows, of course, because the characteristic of the cubic system is the set of three-fold axes inclined to the crystallographic axes; these cannot have any equivalent in two dimensions. It might be thought that, since the projections of a cubic structure on the cube faces have $a = b$ and $\gamma = 90°$, such projections must belong to the square system. This is not so; the plane groups in this system all have four-fold axes of symmetry, and two cubic point groups, 23 and $m3$, do not have this symmetry. Thus the projections of crystals which have these point groups belong to the rectangular system, and the equality of the lengths of the sides of the unit cell must, from the point of view of the two-dimensional representation, be regarded as fortuitous.

Complete descriptions of the 17 plane groups are given in the International Tables, Vol. I (1952).

8.3. *Uses of plane groups.* Since some crystal-structure work is confined to two dimensions, plane groups would appear to have important uses, and they do, for example, provide a basis for the classification of structure-factor formulae (Bragg and Lipson, 1936). Patterson (1935*b*) considered them to be of great value in interpreting $|F|^2$ projections (Chapter 7). Nevertheless, they do not appear to have been greatly used: most workers refer to the space group only, since it is unique for a particular crystal; the three projections parallel to the axes of a monoclinic crystal may belong to three different plane groups, which does not make for simplicity. Moreover, for plane groups, it is sometimes necessary to subdivide the axes, and even to choose new axes, as for the projection of a centred tetragonal cell. It is therefore not surprising that the theory of plane groups has not achieved great prominence in the field of crystal-structure determination.

CHAPTER 3

INTENSITY STATISTICS APPLIED TO SPACE-GROUP DETERMINATION

1. Introduction

1.1. *Patterson function approach.* The determination of space groups by means of systematically absent reflexions is, as we have seen, incomplete in that it frequently fails to distinguish between space groups in a given crystal system. While the ambiguity has not in fact proved to be a serious obstacle in the determination of crystal structures, a clear and unequivocal determination of the space group at the outset of a structure investigation may well lead to more rapid and certain progress, and the statement by Buerger (1946, 1950 *a*, *e*) that the X-ray intensities themselves should provide information in addition to that given by the systematically absent reflexions, is therefore of importance.

Buerger's approach to the problem was made through the theory of the interpretation of the Patterson synthesis (section **1**.3.2). If we accept the conclusion that a particular Patterson synthesis corresponds to one and only one atomic arrangement—a conclusion that is discussed further in sections **6**.6.2 and **7**.3.4—then the symmetry of this atomic arrangement must also be inherent in the Patterson synthesis and hence in the diffracted intensities; Buerger thus considers the characteristic features that different symmetry elements should impress upon Patterson syntheses.

The reasoning is best explained by means of an example. If a structure contains an *a* glide plane through the origin parallel to (010), all the atoms must be related in pairs with co-ordinates (x, y, z) $(\frac{1}{2}+x, \bar{y}, z)$, and thus the Patterson synthesis will show peaks at points $(\frac{1}{2}, 2y, 0)$. There will be other peaks in general positions due to atoms not related by this symmetry element, but along the line $x=\frac{1}{2}$, $z=0$, we should expect an excess of peaks, and if this excess can be detected it gives confirmation of the existence of the glide plane.

Such glide planes are, however, more definitely detected from systematic absences, but the importance of the reasoning is that it applies to symmetry elements, such as mirror planes, which do not lead to systematic absences. If a structure has a mirror plane through the origin parallel to (010), the equivalent points are (x, y, z) and $(x, \bar{y}, z)$ and thus in the Patterson synthesis there will be an excess of peaks in the line $x=0$, $z=0$; if this excess can be detected, it gives confirmation of the existence of a mirror plane which may not be detectable by other means.

The effect of screw axes is more general. A screw axis through the origin along the *b* axis gives equivalent points (x, y, z) and $(\bar{x}, \frac{1}{2}+y, \bar{z})$, and consequently in the Patterson synthesis gives excess of peaks in the plane $y=\frac{1}{2}$. The characteristic of a two-fold rotation axis is excess

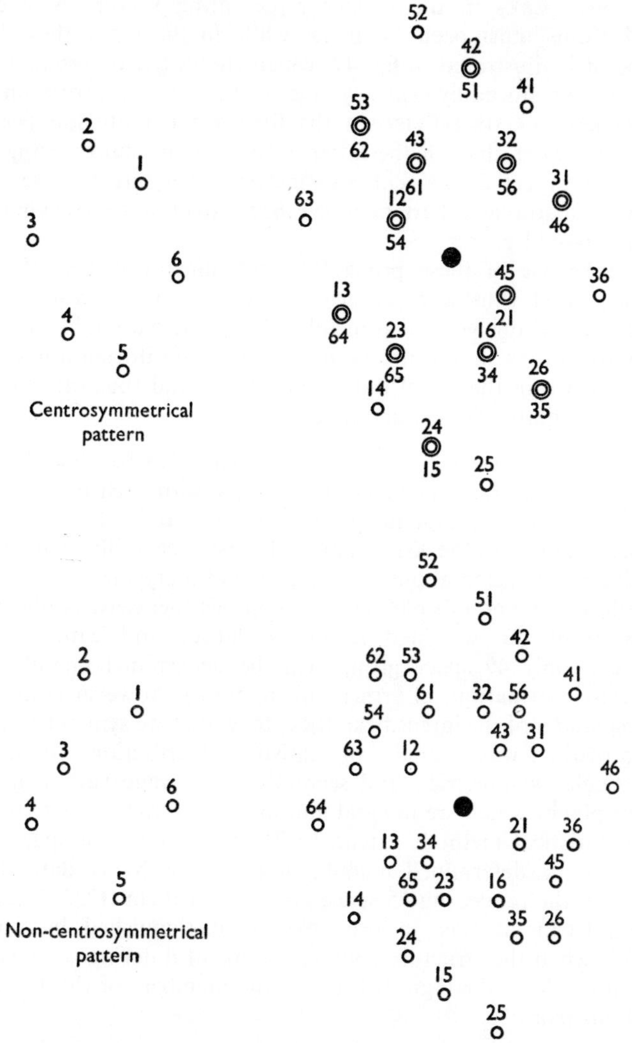

FIG. 47. Representations of vectors produced by centrosymmetrical and non-centrosymmetrical patterns of points. The black spots represent the zero vectors, and the double circles represent overlapping vectors

of peaks in the plane $y=0$, and, again, this axis may not be detectable by any other means.

These principles do not, however, apply to the centre of symmetry, since the Patterson peaks representing vectors between related atoms have co-ordinates ($2x$, $2y$, $2z$), which are quite general. Nevertheless, a distinction still exists between the Patterson syntheses of centro-symmetrical and non-centrosymmetrical structures, for, as Buerger points out, peaks in the former representing vectors between un-related atoms must occur in pairs, while in the latter they do not. This point is illustrated in fig. 47, which shows the representations of the vectors produced by centrosymmetrical and non-centrosymmetrical arrangements of six points; in the former the Patterson peaks are larger and fewer than in the latter. Thus, other things being equal, we should expect a non-centrosymmetrical structure to give a more even and featureless Patterson synthesis than a centrosymmetrical structure would give.

To make use of these principles, three-dimensional syntheses are necessary, and thus a great deal of computational work must be undertaken. From general principles, however, we might expect that the computations should not be necessary; the information sought is contained within the set of diffracted beams, and thus other methods might be available for extracting it.

1.2. *Statistical approach.* The problem may also be viewed through the reciprocal lattice. The reciprocal lattice with each point weighted according to the corresponding structure amplitude $|F|$ is the neatest representation of all the X-ray data and must necessarily contain all the available information about the symmetry of a crystal.

In effect, the methods of Chapter 2 concern themselves only with the symmetry of the weighted reciprocal lattice and with systematic absences; only 49 space groups can be determined unambiguously from this information. Further information is however contained in the *magnitudes* of the intensities; these may indicate symmetry elements in two distinct ways—firstly, by statistical distributions characteristic of particular symmetries, and secondly by average values in certain rows or planes which are integral multiples of average values elsewhere.

The statistical methods extend to 215 the number of space groups which can be determined unambiguously from X-ray data (Rogers, 1950). Of the remaining 15 space groups 4 of them (**I**222, **I**$2_12_12_1$, **I**23 and **I**2_13) can, at least in principle, be distinguished by statistical methods when the structure contains atoms of differing weights, but it is not possible to distinguish between the members of the 11 enantio-morphous pairs.

2. The Centric and Acentric Distribution Functions

2.1. *Ratio test.* Wilson (1949, 1950*a*) has considered the distribution of intensities from a crystal containing a reasonably large number of approximately equal atoms distributed at random. To describe the intensity distribution amongst the individual orders of diffraction we define a quantity P(I), where P(I)δI is the proportion of intensities I (=FF*) which have values lying between I and I+δI. Wilson shows that if the crystal has no symmetry

$$_{1}\mathrm{P(I)}\delta\mathrm{I}=\frac{\exp(-\mathrm{I/S})\delta\mathrm{I}}{\mathrm{S}}, \qquad (49.1)$$

where S is a distribution parameter appropriate to the set of reflexions under consideration. For general *hkl* reflexions referred to a primitive cell, S has the value Σ which is defined by

$$\Sigma=\sum_{j=1}^{N} f_j'^2, \qquad (49.2)$$

where the summation is taken over all the atoms in the unit cell. Possible values of S for less general conditions will be discussed in section **3**.3.2. If, however, the crystal has a centre of symmetry,

$$_{\bar{1}}\mathrm{P(I)}\delta\mathrm{I}=\frac{(\exp-\mathrm{I/2S})\delta\mathrm{I}}{(2\pi\mathrm{SI})^{\frac{1}{2}}} \qquad (49.3)$$

(*49*.1) and (*49*.3) have become known, respectively, as the 'acentric' distribution function and the 'centric' distribution function. It should be noted that the words 'centric' and 'acentric' apply only to properties in reciprocal space and should not be used as substitutes for 'centrosymmetric' and 'non-centrosymmetric'.

These results are equivalent to the properties of Patterson syntheses stated by Buerger, but the fact that they are quantitative makes them of greater use. They are the basis of several practical tests for crystal symmetry.

Thus Wilson (1949) has shown that the mean value of the structure amplitudes is greater for the acentric distribution than for the centric distribution; he has deduced that the ratio of the square of the mean structure amplitude to the mean intensity should have the values

$$\rho=\frac{\langle|\mathrm{F}|\rangle^2}{\langle\mathrm{I}\rangle}=\frac{\pi}{4}\simeq 0{\cdot}785 \text{ for the acentric distribution}$$

$$\text{and } \rho=\frac{2}{\pi}\simeq 0{\cdot}637 \text{ for the centric distribution.}$$

The distinction between the values 0·785 and 0·637 should be readily detectable. Reasonably accurate intensities are required but they need not be put on an absolute scale in making this comparison.

2.2. *Variance test.* Another test proposed by Wilson (1951) is based on the variance, the mean square deviation of I from its mean value ⟨I⟩. He has shown that the specific variance of the intensities,

$$V=\frac{\langle(\mathrm{I}-\langle\mathrm{I}\rangle)^2\rangle}{\langle\mathrm{I}\rangle^2}=\frac{\langle\mathrm{I}^2\rangle}{\langle\mathrm{I}\rangle^2}-1,$$

has the value 2 for the centric distribution and 1 for the acentric distribution. This test, with developments, will be considered further in section 3.4.

2.3. *N*(z) *test.* There may be some reluctance to base a space-group determination on a single item of evidence, as in the ratio and variance tests; the evidence for systematic absences, for example, is accepted only when a reasonably large number of reflexions is considered. In order to make the method more convincing, therefore, Howells, Phillips and Rogers (1950) have devised a way of verifying the complete intensity distribution. They show that the fractions N(z) of reflexions whose intensities are equal to or less than a fraction z of the local average are given, for a non-centrosymmetrical crystal, by the function

$$N(z) = 1 - \exp(-z)$$

and for a centrosymmetrical crystal by the function

$$N(z) = \mathrm{erf}(\tfrac{1}{2}z)^{\frac{1}{2}},$$

where the symbol 'erf' represents the error function (Jahnke and Emde, 1933). These two functions, which are plotted in fig. 50 and which

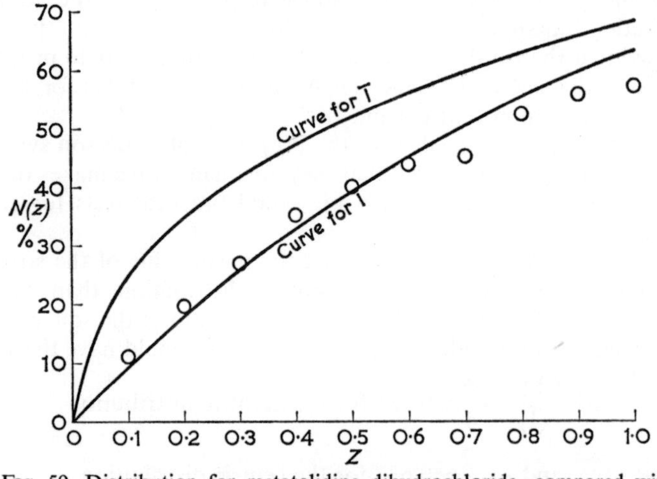

FIG. 50. Distribution for metatolidine dihydrochloride, compared with theoretical curves for 1 and $\bar{1}$

are tabulated below up to $z = 1$, differ appreciably from each other, particularly at lower values of z.

TABLE 50

Values, in percentages, of the two functions representing N(z)

	0·0	0·1	0·2	0·3	0·4	0·5	0·6	0·7	0·8	0·9	1·0
$1 - \exp(-z)$	0·00	9·52	18·13	25·92	32·97	39·35	45·12	50·34	55·07	59·34	63·21
$\mathrm{erf}(\frac{1}{2}z)^2$	0·00	24·81	34·53	41·87	47·38	52·05	56·14	59·72	62·89	65·72	68·33

An extremely important practical point arises from the investigations of Howells, Phillips and Rogers; in assessing the reliability of these methods they discovered that they could often be applied satisfactorily to *zones* of reflexions. There are reasons why this was not to be expected: first, the number of reflexions in a zone is so much smaller than the number of general reflexions that statistical methods might not be applicable; and in projections of structures on to planes, overlapping of atoms might lead to departures from the general distributions upon which the theory rests. These considerations were shown to be unimportant, and clear verification of the space groups of several crystals was demonstrated.

The possibility of confining the calculations to zones of intensities means, of course, that they can be carried out without excessive labour. In addition, however, it leads to the detection of symmetry elements by noting whether they have the effect of producing a centric distribution of intensities or an acentric distribution. For example, a two-fold axis in a structure produces a centric distribution in the reciprocal-lattice section perpendicular to the axis, but not in any other section; a mirror plane gives only acentric distributions. Thus we may distinguish between the space groups P*m*, P2 and P2/*m*—with the *b*-axis unique—by considering the section *h*0*l*, and one other, such as *hk*0: for P*m* the two sections are acentric; for P2, the section *h*0*l* is centric and *hk*0 is acentric; and for P2/*m* both sections are centric. It will therefore be seen that the method is of extreme importance in filling in a gap left by the methods described in section **2**.4.3.

Before actual examples of use are given, one important practical point must be emphasized. The theoretical results apply only to the distribution of intensities produced by a 'random' collection of atoms; they do not apply to any systematic variations produced, for example, by the fall in scattering factors (section **1**.2.4) or by temperature (section **1**.2.5). Intensities should therefore be compared only with others having about the same value of θ. If, however, the ranges of θ are narrow, each will contain too small a number of reflexions for the theory to apply: thus some discretion must be used in deciding what subdivisions to adopt, and the following example will give some idea of a working compromise.

Metatolidine dihydrochloride (Fowweather and Hargreaves, 1950) was known to be monoclinic, but systematic absences showed only the lattice I; consequently the space group could be either No. 8, I*m*; No. 5, I2; or No. 12, I2/*m*. The structure finally adopted had the space group I2, but Howells, Phillips and Rogers (1949) showed that this space group could have been deduced from the intensity data alone. The table of values of intensities I(0*kl*), derived by squaring the values of $|F_0|$ given by Fowweather and Hargreaves, is shown below.

These may be divided into, say, five sets with ranges of 0·2 in sin θ, but this procedure would not be satisfactory, for the lower ranges would not contain enough reflexions for the theory to be properly applicable. Therefore it is better to take larger ranges at low values of θ, and this is reasonable because scattering-factors and the temperature factor do not vary rapidly for such values. Also, for theoretical reasons, the reflexions of lowest angle should be omitted. A reasonable

TABLE 52

Values of $I = |F_0|^2$ for metatolidine dihydrochloride

	k							
l	0	1	2	3	4	5	6	7
0			2500		841		1521	
1		1296		144		100		144
2	49		2209		1369		400	
3		64		256		16		0
4	169		1444		529		25	
5		784		144		361		169
6	729		400		144		49	
7		1521		1225		441		256
8	625		324		0		25	
9		841		1024		324		64
10	169		484		361		100	
11		256		225		144		64
12	2809		1444		400		484	
13		841		121		81		64
14	1024		784		841		324	
15		441		16		256		
16	256		841		576		49	
17		100		16		121		
18	36		225		16		16	
19		676		324		400		
20	0		324		169			
21		784		484		100		
22	4		49		25			
23		361		529		121		
24	16		196		36			
25		256		49				
26	169		100		25			
27		9		36				
28	121		121					
29		49						

choice of subdivision is indicated in table 52, the full lines separating the reflexions into the four ranges of $\sin\theta$, $0-0{\cdot}2$, $0{\cdot}2-0{\cdot}6$, $0{\cdot}6-0{\cdot}8$, $0{\cdot}8-1{\cdot}0$. The first range is disregarded, and the other three—1, 2 and 3—contain 27, 26 and 29 reflexions respectively after omitting the $0k0$ and $00l$ reflexions for reasons discussed in section 3.3.2.

The mean value of I for range 1 is $18256/27 = 676$. Thus the value of $N(0{\cdot}1)$ is obtained by counting the number of reflexions with I less than 68; there is only one—0 4 8—and thus the value of N(0·1) is 1/27 = 0·037. (It is advisable to mark those reflexions that have been dealt with, so that, when the value of N(1·0) has been deduced, it may be confirmed that all those with I less than 676 have been included.) To find the values of N(0·2) we count the number of reflexions with I equal to or less than 135; there are 3, and thus N(0·2) is 0·11. The complete set of results derived in this way for the three ranges is given in table 53.

TABLE 53

Values of N(z), in percentages, for the $0kl$ reflexions of metatolidine dihydrochloride

	z									
Range	0·1	0·2	0·3	0·4	0·5	0·6	0·7	0·8	0·9	1·0
I	3·7	11·1	22·2	33·3	37·0	44·4	48·1	55·5	55·5	55·5
II	23·1	30·8	34·6	38·1	38·5	42·3	42·3	46·2	46·2	50·0
III	6·9	17·2	24·1	34·5	44·8	44·8	44·8	55·2	65·5	65·5
Mean	11·2	19·7	27·0	35·3	40·1	43·8	45·1	52·3	55·7	57·0

As shown in fig. 50, these values lie close to the values for an acentric zone, and thus the space group is not I2/m. The corresponding values for the $h0l$ reflexions show that this zone *has* a centric distribution, and thus the space group is I2.

In principle, the method can also be applied to reflexions with two indices zero; a mirror plane perpendicular to b, for example, should cause only the $0k0$ reflexions to have a centric distribution. In general, however, such rows do not contain enough reflexions for statistical theory to be applicable, but, as was shown earlier in this chapter, other evidence should be available for detecting such symmetry elements; certain parts of the Patterson syntheses should show concentrations of peaks, and these concentrations should be traceable to intensity variations in the reciprocal lattice.

3. AVERAGE-INTENSITY MULTIPLES

3.1. *Special reflexions.* Wilson (1950*a*) has given a precise interpretation to the observations in the preceding paragraph by showing that in certain rows or zones of the weighted reciprocal lattice the local average intensity is increased by a small multiple, the *average-intensity multiple*. He has explained the occurrence of this effect in a particularly simple way. He points out that if, for example, a crystal possesses a mirror plane of symmetry perpendicular to the b-axis, in a projection of the structure on the (010) plane the atoms will overlap in pairs; thus the scattering for the $h0l$ reflexions will simulate that due to half the number of atoms (provided that none is in a special position) each with twice the scattering factor. Thus the local intensity average for a primitive cell (see section 6.5.3), instead of being

$$\sum_{j=1}^{N} f_j^2 = \Sigma$$

will be

$$\sum_{j=1}^{N/2} (2f_j)^2 = 2\Sigma$$

Thus the local intensity average for the *h0l* reflexions should be twice as great as for the general *hkl* reflexions.

Rotation axes lead to similar results for 'central rows' of reflexions—reflexions that are represented by reciprocal-lattice points lying on lines passing through the origin of the reciprocal lattice. Thus a two-fold axis parallel to *b* should cause the 0*k*0 reflexions to be, on the average, twice as strong as the more general reflexions. In general, if equivalent atoms related by a rotation axis coalesce in groups of *n* in the corresponding line projection, the average intensity of reflexions referred to a primitive cell becomes

$$\sum_{j=1}^{N/n} (nf_j)^2 = n\Sigma.$$

Similar considerations can also be applied to glide planes and screw axes.

3.2. *Local average.* The quantity $n\Sigma$ can be identified with the distribution parameter S which occurs in the acentric and centric distribution functions (equations (*49*.1) and (*49*.3)). S is the local average of the intensities of *those reflexions which are not systematically absent throughout the set.* Thus when deriving S for general reflexions the systematic absences in a zone due to a glide are included, but those due to a non-primitive cell are excluded. Glide or centring absences are omitted when considering a zone, but a row of screw absences is then included.

For the general reflexions from a crystal referred to a primitive lattice S has the value Σ. In a centred crystal it has the value 4Σ (face-centring) or 2Σ (end-or body-centring) for the reflexions that actually appear, although clearly the average intensity $\langle I \rangle$ for all reflexions, *including systematically absent reflexions*, remains equal to Σ. For *zones* and *rows* of reflexions, however, both S and $\langle I \rangle$ may be two or more times as great as Σ for the reasons indicated above. S and $\langle I \rangle$ are identical, of course, when considered in relation to symmetry elements not causing systematic absences, but differ for symmetry elements causing systematic absences. For symmetry determination the most useful average-intensity multiple is that given by S/Σ. Table 55 summarizes the zones and rows affected and the multiples appropriate to each symmetry operation.

TABLE 55

Centric sets of reflexions produced by each symmetry element
Symmetry axes chosen parallel to [001]
A=acentric; C=centric

Symmetry elements	General reflexions (*hkl*) Distribution	$n=S/\Sigma$	Transverse zone (*hk*0) Distribution	$n=S/\Sigma$	Parallel row (00*l*) Distribution	$n=S/\Sigma$
1	A	1	A	1	A	1
$\bar{1}$	C	1	C	1	C	1
$2(2_1)$	A	1	C	1	A	2
2(*a*, *b*, *c*, *n*, *d*)	A	1	A	2	C	1
$3(3_{1,2})$	A	1	A	1	A	3
$\bar{3}$	C	1	C	1	C	3
$4(4_{1-3})$	A	1	C	1	A	4
$\bar{4}$	A	1	C	1	C	2
$6(6_{1-5})$	A	1	C	1	A	6
$\bar{6}$	A	1	A	2	C	3

These methods of detecting symmetry elements are of greatest use when three-dimensional data are available, but even in two dimensions they can lead to useful conclusions. For example, we may consider the data contained in table 52, assuming that the space group has not yet been decided upon. If the space group were I2, we should expect the 0*k*0 reflexions to be stronger than the average; if the space group were I*m*, we should expect the 00*l* reflexions, as special cases of the *h*0*l* reflexions, to be stronger than the average; and if the space group were I2/*m*, we should expect both these features to exist. In fact, it is almost immediately obvious that only the 0*k*0 reflexions are outstanding, in agreement with the earlier deduction that the space group is I2.

It is perhaps wise to make a quantitative investigation of the effect, and this should be performed by taking averages over given ranges of θ. The results for the 0*kl* reflexions of metatolidine dihydrochloride are shown in table 56.

Although the numbers of 0*k*0 and 00*l* reflexions are too small to provide data of statistical significance, the conclusions previously drawn are seen to be quite clearly supported. It should be noted that 0*k*0 and 00*l* reflexions have been omitted in computing the value of $\langle I(0kl)\rangle$.

It is now clear why the 0*k*0 and 00*l* reflexions from metatolidine dihydrochloride are omitted in deriving the N(z) distribution curve for 0*kl* reflexions (section (3.2.3)) and in deriving $\langle I(0kl)\rangle$ in table 56. Until the space group is known we are unable to decide whether or not

TABLE 56

Comparison of the values of ⟨I(0k0)⟩ and ⟨I(00l)⟩ with general intensity averages

Range of sin θ	⟨I(0kl)⟩	⟨I(0k0)⟩	⟨I(00l)⟩
0·2–0·6	676	1670	820
0·6–0·8	281	1521	7
0·8–1·0	141	—	145

the 0k0 and 00l reflexions have S-values twice that for the remaining 0kl reflexions: we must, therefore, at this stage, exclude them from the calculations. It is not always necessary to exclude certain sets of reflexions in this way. For example, both 0k0 and 00l reflexions can be included with the 0kl reflexions in any test which attempts to distinguish between the space groups P1 and P$\bar{1}$, because the value of S is the same (Σ) for all types of reflexions in both of these space groups.

Stanley (1955) has discussed the weighting of intensities for statistical surveys when different groups of reflexions have different values of S.

4. General Moment Tests

4.1. *General distributions.* The acentric and centric distributions are valid only when the unit cell contains a large number of crystallographically independent atoms of equal weight distributed at random throughout the unit cell.

Let us consider departures from these ideal conditions and how, as a result, distributions and associated tests are modified.

In some structures the distribution laws are changed substantially by geometrical relationships between atomic positions additional to the symmetry operations of the space group, e.g. extra centres of symmetry or translations-hypersymmetry, discussed in section **3**.6.

Here, we consider modifications required when the atoms are small in number, or differ in weight, or occupy both special and general positions. In practice, the tests in section **3**.2 are found to be satisfactory except when there is one outstandingly heavy atom, or possibly two, in the asymmetric unit.

The tests in section **3**.2 have sometimes been applied satisfactorily to materials with heavy atoms, but the chance of success depends upon the space group. It is clearly desirable to have a test for which there are no doubts about the validity of the underlying conditions. At first sight the problem is difficult, because when atoms in the unit of pattern are small in number or differ in weights then the distribution of intensities depends on the presence of other symmetry elements besides centres. It appears that we have to consider the intensity distribution for each individual space group: indeed, if we consider special positions there may be several different types of distribution for a given space group.

General methods for evaluating intensity distributions for different space groups are available (e.g. Karle and Hauptman, 1953; Hauptman and Karle, 1953; Klug, 1958). But they could not be readily applied to space-group determination and in practice distributions have been evaluated for certain special cases only (Collin, 1955; Hargreaves, 1955, 1956; Sim, 1958).

One point emerging from these special cases is that, for some space groups, the tests in section **3**.2 may give completely wrong results when there are serious departures from the simplifying assumptions made in deriving these tests.

For example, if a crystal with space group $P\bar{1}$ contains one atom only in the asymmetric unit or, what is effectively equivalent, an asymmetric unit containing one heavy atom which completely dominates the remaining lighter atoms, then the N(z) cumulative distribution is given by the full line in fig. 57. This may be compared with the dashed

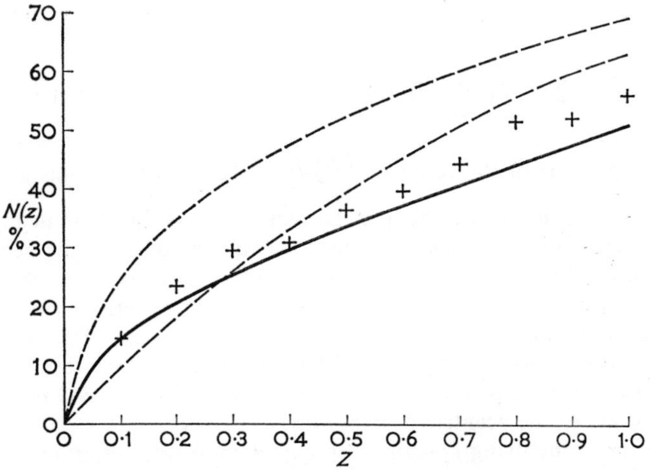

FIG. 57. Distribution curve for compound containing antimony, showing preponderant influence of heavy atom

lines representing the acentric and centric distributions. Although the full line represents the curve for a centro-symmetrical structure it clearly lies nearer to the acentric than to the centric N(z) curve. The use of the N(z) test or any other statistical test based on the acentric and centric distributions would suggest—wrongly—that a structure producing the full line is non-centrosymmetric. A practical example is presented by the crosses in fig. 57 which show a plot of the experimental N(z) distribution for a structure, with space group P$\bar{1}$, containing 2 molecules of $C_{20}H_{17}O_2Sb$ in the unit cell: the effect of the antimony atom (atomic number 51) is clear.

4.2. *Moments of intensity.* It is possible to express the distribution of a set of intensities in terms of the moments $\langle I^r \rangle$, the rth moment of intensity being defined as the average value of I^r. A comparison of theoretical and experimental moments of intensity is therefore equivalent to comparing theoretical and experimental intensity distributions and provides a much simpler test when the theoretical distributions are non-standard types which have to be computed for a particular structure. In practice it is more convenient to compare theoretical and experimental moments of z ($=I/\langle I \rangle$), the rth moment of z being given by $\langle z^r \rangle = \langle I^r \rangle / \langle I \rangle^r$.

The specific variance V is related to the second moment of z by the equation

$$\langle z^2 \rangle = V + 1.$$

Wilson (1951) has shown that

$$V = 1 - \sum_{j=1}^{N} f_j^4 \Big/ \left(\sum_{j=1}^{N} f_j^2 \right)^2 \quad \text{for a crystal with no symmetry and}$$

$$V = 2 - 3 \sum_{j=1}^{N} f_j^4 \Big/ \left(\sum_{j=1}^{N} f_j^2 \right)^2 \quad \text{for a crystal with centrosymmetry only.}$$

Since $\sum_{j=1}^{N} f_j^4$ is of the order of $\left(\sum_{j=1}^{N} f_j^2 \right)^2 \Big/ N$ when the atoms are approximately equal in weight, the 'correction terms' in f_j^4 are negligible for N large: therefore, as previously stated (section 3.2), the acentric and centric distribution functions give values of 1 and 2 respectively for the specific variance. When N is small, however, or the atoms differ in weight, the 'correction term' may be quite large. For example, in a centrosymmetrical crystal with N = 2 the 'correction term' of 3/2 is sufficiently large to reduce V to a value which is less by $\frac{1}{2}$ than that appropriate to the acentric distribution.

The terms involving f_j^4—and, for higher moments, additional terms in $f_j^6, f_j^8, \ldots$—take on different values for other symmetry elements or combinations of symmetry elements. Foster and Hargreaves (1963*a*) have examined the general problem of deriving theoretical moments for different space-group symmetries and have obtained expressions (1963*b*), which are presented in table 59, for the first three moments of intensity in all but two of the 74 space groups and the 9 related plane groups in the triclinic, monoclinic and orthorhombic systems: the exceptions are F*ddd* and F*dd*2 which are uniquely determinable from systematically absent reflexions.

TABLE 59

Formulae used in calculating theoretical moments;
all atoms in general positions

Geometrical Structure Factor			Moments of Intensity
1.	$A=\cos\theta$	$B=\sin\theta$	$\langle I_a \rangle = S(2)$
	$A=\sin\theta$	$B=\cos\theta$	$\langle I_a^2 \rangle = 2S^2(2) - S(4)$
			$\langle I_a^3 \rangle = 6S^3(2) - 9S(2)S(4) + 4S(6)$
2.	$A=\cos\theta$	$B=0$	$\langle I_a \rangle = \frac{1}{2}S(2)$
	$A=\sin\theta$	$B=0$	$\langle I_a^2 \rangle = \frac{3}{4}S^2(2) - \frac{3}{8}S(4)$
			$\langle I_a^3 \rangle = \frac{15}{8}S^3(2) - \frac{45}{16}S(2)S(4) + \frac{5}{4}S(6)$
3.	$A=\cos\theta\cos\phi$	$B=\cos\theta\sin\phi$	$\langle I_a \rangle = \frac{1}{2}S(2)$
	$A=\cos\theta\sin\phi$	$B=\cos\theta\cos\phi$	$\langle I_a^2 \rangle = \frac{1}{2}S^2(2) - \frac{1}{8}S(4)$
	$A=\cos\theta\sin\phi$	$B=\sin\theta\sin\phi$	$\langle I_a^3 \rangle = \frac{3}{4}S^3(2) - \frac{9}{16}S(2)S(4) + \frac{1}{8}S(6)$
	$A=\sin\theta\sin\phi$	$B=\sin\theta\cos\phi$	
4.	$A=\cos\theta\cos\phi$	$B=0$	$\langle I_a \rangle = \frac{1}{4}S(2)$
	$A=\cos\theta\sin\phi$	$B=0$	$\langle I_a^2 \rangle = \frac{3}{16}S^2(2) - \frac{3}{64}S(4)$
	$A=\sin\theta\sin\phi$	$B=0$	$\langle I_a^3 \rangle = \frac{15}{64}S^3(2) - \frac{45}{256}S(2)S(4) + \frac{5}{128}S(6)$
5.	$A=\cos\theta\cos\phi\cos\psi$	$B=\sin\theta\sin\phi\sin\psi$	$\langle I_a \rangle = \frac{1}{4}S(2)$
	$A=\cos\theta\sin\phi\sin\psi$	$B=\sin\theta\cos\phi\cos\psi$	$\langle I_a^2 \rangle = \frac{1}{8}S^2(2) - \frac{1}{64}S(4)$
			$\langle I_a^3 \rangle = \frac{3}{32}S^3(2) - \frac{9}{256}S(2)S(4) + \frac{1}{256}S(6)$
6.	$A=\cos\theta\cos\phi\cos\psi$	$B=\cos\theta\cos\phi\sin\psi$	$\langle I_a \rangle = \frac{1}{4}S(2)$
	$A=\cos\theta\sin\phi\sin\psi$	$B=\cos\theta\sin\phi\cos\psi$	$\langle I_a^2 \rangle = \frac{1}{8}S^2(2) + \frac{1}{64}S(4)$
	$A=\cos\theta\sin\phi\sin\psi$	$B=\sin\theta\sin\phi\sin\psi$	$\langle I_a^3 \rangle = \frac{3}{32}S^3(2) + \frac{9}{256}S(2)S(4) - \frac{1}{32}S(6)$
7.	$A=\cos\theta\cos\phi\cos\psi$	$B=0$	$\langle I_a \rangle = \frac{1}{8}S(2)$
	$A=\cos\theta\cos\phi\sin\psi$	$B=0$	$\langle I_a^2 \rangle = \frac{3}{64}S^2(2) + \frac{3}{512}S(4)$
	$A=\cos\theta\sin\phi\sin\psi$	$B=0$	$\langle I_a^3 \rangle = \frac{15}{512}S^3(2) + \frac{45}{4096}S(2)S(4) - \frac{5}{512}S(6)$
	$A=0$	$B=\sin\theta\sin\phi\sin\psi$	
	$A=0$	$B=\sin\theta\sin\phi\cos\psi$	
	$A=0$	$B=\sin\theta\cos\phi\cos\psi$	

θ, ϕ and ψ each represent either $2\pi hx$, $2\pi ky$ or $2\pi lz$, $\langle I_a^r \rangle$ is the rth moment of intensity for the asymmetric unit of the cell and $S(t) = \sum_1^n f_i^t$; where f_i is the scattering factor of the ith atom and *the summation is taken over the* n *atoms in the asymmetric unit within the unit cell.*

In table 59, A and B are the geometrical structure-factor formulae listed for each space group in the International Tables for Crystallography; constants, *m*, representing the number of equivalent general positions are omitted from these formulae. When *m*'s are left out, the 81 space groups and plane groups considered are represented by the different groups of structure-factor expressions—7 only, in number—

listed in table 59. The corresponding expressions for the first three moments, $\langle I_a \rangle$, $\langle I_a^2 \rangle$ and $\langle I_a^3 \rangle$, are the same for all structure factors within a given group. $\langle I_a \rangle$, $\langle I_a^2 \rangle$ and $\langle I_a^3 \rangle$ should be multiplied by constants—powers of m—to convert them to true intensity moments $\langle I \rangle$, $\langle I^2 \rangle$ and $\langle I^3 \rangle$: but these constants can be omitted when all atoms occupy general positions since they are eliminated in evaluating moments of z from $\langle z^r \rangle = \langle I_a^r \rangle / \langle I_a \rangle^r = \langle I^r \rangle / \langle I \rangle^r$; their omission greatly simplifies table 59 and allows the summations S(t) to be taken over the atoms in the asymmetric unit only, rather than over the full unit cell. Any convenient table of atomic scattering factors may be used in evaluating the summations S(t): very accurate values are not required and temperature corrections are unnecessary.

When the material giving rise to the X-ray reflexions consists of more than one type of atom, the moments of z will be θ-dependent because of the variation with θ in the *relative* magnitudes of the scattering factors for different atoms. It may then be necessary to divide the reflexions into a few ranges of θ and to determine the theoretical moments at the centre of each range. With most materials, however, the *relative* values of the scattering factors of the different constituent atoms do not vary much with θ so that the θ-variation in moments is negligible and the experimental moments can be derived, from the outset, for the whole set of reflexions. The following example illustrates this point and also the general procedure for using moments as a test for symmetry.

A triclinic cell contained 2 molecules of 9-paracarbethoxyphenyl-9-stibiafluorene ($C_{20}H_{17}O_2.Sb$) and the problem was to distinguish between P1 and P$\bar{1}$. The geometrical structure factor for reflexions $hk0$ and space group P1 is

$$A = \cos 2\pi(hx + ky); \quad B = \sin 2\pi(hx + ky),$$

whence the first set of expressions in table 59 gives

$$\langle z^2 \rangle = \langle I_a^2 \rangle / \langle I_a \rangle^2 = 2 - S(4)/S^2(2)$$

and

$$\langle z^3 \rangle = \langle I_a^3 \rangle / \langle I_a \rangle^3 = 6 - 9S(4)/S^2(2) + 4S(6)/S^3(2).$$

For P$\bar{1}$, $A = \cos 2\pi(hx + ky)$; $B = 0$, whence the second set of expressions in table 59 gives

$$\langle z^2 \rangle = 3 - 3S(4)/2S^2(2)$$

and

$$\langle z^3 \rangle = 15 - 45S(4)/2S^2(2) + 10S(6)/S^3(2).$$

Theoretical moments calculated from these expressions are compared with the experimental moments in table 61. Both the weighted average values and those for the individual ranges indicate clearly that the space group is P$\bar{1}$.

The last line in table 61 gives theoretical moments for the acentric and centric distributions. It will be seen that if these moments had been compared with the experimental values, then the space group would have been wrongly chosen as P1.

TABLE 61

Comparison of experimental and theoretical moments of z for the $hk0$ reflexions of 9-paracarbethoxyphenyl-9-stibiafluorene

sin θ range	Number of reflexions	$\langle z^2 \rangle$ Experimental	$\langle z^2 \rangle$ Theoretical P1	$\langle z^2 \rangle$ Theoretical $P\bar{1}$	$\langle z^3 \rangle$ Experimental	$\langle z^3 \rangle$ Theoretical P1	$\langle z^3 \rangle$ Theoretical $P\bar{1}$
0·20–0·38	29	1·82	1·21	1·80	4·5	1·70	4·20
0·38–0·50	29	1·83	1·16	1·74	3·9	1·50	3·78
0·50–0·70	71	1·98	1·16	1·74	4·2	1·50	3·78
0·70–0·85	62	2·69	1·16	1·74	7·2	1·50	3·78
0·85–1·00	55	1·75	1·18	1·76	3·6	1·55	3·95
Weighted average values for all reflexions		2·07	1·17	1·75	4·8	1·54	3·87
Acentric and centric distributions			2	3		6	15

The theoretical moments in table 61 do not change much with sin θ and it can be seen that the weighted average values differ very little from the values near the centre of the full range (sin $\theta \sim 0{\cdot}6$). It would have been simpler, and perfectly satisfactory in this case, to group all the reflexions into a single range.

5. ATOMS IN SPECIAL POSITIONS

The contributions to X-ray scattering made by atoms in special positions may follow quite different distribution laws from the contributions made by atoms in general positions. Statistical tests therefore require special consideration when atoms occupy special positions, though in practice the influence of such atoms is likely to be important only when they are very heavy as compared with atoms in general positions. Collin (1955) has considered the effect on the acentric and centric distributions of a heavy atom in a fixed position and has deduced the resulting modifications in the N(z) distribution functions. Hargreaves (1956) has discussed the N(z) distributions appropriate to an outstandingly heavy atom in any special position in the 12 plane groups of lowest symmetry. A more general approach is afforded by a simple extension of the moment tests discussed in section 3.4.2.

The geometrical structure-factor formula for atoms in general positions changes to one with fewer variables for atoms in special positions. Quantities $\langle I_g^r \rangle$ and $\langle I_s^r \rangle$ may be evaluated using the formulae in table 59 but with the summations S(t) extending, respectively, over the atoms in general positions only and over the atoms in special positions only. $\langle I_a \rangle$, $\langle I_a^2 \rangle$ and $\langle I_a^3 \rangle$ can then be calculated from the expressions given in table 62.

TABLE 62

Formulae used in calculating theoretical moments; atoms in general and in special positions

$$\langle I_a \rangle = \langle I_g \rangle + \lambda^2 \langle I_s \rangle$$
$$\langle I_a^2 \rangle = \langle I_g^2 \rangle + \lambda^4 \langle I_s^2 \rangle + K_1 \lambda^2 \langle I_g \rangle \langle I_s \rangle$$
$$\langle I_a^3 \rangle = \langle I_g^3 \rangle + \lambda^6 \langle I_s^3 \rangle + K_2 \lambda^4 \langle I_g \rangle \langle I_s^2 \rangle + K_2 \lambda^2 \langle I_g^2 \rangle \langle I_s \rangle.$$

λ is the ratio $\dfrac{\text{number of equivalent special positions in the unit cell}}{\text{number of equivalent general positions in the unit cell}}$, the value of K_1 is 6 for centrosymmetrical and 4 for non-centrosymmetrical plane groups and space groups, and the value of K_2 is 15 for centrosymmetrical and 9 for non-centrosymmetrical plane groups and space groups.

Each atom in a special position is counted as one complete atom in the summations S(t) used to evaluate $\langle I_s^r \rangle$, even though atoms in special positions contribute only a fraction of their scattering power to the asymmetric unit; the constants λ introduce the appropriate corrections for the fractional contributions from atoms in special positions.

If the special positions are fixed points, with no variable parameters, none of the expressions in table 59 is appropriate. It is then usually necessary, with a single set of equivalent fixed points, to divide the reflexions into two groups. For one group half the atoms at fixed points scatter in phase with respect to each other but out of phase with respect to the other half so that $\langle I_s^r \rangle = 0$; for the other group all the atoms scatter in phase and we have $\langle I_s^r \rangle = (\Sigma f_s)^{2r}$.

Complications arise when atoms occupy more than one type of special position. The necessary modifications, and examples of the use of moment tests for atoms in special positions, are discussed by Foster and Hargreaves (1963*b*).

6. HYPERSYMMETRY

The success of the methods described in sections **3**.2 and **3**.4 depends upon the randomness of the distribution of the atoms within the unit cell. Wilson (1949) pointed out that symmetry operations unrelated to the space group may give rise to abnormal intensity distributions and this was first confirmed by the discovery of the hypercentric intensity distribution (Lipson and Woolfson, 1952). The hypercentric distribution arises when two molecules, each with a non-crystallographic centre of symmetry, occupy general positions in a centrosymmetric space group. They are then necessarily parallel and their Fourier transform is modulated by a sinusoidal fringe system which increases the variance beyond that of the centric distribution.

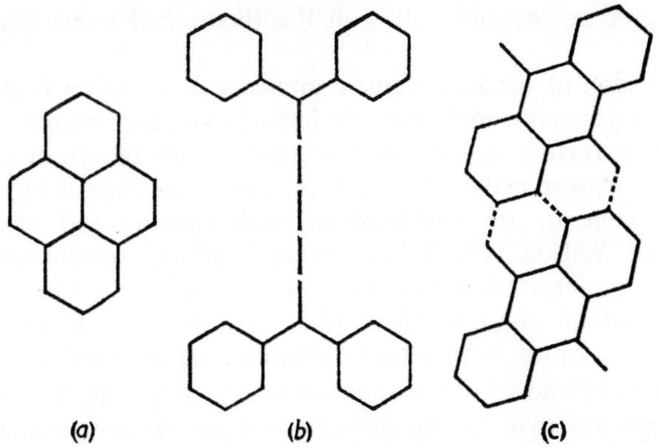

FIG. 63 (i). Three molecules that give hypercentric distributions. (*a*) pyrene and (*b*) 1 : 1 : 6 : 6-tetraphenylhexapentaene are centrosymmetric. (*c*) flavanthrone is also centrosymmetric and can be regarded as composed of two centrosymmetrically related parts

The theoretical cumulative distributions N(z) for the hypercentric, centric and acentric distributions are compared in fig. 63 (ii). Three molecules which might be expected to give rise to the hypercentric distribution are shown in fig. 63 (i). Pyrene (Robertson and White, 1947*a*) and 1 : 1 : 6 : 6 tetraphenylhexapentaene (Woolfson, 1953) have four molecules in unit cells with space group $P2_1/a$ and although flavanthrone with space group $P2_1/a$ (Stadler, 1953) has only two molecules in the unit cell, each molecule can be regarded as composed of two centrosymmetrical parts. The *h*0*l* distribution curves for these three

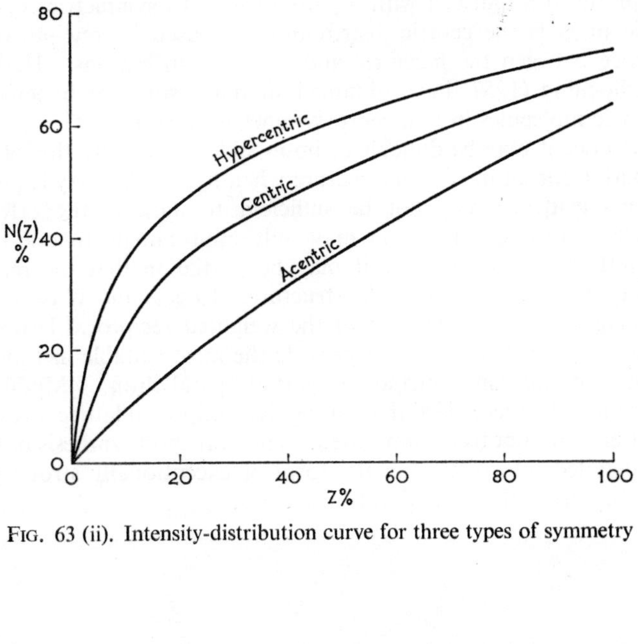

FIG. 63 (ii). Intensity-distribution curve for three types of symmetry

crystals agree reasonably well with the theoretical hypercentric N(z) curve.

An extension of the hypercentric intensity distribution occurs when each centrosymmetric molecule consists of two centrosymmetric parts related by a further non-crystallographic centre of symmetry. The modulation pattern is then the product of two sinusoidal fringe systems which, in general, are unrelated in both spacing and orientation. Rogers and Wilson (1953) have generalized this extension to any number of non-crystallographic centres of symmetry. They have also considered other non-crystallographic arrangements leading to the repetition of a motif in parallel orientation. It is found that, for the space groups P1 and P$\bar{1}$, the variance is increased by parallel repetitions to values greater than for the acentric and centric distributions. The increase may be substantial and disturbing when considered in relation to space-group determination. For example, two parallel non-centrosymmetric motifs related by a non-crystallographic translation in a non-centrosymmetric space group give the same (centric) distribution as when they are in centrosymmetric antiparallelism.

If, in addition to centres of symmetry, the space group contains other elements of symmetry, such as m, molecules directly related by the crystallographic centres of symmetry are parallel in pairs, but those related only by other symmetry elements are not, in general, parallel. The fringe systems of the parallel pairs will be partially obliterated by the unrelated additive fringe systems of other pairs, and the variance will be reduced to a value somewhere between that of the centric distribution and that of the appropriate hypercentric distribution. Wilson (1956) has shown that to a first approximation the distribution appropriate to a unit cell with p pairs of n-centrosymmetric crystallographic units is the centric distribution increased by one-pth of the difference between the n-centric and centric distributions. Herbstein and Schoening (1957) have obtained similar results for hypercentrosymmetric molecules in non-centrosymmetric crystals.

In practice it may be difficult or impossible to evaluate the intensity distribution for an unknown structure when hypersymmetry is present. Chemical evidence may not be sufficient to indicate the extent of parallelism, or the parallelism may only approximate to one of the types hitherto considered, or it may be partial in that the repeated motifs do not account for all the structure. Rogers and Wilson (1953) have suggested that inspection of the weighted reciprocal lattice and the study of the Patterson map provide the most suitable methods for detecting parallelism, including partial parallelism. Modulation patterns may be recognized in the weighted reciprocal lattice, providing the patterns are not too complicated. The Patterson synthesis provides more detailed information in the form of exceptionally strong peaks originating from the repetition translations.

7. Practical Difficulties

The statistical tests for symmetry are subject to several possible sources of error, some of which have been considered in earlier sections of this chapter.

One difficulty arises when the number of experimentally observed intensities is too small for an accurate statistical analysis. Whenever possible, statistical tests should be performed with three-dimensional *hkl* reflexions rather than reflexions with one or two indices zero. The larger number of reflexions available in three dimensions permits more reliable statistical averaging; in addition, the results are less likely to be seriously influenced by hypersymmetry, by the overlap of atoms in projection and by the inadequate statistical averaging which may occur if a heavy atom happens to fall, in projection, very near to a special position.

Hypersymmetry always increases the variance. Overlap may increase or decrease the variance, depending upon the space group, but the errors which it introduces are likely to be important only with one-dimensional data, or two-dimensional data from crystals with unit cells containing a small number of atoms or one very heavy atom.

The effects, on the various statistical tests, of both random and systematic errors in the observed intensities, have been considered in detail by Rogers, Stanley and Wilson (1955). The tests are particularly sensitive to errors in the determination of $\langle I \rangle$ as a function of $\sin^2 \theta$; procedures for deriving this curve are described by Howells, Phillips and Rogers (1950). Different tests are unequally affected by any given error and it may, therefore, be desirable to apply more than one test to a given problem.

CHAPTER 4

CALCULATION OF STRUCTURE FACTORS

1. STRUCTURE-FACTOR FORMULAE

1.1 *Formulae for different space groups.* The expression for the structure factor derived in Chapter 1 (equation *10.3*),

$$F(hkl) = \sum_{n=1}^{N} f_n \exp 2\pi i(hx_n + ky_n + lz_n),$$

is valid for any space group. In Chapter 2, however, we have seen that the atomic positions in the unit cell are usually symmetrically related, and important simplifications of equation *10.3* can be made by collecting the atoms together in their equivalent groups (section 2.5.1). An expression may be derived for one such group, and then the summation need only be made over the number of groups, which is necessarily smaller than the number of atoms.

The simplest illustration is provided by the space group P$\bar{1}$. For each atom at the point x, y, z there is a corresponding atom at the point $\bar{x}$, $\bar{y}$, $\bar{z}$. The contribution of these two atoms to the structure factor is

$$f \exp \{2\pi i(hx + ky + lz)\} + f \exp \{-2\pi i(hx + ky + lz)\}$$
$$= 2f \cos 2\pi(hx + ky + lz).$$

Thus if we wish to calculate structure factors for a crystal with space group P$\bar{1}$, the expression used is

$$F(hkl) = 2 \sum_{n=1}^{N/2} f_n \cos 2\pi(hx_n + ky_n + lz_n), \qquad (66.1)$$

the summation now being made over half the unit cell; any atom related to an atom already considered is not included in the summation.

The simplification introduced by collecting equivalent atoms together is not always so marked. Consider, for example, space group No. 3, P2, with a two-fold axis along b. The equivalent points are x, y, z and $\bar{x}$, y, $\bar{z}$. The contribution to the structure factor of atoms at these two points is

$$f \exp \{2\pi i(hx + ky + lz)\} + f \exp \{2\pi i(-hx + ky - lz)\}$$
$$= 2f \exp \{2\pi iky\} \cos 2\pi(hx + lz). \qquad (66.2)$$

Thus the contribution of the two atoms is again reduced to a single expression, but it is more complicated than that in equation *66.1*.

Moreover, it will be noted that the expression *66.1* is real, whereas the expression *66*.2 is complex. Since the only symmetry involved in the derivation of *66*.1 is the centre of symmetry at the origin, it must follow that it is this property which causes the structure factor to be real. If the space group has no centre of symmetry, or if the centre of symmetry is not at the origin, the structure factor will not be real for all values of h, k and l, although it may be so for special values of these indices. For example, in space group No. 3, P2, the structure factor is shown by equation *66*.2 to be real if $k=0$. Use can be made of such relationships, as will be shown in Chapter 8.

The importance of having real structure factors is such that, wherever possible, the origin of co-ordinates in a space group is placed at a centre of symmetry. This explains why the symmetry representation of the space group C*mca* in section **2**.5.2 appears to differ from that in the International Tables; in these tables the origin is taken at a centre of symmetry, whereas the deduction of the representation made in section **2**.5.2 happened to put this centre of symmetry at $(0\frac{1}{4}\frac{1}{4})$. The equivalent points, of course, also differ from those given in the International Tables.

For purposes of computation, expressions such as *66*.2 have to be resolved into real and imaginary parts.

$$2f\exp\{2\pi iky\}\cos 2\pi(hx+lz)$$
$$=2f\cos 2\pi ky\cos 2\pi(hx+lz)+i2f\sin 2\pi ky\cos 2\pi(hx+lz).$$

Thus the two quantities A′ and B′ of equation *11*.1 are

$$\left.\begin{aligned} A' &= 2\sum f\cos 2\pi ky\cos 2\pi(hx+lz),\\ B' &= 2\sum f\sin 2\pi ky\cos 2\pi(hx+lz).\end{aligned}\right\}\quad (67)$$

The corresponding expressions for the 230 space groups are given in the International Tables Vol. I (1952). In these tables, the summation sign and the symbol for the scattering factor are omitted, and the resulting expressions are termed simply A and B.

1.2. *Formulae for different classes of reflexion.* Expressions such as those in *66*.1 and *67* can be evaluated for different values of x, y and z, and h, k and l. For some space groups, however, it may so happen that further simplification can be introduced by separating the reflexions into various classes with indices having various properties; this is so when the space group contains screw axes and glide planes.

We may see this by considering the space group No. 4, $P2_1$, of which the general equivalent points are x, y, z and $\bar{x}, \frac{1}{2}+y, \bar{z}$. Then

$$A=\cos 2\pi(hx+ky+lz)+\cos 2\pi(-hx+ky-lz+\tfrac{1}{2}k).$$

If k is even this reduces to

$$A=2\cos 2\pi ky\cos 2\pi(hx+lz),$$

and if k is odd, it reduces to

$$\begin{aligned} A &= \cos 2\pi(hx+ky+lz) - \cos 2\pi(hx-ky+lz) \\ &= -2 \sin 2\pi ky \sin 2\pi(hx+lz). \end{aligned} \qquad (68.1)$$

In a similar way, for even values of k, B reduces to

$$B = 2 \sin 2\pi ky \cos 2\pi(hx+lz),$$

and for odd values of k, to

$$B = 2 \cos 2\pi ky \sin 2\pi(hx+lz). \qquad (68.2)$$

Formulae for all the space groups are contained in the International Tables (1952). Nevertheless it is recommended that the expressions for each space group should be worked out as required, the International Tables being used only as a check.

1.3. *Formulae for atoms in special positions.* The formulae in the International Tables are applicable to atoms in general equivalent positions, but they can readily be adapted for atoms in special positions. The adaptation, however, does not consist merely in the substitution, in the general formula, of the values of x, y and z representative of the special positions; the multiplicity of these special positions is also involved. The general rule is that the contribution of an atom in a special position has to be multiplied by the ratio of the multiplicity of the set of special positions (section **2**.6.2) to that of the set of general positions. Thus for a structure with space group No. 2, $P\bar{1}$, containing an atom of scattering factor f in the position 000, and 2N other atoms of scattering factor f_n in general positions (x_n, y_n, z_n), the expression for the structure factor is

$$F = f + 2 \sum_{n=1}^{N} f_n \cos 2\pi(hx_n + ky_n + lz_n). \qquad (68.3)$$

In the more complicated space groups many more possibilities may arise. For example, in space group No. 64, $Cmca$, with a centre of symmetry at the origin, the following sets of equivalent positions occur:

4:	(*a*) 000; etc.	(*b*) $\frac{1}{2}$00; etc.
8:	(*c*) $\frac{1}{4}\frac{1}{4}$0; etc.	(*d*) x00; etc.
	(*e*) $\frac{1}{4}y\frac{1}{4}$; etc.	(*f*) 0yz; etc.
16:	(*g*) xyz; etc.	

In order to find the contributions given by atoms in each of these seven sets, we consider the formulae in Lonsdale's tables (1936). For $h+k$ even, $k+l$ even,

$$A = 16 \cos 2\pi hx \cos 2\pi ky \cos 2\pi lz.$$

Application of the rule just stated leads to the following expressions for the contributions of atoms in the various sets of equivalent positions:

$$\left.\begin{aligned}
&(a)\ A = 16 \times \tfrac{4}{16} &&= 4\\
&(b)\ A = 16 \cos \pi h \times \tfrac{4}{16} &&= 4 \cos \pi h\\
&(c)\ A = 16 \cos \pi h/2 . \cos \pi k/2 \times \tfrac{8}{16} &&= 8 \cos \pi h/2 \cos \pi k/2\\
&(d)\ A = 16 \cos 2\pi hx \times \tfrac{8}{16} &&= 8 \cos 2\pi hx\\
&(e)\ A = 16 \cos \pi h/2 . \cos 2\pi ky . \cos \pi l/2 \times \tfrac{8}{16} &&= 8 \cos \pi h/2 \cos 2\pi ky . \cos \pi l/2\\
&(f)\ A = 16 \cos 2\pi ky . \cos 2\pi lz \times \tfrac{8}{16} &&= 8 \cos 2\pi ky \cos 2\pi lz
\end{aligned}\right\}$$

Expressions such as these are not yet tabulated for the different space groups, and indeed it is hardly necessary that they should be so, since they are easily derived from the general formulae.

1.4. *Space-group absences from structure-factor formulae.* The systematic absences of the space-groups are deducible from the structure-factor formulae, and this provides a way of checking these formulae: the structure factor should be zero for the indices corresponding to absent reflexions, independently of particular values of x, y and z. Zero values arise, for example, if the structure-factor formula contains a sine term which is zero if a certain index or combination of indices is zero.

The formulae for space group No. 2, $P\bar{1}$ are

$$A = 2 \cos 2\pi(hx + ky + lz),$$
$$B = 0.$$

and, since a sine term is not included, F is not zero for any particular combination of indices; correspondingly, there are no systematic absences for this space group. For the space group $P2_1$ however, equations *68*.1 and *68*.2 include sine terms that lead to the following results:

For k even, $B = 0$ if $k = 0$,
and for k odd, $A = 0$ if $h = l = 0$ (k cannot, of course, be zero),
and $B = 0$ if $h = l = 0$.

Thus we see that the only combinations of indices that lead to zero values for *both* A and B are that k should be odd, and h and l both zero; this is the set of absent reflexions that characterize the screw axis.

The fact that B is zero for certain reflexions while A is not is also important. In space group No. 4, $P2_1$, B is zero for all reflexions with $k = 0$, and this means that, although the space group has not a centre of symmetry, the projection of the structure on the plane (010) has such a centre. This symmetry is, of course, the projection of the screw axis on the (010) plane. The presence of centres of symmetry in projections can be very useful; in space group No. 19, $P2_12_12_1$, for example, the three projections parallel to the axes each have centro-symmetry, and so the structure factors for the three principal zones can all be real. They will not be real, however, if the same origin is maintained for each projection, since the three screw axes do not intersect, but the gain in putting the origin at a centre of symmetry is so great that it is worth while choosing a different origin for each of the projections (section **4**.1.1).

2. Systematic Methods of Calculation

2.1. *Layout of calculations.* The beginner in crystal structure analysis will find it worth while to make some calculations of structure factors without using a computer, as this can be a help in understanding the computer program. Planning the operation in advance is essential, and a possible procedure is best described by means of an actual example.

Table 71 shows some calculations of structure factors for the compound cryolite, Na_3AlF_6 (Náray-Szabó and Sasvari, 1938), which belongs to the space group No. 14, $P2_1/n$, with atoms in the following positions:

2Al in (*a*) $0, 0, 0;\ \frac{1}{2}, \frac{1}{2}, \frac{1}{2}$.
2Na in (*b*) $0, 0, \frac{1}{2};\ \frac{1}{2}, \frac{1}{2}, 0$.
4Na in (*c*) $x, y, z;\ \bar{x}, \bar{y}, \bar{z};\ \frac{1}{2}+x, \frac{1}{2}-y, \frac{1}{2}+z;\ \frac{1}{2}-x, \frac{1}{2}+y, \frac{1}{2}-z,$
with $x=0{\cdot}50,\ y=-0{\cdot}05_5,\ z=0{\cdot}24$.
12F in (*c*) with $x_1=0{\cdot}06_5,\ y_1=0{\cdot}06,\ z_1=0{\cdot}22,$
$x_2=-0{\cdot}29,\ y_2=0{\cdot}16,\ z_2=0{\cdot}03,$
$x_3=0{\cdot}15,\ y_3=0{\cdot}28,\ z_3=-0{\cdot}06.$

For this space group, the structure-factor formulae fall into two classes, and the sets of indices should be divided into these two sets—those with $h+k+l$ even and those with $h+k+l$ odd. The formulae are

$$A = 4\cos 2\pi(hx+lz)\cos 2\pi ky \quad \text{for } h+k+l \text{ even}$$

and

$$A = -4\sin 2\pi(hx+lz)\sin 2\pi ky \quad \text{for } h+k+l \text{ odd.}$$

Since the space group has a centre of symmetry at the origin, $B=0$ for all reflexions.

Table 71 shows the calculations for fifteen reflexions with $h+k+l$ even, the complete structure-factor equation being

$$F(hkl) = 2f_{Al} + 2(-1)^l f_{Na} + 4f_{Na}\cos 2\pi(hx+lz)\cos 2\pi ky + 4f_F\sum_{n=1}^{3}\cos 2\pi(hx_n+lz_n)\cos 2\pi ky_n.$$

The corresponding equation for reflexions with $h+k+l$ odd is

$$F(hkl) = 4f_{Na}\sin 2\pi(hx+lz)\sin 2ky + 4f_F\sum_{n=1}^{3}\sin 2\pi(hx_n+lz_n)\sin 2\pi ky_n,$$

the contributions from the atoms in special positions being zero.

TABLE 71

Calculation of structure factors for Cryolite, Na_3AlF_6

$hk0$	$2f_{Al}$	$2f_{Na}$	$4f_{Na}$	cos $2\pi hx$	cos $2\pi ky$	Prod.	$4f_F$	cos $2\pi hx_1$	cos $2\pi ky_1$	Prod.$_1$	cos $2\pi hx_2$	cos $2\pi ky_2$	Prod.$_2$	cos $2\pi hx_3$	cos $2\pi ky_3$	Prod.$_3$	$\sum_1^3$ Prod.	F contrib.	F $(hk0)$
200	**18·5**	**16·9**	33·8	1·000	1·000	**33·8**	26·0	0·684	1·000	0·684	$\overline{0{\cdot}876}$	1·000	$\overline{0{\cdot}876}$	$\overline{0{\cdot}309}$	1·000	$\overline{0{\cdot}309}$	$\overline{0{\cdot}501}$	$\overline{\mathbf{13{\cdot}0}}$	56·2
400	**14·0**	**11·5**	23·0	1·000	1·000	**23·0**	14·5	$\overline{0{\cdot}063}$	1·000	$\overline{0{\cdot}063}$	0·536	1·000	0·536	$\overline{0{\cdot}809}$	1·000	$\overline{0{\cdot}809}$	$\overline{0{\cdot}336}$	$\overline{\mathbf{4{\cdot}7}}$	43·8
600	**10·0**	**7·2**	14·4	1·000	1·000	**14·4**	9·5	$\overline{0{\cdot}770}$	1·000	$\overline{0{\cdot}770}$	$\overline{0{\cdot}063}$	1·000	$\overline{0{\cdot}063}$	0·809	1·000	0·809	$\overline{0{\cdot}024}$	$\overline{\mathbf{0{\cdot}2}}$	31·4
110	**20·7**	**18·5**	37·0	$\overline{1{\cdot}000}$	0·941	$\overline{\mathbf{34{\cdot}8}}$	29·5	0·918	0·930	0·854	$\overline{0{\cdot}249}$	0·536	$\overline{0{\cdot}133}$	0·588	$\overline{0{\cdot}187}$	$\overline{0{\cdot}110}$	0·611	**18·0**	22·4
310	**15·7**	**13·7**	27·4	$\overline{1{\cdot}000}$	0·941	$\overline{\mathbf{25{\cdot}8}}$	19·0	0·339	0·930	0·315	0·684	0·536	0·367	$\overline{0{\cdot}951}$	$\overline{0{\cdot}187}$	0·178	0·860	**16·3**	19·9
510	**11·7**	**8·8**	17·6	$\overline{1{\cdot}000}$	0·941	$\overline{\mathbf{16{\cdot}6}}$	11·5	$\overline{0{\cdot}454}$	0·930	$\overline{0{\cdot}422}$	$\overline{0{\cdot}951}$	0·536	$\overline{0{\cdot}510}$	0·000	$\overline{0{\cdot}187}$	0·000	$\overline{0{\cdot}932}$	$\overline{\mathbf{10{\cdot}7}}$	$\overline{6{\cdot}8}$
710	**8·2**	**5·8**	11·6	$\overline{1{\cdot}000}$	0·941	$\overline{\mathbf{10{\cdot}9}}$	8·0	$\overline{0{\cdot}960}$	0·930	$\overline{0{\cdot}893}$	0·982	0·536	0·526	0·951	$\overline{0{\cdot}187}$	$\overline{0{\cdot}178}$	$\overline{0{\cdot}545}$	$\overline{\mathbf{4{\cdot}4}}$	$\overline{1{\cdot}3}$
020	**18·7**	**17·0**	34·0	1·000	0·770	**26·2**	26·0	1·000	0·729	0·729	1·000	$\overline{0{\cdot}426}$	$\overline{0{\cdot}426}$	1·000	$\overline{0{\cdot}930}$	$\overline{0{\cdot}930}$	$\overline{0{\cdot}627}$	$\overline{\mathbf{16{\cdot}3}}$	45·6
220	**16·5**	**14·8**	29·6	1·000	0·770	**22·8**	21·0	0·684	0·729	0·498	$\overline{0{\cdot}876}$	$\overline{0{\cdot}426}$	0·369	$\overline{0{\cdot}309}$	$\overline{0{\cdot}930}$	0·287	1·154	**24·3**	78·4
420	**13·0**	**10·3**	20·6	1·000	0·770	**15·9**	13·0	$\overline{0{\cdot}063}$	0·729	$\overline{0{\cdot}046}$	0·536	$\overline{0{\cdot}426}$	$\overline{0{\cdot}228}$	$\overline{0{\cdot}809}$	$\overline{0{\cdot}930}$	0·752	0·478	**6·2**	45·4
620	**8·7**	**6·2**	12·4	1·000	0·770	**9·5**	8·5	$\overline{0{\cdot}770}$	0·729	$\overline{0{\cdot}561}$	$\overline{0{\cdot}063}$	$\overline{0{\cdot}426}$	0·027	0·809	$\overline{0{\cdot}930}$	$\overline{0{\cdot}752}$	$\overline{1{\cdot}286}$	$\overline{\mathbf{10{\cdot}9}}$	13·5
130	**15·9**	**13·9**	27·8	$\overline{1{\cdot}000}$	0·509	$\overline{\mathbf{14{\cdot}1}}$	19·0	0·918	0·426	0·391	$\overline{0{\cdot}249}$	$\overline{0{\cdot}992}$	0·247	0·588	0·536	0·315	0·953	**18·1**	33·8
330	**13·5**	**11·0**	22·0	$\overline{1{\cdot}000}$	0·509	$\overline{\mathbf{11{\cdot}2}}$	14·0	0·339	0·426	0·144	0·684	$\overline{0{\cdot}992}$	$\overline{0{\cdot}679}$	$\overline{0{\cdot}951}$	0·536	$\overline{0{\cdot}510}$	$\overline{1{\cdot}045}$	$\overline{\mathbf{14{\cdot}6}}$	$\overline{1{\cdot}3}$
530	**10·4**	**7·5**	15·0	$\overline{1{\cdot}000}$	0·509	$\overline{\mathbf{7{\cdot}6}}$	10·0	$\overline{0{\cdot}454}$	0·426	$\overline{0{\cdot}193}$	$\overline{0{\cdot}951}$	$\overline{0{\cdot}992}$	0·944	0·000	0·536	0·000	0·751	**7·5**	17·8
730	**7·4**	**5·4**	10·8	$\overline{1{\cdot}000}$	0·509	$\overline{\mathbf{5{\cdot}5}}$	7·5	$\overline{0{\cdot}960}$	0·426	$\overline{0{\cdot}409}$	0·982	$\overline{0{\cdot}992}$	$\overline{0{\cdot}974}$	0·951	0·536	0·510	$\overline{0{\cdot}873}$	$\overline{\mathbf{6{\cdot}5}}$	0·8
1	2	3	4	5	6	7	8	9	10	11	12	13	14	15	16	17	18	19	20
						4 × 5 × 6				9 × 10			12 × 13			15 × 16	11+14 +17	8 × 18	2+3+ 7+19

The columns are numbered in sequence, and the numbers below certain columns show how the quantities in them are derived. The quantities in heavy type are the contributions to the structure factor.

2.2. *Atomic scattering factors.* As explained in section **1**.2.4, values of scattering factors have been derived theoretically and have been recorded as functions of $\sin\theta/\lambda$; tables are given in Appendix IV in Volume I and these are used in table 71. To make use of these values they should be plotted against $\sin\theta$ for the radiation used and a smooth curve drawn through the points; the scattering factor for any particular value of $\sin\theta$ can then be obtained from this graph. More recent values of scattering factors are given in Volume III of the International Tables (1962), accompanied by an extensive review of the literature of the subject.

For work carried out by computers, however, a different approach is desirable: it is not efficient to ask the computer to extract values of a function from a table; it is easier to present it with an analytical function that it can evaluate itself. Vand, Eiland and Pepinsky (1957) have shown that a function of the form

$$f(s) = \mathrm{A}\exp(-as^2) + \mathrm{B}\exp(-bs^2) + \mathrm{C},$$

where $s = (\sin\theta)/\lambda$, can be used, and Forsyth and Wells (1959) give a table of the values of the five constants – A, a, B, b, and C—that reproduce the accepted scattering-factor curves of all the atoms, and some ions, ranging from hydrogen to uranium.

2.3. *Temperature factor.* If absolute values of the intensities have been determined experimentally it should be found that for the low-angle reflexions reasonable agreement is obtained with the scattering factors discussed in the last section, but that, as the angle increases, the calculated values gradually become systematically greater than the observed ones. This effect, of course, is caused by temperature, which has not been taken into account in computing the atomic scattering factors (section **1**.2.5). It can be taken into account by multiplying the scattering factors by a quantity $\exp(-\mathrm{B}\sin^2\theta/\lambda^2)$, but the value of B will not in general be known. Some estimate of its value can be found from the comparison of the calculated and observed intensities. Thus, if I_o is the observed value and I_c the calculated value of an intensity of reflexion, we have that

$$\mathrm{I}_o = \mathrm{I}_c \exp(-2\mathrm{B}\sin^2\theta/\lambda^2)$$

or

$$\log_e \frac{\mathrm{I}_c}{\mathrm{I}_o} = 2\mathrm{B}\sin^2\theta/\lambda^2. \qquad (72)$$

Thus, if the logarithms of the ratios of the observed and calculated intensities are plotted against $\sin^2\theta/\lambda^2$, the slope of the graph should give the value of B. Fig. 73, from the results of Bradley and Lu (1937) for Cr_2Al, provides an example of the determination of B in this way.

A knowledge of the value of B before the structure is even approximately known would, however, be more useful, and this knowledge can be derived by a method due to Wilson (1942). Wilson makes use of the fact, referred to later (section 6.5.3), that the mean value of $|F|^2$ is equal to the value of $\sum f^2$ at a particular value of θ. Thus by dividing

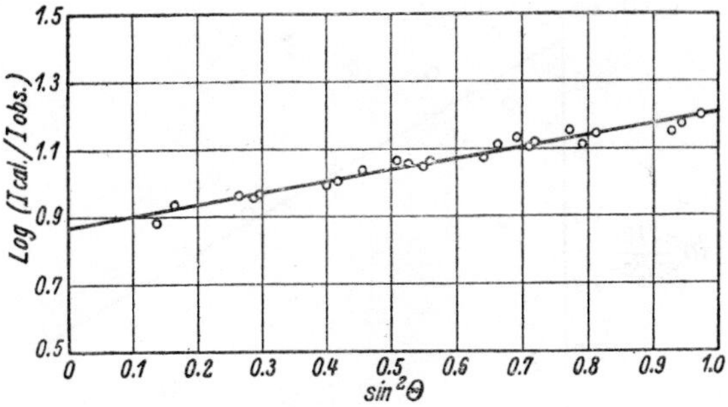

FIG. 73. Derivation of temperature constant for Cr_2Al (Bradley and Lu, 1937)

the reflexions into groups covering narrow ranges of θ, the f curve could be directly derived. It is more usual, however, to assume the theoretical form of f curve, and to use Wilson's method to derive the constant B; this is necessary when the crystal contains atoms of different scattering factors which may vary differently with θ.

The method can be illustrated by means of the data contained in table 52, the ranges of sin θ being divided more finely, than was required in section 3.2.2. The mean values for the intensities are shown in the following table, together with the other data which are needed.

TABLE 73

Deduction of value of temperature constant B for metatolidine dihydrochloride, $C_{14}H_{16}N_2.2HCl$

$\langle \sin \theta \rangle$	$\langle \sin^2 \theta/\lambda^2 \rangle$	$\langle I \rangle$	$\langle f_0^2 \rangle$	$\langle I \rangle/\langle f_0^2 \rangle$	$\log_e\{\langle I \rangle/\langle f_0^2 \rangle\}$
·30	·04	875	20·8	42	3·74
·50	·10	612	13·2	46	3·83
·65	·18	315	9·9	32	3·47
·75	·24	263	8·6	31	3·43
·85	·30	204	7·4	28	3·32
·95	·38	77	6·8	11	2·40

The value of $\langle f_0^2 \rangle$ is taken as the mean of the squares of the scattering factors of carbon, nitrogen and chlorine weighted in the proportions 7 : 1 : 1.

To find the value of B, the logarithms of the values of $\langle I \rangle / \langle f_0^2 \rangle$ are plotted against $\sin^2 \theta/\lambda^2$ as shown in fig. 74; the slope of the graph gives the value of 2B.

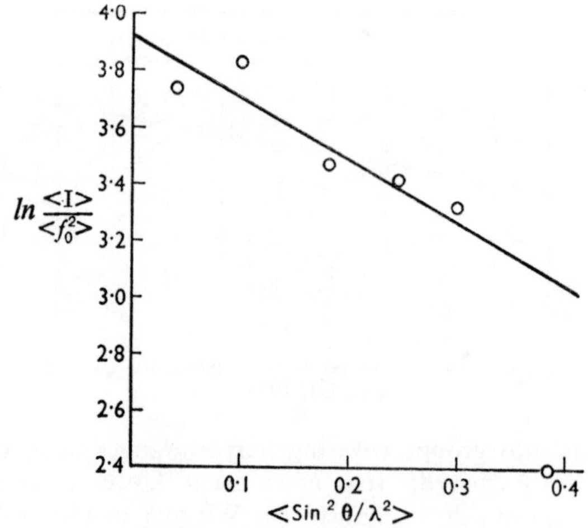

FIG. 74. Graph for finding the temperature factor for metatolidine dihydrochloride. (The last point is unreliable and has been ignored)

Although this procedure is reasonably satisfactory for giving the values of scattering factors, some workers may prefer to use empirical scattering factors, such as those given by Robertson (1935*c*) for carbon. Since these scattering factors already include the effects of temperature, they should be much closer approximations than the values of f_0. But they should be used with caution, since they may not apply accurately to the particular crystal under examination. The more objective procedure just outlined would seem to be preferable.

2.4. *Unitary scattering factors.* Scattering factors of atoms all have maximum values equal to the atomic numbers at zero angle of scattering, and fall off asymptotically to zero at large angles. The rate of fall-off differs from atom to atom; as described in Appendix IV of Volume I, the scattering-factor curves of atoms with Thomas-Fermi electron distributions, and with atomic numbers greater than about 55 (caesium), are similar only if plotted on different scales of $\sin \theta/\lambda$. The extent of the similarity of the various *f*-curves has been discussed by Harker and Kasper (1948), who have produced the diagram shown in fig. 75 in which the *f*-curves are shown normalized to have unit value at $\sin \theta/\lambda = 0$; it will be observed that the curves vary erratically in the region of low atomic numbers, but that they gradually become more regular as the atomic numbers increase.

The ordinates of the curves shown in fig. 75 are known as unitary

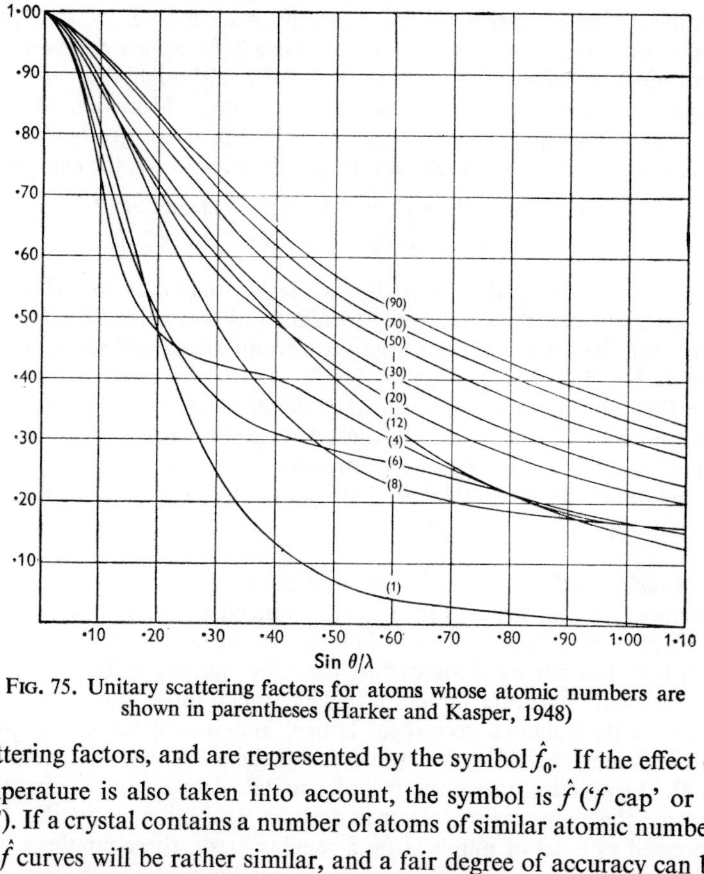

FIG. 75. Unitary scattering factors for atoms whose atomic numbers are shown in parentheses (Harker and Kasper, 1948)

scattering factors, and are represented by the symbol $\hat{f}_0$. If the effect of temperature is also taken into account, the symbol is $\hat{f}$ ('f cap' or 'f hat'). If a crystal contains a number of atoms of similar atomic number, the $\hat{f}$ curves will be rather similar, and a fair degree of accuracy can be achieved by assuming that they are exactly equal. This simplifies the calculations to a great extent, and is necessary for some of the methods of structure-factor calculation described in section **4**.3.2; the device should not be used, however, except for preliminary calculations.

2.5. *Adaptation to projections of low symmetry.* When the function $\cos 2\pi(hx+ky)$ is involved, the methods described in section **4**.2.1 can be used if this expression is put into the form $\cos 2\pi hx \cos 2\pi ky - \sin 2\pi hx \sin 2\pi ky$. The work involved is not thereby doubled, as may be supposed, because the same set of calculations will serve for both the $hk0$ and $h\bar{k}0$ reflexions, the only difference being the change in sign of the second part of the expression. If the direct evaluation of $\cos 2\pi(hx+ky)$ is preferred, the reflexions should again be grouped in sets with constant h (or k).

2.6. *Adaptation to projections of higher symmetry.* For symmetries higher than orthorhombic, more complicated expressions arise. For example, in some tetragonal space groups, such as No. 89, P422, the expression $\cos 2\pi hx \cos 2\pi ky + \cos 2\pi kx \cos 2\pi hy$ appears; these two parts must, of course, be treated separately, although they are concerned with only one equivalent set of atoms. More complicated expressions can also appear; for example, the space group No. 92, $P4_12_12$, introduces, for reflexions with $2h+2k+l=4n+1$, the expression

$$-\cos \pi(h+k)(x+y) \sin \pi(h-k)(x-y) \sin 2\pi lz$$
$$+\sin \pi(h-k)(x+y) \cos \pi(h+k)(x-y) \cos 2\pi lz.$$

This can best be evaluated in terms of the quantities $(h+k)/2$ and $(h-k)/2$, but this does not apply to reflexions for which $2h+2k+l$ is even. Similar considerations apply to certain hexagonal space groups such as No. 178, $P6_122$.

In the cubic system there are either three, six or twelve products in the expressions for A or B, and these have to be treated separately by calculation. Nevertheless, the expressions are not complicated and appear much less formidable than some that occur in hexagonal space groups.

2.7. *Fourier methods.* The similarity of equation *10*.3, which gives the structure factor in terms of the atomic arrangement, and equation *12*.2, which gives the electron density in terms of the structure factors, suggests that Fourier methods can be used for computing both electron densities and structure factors. In fact, the Fourier transform of a crystal is its weighted reciprocal lattice, and thus a set of structure factors is merely the Fourier transform of the electron density (section **1**.3.3). In practice, therefore, in order to calculate a zone of structure factors, the appropriate electron-density projection must be first expressed as a set of numbers on a regular mesh, these numbers then being used as Fourier coefficients in one of the ways to be described in the next chapter; the sum of the series then gives the required structure factors. This subject will be considered in more detail in sections **5**.3.3 and **5**.3.4.

3. Methods for Isolated Reflexions

3.1. *Introduction.* The methods described in the preceding sections are suitable only when a complete two-dimensional or three-dimensional set of structure factors has to be calculated. This, however, is often not required; in the initial stages of the determination of a crystal structure it is more important to establish the correctness or otherwise of a few reflexions, and for this purpose only a few, perhaps unrelated, structure factors need be calculated. In these circumstances each structure factor has to be tackled individually; extreme accuracy is less important than reliability and rapidity, and consequently methods have to be adapted to provide these properties. Calculation can still, of course, be used, but several suggestions have been made which seem to offer more possibilities of easing the work of the initial stages of a structure determination.

3.2 *Structure-factor graphs.* Since in the initial stages we can confine our attention to any chosen reflexions, it is natural to choose those that are most easily calculated, that is, those with one or two indices zero. The latter limitation is usually too severe, and so structure work frequently begins with consideration of intensities with one index zero.

For such reflexions, in the systems of lower symmetry, only two coordinates are involved in the structure-factor formulae, and thus it is possible to evaluate the expression at all points within the unit cell and express these values on a two-dimensional diagram; the contribution to the structure factor of any atom can then be found by multiplying the value of the expression at the atomic position by the atomic scattering factor.

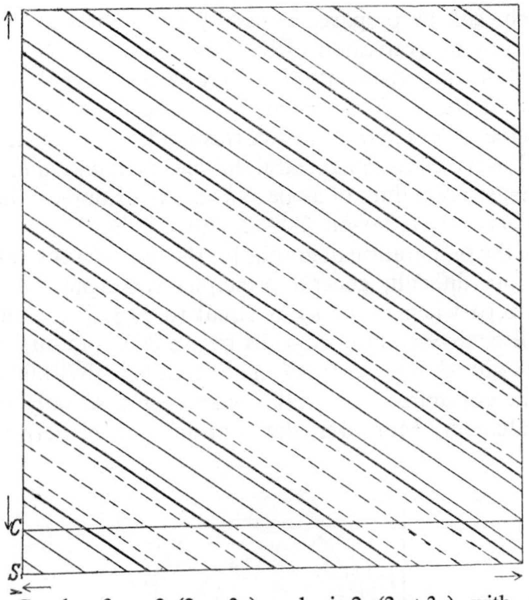

FIG. 77. Graph of $\cos 2\pi(2x+3y)$ and $\sin 2\pi(2x+3y)$ with contours drawn at 1·0 and 0·5 (thin full lines), 0 (thick lines), and $\overline{0{\cdot}5}$ and $\overline{1{\cdot}0}$ (thin broken lines) (Bragg and Lipson, 1936). C is the origin for the cosine function and S for the sine function

Bragg and Lipson (1936) have suggested that the representation of the structure factor should take the form of contours of constant value, and they proposed that these diagrams should be called structure-factor graphs. Although there are many different formulae to be dealt with, and the graphs would not be of value unless a considerable number of sets of indices were available, the difficulties are not as formidable as might be expected. As we have seen in section **2**.8.2, there are only 17 plane groups and therefore the number of separate formulae to be considered is much smaller than the number required for the 230 space groups. The production of structure-factor graphs for limited ranges of indices is therefore quite practicable. The unit cell may, of course, be considered as a square, since the structure factors depend only upon the parameters and not upon the unit-cell dimensions.

It was originally thought by Bragg and Lipson that the structure-factor graphs would be of greatest use for crystals of high symmetry, where the structure-factor formulae (section **4**.1.1) are of greatest complexity. It has turned out, however, that they have been of much greater use for crystals of low symmetry, merely because such crystals occur most frequently. All triclinic, monoclinic and orthorhombic crystals, and projections on the prism faces of tetragonal and hexagonal crystals, are covered by expressions of the type $\cos 2\pi(hx+ky)$ and $\cos 2\pi hx \cos 2\pi ky$.

The graphs can be prepared either by calculation of the shapes of the contours or by evaluation of the function at specific points in the unit cell and drawing the contours by graphical interpolation. For the function $\cos 2\pi(hx+ky)$ the former method is used; obviously a constant value of $\cos 2\pi(hx+ky)$ corresponds to a constant value of $hx+ky$ and so the contours are straight lines of equation $hx+ky=$ constant, that is, straight lines of slope $-k/h$. An example—the structure-factor graphs for the reflexion 230—is shown in fig. 77.

Although the preparation of graphs for the function $\cos 2\pi hx \cos 2\pi ky$ is rather more difficult, general principles can again be used. The function is zero when hx or ky is equal to $\frac{1}{4}, \frac{3}{4}, \frac{5}{4}, \ldots$, and thus the unit cell will be divided into sub-cells by straight contours corresponding to zero—nodal lines, as they may be called. Within the various sub-cells, the contours have similar shapes, and so only one sub-cell need be evaluated. Moreover, the contours can be derived from the

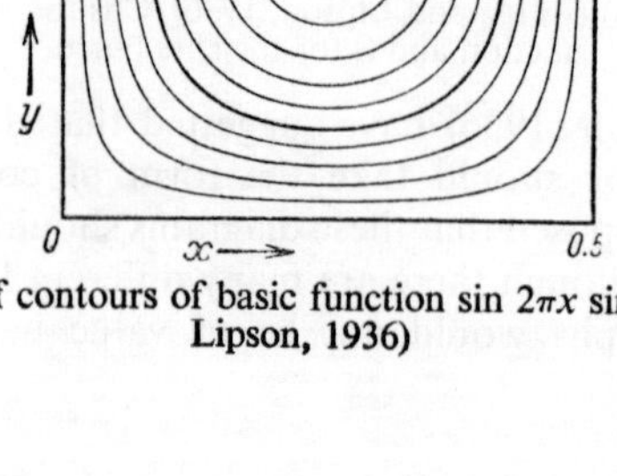

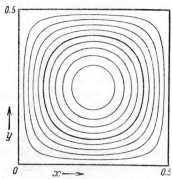

FIG. 78. Graph of contours of basic function $\sin 2\pi x \sin 2\pi y$ (Bragg and Lipson, 1936)

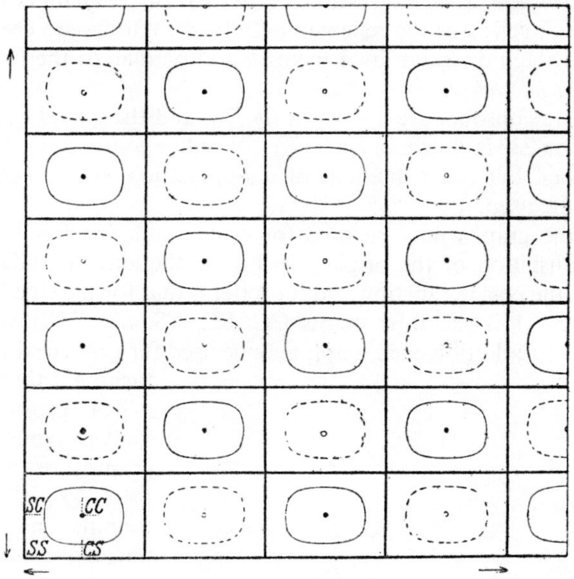

FIG. 79(i). Graph of function $\stackrel{\cos}{\underset{\sin}{\cdot}} 4\pi x \times \stackrel{\cos}{\underset{\sin}{\cdot}} 6\pi y$, with contours drawn at 1·0 (black spots), 0·5 (thin full lines), 0 (thick lines) $\overline{0{\cdot}5}$ (thin broken lines) and $\overline{1{\cdot}0}$ (small circles). The arrows indicate the cell dimensions (Bragg and Lipson, 1936)

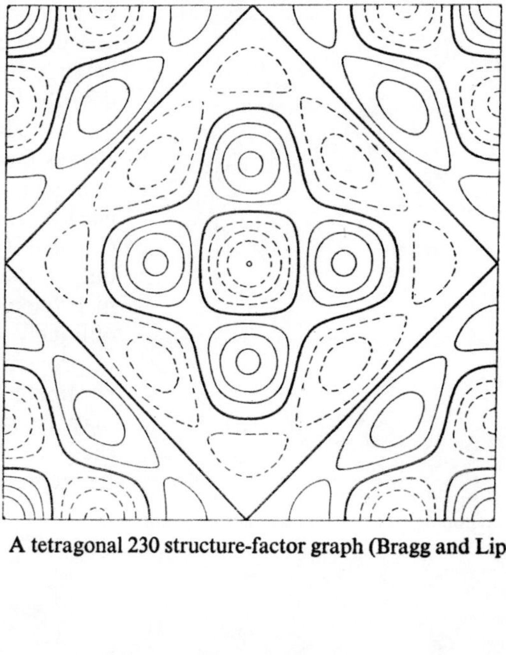

FIG. 79 (ii). A tetragonal 230 structure-factor graph (Bragg and Lipson, 1936)

contours for the basic expression $\sin 2\pi x \sin 2\pi y$, which are based on a square sub-cell; for the reflexion $hk0$ these contours are compressed parallel to the a direction by a factor h and parallel to the b direction by a factor k.

The basic contours are shown in fig. 78, and their modification for the reflexion 230 is shown in fig. 79 (i). Negative contours are shown by broken lines, but other methods of differentiation, such as colouring, may also be used.

The same graphs may be used for cosine and sine functions by a simple translation of the origin. In fig. 77 the letter C indicates the origin for the cosine function and the letter S that for the sine function, and in fig. 79 (i) the four points CC, SC, CS and SS have similar meanings. In addition each graph may be used for the reflexion $kh0$ by turning it through 90°.

FIG. 80. A hexagonal $12\bar{3}0$ structure-factor graph (Bragg and Lipson, 1936)

For projections of higher symmetry the graphs, as shown in figs. 79 (ii) and 80, become more complicated; methods of preparing some of them have been described by Beevers and Lipson (1938). In using such graphs, only those points within the asymmetric unit of pattern need be inserted, special positions being allowed for as described in section **4**.1.3. This may not always mean that only non-equivalent points need be considered; as Chrobak (1937) points out, if there are symmetry elements inclined obliquely to the plane of projection, all three parameters x, y and z may be involved and these cannot possibly be represented by a point with two coordinates. For example, the triad axes of the cubic system produce equivalent points with relationships of the type *xyz*, *yzx*, *zxy*, and in two dimensions these would have to be represented by the three points *xy*, *yz*, *zx*. For this reason, the structure-factor graphs for some of the cubic systems do not reduce to those for the basal plane of the tetragonal system, as might be expected; for example, the graphs for the space group No. 195, P23, reduce to those for the plane group *pmm* (cf. section **2**.8.2).

For rough work, the graphs are most simply used by plotting the atomic co-ordinates on tracing paper and placing them successively over the different graphs. This is illustrated in figs. 81(*a*) and (*b*), which show the evaluation of two of the structure factors included in table 71. For accurate work, variation in the dimensions of the paper on which the graphs are drawn must be allowed for and Bunn (1961) describes how this may be done for the function $\cos 2\pi(hx+ky)$; for other functions this limitation renders it improbable that high accuracy can be obtained with the graphs.

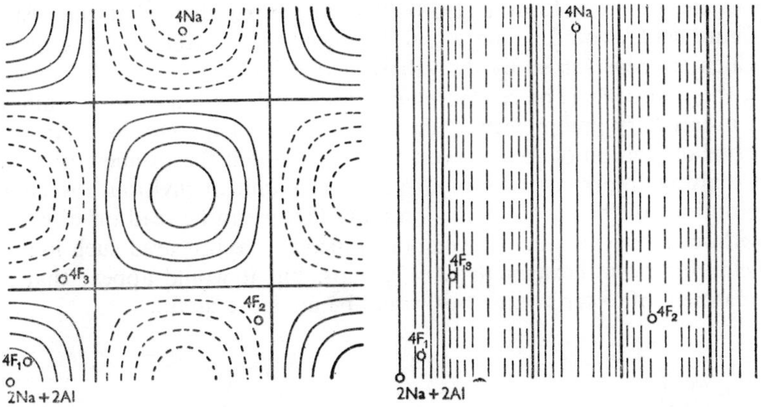

FIG. 81 (*a*) 110 and (*b*) 200 structure-factor graph for cryolite, showing positions of atoms. The thick lines are zero contours and the broken lines are negative

A further use of the graphs becomes manifest from figs. 81(*a*) and (*b*). It will be noted that certain atoms lie in regions where their contribution to the structure factor changes slowly, whereas other atoms lie on quite steep slopes. Thus, if the agreement between observed and calculated intensity is unsatisfactory, it is obvious which atoms should be moved and in which way. For example, if we wish to increase the intensity of the 200 reflexion the F_1 or the F_3 atoms must be moved to positions with smaller *x* parameters; both these sets of atoms lie on steep gradients. A slight change in the positions of the general sodium atoms would be useless, since these lie on maxima; and giving F_2 a larger *x* parameter would have a small effect, since this atom lies near a minimum. Consideration of a number of graphs for different reflexions can give useful evidence about possible atomic shifts, as described by Bunn (1945, p. 268).

3.3. *Use of structure-factor graphs for general intensities.* Although the structure-factor graphs were devised for reflexions with one index zero, they can be used also for general reflexions. Suppose, for example, that the structure-factor formula is $\cos 2\pi hx \cos 2\pi ky \cos 2\pi lz$. For $l=1$, we may write down the value of $\cos 2\pi z$ against the position of each atom in the projection, and when the value of $\cos 2\pi hx \cos 2\pi ky$ is read from the chart it can be multiplied by $\cos 2\pi z$ on a slide rule, the product being entered directly in the table. A separate diagram is thus needed for each value of l and for the different structure-factor expressions that involve changes in the function of lz.

3.4. *Figure fields.* Certain difficulties occur in the use of structure-factor graphs, particularly near maxima and minima, where the gradients are changing rapidly; here interpolation becomes rather difficult, and Beevers and Lipson (1938) have suggested that what they call 'figure fields' would be more useful. These are structure-factor graphs which are represented by the values of the functions at specific points in the unit cell. (For certain plane groups calculation of these values is a necessary preliminary to the construction of the graphs.) An interval of division of the cell must be chosen, and if the atomic positions are always represented as multiples of this unit of division, the contributions of the atoms to the structure factor can be read off directly without interpolation. Beevers and Lipson have prepared such figure fields for some hexagonal plane groups, but it would appear that a treatment of lower symmetries would be far more useful.

CHAPTER 5

SUMMATION OF FOURIER SERIES

1. General Formulae

1.1 *Elimination of complex quantities.* Equation (*12*.2)

$$\rho(x, y, z) = \frac{1}{V} \Sigma \Sigma \Sigma \, F(hkl) \exp\{-2\pi i(hx + ky + lz)\}$$

is not suitable for quantitative evaluation of electron densities since it contains complex quantities; these quantities must therefore be resolved into their real and imaginary parts. The process of resolution may be described most simply by considering a single term only—$F(hkl) \exp\{-2\pi i(hx+ky+lz)\}$, which can be expressed as

$$\{A'(hkl) + iB'(hkl)\}\{\cos 2\pi(hx+ky+lz) - i \sin 2\pi(hx+ky+lz)\},$$

where A′ and B′ are the two components of F (section **1**.2.6). We may now combine this expression with that for the conjugate term $(\bar{h}\bar{k}\bar{l})$, which gives:

$$\begin{aligned} &\{A'(hkl) + iB'(hkl)\}\{\cos 2\pi(hx+ky+lz) - i \sin 2\pi(hx+ky+lz)\} \\ &+ \{A'(\bar{h}\bar{k}\bar{l}) + iB'(\bar{h}\bar{k}\bar{l})\}\{\cos 2\pi(hx+ky+lz) + i \sin 2\pi(hx+ky+lz)\} \\ &= 2A'(hkl) \cos 2\pi(hx+ky+lz) + 2B'(hkl) \sin 2\pi(hx+ky+lz), \qquad (83.1) \end{aligned}$$

since $A'(\bar{h}\bar{k}\bar{l}) = A'(hkl)$ and $B'(\bar{h}\bar{k}\bar{l}) = -B'(hkl)$. This expression is suitable for numerical calculation, if all the values of $A'(hkl)$ and $B'(hkl)$ are known.

In performing the summation, it must be remembered that the expression does not apply to the term 000, which has no conjugate (or more strictly, is its own conjugate). Thus the factor 2 in expression *83*.1 has to be omitted for this term only, and the expression for the electron density is

$$\rho(x, y, z) = \frac{1}{V}\left[F(000) + 2 \sum_{h=0}^{\infty} \sum_{k=-\infty}^{\infty} \sum_{l=-\infty}^{\infty} A'(hkl) \cos 2\pi(hx+ky+lz) + B'(hkl) \sin 2\pi(hx+ky+lz)\right], \qquad (83.2)$$

the summation being taken over only half the complete reciprocal lattice, excluding the term for which $h = k = l = 0$.

Equation *83*.2 gives the general expression from which all others are derived, and it is probably the best form for evaluation. It can, however, be expressed more simply if a phase angle α is introduced (section **1**.3.1); this angle is defined by the equations

$$\left.\begin{aligned} &A'(hkl) = |F(hkl)| \cos \alpha(hkl), \\ \text{and} \quad &B'(hkl) = |F(hkl)| \sin \alpha(hkl). \\ \text{whence} \quad &\tan \alpha(hkl) = B'(hkl)/A'(hkl). \end{aligned}\right\} \qquad (83.3)$$

Equation *83.2* becomes

$$\rho(x, y, z) = \frac{1}{V}\left[F(000) + 2\sum_{h=0}^{\infty}\sum_{k=-\infty}^{\infty}\sum_{l=-\infty}^{\infty}|F(hkl)|\cos\{2\pi(hx+ky+lz) - \alpha(hkl)\}\right]. \quad (84)$$

1.2. *Formulae for different space groups.* Although equation *84* holds generally for all crystals, some simplification in its application may be obtained by making use of any symmetry that the weighted reciprocal lattice might possess. For example, if a crystal has a centre of symmetry at the origin, $F(hkl) = F(\bar{h}\bar{k}\bar{l})$; the structure factors are therefore all real (section **4**.1.1.) and the expression for the electron density becomes

$$\rho(x, y, z) = \frac{1}{V}\left[F(000) + 2\sum_{h=0}^{\infty}\sum_{k=-\infty}^{\infty}\sum_{l=-\infty}^{\infty}F(hkl)\cos 2\pi(hx+ky+lz)\right].$$

Corresponding results follow from the presence of other types of symmetry elements; for example, if the crystal has a two-fold axis along the b axis (space group No. 3, P2), the relationship between the structure factors is that $F(hkl) = F(\bar{h}k\bar{l})$; thus if we combine the terms $F(hkl)$, $F(\bar{h}k\bar{l})$, $F(h\bar{k}l)$ and $F(\bar{h}\bar{k}\bar{l})$ we obtain

$$\rho(x, y, z) = \frac{1}{V}\left[F(000) + 2\sum\sum\sum |F(hkl)|\cos\{2\pi(hx+ky+lz) - \alpha(hkl)\} + |F(\bar{h}k\bar{l})|\cos\{2\pi(-hx+ky-lz) - \alpha(\bar{h}k\bar{l})\}\right]$$

the summation not including the term F(000).

Because of the relationship between the structure factors, $|F(hkl)| = |F(\bar{h}k\bar{l})|$ and $\alpha(hkl) = \alpha(\bar{h}k\bar{l})$, and thus the separate terms in the summation are

$$4|F(hkl)|\cos 2\pi(hx+lz)\cos\{2\pi ky - \alpha(hkl)\}.$$

This result will not however apply to the terms $F(0k0)$ and $F(h0l)$, since there are not four of them to make a set. The complete expression for the electron density therefore includes the expressions F(000),

$$2\sum_{k=1}^{\infty}|F(0k0)|\cos\{2\pi ky - \alpha(0k0)\}$$

and

$$2\sum_{h=0}^{\infty}\sum_{l=-\infty}^{\infty}F(h0l)\cos 2\pi(hx+lz),$$

the general triple summation not including these terms, and the double summation not including the term F(000).

An extra complication arises for space groups that contain screw axes and glide planes. In the space group No. 11, $P2_1/m$, for example, the structure-factor formulae are

$$A = 4\cos 2\pi(hx+lz)\cos 2\pi ky,\ B=0,\ \text{if } k \text{ is even,}$$

and

$$A = -4\sin 2\pi(hx+lz)\sin 2\pi ky,\ B=0,\ \text{if } k \text{ is odd.}$$

Thus the relationships between the structure factors are different for these two classes of reflexion; for those with k even, the relationships are $F(hkl)=F(h\bar{k}l)=F(\bar{h}k\bar{l})=F(\bar{h}\bar{k}\bar{l})$, while for those with k odd the relationships are $F(hkl)=-F(h\bar{k}l)=-F(\bar{h}k\bar{l})=F(\bar{h}\bar{k}\bar{l})$. The summation for the terms with k even is thus different from the summation for terms with k odd, which contains expressions such as:

$$\begin{aligned} &F(hkl)\cos 2\pi(hx+ky+lz)+F(\bar{h}k\bar{l})\cos 2\pi(-hx+ky-lz)\\ &\quad =F(hkl)\cos 2\pi(hx+ky+lz)-F(hkl)\cos 2\pi(-hx+ky-lz)\\ &\quad =-2F(hkl)\sin 2\pi(hx+lz)\sin 2\pi ky. \end{aligned}$$

The expression for the electron density then includes the general terms

$$4\sum_{-\infty}^{+\infty}\sum_{2}^{\infty}\sum_{0}^{\infty} F(hkl)\cos 2\pi(hx+lz)\cos 2\pi ky, \quad (k \text{ even})$$

and

$$-4\sum_{-\infty}^{+\infty}\sum_{1}^{\infty}\sum_{0}^{\infty} F(hkl)\sin 2\pi(hx+lz)\sin 2\pi ky, \quad (k \text{ odd}) \qquad (85.1)$$

the multiplicities of the special terms F(000), F(0*k*0) and F(*h*0*l*) being the same as those set out on page 84. (It will be noted that, since this space group has a centre of symmetry, we can specify the structure factors themselves, not merely their moduli.)

In the International Tables (1952) the expression for the electron density in terms of the general structure factors only is given. For the space group No. 11, $P2_1/m$, the expression is

$$\rho(XYZ)=$$

$$\frac{4}{V_c}\Big\{\sum_{0}^{\infty}\sum_{0}^{\infty}\sum_{0}^{\infty}{}^{l=2n}[F(hkl)\cos 2\pi(hX+kY)+F(\bar{h}kl)\cos 2\pi(-hX+kY)]\cos 2\pi lZ$$

$$-\sum_{0}^{\infty}\sum_{0}^{\infty}\sum_{0}^{\infty}{}^{l=2n+1}[F(hkl)\sin 2\pi(hX+kY)+F(\bar{h}kl)\sin 2\pi(-hX+kY)]\sin 2\pi lZ\Big\}. \qquad (85.2)$$

It will be noted that the coordinates (XYZ) of a general point in the unit cell are printed differently from the coordinates (*xyz*) representing an atomic position. In this book, no differentiation has been made.

1.3. *Projections on to planes and lines.* The summation of series such as *84* and *85*.1 involves considerable work since *all* the reflexions observable have to be considered. A reduction in the amount of work can be achieved by considering the projection of a structure on to a plane (Bragg, 1929*a*). The information obtained is less than that given by three-dimensional summations, but the work is curtailed by such a large factor that for some time only two-dimensional methods were considered practicable; with present-day resources (section 5.3.2), however, three-dimensional computations are quite practicable and are much used.

The electron density projected on to a point (x, y) in the (001) face of the unit cell is given by the equation:

$$\begin{aligned}\rho(x, y) &= \int_0^1 \rho(x, y, z)c\,dz \\ &= \frac{c}{V}\int_0^1 \Sigma\,\Sigma\,\Sigma\,F(hkl)\exp\{-2\pi i(hx+ky+lz)\}\,dz \\ &= \frac{1}{A_c}\Sigma\,\Sigma\,\Sigma\,F(hkl)\exp\{-2\pi i(hx+ky)\}\int_0^1 \exp\{-2\pi ilz\}\,dz,\end{aligned}$$

where A_c is the area of the projection of the unit cell. Since $\exp 2\pi ilz = \cos 2\pi lz + i \sin 2\pi lz$, the integral is zero for all values of l except zero; when l is zero, the integral is unity and the equation becomes:

$$\rho(x, y) = \frac{1}{A_c}\sum_h \sum_k F(hk0)\exp\{-2\pi i(hx+ky)\}. \qquad (86)$$

We see therefore that the projected electron density can be obtained from the data given by a single zone of X-ray reflexions.

Similar equations apply to projections on other faces of the unit cell, and the same theory may be applied to oblique planes also; in general, if we make use of that section of the reciprocal lattice for which $ph+qk+rl=0$, we obtain the electron density projected on the plane (pqr). Naturally the most information will be obtained when the period of repetition in the direction of the projection is small, and this will usually happen when the electron density is projected along one of the crystallographic axes. But exceptional cases may arise when this is not so, and other directions of projection should then be considered; centred lattices, in particular, can lead to such conditions. For example, if a crystal has a lattice C, a Fourier series with the values of $F(hhl)$ as coefficients will give the electron density projected on the plane $(1\bar{1}0)$. An atom at the point x, y, z will project exactly at the same position as an atom at $\frac{1}{2}+x, \frac{1}{2}+y, z$, and thus, in effect, the period of repetition in the direction of projection is $\frac{1}{2}(a^2+b^2)^{\frac{1}{2}}$; this may be less than a or b separately.

Electron densities can also be projected on to lines. For the projection on to a cell edge we have

$$\begin{aligned}\rho(x) &= \int_0^1 \rho(x, y)b\,dy \\ &= \frac{bc}{V}\sum_h \sum_k F(hk0)\exp\{-2\pi ihx\}\int_0^1 \exp\{-2\pi iky\}\,dy\end{aligned}$$

$$=\frac{bc}{V}\sum_h F(h00)\exp\{-2\pi ihx\}, \tag{87.1}$$

since the integral is zero unless $k=0$. To evaluate $\rho(x)$ we need to know only the structure factors of a set of orders from a single set of planes, but, of course, the information is of much less value.

1.4. *Partial three-dimensional summations.* Booth (1945*c*) has suggested two methods which are a compromise between two-dimensional and three-dimensional analysis. The first is the projection of the contents of the unit cell lying between two planes, say $z=z_1$ and $z=z_2$ (the bounded projection). If interest lies in the x and y parameters of atoms that are known to lie between these two planes, there is no need to confine attention to the precise planes in which these atoms lie.

Let us call the density projected in this way $\rho_{12}(x, y)$. Then

$$\begin{aligned}\rho_{12}(x, y) &= \int_{z_1}^{z_2}\rho(x, y, z)c\,dz\\ &= \frac{c}{V}\int_{z_1}^{z_2}\sum\sum\sum F(hkl)\exp\{-2\pi i(hx+ky+lz)\}\,dz\\ &= \frac{1}{A_c}\sum\sum\sum\frac{F(hkl)}{-2\pi il}[\exp\{-2\pi i(hx+ky+lz_2)\}\\ &\qquad\qquad -\exp\{-2\pi i(hx+ky+lz_1)\}]\\ &= \frac{1}{A_c}\sum\sum\sum\frac{F(hkl)}{2\pi l}[\sin 2\pi(hx+ky+lz_2)\\ &\qquad +i\cos 2\pi(hx+ky+lz_2)-\sin 2\pi(hx+ky+lz_1)\\ &\qquad -i\cos 2\pi(hx+ky+lz_1)]\\ &= \frac{1}{A_c}\sum\sum\sum\frac{F(hkl)}{2\pi l}\left[2\cos 2\pi\left(hx+ky+l\frac{z_2+z_1}{2}\right)\sin \pi l(z_2-z_1)\right.\\ &\qquad \left.-2i\sin 2\pi\left(hx+ky+l\frac{z_2+z_1}{2}\right)\sin \pi l(z_2-z_1)\right]\\ &= \frac{1}{A_c}\sum\sum\sum\frac{F(hkl)}{\pi l}\sin \pi l(z_2-z_1)\\ &\qquad \left\{-\exp 2\pi i\left(hx+ky+l\frac{z_2+z_1}{2}\right)\right\}.\end{aligned}$$

By methods similar to those used in section **5**.1.1, this expression can be shown to be equal to

$$\frac{1}{A_c}\sum\sum\sum\frac{F(hkl)}{\pi l}\sin\pi l(z_2-z_1)\cos 2\pi\left\{hx+ky+l\frac{z_2+z_1}{2}-\alpha(hkl)\right\}, \tag{87.2}$$

the summation now being taken over half the reciprocal lattice.

The summation may be made by combining the quantity $l(z_2+z_1)/2$ with $\alpha(hkl)$, and then proceeding in the way described in section **5**.1.1

—that is, the A and B parts of the coefficients should be calculated. For a crystal with a centre of symmetry the summation may be expressed as

$$\frac{1}{A_c}\sum\sum\sum\left[\frac{F(hkl)\sin\pi l(z_2-z_1)\cos\pi l(z_2+z_1)}{\pi l}\cos 2\pi(hx+ky)\right.$$
$$\left.-\frac{F(hkl)\sin\pi l(z_2-z_1)\sin\pi l(z_2+z_1)}{\pi l}\sin 2\pi(hx+ky)\right]. \quad (88)$$

The quantities F(hkl) have therefore to be multiplied by factors that, for given values of z_2 and z_1, are functions of l only, and can therefore be evaluated separately for the few different values of l to be considered. The new coefficients having been obtained, the summation follows the ordinary lines of a two-dimensional summation.

It will be noted that, though the computational work is not large, all the values of F(hkl) have to be known, and thus the labour of data reduction is still as large as for a complete three-dimensional synthesis. In special cases, this labour can be reduced to some extent. For example, if we wish to project the contents of half the unit cell, $z_2-z_1=\frac{1}{2}$, and thus the value of $\sin\pi l(z_2-z_1)$ is zero if l is even; consequently, the reflexions with l even, but not zero, need not be measured. If l is zero, the quantity $\{\sin\pi l(z_2-z_1)\}/\pi l$ is equal to z_2-z_1 and so the terms with l zero do not disappear when $z_2-z_1=\frac{1}{2}$.

Booth (1945*c*) has also shown how it is possible to add together the electron densities in several parallel sections by methods that are no more tedious than those for a single section. This operation would be useful if one required, say, the x and y parameters of several different atoms whose z parameters were already known; the parameters must, of course, be known approximately as the result gives no indication of which x and y parameters are associated with a particular z parameter.

2. Reduction of Formulae for Systematic Calculation

2.1. *General principles for three-dimensional summations.* We have seen in section 5.1.1 how the expression for the electron density in a crystal can be reduced to include real quantities only; but there still remains the practical problem of performing the summation. Equation *83.2*, despite its apparently greater complexity, forms a better starting point than equation *84*, since it does not contain the quantities $\alpha(hkl)$, which may have any value between 0° and 360°. Nevertheless, equation *83.2* still includes the terms $\cos 2\pi(hx+ky+lz)$ and $\sin 2\pi(hx+ky+lz)$, and thus each index cannot be considered separately, as they could be if terms such as $\cos 2\pi hx \cos 2\pi ky \cos 2\pi lz$ occurred. This difficulty can be overcome by expanding $\cos 2\pi(hx+ky+lz)$ and $\sin 2\pi(hx+ky+lz)$ into the forms:

$$\cos 2\pi(hx+ky+lz) = \cos 2\pi hx \cos 2\pi ky \cos 2\pi lz - \cos 2\pi hx \sin 2\pi ky \sin 2\pi lz$$
$$- \sin 2\pi hx \cos 2\pi ky \sin 2\pi lz - \sin 2\pi hx \sin 2\pi ky \cos 2\pi lz$$

and $\sin 2\pi(hx+ky+lz) = \sin 2\pi hx \cos 2\pi ky \cos 2\pi lz$

$$+ \cos 2\pi hx \sin 2\pi ky \cos 2\pi lz + \cos 2\pi hx \cos 2\pi ky \sin 2\pi lz$$
$$- \sin 2\pi hx \sin 2\pi ky \sin 2\pi lz.$$

The disadvantage of expanding each single term into four is offset by the fact that the calculations need to be carried out for only one eighth of the unit cell; the separate terms can be changed in sign appropriately to provide the electron densities at the points (x, y, z), $(\bar{x}, y, z)$, $(x, \bar{y}, z)$, $(x, y, \bar{z})$, $(x, \bar{y}, \bar{z})$, $(\bar{x}, y, \bar{z})$, $(\bar{x}, \bar{y}, z)$ and $(\bar{x}, \bar{y}, \bar{z})$.

The advantage of expressing the separate terms as triple products is brought out by considering the problem in detail. The general case of a crystal with no symmetry has been discussed by Goodwin and Hardy (1938), but the principles can be explained rather more simply by considering terms of the form $F(hkl) \cos 2\pi hx \cos 2\pi ky \cos 2\pi lz$, which arise in the orthorhombic system. The summation can be written as

$$\sum_l [\sum_k \{\sum_h F(hkl) \cos 2\pi hx\} \cos 2\pi ky] \cos 2\pi lz.$$

The expression between the braces is a one-dimensional series, and can be summed for particular values of k and l, the ordinates of the curve so obtained representing values of each summation for particular values of x; by completing the summations for the various groups of reflexions with given values of k and l we obtain quantities that are characteristic of certain values of x, k and l: let us call them $C(x, k, l)$.

The summation now is

$$\sum_l [\sum_k C(x, k, l) \cos 2\pi ky] \cos 2\pi lz.$$

We can now divide the values of $C(x, k, l)$ into sets with constant l, and again perform separate one-dimensional summations, each ordinate of which now is a quantity characteristic of a particular value of x, y and l: let us call it $C(x, y, l)$. The final summation is then

$$\sum_l C(x, y, l) \cos 2\pi lz.$$

In this way the process of summing a three-dimensional series has been reduced to a succession of one-dimensional summations.

Because of the complexity of the rigorous expressions involved in the complete process of three-dimensional Fourier synthesis, the rest of this chapter will be mainly concerned with two-dimensional methods; these methods bring out the essential principles involved, and can easily be extended to three dimensions if required.

2.2. *General principles for two-dimensional summations.* We have seen from equations *83.1* and *83.2* that the general expression for the electron density projected on to a plane contains terms such as

$$A'(hk0) \cos 2\pi(hx+ky) + B'(hk0) \sin 2\pi(hx+ky),$$

which can be written as

$$A'(hk0) \cos 2\pi hx \cos 2\pi ky - A'(hk0) \sin 2\pi hx \sin 2\pi ky$$
$$+ B'(hk0) \sin 2\pi hx \cos 2\pi ky + B'(hk0) \cos 2\pi hx \sin 2\pi ky. \quad (90.1)$$

This expression, it will be remembered, was obtained by combining the two terms $(hk0)$ and $(\bar{h}\bar{k}0)$; the corresponding expression for the terms $(\bar{h}k0)$ and $(h\bar{k}0)$ is

$$A'(\bar{h}k0) \cos 2\pi hx \cos 2\pi ky + A'(\bar{h}k0) \sin 2\pi hx \sin 2\pi ky$$
$$- B'(\bar{h}k0) \sin 2\pi hx \cos 2\pi ky + B'(\bar{h}k0) \cos 2\pi hx \sin 2\pi ky. \quad (90.2)$$

If we combine expressions *90*.1 and *90*.2 we obtain

$$[A'(hk0) + A'(\bar{h}k0)] \cos 2\pi hx \cos 2\pi ky$$
$$- [A'(hk0) - A'(\bar{h}k0)] \sin 2\pi hx \sin 2\pi ky$$
$$+ [B'(hk0) - B'(\bar{h}k0)] \sin 2\pi hx \cos 2\pi ky$$
$$+ [B'(hk0) + B'(\bar{h}k0)] \cos 2\pi hx \sin 2\pi ky. \quad (90.3)$$

The advantage of this form of expression has been described in the previous section: that is, it is possible to combine terms with the same value of one index, say k.

If we write

$$A_1 = A'(hk0) + A'(\bar{h}k0), \qquad A_2 = A'(hk0) - A'(\bar{h}k0),$$
$$B_1 = B'(hk0) + B'(\bar{h}k0) \text{ and } B_2 = B'(hk0) - B'(\bar{h}k0),$$

expression *90*.3 can be written as

$$(A_1 \cos 2\pi hx + B_2 \sin 2\pi hx) \cos 2\pi ky$$
$$- (A_2 \sin 2\pi hx - B_1 \cos 2\pi hx) \sin 2\pi ky.$$

The summation may then be expressed as

$$\sum_k [\sum_h A_1(hk0) \cos 2\pi hx + B_2(hk0) \sin 2\pi hx] \cos 2\pi ky$$
$$- \sum_k [\sum_h A_2(hk0) \sin 2\pi hx - B_1(hk0) \cos 2\pi hx] \sin 2\pi ky.$$

The expressions in square brackets may be evaluated in preliminary tables which give the coefficients to be used in the final summations. In other words, we evaluate the expressions in the square brackets for groups of reflexions with a given value of k, and the result is a series of ordinates at particular values of x; we may therefore call the quantities obtained $C(k, x)$. Similarly, the quantities obtained from the other brackets may be called $S(k, x)$. The final summation is then

$$\sum_k [C(k, x) \cos 2\pi ky - S(k, x) \sin 2\pi ky].$$

It will be noted that, since we have taken the terms together in groups of four, with all possible changes of sign, the summation must be taken over positive values of the indices only. Moreover, the considerations mentioned in section **5**.1.2 concerning the special terms such as $h00$ also apply, and the precise expression for the electron density is

$$\rho(x, y) = \frac{1}{A_c}\Big[F(000) + 2\sum_{h=1}^{\infty}\{A'(h00)\cos 2\pi hx + B'(h00)\sin 2\pi hx\}$$

$$+ 2\sum_{k=1}^{\infty}\{A'(0k0)\cos 2\pi ky + B'(0k0)\sin 2\pi ky\}$$

$$+ 2\sum_{k=1}^{\infty}\left\{\sum_{h=1}^{\infty}(A_1(hk0)\cos 2\pi hx + B_2(hk0)\sin 2\pi hx)\right\}\cos 2\pi ky$$

$$- 2\sum_{k=1}^{\infty}\left\{\sum_{h=1}^{\infty}(A_2(hk0)\sin 2\pi hx - B_1(hk0)\cos 2\pi hx)\right\}\sin 2\pi ky\Big]. \quad (91.1)$$

2.3. *Two-dimensional summations for the space group $P\bar{1}$.* The space group No. 2, $P\bar{1}$, is particularly important because, as we have seen in section **4**.1.1, the structure factors are real and there are thus only two possibilities to consider—that a particular F is positive or negative. In addition, since the coefficients of a Patterson series (section **1**.3.2) are all real, the method of summation can always be based upon the methods devised for the space group $P\bar{1}$.

The summations are simpler for this space group because the imaginary components of the structure factors are zero, and thus $A'(hk0) = F(hk0)$. The expression for the electron density is therefore

$$\rho(x, y) = \frac{1}{A_c}\Big[F(000) + 2\sum_{h=1}^{\infty}F(h00)\cos 2\pi hx + 2\sum_{k=1}^{\infty}F(0k0)\cos 2\pi ky$$

$$+ 2\sum_{h=1}^{\infty}\left\{\sum_{k=1}^{\infty}\{F(hk0) + F(\bar{h}k0)\}\cos 2\pi hx\right\}\cos 2\pi ky$$

$$- 2\sum_{h=1}^{\infty}\left\{\sum_{k=1}^{\infty}\{F(hk0) - F(\bar{h}k0)\}\sin 2\pi hx\right\}\sin 2\pi ky\Big]. \quad (91.2)$$

2.4. *Adaptation to other space groups.* It is obvious that relationships between the structure factors may simplify the equations *91*.1 and *91*.2 still further. The space groups considered in section **5**.1.2 provide examples of this simplification. In the space group No. 3, P2, $F(hk0) = F(\bar{h}k0)$, which means that $A'(hk0) = A'(\bar{h}k0)$ and $B'(hk0) = B'(\bar{h}k0)$. Since also we have the general relationships $A'(hk0) = A'(\bar{h}\bar{k}0)$ and $B'(hk0) = -B'(\bar{h}\bar{k}0)$,

$$A_1(hk0) = 2A'(hk0), \qquad A_2 = 0,$$
$$B_1(hk0) = 2B'(hk0), \text{ and } B_2 = 0;$$

TABLE 92

Values of F($hk0$) for $CuSO_4.5H_2O$

$F(hk0) = F(\bar{h}\bar{k}0)$

k \ h	$\bar{8}$	$\bar{7}$	$\bar{6}$	$\bar{5}$	$\bar{4}$	$\bar{3}$	$\bar{2}$	$\bar{1}$	0	1	2	3	4	5	6	7	8
0	8	11	12	0	28	0	33	26	129	26	33	0	28	0	12	11	8
1		11	0	20	0	21	$\overline{18}$	30	0	18	10	19	$\overline{10}$	0	0	0	
2		0	0	0	0	$\overline{21}$	0	$\overline{17}$	12	$\overline{32}$	17	$\bar{7}$	10	0	9	0	
3		0	0	18	7	26	$\overline{20}$	23	11	50	17	18	7	16	6	8	
4		0	18	13	26	8	27	17	0	0	17	10	8	0	10		
5		0	0	0	0	12	0	0	$\overline{14}$	11	$\overline{15}$	0	$\overline{10}$	0	0		
6		0	0	0	7	0	16	0	12	14	15	0	9	0	0		
7		7	0	13	9	19	15	21	15	18	0	19	7	15			
8		0	10	0	0	0	16	$\bar{8}$	12	0	11	0	0	0			
9			0	0	0	0	$\overline{11}$	0	0	0	0	7	0				
10			8	0	12	0	14	7	16	0	10	0	12				
11				13	0	12	0	17	0	8	0	7					
12				0	0	0	0	0	0	0	0						
13					0	0	0	11	0	7							

the insertion of these values in equation *91*.1 then gives an equation that is equivalent to that in the International Tables (1952) for this space group.

In the space group No. 11, $P2_1/m$, which has a centre of symmetry, the B's are zero, and in addition there are the following relations between the structure factors:

$$F(hk0) = F(h\bar{k}0) \text{ if } k \text{ is even,}$$

and

$$F(hk0) = -F(h\bar{k}0) \text{ if } k \text{ is odd.}$$

If we substitute these relationships in equation *91*.2 we arrive at a relationship equivalent to equation *85*.2 with l equal to zero.

2.5. *Illustration of the method of two-dimensional summation.* The principles outlined in the preceding sections are perhaps best understood by reference to an actual example. The data shown in table 92 are those given by Beevers and Lipson (1934) for $CuSO_4.5H_2O$. The crystal has a centre of symmetry so that all the structure factors are real; otherwise, two tables would have been needed—one for the A parts of the structure factors and one for the B parts. In addition, since F($hk0$) and F($\bar{h}\bar{k}0$) are equal only half the reciprocal lattice need be shown.

TABLE 93 (i)

Values of $2A_1 = 2[F(hk0) + F(\bar{h}k0)]$

		h								
		0	1	2	3	4	5	6	7	8
	0	129	52	66	0	56	0	24	22	16
	2	24	$\bar{98}$	34	$\bar{56}$	20	0	18	0	
	4	0	34	88	36	68	26	56	0	
k	6	24	28	62	0	32	0	0	0	
	8	24	$\bar{16}$	54	0	0	0	20	0	
	10	32	14	48	0	48	0	16		
	12	0	0	0	0	0	0			
	1	0	96	$\bar{16}$	80	$\bar{20}$	40	0	22	
	3	22	146	$\bar{6}$	88	28	68	12	16	
	5	$\bar{28}$	22	$\bar{30}$	24	$\bar{20}$	0	0	0	
k	7	30	78	30	76	32	56	0	14	
	9	0	0	$\bar{22}$	14	0	0	0		
	11	0	50	0	38	0	26			
	13	0	36	0	0	0				

TABLE 93 (ii)

Values of $2A_2 = 2[F(hk0) - F(\bar{h}k0)]$

		h								
		0	1	2	3	4	5	6	7	8
	0	0	0	0	0	0	0	0	0	0
	2	0	$\bar{30}$	34	28	20	0	18	0	
	4	0	$\bar{34}$	$\bar{20}$	4	$\bar{36}$	$\bar{26}$	$\bar{16}$	0	
k	6	0	28	$\bar{2}$	0	4	0	0	0	
	8	0	16	$\bar{10}$	0	0	0	$\bar{20}$	0	
	10	0	$\bar{14}$	$\bar{8}$	0	0	0	$\bar{16}$		
	12	0	0	0	0	0	0			
	1	0	$\bar{24}$	56	$\bar{4}$	$\bar{20}$	$\bar{40}$	0	$\bar{22}$	
	3	0	54	74	$\bar{16}$	0	$\bar{4}$	12	16	
	5	0	22	$\bar{30}$	$\bar{24}$	$\bar{20}$	0	0	0	
k	7	0	$\bar{6}$	$\bar{30}$	0	$\bar{4}$	4	0	$\bar{14}$	
	9	0	0	22	14	0	0	0		
	11	0	$\bar{18}$	0	$\bar{10}$	0	$\bar{26}$			
	13	0	8	0	0	0				

The next step is to prepare tables of values of $2A_1$, which is equal to $2[F(hk0)+F(\bar{h}k0)]$, and of $2A_2$, which is equal to $2[F(hk0)-F(\bar{h}k0)]$. The relative weights of the various coefficients, as expressed in equations such as *91*.1, are obtained by including only the single value of F(000), of $A_1(h00)$, of $A_2(h00)$, of $A_1(0k0)$, and of $A_2(0k0)$; the general rule is that such special quantities should be included only in the ratio of the number of times they appear in the reciprocal lattice. The resulting quantities are shown in tables 93 (i) and 93 (ii).

It is now necessary to compute values of the function $2\sum_{n} A_1 \cos 2\pi hx$ and $2\sum_{n} A_2 \sin 2\pi hx$. There is, of course, no reason why these quantities should be summed first; the summations can be made equally well by taking the k summations first. In this case, there is some advantage in so doing: the indices k cover a larger range (up to 13) than do the indices h (up to 8); thus by making the summations first with respect to k the larger range of index is confined to the preliminary tables, and the final tables, which are much more extensive, include only the smaller range of index.

In order to effect the summations numerically, ordinates at particular values of the parameter y have to be determined, and a decision has to be made concerning the intervals into which the projection should be divided. Ideally, the interval of division should be very small, but the work of computation increases as the size of the interval decreases. On the other hand, if the interval is made large to reduce the work of computation, some detail may be lost in the final projection. It is therefore necessary to consider with some care what fineness of interval forms a reasonable compromise between these two considerations.

2.6. *Interval of division of projection.* The argument that leads to a suitable interval of division is essentially physical. As we have seen in section **1**.3.1, Fourier methods provide a mathematical way of deriving the image of a crystal structure, and the detail shown in this image is limited by the resolving power of the optical instrument used to derive it. For ordinary optical instruments the limit of resolution is given by the expression $0{\cdot}6\lambda/\sin\theta_m$, where λ is the wave-length of the radiation and θ_m is the maximum angle which the rays entering the entrance pupil of the instrument make with the axis.

It is shown in Volume II (p. 400) that the limit of resolution of the X-ray goniometer is $0{\cdot}6\lambda/2\sin\theta_m$, where θ_m is the maximum Bragg angle observed (Bragg and West, 1930). For CuKα radiation, of wave-length 1·5 Å, the value is about 0·45 Å if all reflexions with Bragg angles up to $\pi/2$ are observed. In order to make sure that the electron-density peaks are reasonably well defined it is necessary that the interval of division should be considerably less than this; if, for example, we had made the interval equal to 0·45 Å, it would have been possible for the dip between two barely resolved atoms to have been omitted completely. For results obtained with CuKα radiation with $\theta_m \simeq \pi/2$, we may say that an interval of division of, at most, 0·2 Å is necessary. For $CuSO_4.5H_2O$, the b edge of the unit cell (10·7 Å) should be divided into about 50 parts, and the a edge (6·1 Å) into about 30 parts.

It is more directly useful to express the interval of division in terms of the highest indices used, since then both λ and θ are taken into consideration. Suppose we assume that the interval is to be about 0·4 of the limit of resolution, that is, about $0{\cdot}12\lambda/\sin\theta_m$. Then the number n of intervals along a cell edge, a, is given by the equation

$$n = \frac{a \sin\theta_m}{0{\cdot}12\lambda}.$$

The highest observable index, h_m, is given by the equation

$$h_m = \frac{2a \sin\theta_m}{\lambda}.$$

Therefore n is equal to $4h_m$. That is, the number of intervals into which a cell edge should be divided should be at least four times the highest corresponding index. For the projection of $CuSO_4.5H_2O$, for which the highest indices are $h_m = 8$ and $k_m = 13$, the cell edges should be divided into 32 and 52 parts respectively, in reasonable agreement with the previous deduction.

It is, of course, inconvenient to adopt different values of subdivision for each crystal, and convention has now settled upon particular values which are related to the numbers used in angular measure. The most common number of parts is 60, corresponding to an interval of 6° in a complete period of 360°. For small cell edges, of the order of 6 Å, 12° may be used, and for larger cell edges of the order of 20–30 Å, 3° subdivision is now common. Still finer subdivisions of about 1° have also been suggested.

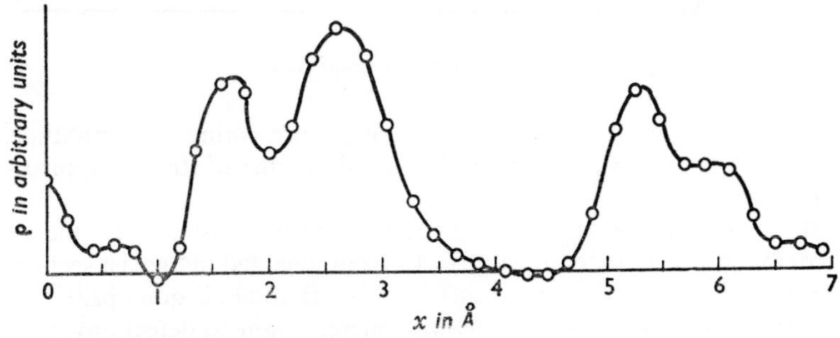

FIG. 95. Electron density along line in $CuSO_4 . 5H_2O$, calculated at intervals of 0·203 Å (x/30). This subdivision is rather coarse, and, although it ensures that no peaks are missed, some of them, such as that near 1·7 Å, are rather poorly defined

Emphasis must be laid upon the fact that these rules give only the minimum number of parts into which the cell edges should be divided; fig. 95, from an actual Fourier synthesis (table 100), shows how this fineness gives only a barely acceptable definition of the peaks. For work of the highest accuracy we have too little margin of safety, and a finer subdivision should be used. Mathematically, also, the results are hardly satisfactory; for the highest index, 8, with a subdivision of 12°, the sine curve is represented by points 96° apart—hardly an acceptable substitute for a sine curve! Nevertheless, it has been found in practice that the rules given work reasonably well; an interesting discussion of the matter will be found following a paper by Beevers (1939).

3. Methods of Computation

3.1. *Beevers-Lipson strips.* The most popular devices used for Fourier summations consist of strips of card upon which are printed numbers representing the ordinates of the various terms to be included. The simplest of such sets of strips is that produced by Lipson and Beevers (1936). In these strips, two variables are incorporated, one representing the amplitude of the term and the other representing the index: the amplitudes are recorded on separate strips in steps of unity from 1 to 99, the negative values, from −1 to −99, being recorded on the backs; there is one set of such strips for each index from 0 to 20 for the cosine terms and 1 to 20 for the sine terms.

The values of the ordinates for each term are recorded on the strip at intervals of 6°, each ordinate being given to the nearest digit, as shown in fig. 96. In this figure a cosine and a sine strip are shown, the

76	C 7	76	56	8	$\bar{45}$	$\bar{74}$	$\bar{66}$	$\bar{23}$	31	69	72	38	$\bar{16}$	$\bar{61}$	$\bar{76}$	$\bar{51}$	0
19	S 6	0	11	18	18	11	0	$\bar{11}$	$\bar{18}$	$\bar{18}$	$\bar{11}$	0	11	18	18	11	0

FIG. 96. Two Beevers-Lipson strips

sequence of symbols at the left-hand side representing the amplitude, cosine (C) or sine (S), and index. The total number of strips is approximately 4000.

It will be noted that, although the interval of division is 6°, the indices exceed the maximum value of 15 recommended in the last section. The reason for this is that the inclusion of 20 orders is quite justifiable for preliminary work, where one may merely want to detect any gross errors; but for final accurate work, the strips should not be used much above the index 15. If higher indices than this have to be included, then the 6° strips are not adequate.

In fig. 96 only one quarter of the complete function is included. This modification is possible because any cosine or sine curve can be built up by repetition of the first quadrant by either inversion about a point or reflexion across a line; for example, the curve $y = \cos 2\pi x$ can be derived from the first quadrant by inversion about the point $(\frac{1}{4}, 0)$, reflexion across the line $x = \frac{1}{2}$, and inversion about the point $(\frac{3}{4}, 0)$ (fig. 97).

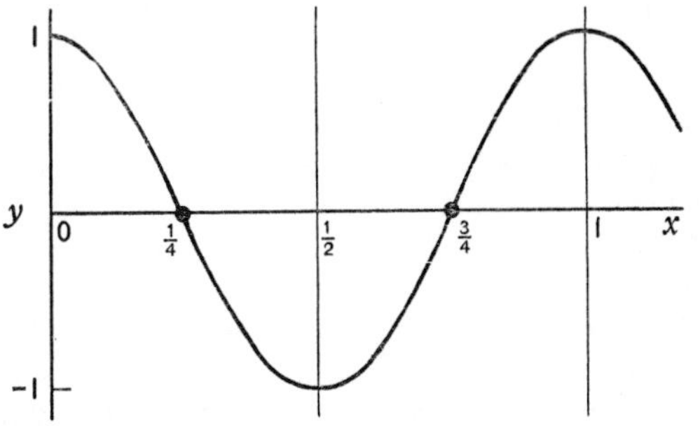

FIG. 97. Curve $y = \cos 2\pi x$, showing lines of symmetry at $x = 0, \frac{1}{2}, 1$ and points of antisymmetry at $x = \frac{1}{4}, \frac{3}{4}$

The function is said to be symmetrical about the value $x = \frac{1}{2}$ and anti-symmetrical about the values $x = \frac{1}{4}$, $x = \frac{3}{4}$. These relationships hold for all the curves $y = \cos 2\pi hx$ for which h is odd; the relationship for the curves for even values of h and for the two corresponding sine curves can be easily derived.

Thus to derive the complete cycle from any one cosine strip with odd index, the numbers on the strip are first read off to give the values for $x = 0$ to $x = \frac{1}{4}$; these numbers are then read off in the reverse direction with the signs changed for $x = \frac{1}{4}$ to $\frac{1}{2}$; they are read in the original direction, again with changed signs, for $x = \frac{1}{2}$ to $\frac{3}{4}$; and finally they are read in the reverse direction, with the signs changed back to their original values, for $x = \frac{3}{4}$ to 1. Since these rules apply to all the terms with h odd, they also apply to their sum. It is therefore worth while separating the cosine terms with even index from those with odd index; the sum of the even terms is symmetrical about $x = \frac{1}{4}$ and the sum of the odd terms is anti-symmetrical about $x = \frac{1}{4}$, and so the sum up to $x = \frac{1}{2}$ can be obtained by adding the corresponding sums up to $x = \frac{1}{4}$, and subtracting them to obtain the sums up to $x = \frac{1}{2}$. This process is shown in table 98. The sums of sine terms are obtained by making use of the symmetry of the sine curve; a set of summations is shown in table 99.

There can be no doubt about the operation of the symmetrical and anti-symmetrical relations; at a point where a function is symmetrical the ordinate is equal to the amplitude (positive or negative), and where it is anti-symmetrical the ordinate is equal to zero.

As we have seen, the strips are useful only for crystals whose cell edges do not greatly exceed 10 Å in length. For larger unit cells, finer subdivision is required, and for this reason a new version of the strips has been produced by Beevers (1952). In these strips the interval of division is 3°, and therefore twice as many ordinates appear. In order that the strips should not be unmanageably long, the even ordinates are printed on one side and the odd ordinates on the other, and so only the same number of figures has to be accommodated in a given length; on the other hand, a separate strip has to be printed for negative amplitudes, so that, for a given index, twice as many strips are required. It will be noted that the even sides show exactly the same quantities as the 6° strips.

Since the interval of division is halved, the strips can be used for rough work up to indices of 40. For economy, however, strips are provided only up to 30, and they can be extended beyond this value by the following artifice: for cosines, the even ordinates present the same values for indices h and $60-h$, and the odd ordinates for these two indices differ only in sign. Thus, if we wish to include, say, a curve with index 31, we choose the corresponding amplitude with index 29, take the given values on the even side of the strip, and values with the signs changed on the odd side of the strip. For sines, the rules are reversed: for even ordinates of index h, the signs of the numbers on the strip for $60-h$ are reversed, and for the odd ordinates the signs are unchanged.

TABLE 98

Preliminary summations

Evaluation of $\sum_k 2A_1 \cos 2\pi ky$, for $h=3$

	y (60ths)																
	0	1	2	3	4	5	6	7	8	9	10	11	12	13	14	15	
$\bar{56}$ C 2	$\bar{56}$	$\bar{55}$	$\bar{51}$	$\bar{45}$	$\bar{37}$	$\bar{28}$	$\bar{17}$	$\bar{6}$	6	17	28	37	45	51	55	56	(0)
36 C 4	36	33	24	11	$\bar{4}$	$\bar{18}$	$\bar{29}$	$\bar{35}$	$\bar{35}$	$\bar{29}$	$\bar{18}$	$\bar{4}$	11	24	33	36	(36)
	$\bar{20}$	$\bar{22}$	$\bar{27}$	$\bar{34}$	$\bar{41}$	$\bar{46}$	$\bar{46}$	$\bar{41}$	$\bar{29}$	$\bar{12}$	10	33	56	75	88	92	(36)
80 C 1	80	80	78	76	73	69	65	59	54	47	40	33	25	17	8	0	(804)
88 C 3	88	84	71	52	27	0	$\bar{27}$	$\bar{52}$	$\bar{71}$	$\bar{84}$	$\bar{88}$	$\bar{84}$	$\bar{71}$	$\bar{52}$	$\bar{27}$	0	($\bar{234}$)
24 C 5	24	21	12	0	$\bar{12}$	$\bar{21}$	$\bar{24}$	$\bar{21}$	$\bar{12}$	0	12	21	24	21	12	0	(57)
76 C 7	76	56	8	$\bar{45}$	$\bar{74}$	$\bar{66}$	$\bar{23}$	31	69	72	38	$\bar{16}$	$\bar{61}$	$\bar{76}$	$\bar{51}$	0	($\bar{62}$)
14 C 9	14	8	$\bar{4}$	$\bar{13}$	$\bar{11}$	0	11	13	4	$\bar{8}$	$\bar{14}$	$\bar{8}$	4	13	11	0	(20)
38 C 11	38	15	$\bar{25}$	$\bar{36}$	$\bar{4}$	33	31	$\bar{8}$	$\bar{37}$	$\bar{22}$	19	38	12	$\bar{28}$	$\bar{35}$	0	($\bar{9}$)
	320	264	140	34	$\bar{1}$	15	33	22	7	5	7	$\bar{16}$	$\bar{67}$	$\bar{105}$	$\bar{82}$	0	(576)
Sum	300	242	113	0	$\bar{42}$	$\bar{31}$	$\bar{13}$	$\bar{19}$	$\bar{22}$	$\bar{7}$	17	17	$\bar{11}$	$\bar{30}$	6	92	
Difference	$\bar{340}$	$\bar{286}$	$\bar{167}$	$\bar{68}$	$\bar{40}$	$\bar{61}$	$\bar{79}$	$\bar{63}$	$\bar{36}$	$\bar{17}$	3	49	122	180	170		
	30	29	28	27	26	25	24	23	22	21	20	19	18	17	16	15	
	y (60ths)																

Two other important modifications are also introduced in the strips. First, for work in which two-figure accuracy is thought to be insufficient, strips of amplitude 100, 200, etc., are included; thus when three-figure quantities arise, they can be obtained by the combination of two strips. This means that the work of addition will be slowed down somewhat, since extra strips are introduced, and also the errors are bigger than if a single strip were used, since the rounding-off errors in the two may combine. It is doubtful, however, whether this latter consideration is likely to be significant, since the strips should give results accurate to about 0·2 per cent.

The other modification is a means for checking the additions. The usual method of checking is to repeat each addition, but it is surprising how easily an error can be repeated. An entirely independent check is preferable, and this is provided by the total of the figures on each strip printed in parentheses at the right-hand end; the sum of these quantities should then be equal to the sum of the totals of the individual

TABLE 99

Evaluation of $\sum_{k} 2A_2 \sin 2\pi k y$, for $h=3$

	y (60ths)																
	0	1	2	3	4	5	6	7	8	9	10	11	12	13	14	15	
$\bar{4}$ S 1	0	0	$\bar{1}$	$\bar{1}$	$\bar{2}$	$\bar{2}$	$\bar{2}$	$\bar{3}$	$\bar{3}$	$\bar{3}$	$\bar{3}$	$\bar{4}$	$\bar{4}$	$\bar{4}$	$\bar{4}$	$\bar{4}$	($\overline{40}$)
$\overline{16}$ S 3	0	$\bar{5}$	$\bar{9}$	$\overline{13}$	$\overline{15}$	$\overline{16}$	$\overline{15}$	$\overline{13}$	$\bar{9}$	$\bar{5}$	0	5	9	13	15	16	($\overline{42}$)
$\overline{24}$ S 5	0	$\overline{12}$	$\overline{21}$	$\overline{24}$	$\overline{21}$	$\overline{12}$	0	12	21	24	21	12	0	$\overline{12}$	$\overline{21}$	$\overline{24}$	($\overline{57}$)
14 S 9	0	11	13	4	$\bar{8}$	$\overline{14}$	$\bar{8}$	4	13	11	0	$\overline{11}$	$\overline{13}$	$\bar{4}$	8	14	(20)
$\overline{10}$ S 11	0	$\bar{9}$	$\bar{7}$	3	10	5	$\bar{6}$	$\overline{10}$	$\bar{2}$	8	9	$\bar{1}$	$\overline{10}$	$\bar{7}$	4	10	($\bar{3}$)
	0	$\overline{15}$	$\overline{25}$	$\overline{31}$	$\overline{36}$	$\overline{39}$	$\overline{31}$	$\overline{10}$	20	35	27	1	$\overline{18}$	$\overline{14}$	2	12	($\overline{122}$)
28 S 2	0	6	11	16	21	24	27	28	28	27	24	21	16	11	6	0	(266)
4 S 4	0	2	3	4	4	3	2	1	$\bar{1}$	$\bar{2}$	$\bar{3}$	$\bar{4}$	$\bar{4}$	$\bar{3}$	$\bar{2}$	0	(0)
	0	8	14	20	25	27	29	29	27	25	21	17	12	8	4	0	(266)
Sum	0	$\bar{7}$	$\bar{9}$	$\overline{11}$	$\overline{11}$	$\overline{12}$	$\bar{2}$	19	47	60	48	18	$\bar{6}$	$\bar{6}$	6	12	
Difference	0	$\overline{23}$	$\overline{39}$	$\overline{51}$	$\overline{61}$	$\overline{66}$	$\overline{60}$	$\overline{39}$	$\bar{7}$	10	6	$\overline{16}$	$\overline{30}$	$\overline{22}$	$\bar{2}$		
	30	29	28	27	26	25	24	23	22	21	20	19	18	17	16	15	
	y (60ths)																

Note that the numbers in these tables are derived either from the 6° strips or from the even sides (denoted by CE or SE) of the 3° strips. For division into 12°, either alternate columns only are added, or the indices are doubled.

TABLE 100: Final summations for $y=7/60$ths

The results of the summations shown in tables such as 98 and 99 (one for each h index) are now used as Fourier coefficients. For example, the coefficients for index 3 at $y=7/60$ths are $\overline{19}$ for the cosine term and 19 for the sine term. The h indices are doubled in order to give 12° subdivision of x.

	x (30ths)																
	0	1	2	3	4	5	6	7	8	9	10	11	12	13	14	15	
186 C 0	186	186	186	186	186	186	186	186	186	186	186	186	186	186	186	186	(2976)
$\overline{52}$ C 2	$\overline{52}$	$\overline{51}$	$\overline{48}$	$\overline{42}$	$\overline{35}$	$\overline{26}$	$\overline{16}$	$\bar{5}$	5	16	26	35	42	48	51	52	(0)
48 C 4	48	44	32	15	$\bar{5}$	$\overline{24}$	$\overline{39}$	$\overline{47}$	$\overline{47}$	$\overline{39}$	$\overline{24}$	$\bar{5}$	15	32	44	48	(48)
$\overline{19}$ C 6	$\overline{19}$	$\overline{15}$	$\bar{6}$	6	15	19	15	6	$\bar{6}$	$\overline{15}$	$\overline{19}$	$\overline{15}$	$\bar{6}$	6	15	19	(0)
8 C 8	8	5	$\bar{1}$	$\bar{6}$	$\bar{8}$	$\bar{4}$	2	7	7	2	$\bar{4}$	$\bar{8}$	$\bar{6}$	$\bar{1}$	5	8	(6)
$\overline{20}$ C 10	$\overline{20}$	$\overline{10}$	10	20	10	$\overline{10}$	$\overline{20}$	$\overline{10}$	10	20	10	$\overline{10}$	$\overline{20}$	$\overline{10}$	10	20	(0)
$\overline{10}$ C 12	$\overline{10}$	$\bar{3}$	8	8	$\bar{3}$	$\overline{10}$	$\bar{3}$	8	8	$\bar{3}$	$\overline{10}$	$\bar{3}$	8	8	$\bar{3}$	$\overline{10}$	($\overline{10}$)
34 C 14	34	4	$\overline{33}$	$\overline{11}$	31	17	$\overline{28}$	$\overline{23}$	23	28	$\overline{17}$	$\overline{31}$	11	33	$\bar{4}$	$\overline{34}$	(0)
16 C 16	16	$\bar{2}$	$\overline{16}$	5	15	$\bar{8}$	$\overline{13}$	11	11	$\overline{13}$	$\bar{8}$	15	5	$\overline{16}$	$\bar{2}$	16	(16)
	191	158	132	181	206	140	84	133	197	182	140	164	235	286	302	305	(3036)
$\overline{78}$ S 2	0	$\overline{16}$	$\overline{32}$	$\overline{46}$	$\overline{58}$	$\overline{68}$	$\overline{74}$	$\overline{78}$	$\overline{78}$	$\overline{74}$	$\overline{68}$	$\overline{58}$	$\overline{46}$	$\overline{32}$	$\overline{16}$	0	($\overline{744}$)
{100 S 4	0	41	74	95	99	87	59	21	$\overline{21}$	$\overline{59}$	$\overline{87}$	$\overline{99}$	$\overline{95}$	$\overline{74}$	$\overline{41}$	0	(0)
{76 S 4	0	31	56	72	76	66	45	16	$\overline{16}$	$\overline{45}$	$\overline{66}$	$\overline{76}$	$\overline{72}$	$\overline{56}$	$\overline{31}$	0	(0)
19 S 6	0	11	18	18	11	0	$\overline{11}$	$\overline{18}$	18	$\overline{11}$	0	11	18	18	11	0	(58)
8 S 8	0	6	8	5	$\bar{2}$	$\bar{7}$	$\bar{8}$	$\bar{3}$	3	8	7	2	$\bar{5}$	$\bar{8}$	$\bar{6}$	0	(0)
$\overline{66}$ S 10	0	$\overline{57}$	$\overline{57}$	0	57	57	0	$\overline{57}$	$\overline{57}$	0	57	57	0	$\overline{57}$	$\overline{57}$	0	($\overline{114}$)
18 S 12	0	17	11	$\overline{11}$	$\overline{17}$	0	17	11	$\overline{11}$	$\overline{17}$	0	17	11	$\overline{11}$	$\overline{17}$	0	(0)
12 S 14	0	12	2	$\overline{11}$	$\bar{5}$	10	7	$\bar{9}$	9	7	10	$\bar{5}$	$\overline{11}$	2	12	0	(12)
	0	45	80	122	161	145	35	$\overline{117}$	$\overline{207}$	$\overline{191}$	$\overline{147}$	$\overline{151}$	$\overline{200}$	$\overline{218}$	$\overline{145}$	0	($\overline{788}$)
Difference	191	113	52	59	45	$\bar{5}$	49	250	404	373	287	315	435	504	447	305	
Sum	191	203	212	303	367	285	119	16	$\overline{10}$	$\bar{9}$	$\bar{7}$	13	35	68	157		
	30	29	28	27	26	25	24	23	22	21	20	19	18	17	16	15	
	x (30ths)																

columns. This means of checking is shown in tables 98 and 99. A reliable computer should find that this device saves a considerable time, as each column need be added only once. If, however, mistakes are frequent, the device will add considerably to the labour since, although it indicates mistakes, it gives no hint of their location. For this reason, it is better not to add a large number of strips at once, unless an adding machine is used; about ten is ideal.

3.2. *Summary.* There is little doubt that the electronic computer has rendered unnecessary some of the methods described in this chapter; it provides a means of producing the result of a two-dimensional or three-dimensional summation extremely rapidly. Nevertheless, the older methods should still be used by new students because they give a basic understanding of the computational processes; students must beware of accepting results without knowing how they are derived, and of concluding that Fourier summation is a process that can be carried out *only* by means of a computer.

3.3. *General application of Fourier methods to computation of structure factors.* The defect of the methods described in the previous section is that the atoms have to be assumed to be points, and that the results have therefore to be finally modified by the standard scattering-factor curve; this is unsatisfactory if atoms of widely differing atomic number are concerned. This difficulty can be overcome by representing each atom by a complete set of electron-density values at specific points, which can be taken as multiples of 3°. The specific values may be obtained from atoms in known crystal structures, and the Fourier synthesis then gives the set of structure factors directly, corrected for the variation of electron density within the various atoms, different as these may be. Full details of the method are described by Sayre (1951).

It will be noted that the Fourier method can be used directly only if the crystal has a centre of symmetry; otherwise the coefficients for the points x, y, z and $\bar{x}$, $\bar{y}$, $\bar{z}$ are not equal. This difficulty may be overcome by evaluating the real and imaginary parts of the structure factors separately; to determine the former we add to the structure another one related to it by a centre of symmetry, and to determine the latter we add an anti-symmetrically related structure, that is, with negative electron densities.

The method allows the introduction of departures from the ideal simplicity of the spherical atom, such as electron distributions in bonds, and this may become of increasing importance as the accuracy of structural analysis increases. There is, however, a theoretical difficulty which is discussed by Sayre. By taking, as a basis for the calculation, the electron densities at regularly arranged points, a spurious regularity is inserted and a systematic error is introduced; we have replaced a continuous function by a set of point scatterers and so the diffraction pattern consists of sets of spectra instead of one set only. For example, if the unit cell is sampled at n points spaced in one dimension, the nth order of diffraction would be equal in amplitude to the zero order, and in general the qth order would be equal to the $(n \pm q)$th. Thus the calculation of any structure factor q will include also the $(n-q)$th from the first set of spectra, the $(2n-q)$th from the second set, and so on.

To overcome this difficulty it is necessary to ensure that the various sets of spectra do not overlap—that is, for the highest index q observed, the $(n-q)$th and higher orders should be negligible. In other words n must be made so large that the sets of orders are well spaced from each other. If, for example, we wish to deal with 15 orders, n must be made much greater than 30, for if it were only 30, the 15th order would be doubled. To allow a margin of safety, it would be advisable to make n about 45, and so we arrive at the general rule that, if we wish to calculate structure factors in this way, the number of points at which the electron density should be sampled in any one direction should be about three times the highest index observed in that direction. This rule is similar to that deduced for the subdivision of cell edges for Fourier synthesis (section **5**.2.6); the two matters are, of course, closely related.

3.4. *Computation of Fourier transforms.* The Fourier transform of a single unit of pattern can be derived by means of methods that are essentially the same as those described in the last section. In fact, of course, the weighted reciprocal lattice, as explained in section **1**.3.3, is the Fourier transform of the single unit, evaluated at specific points. The reciprocal lattice is, however, a very poor representation, because the points of evaluation are too widely spaced; this must be so if the unit has the same order of magnitude as the spacings of the crystal, and in order to evaluate the Fourier transform in reasonable detail it is necessary to postulate a hypothetical crystal in which the spacings are several times as large as the dimensions of the unit: then the reciprocal lattice—the sampling mesh—is much finer.

Obviously a great deal of work is entailed in this calculation. If the sampling mesh is three times as fine as the reciprocal lattice, the amount of work involved in the calculation of a two-dimensional transform is nine times as great as for the calculation of the reciprocal lattice, and if the three-dimensional transform is required the work is 27 times as great. On the other hand, for some of the purposes for which the transform is required, only the central portion of the transform is needed, and so the work of evaluation can be reduced.

4. Representation of Results

4.1. *Plotting of contours.* The methods of Fourier summation so far described give values of the electron density at specific points in the unit cell, and, although some of the earlier papers expressed the results in this way, it is now generally agreed that the results expressed as a set of contours of constant electron density are much more useful.

We have therefore to consider ways of deriving these contours from the numerical data. Two ways are possible—drawing the contours between the numbers by subjective judgment, and obtaining the positions of specific values of electron density by graphical interpolation. The former method is much more rapid, and is certainly good enough for much work, particularly in the preliminary stages of a structure determination. If accuracy is required, however, contours should not be derived by subjective methods. Curves should be drawn of the values of electron density along the rows of points for which the calculations have been performed, and the co-ordinates at which the electron density attains the values to be plotted obtained by interpolation.

The smoothness of the contours produced by any method is to some extent a verification of the correctness of the computations, for if any variations are found which are on a finer scale than the limit of resolution, they must be erroneous. Moreover, some Fourier diagrams show unjustifiable ripples in the contours; the best *smooth* curve should always be drawn between the points, in the way accepted for other forms of graphical representation.

The main reason for accurate drawing of contours is the determination of atomic positions. As described in Chapter 12, however, there are other, more accurate, ways of obtaining these positions, and the care taken in careful drawing of contours is often largely wasted. Even when accuracy is required, only the regions near the peak positions need be carefully drawn. The justification for drawing the lower contours accurately is that they may show unexpected detail, such as hydrogen atoms (Morrison, Binnie and Robertson, 1948) or departures of the atoms from spherical form.

In three dimensions, further problems arise. Obviously, in the two dimensions available, exact representation is not possible, and the usual procedure is to extract important parts of certain projections and to place them in juxtaposition to show as graphically as possible the relative positions of the various atoms in the molecule; an example, due to Jeffrey (1945), is shown in fig. 104.

In drawing a two-dimensional projection, it must be remembered that if the direction of projection is parallel to a crystal axis, it is not necessarily perpendicular to a face of the unit cell. Thus the parallelogram that limits the area of the projection may not have the shape of the face of the unit cell; the shape is that of the projection of this face on a plane perpendicular to the direction of projection. If the direction of projection is markedly oblique to the face of the unit cell, a noticeable distortion of the atomic shapes will be produced if the wrong area of projection is used.

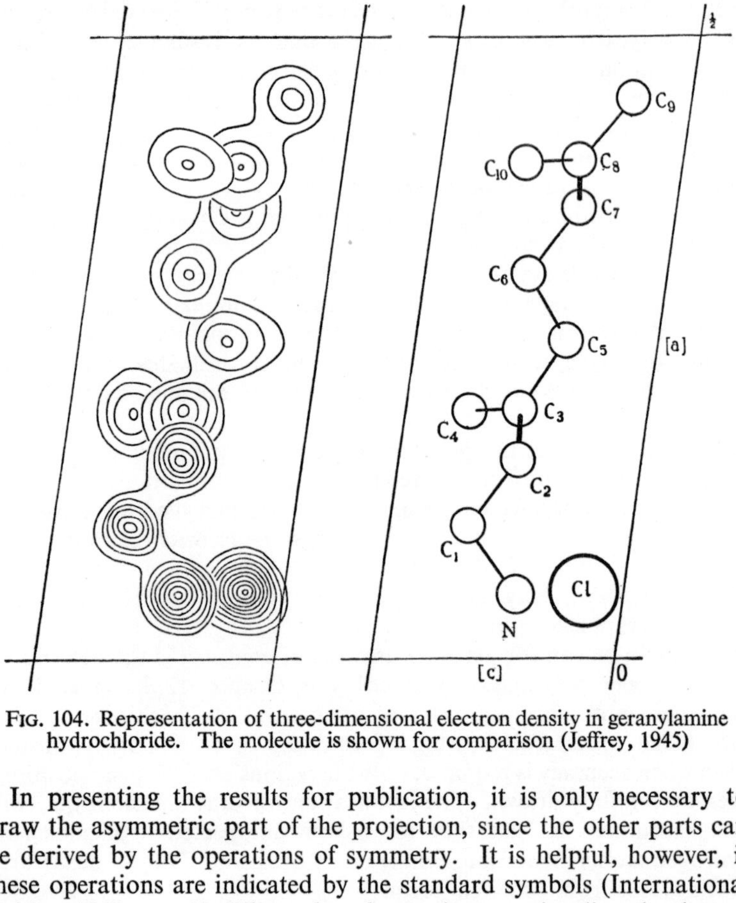

FIG. 104. Representation of three-dimensional electron density in geranylamine hydrochloride. The molecule is shown for comparison (Jeffrey, 1945)

In presenting the results for publication, it is only necessary to draw the asymmetric part of the projection, since the other parts can be derived by the operations of symmetry. It is helpful, however, if these operations are indicated by the standard symbols (International Tables, 1952, pp. 49, 50) so that the reader can visualize clearly and unambiguously the relationships of the various atomic peaks to each other.

4.2. *Electron counts.* Electron-density maps are much used for finding the positions of atoms, but in principle they contain other information as well—the numbers of electrons contained in the atoms. There is no difficulty in distinguishing between carbon, nitrogen and oxygen atoms for example, but more interesting questions concerning their state of ionization are in practice rather difficult to answer. Systematic errors introduced by Fourier-series termination make it scarcely worth while to integrate the density over selected areas or volumes, except on maps of the difference density (section **12**.2.5). The interpretation of the results obtained in this way is not usually clear-cut; if a sphere could be drawn round an atom in such a way as to pass through regions in

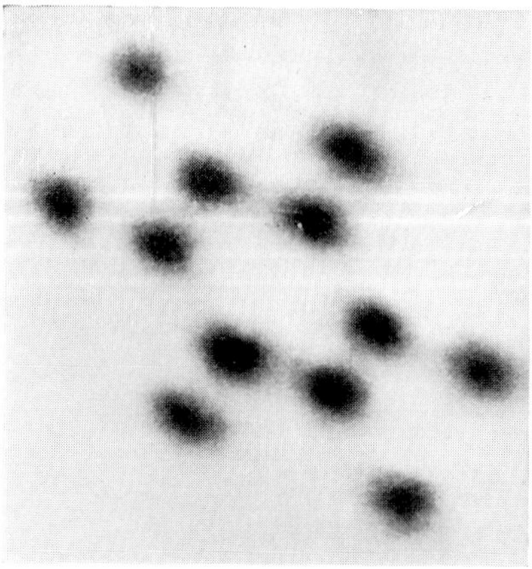

FIG. 105 (i). Optical synthesis of hexamethylbenzene, produced by means of Huggins masks

FIG. 105 (ii). Set of fringes used in Pepinsky's machine. Each horizontal line is modulated by a sine wave of appropriate wavelength, and successive lines have appropriate shifts of phase to produce the sloping fringes shown. An extra modulation of 60 c.p.s. is also superimposed to make the lines stand out; in practice the fringes appear perfectly continuous

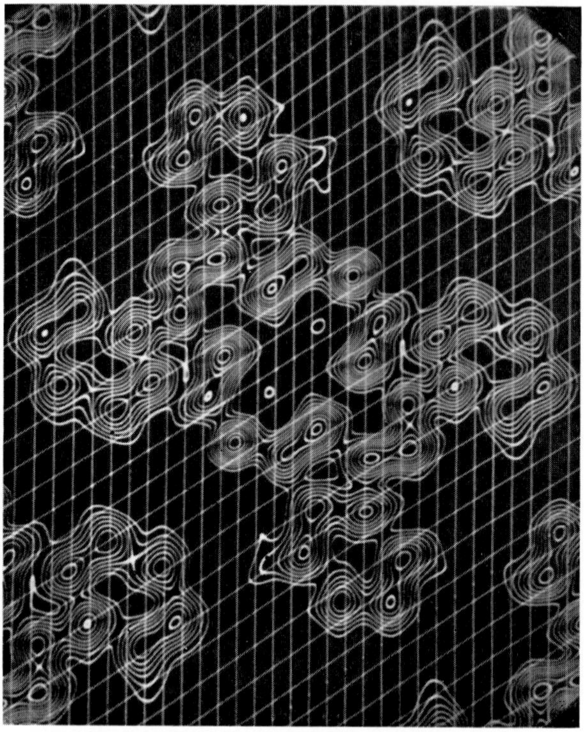

FIG. 105 (iii). Electron-density projection of phthalocyanine produced by Pepinsky's machine

which the electron density was essentially zero there would be no difficulty, but this is seldom the case in practice. However Witte and Wolfel (1958) have been able to show, for example, that the X-ray data for sodium chloride are consistent with the atoms being fully ionized (see also Chapter 12).

Care must also be taken to put the structure factors on a reasonably accurate absolute scale, either by an experimental method (see for example McDonald, 1960) or by using the method of least squares to determine the scaling factor (section **12**.3.5), excluding data for which $(\sin \theta)/\lambda$ is less than say 0·5Å^{-1}.

5. Optical Methods of Fourier Synthesis

5.1. *Bragg's photographic method.* We have seen in section **1**.4.3 that the process of Fourier summation is essentially the adding of sets of fringes. W. L. Bragg (1929*b*) suggested that, for two dimensions, the process can be carried out photographically and showed (Volume I, p. 229) the successful application of this idea to three projections of diopside. Since it is not possible to produce negative values, the fringes were of the form $1 + \cos 2\pi(hx + ky)$, and these were projected on to a sheet of photographic paper on which the unit cell was drawn; for different reflexions the indices were controlled by the magnification and the orientation, the signs (the structure is centrosymmetrical) by placing either a maximum or a minimum at the origin, and the amplitudes by the exposure.

The result is a representation, with a magnification of about 10^8, of what would be seen by means of an 'X-ray microscope' if the eye were sensitive to X-rays. The image is, of course, not a true one since the atomic peaks appear on a background that is much too high, but by suitable photographic processing the method can be made to produce striking results, as shown by the examples in Volume I. The method has not, however, been widely adopted, partly because it yields only qualitative results, and partly because it requires a great deal of care to avoid mistakes, since four quantities have to be controlled for every reflexion.

A more manageable procedure has been adopted by Huggins (1944), who produced, on 35 mm. film, sets of masks representing the fringes for indices up to ten, on the basis of a square unit cell. Each mask contains fringes with the right spacing and orientation, and there are separate masks for positive and negative signs; the exposure for each mask is made proportional to the structure amplitude. This procedure is quite rapid, and a quite extensive two-dimensional synthesis can be completed in about two hours; an example is shown in fig. 105(i).

The qualitative nature of the results is however an important disadvantage, and has been overcome in a device which has been of considerable use in the solution of crystallographic problems. The device is that described by Pepinsky (1947). The beam in a cathode-ray tube is made to trace out one of the sets of fringes, as shown in fig. 105 (ii). Any sets of fringes up to indices of 20 can be produced in this way, and their amplitudes suitably controlled; by producing them simultaneously the Fourier synthesis would appear in form similar to that given by the method of Bragg and Huggins. It is, however, possible to present the result in the form of contours, a typical example being shown in fig. 105 (iii).

For speed, this device would appear to have reached the acme of perfection; the time taken for a synthesis is effectively only the time taken to set the amplitude controls. The device can deal with complex coefficients, can represent non-orthogonal unit cells, can give sections of three-dimensional syntheses, and can deal with indices up to 20. The only disadvantages would appear to be its cost and its complexity.

The photographic method has, however, been given a new lease of life by von Eller (1955*a*) who has devised an instrument—le photosommateur harmonique—that makes the addition of the Fourier components extremely simple. Starting with the mask of fringes that give a sinusoidal distribution of transmitted intensity, it reduces to a minimum the task of projecting each set of fringes in the appropriate way; the spacing and orientation are controlled together by moving a pointer to the corresponding point on a reciprocal-lattice section; the phase can be adjusted to any required value and the fringes exposed for a time proportional to the structure amplitude. Both the phase and amplitude can be recorded at each reciprocal-lattice point and so there is little likelihood of a mistake.

The photosommateur makes an ideal teaching device, since the operator can see clearly what he is doing at each stage. It is also helpful in research, as a preliminary to computation; an example of the results obtainable (Eller-Pandraud 1960) is shown in fig. 106 (Plate III).

5.2. *The X-ray microscope.* The methods described in the previous section, effective though they have become in the hands of the electronicists, are essentially an artificial and cumbersome way of doing what waves can do much more elegantly themselves if the right conditions are presented to them—that is, if they are passed through an apparatus that causes them to interfere in the way described in section 1.4.3. W. L. Bragg has shown that it is possible, in certain circumstances, for the X-ray data to be simulated by a set of holes through which light can be passed, the transmitted light then being brought to a focus to give the required image.

The process may be described in the following way. We have seen that each Fourier component is, in two dimensions, a set of fringes. Such fringes can be produced by the interference of light passing

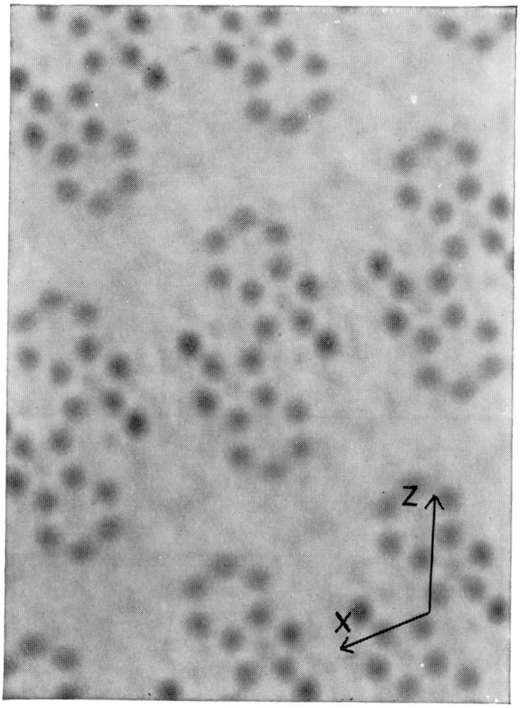

FIG. 106
Projection of structure of isoindigo, obtained by means of the photosommateur harmonique

through two small holes; the spacing of the fringes is inversely proportional to the distance between the holes, the fringes are perpendicular to the line joining the holes, and the intensity is proportional to the area of the holes. Consideration of the description of the reciprocal lattice (section 1.2.3) shows that the set of holes required to produce the image of a given crystal structure is represented by the reciprocal lattice of the crystal. The mask of holes for diopside (Bragg, 1939) is shown in fig. 107.

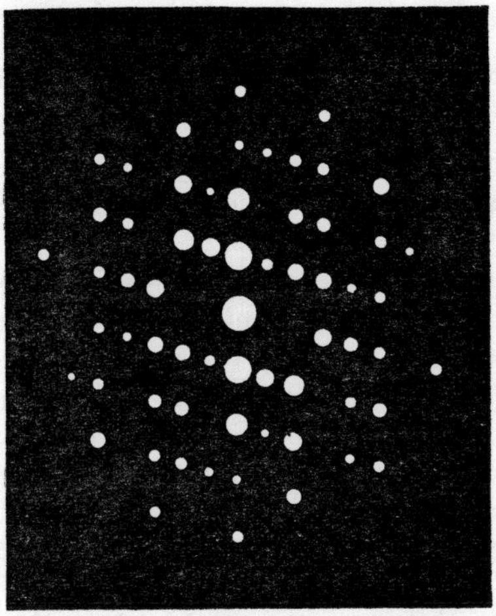

FIG. 107. Mask representing the $h0l$ reciprocal lattice section of diopside (Bragg, 1939)

To observe the diffraction pattern of the mask, we can use the apparatus (Bragg and Lipson, 1943) shown in fig. 290. Parallel light falls on the mask, and the transmitted light is brought to a focus in the focal plane of the second lens, where an image of the structure should appear. The result for the mask shown in fig. 107 is shown in fig. 108(i); in fig. 108(iv) the corresponding projection is shown and it will be seen that there is close correspondence.

There is, however, a difficulty that has so far prevented any general use of the method; there is no simple way of introducing phase shifts, and so the method can be used only if all the phases are zero. This is so if the structure has a heavy atom at the origin, and for diopside, $CaMg(SiO_3)_2$, this condition applies because calcium and magnesium atoms overlap exactly in the projection shown in fig. 108(iv).

Two methods have been successfully used for introducing the phase shifts required for more general crystal projections. Buerger (1951) places over each reciprocal-lattice hole a mica plate so tilted as to produce the appropriate increase in the optical path of the light passing through it; in order that the paths of the light passing through all the

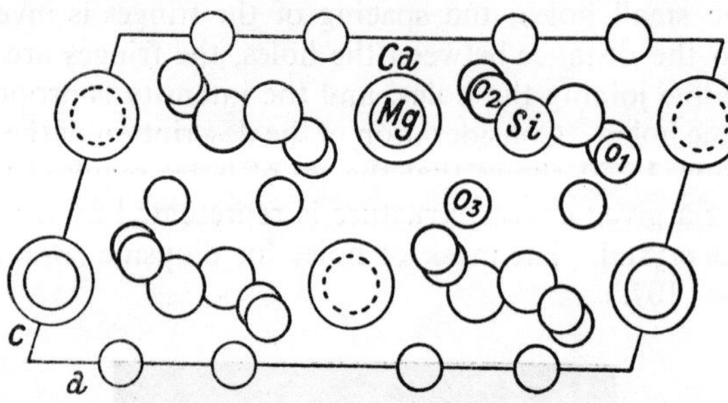

FIG. 108 (iv). Representation of projection of structure of diopside on (010) (Compare fig. 108(i))

holes shall be accurately comparable, the mica plates are cut from the same uniform cleavage sheet. Buerger's results for marcasite, FeS_2, are shown in fig. 108(ii).

The second method, described by Hanson, Taylor and Lipson (1951), also uses mica plates cut from a uniform sheet. The reciprocal lattice, however, is represented by a set of equal holes, which are placed between crossed Nicols in the optical diffractometer (Hughes and Taylor, 1953) shown in fig. 290. Each mica plate has two positions of extinction, which are such that when they lie in the plane of polarization of the polarizer and analyser, no light is transmitted; but when the mica plate is rotated in its own plane through an angle ϕ, the amplitude of the transmitted light is proportional to $\sin 2\phi$. Thus the intensities associated with the different reciprocal lattice points can be simulated by different values of ϕ. Different signs for the structure factors can be simulated by rotating the mica plate either clockwise or anticlockwise.

An image of the (010) projection of the structure of hexamethylbenzene is shown in fig. 108 (iii), and Hanson and Lipson (1952*b*) have suggested how the device could be used for the trial-and-error method of sign determination for centrosymmetrical projections (section **10**.3.1). It cannot be used for other projections, but since optical methods are not likely to achieve a high degree of accuracy, their application to non-centrosymmetrical projections would not appear to be particularly fruitful; Harburn and Taylor (1962), however, have described an optical method for Fourier synthesis for non-centrosymmetric crystals.

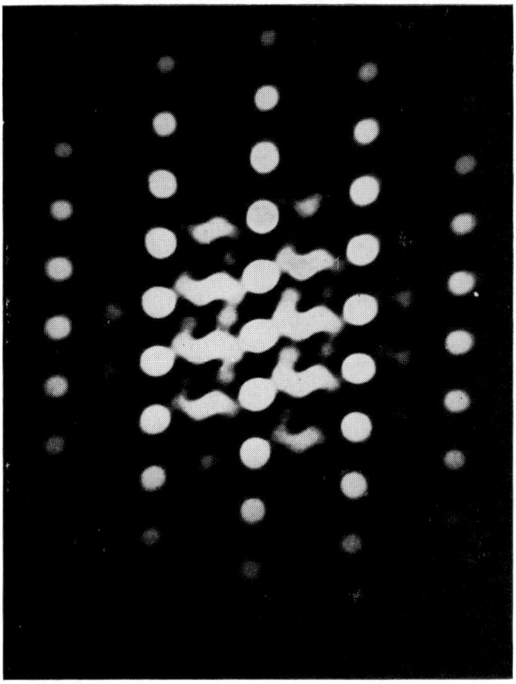

FIG. 108 (i). Optical synthesis of diopside obtained from mask shown in figure 107 with representation of projection of structure for comparison (fig. 108 (iv)) (Bragg, 1939)

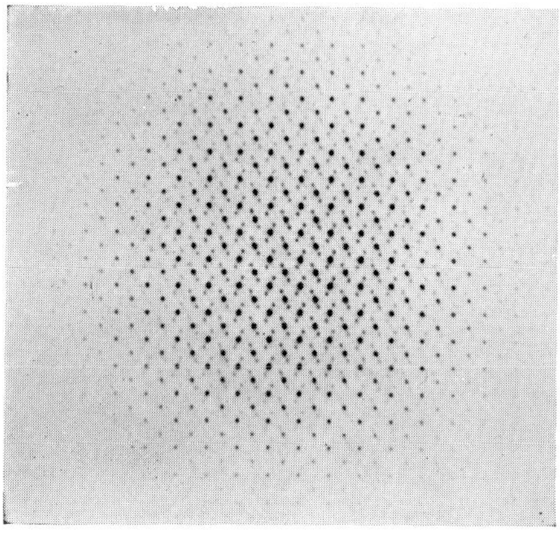

FIG. 108 (ii). Optical synthesis of marcasite, FeS_2 (Buerger, 1951)

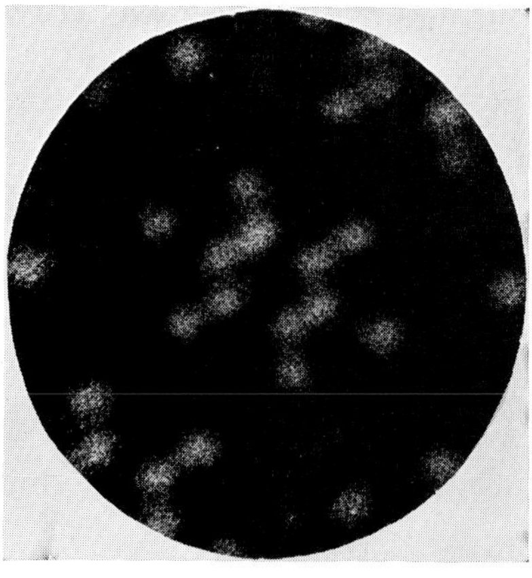

FIG. 108 (iii). Optical synthesis of hexamethyl benzene (Hanson, 1952)

CHAPTER 6

TRIAL-AND-ERROR METHODS

1. INTRODUCTION

It has been shown in Chapter 1 that the process of crystal-structure determination cannot in general be direct, because, in the process of recording the diffraction pattern of a crystal, knowledge of the relative phases of the various diffracted beams is lost. Consequently we know only the amplitudes, and we are thus confronted with the problem of finding the structure from these alone. Although this information is incomplete, it is almost always sufficient because other information is also available—that the crystal structure contains discrete atoms which behave approximately as spherically symmetrical regions of electron density, and that there are no regions of negative electron density. Thus, although there is an infinity of distributions of electron density—positive and negative—that would diffract X-rays in the way observed, there is usually only one that can be interpreted as a collection of atoms.

The problem that has to be solved, therefore, is the derivation of this unique solution for a given collection of structure amplitudes, and usually the only method available is to postulate an atomic arrangement that conforms with the space-group symmetry, and to find, by calculation or otherwise, what structure amplitudes it would give for certain reflexions: if these amplitudes agree roughly with those observed, then the postulation is probably correct, and can be proved to be so by continuing the calculations for other reflexions; but if there are some violent disagreements, then the postulation is wrong, and another must be tried. This process is, for obvious reasons, known as 'trial and error'.

Naturally, a great deal of experience is necessary to use the method effectively. While an incorrect structure will give recognizably incorrect results, an approximation to the right structure will give only approximately correct results and so may easily be dismissed as wrong. It is important, therefore, to recognize when agreement between calculated and observed structure amplitudes is possibly acceptable, and in this recognition lies the whole art of the method. There are no golden rules for success; almost everything depends upon individual experience, and perhaps even intuition, in recognizing what possibilities to dismiss and what possibilities to proceed with.

Because of this lack of certainty in the method, it is important to make use of any hints, however slight, that might be gained about the positions of the atoms in the unit cell. Such hints may be given by experience from other crystals, by the physical and chemical properties of the compound, or by the X-ray intensities themselves. This chapter is chiefly concerned with summarizing—as far as they can be summarized—the general principles of the use of these devices.

2. Spatial Considerations

2.1. *Atomic radii.* The most important information that has been gained from crystal structures that have been determined is that of atomic sizes, and this information can, in its turn, be used in devising possible configurations of atoms in unknown structures. It is, of course, not to be expected that atoms behave as solid balls, but, nevertheless, it is found that, within narrow limits, a radius can be assigned to each different atom in crystals of similar nature.

This last qualification is important. The distance between two atoms depends upon the type of force between them; for example, the force between two metal atoms in an alloy is very different from that between one of these atoms and an acid radical in an inorganic salt. Fortunately, the number of essentially different forces is quite small, and attention may be confined to the two types, ionic and covalent or metallic (Volume I, pp. 114 and 119).

The forces between an atom and its neighbours may be different in different directions, and thus we may find that no effective value of atomic radius can be found. This is so, for example, in the metals zinc and cadmium, which behave, when unalloyed, as though composed of atoms with the shapes of elongated ellipsoids of revolution; in alloys, however, all atoms seem to adopt spherical shapes fairly accurately. In organic crystals, the behaviour of the atoms is much more consistent; the forces between the atoms in a molecule are much stronger than the forces—the van der Waals forces—between atoms in different molecules, and thus atoms must be considered as having much larger radii when these latter forces are concerned. The distances between carbon atoms in adjacent molecules are about 3·4–3·8 Å, whereas the covalent diameter for carbon is only about 1·4 Å.

The data in the tables of atomic radii must not be taken as precise; in view of the nature of atomic structure it would be surprising if the radii of the atoms were accurately invariant. In using the data, therefore, some latitude should be allowed; 0·2–0·3 Å is a possible variation. Goldschmidt (1929) has shown how these variations can be partly accounted for by differences in coordination—that is, by differences in environment—but since, in attempting to derive an unknown structure the coordination of certain atoms may not be known with certainty, it is preferable to accept a vagueness in the atomic radii that will allow for this uncertainty.

While we know that the final structure evolved for a crystal must have acceptable atomic radii, we are more concerned here with methods of making use of these radii in postulating structures for trial. It must be admitted that atomic radii are not often of great use in themselves, but nevertheless fairly complicated problems have arisen which have been almost completely solved by packing considerations alone.

Cyanite, for example, was solved in this way by Taylor and Jackson (1928). The unit cell has dimensions $a = 7{\cdot}09$, $b = 7{\cdot}72$, $c = 5{\cdot}56$ Å, $\alpha = 90°05'$, $\beta = 101°02'$, $\gamma = 105°44'$, and contains $4(Al_2SiO_5)$; thus, since the crystal is centrosymmetric, forty-eight parameters are needed to define the atomic positions unless some of the atoms are in special positions; this number of parameters would even now be regarded as presenting a formidable problem. The clue to the structure, however, was given by the packing of the oxygen atoms. The oxygen atoms, with radii of 1·35 Å, are much larger than the aluminium atoms (0·55 Å) and the silicon atoms (0·4 Å), and thus, as far as space is concerned, to a first approximation these latter atoms may be neglected.

With this assumption, calculation shows that each oxygen atom occupies a volume of 13·6 Å^3. Now the volume occupied by an atom of radius r in a close-packed structure is $4\sqrt{2}r^3$; this can be seen by noting that the unit cell of the cubic close-packed structure contains four atoms and has a cell dimension of $2\sqrt{2}r$. For a close-packed structure of atoms of radius 1·35 Å, the volume per atom would be 13·9 Å, and this is so close to the value deduced for the oxygen atoms in cyanite that these atoms must be approximately close-packed.

There are, however, many close-packed structures, ranging from cubic to hexagonal (Volume I, p. 144), and it is necessary to find in which one a unit cell of the observed dimensions can be found. The dimensions themselves give some help; c ($= 5{\cdot}56$ Å) is equal to two atomic diameters, which is a repeat distance found in all close-packed structures, and b ($= 7{\cdot}72$ Å) is equal to $4\sqrt{2}r$, a distance that occurs most frequently in the cubic close-packed structure. Closer inspection of this structure shows that it is possible to choose a unit cell defined by the vectors $-\frac{3}{2}\mathbf{a} + \mathbf{b} - \frac{1}{2}\mathbf{c}$, $2\mathbf{c}$ and $\mathbf{a} + \mathbf{b}$, where $\mathbf{a}$, $\mathbf{b}$ and $\mathbf{c}$ are the vectors defining the edges of the cubic unit cell. Since the magnitudes of these vectors are $2{\cdot}7\sqrt{2}$ Å $= 3{\cdot}82$ Å, the edges of the chosen unit cell are $\sqrt{14} \times 1{\cdot}91$ Å (7·15 Å), $4 \times 1{\cdot}91$ Å (7·64 Å) and $2\sqrt{2} \times 1{\cdot}91$ Å (5·40 Å), in close agreement with those observed. The cosines of the interaxial angles are 0, $-1/\sqrt{28}$, and $-1/\sqrt{14}$, which give $\alpha = 90°$, $\beta = 100{\cdot}9°$ and $\gamma = 105{\cdot}5°$, also in good agreement with the observed angles.

Thus the chosen unit cell needs but little distortion to give the dimensions found experimentally, and so, if the reasoning is correct, the positions of the oxygen atoms may be taken as approximating to the positions of the atoms in the underlying close-packed structure.

The positions of the aluminium and silicon atoms, however, have still to be found before the structure can be proved to be correct, and to find these positions other considerations have to be used.

2.2. *Grouping of atoms.* Knowledge of other silicate structures provides important clues. Silicon atoms are always linked to four oxygen atoms, and hence only the tetrahedral interstices in the close-packed grouping of oxygen atoms need be tried; aluminium, on the other hand, tends to occupy octahedral interstices, although it can sometimes replace silicon in tetrahedral interstices. Since there are fewer octahedral than tetrahedral interstices in the structure, the aluminium atoms may be placed first, and the silicon atoms then distributed reasonably uniformly in the tetrahedral spaces available. Some trial placings are, of course, necessary, but the number of possibilities, at least for the aluminium atoms, is not large.

A diagram of the complete structure, showing also its relation to the underlying face-centred cubic arrangement of oxygen atoms, is shown in fig. 112.

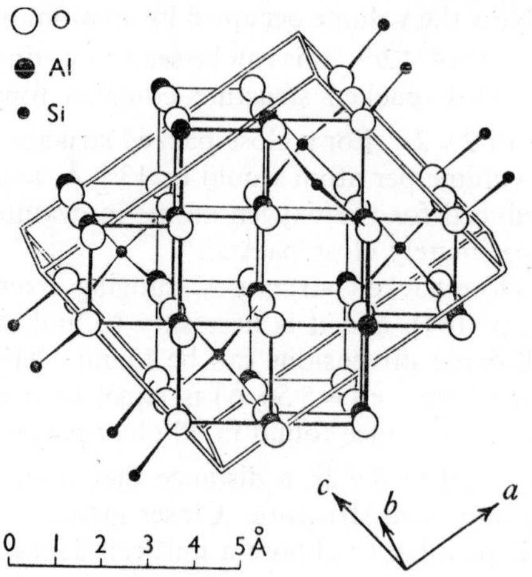

FIG. 112. Unit cell of cyanite (double lines showing relationship to cubic structure)

Such information is usually available about inorganic structures, since the dimensions of many ions are now known (Wells, 1950). For example, the SO_4 group consists of a sulphur atom at the centre of a tetrahedron of oxygen atoms of radius 1·25 Å; thus in sulphates, the SO_4 group can be treated as a single unit with six parameters—three translational and three rotational—instead of the fifteen that would be needed if the atoms were treated as independent.

In addition to this knowledge of the shapes of ions, much is known of the functions of other units, such as molecules of water and ammonia (Jensen, 1948). In the simplest cases, water molecules form symmetrical complexes around the cations—tetrahedral if the cation is small and octahedral if it is rather larger—and thus such complexes may also be treated as units in the structure. The assumption is not always correct —$SrCl_2.6H_2O$, for example, does not contain a complex $Sr.6H_2O$ (Jensen, 1940)—but it is often worth trying.

These principles are usually not sufficient for dealing with all the atoms in a structure. For example, $NiSO_4.7H_2O$ (Beevers and Schwartz, 1935) has to be treated as though it were composed of SO_4 groups, $Ni.6H_2O$ groups, and single H_2O molecules; the total number of parameters needed to specify the dispositions of these units is 15, a number too great to be handled by spatial methods alone, particularly since the space group, No. 19, $P2_12_12_1$, gives no help in limiting the atomic positions.

In organic structures, the scope for spatial methods is much wider, since a great deal is often known about the relative positions of the atoms in the molecules. Often, the complete stereochemistry of the molecule is known; it is then possible to make models and to fit these together in the unit cell with the space-group symmetry so that approximately correct van der Waals' distances occur between the separate molecules. As emphasized in the previous section, these distances must not be accepted precisely; although generally over 3 Å, they may be less, when they are usually attributed to the presence of hydrogen bonds (Bernal and Megaw, 1935). Thus a certain amount of uncertainty should be allowed for in the models used. Kitaygorodsky (1961) has given a quantitative discussion of the problems involved in the packing of near-spherical molecules.

In order to make the best use of the available data, the models of the molecules should take up approximately the space corresponding to the van der Waals' radii of the atoms. Since these radii are greater than the covalent radii, the balls representing the atoms have to be cut off by planes at distances from the centres corresponding to these covalent radii. Thus one atom may have to be represented by a different model according to its state of combination. A carbon atom in a CH_3 group, for example, may be represented by a sphere cut off by a single plane, corresponding to the single bond with which it is joined to the rest of the molecule, whereas the carbon atom in diamond has to be represented by a sphere cut off by four tetrahedrally disposed planes. Fig. 113 shows a diagram of a model of an organic molecule made in this way. Components for making these models, coloured according to a code (J. Sci. Instr. (1947), **24,** 249), are obtainable commercially.

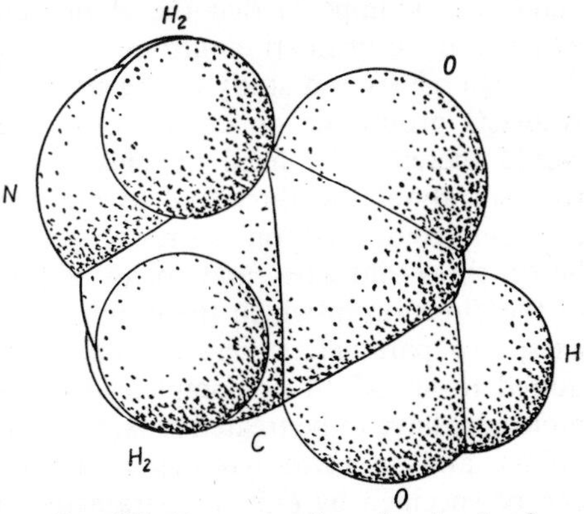

FIG. 113. Representation of molecule of glycine, $NH_2 . CH_2 . COOH$ (Bunn, 1961)

While such models are excellent for finding possible modes of fitting of molecules in the unit cell, they are less useful in giving the structural parameters, since the centres of the balls cannot easily be located. For this purpose a completely different type of model is required; the molecule is made in the form of a wire skeleton, the components of which represent the interatomic bonds. Atom centres will, in general, be at junctions of wires or at bends (Hughes and Taylor, 1958), and can be located by casting a shadow of the model from a distant source of light on to a drawing of the unit cell, or by other methods (Hughes, Phillips, Rogers and Wilson, 1949; Low and Waldram, 1949). Such shadows give the parameters of the atoms with an accuracy sufficient for calculating values of the structure factors of low-order reflexions.

2.3. *Use of symmetry elements.* In section **6**.2.2 it was pointed out that ions such as SO_4 have characteristic shapes that do not vary from crystal to crystal. These shapes are often symmetrical, and the relations between the symmetry of the ion and the symmetry of the space group sometimes impose severe limitations on the possible positions of ions. For example, in section **2**.7.1, it was seen that in potassium alum, $KAl(SO_4)_2.12H_2O$, the potassium and aluminium atoms lie on centres of symmetry, and the sulphur atoms lie on three-fold axes. Even without the evidence that all the centres of symmetry are already occupied, the deduction could have been made that the sulphur atoms do not occupy these positions, because the SO_4 group has no centre of symmetry. The data on point symmetry in the International Tables Vol. I (1952) can be very helpful in giving quickly the symmetries at the various positions in a space group, although, of course, this information can be readily derived from the space-group diagram itself. If we make the assumption that the aluminium atoms form the centres of octahedral co-ordination groups of water molecules, the following facts emerge from a study of the space group No. 205, Pa3: first, the $Al.6H_2O$ groups lie on centres of symmetry on three-fold axes, and would therefore be fixed by only one parameter (corresponding to rotation about the three-fold axes); secondly, the potassium atoms are completely fixed, on centres of symmetry; thirdly, the SO_4 groups lie on three-fold axes, and so, in addition to the lack of knowledge of the direction in which the groups are pointing along the three-fold axes, two parameters, one translational and one rotational, are required to specify their complete dispositions. The remaining water molecules have to be treated separately as occupying a set of equivalent points, and so three parameters are involved. Thus the structure can be specified by only six parameters, a number that would not be too large to handle, in view of the other facts that are now known of the functions of water of crystallization (Jensen, 1948). That the structure was not so worked out (Cork, 1927) was due both to lack of this knowledge and to the misleading information obtained by other methods (section **8**.3.3).

Important information about the location of molecules in an organic crystal can often be obtained in a similar way. For example, durene (Robertson, 1933) belongs to the space group No. 14, $P2_1/a$, and has a unit cell which contains two molecules. These two molecules cannot be placed in general positions, which are four-fold, and therefore we can deduce immediately that they are distributed around special positions. The only special positions in this space group are centres of symmetry, and thus the centres of the molecules are completely fixed. It may appear at first sight that the space-group data allow of four possibilities, but, for reasons similar to those mentioned in section **2**.7.1, it does not matter which centres are chosen.

The reasoning proved incidentally that the durene molecule was centrosymmetrical. This was known initially and therefore the deduction was not in itself of great importance. Sometimes, however, such deductions, even without complete structure determination, can give useful information about the stereochemistry of a molecule. For example, metatolidine dihydrochloride (Fowweather and Hargreaves, 1950) is monoclinic with space group either No. 5, I2 or No. 8, I*m*; it cannot be No. 12, I2/*m* because the crystals are pyroelectric (section **6**.3.1). The unit cell contains two molecules, and, therefore, since the general equivalent positions are four-fold, the molecules must lie in special positions. A schematic form of the molecule is shown in fig. 115, and it will be seen that it may have either a two-fold axis or a mirror plane of symmetry; the latter would demand that a plane of symmetry in the space group should coincide either with the plane of the molecule or with a plane perpendicular to this and to the length of the molecule. Neither of these possibilities can occur, since the molecule is too long to be accommodated in these orientations in the unit cell. Thus the molecule must have a two-fold axis, in agreement with the conclusion reached in section **3**.2.3.

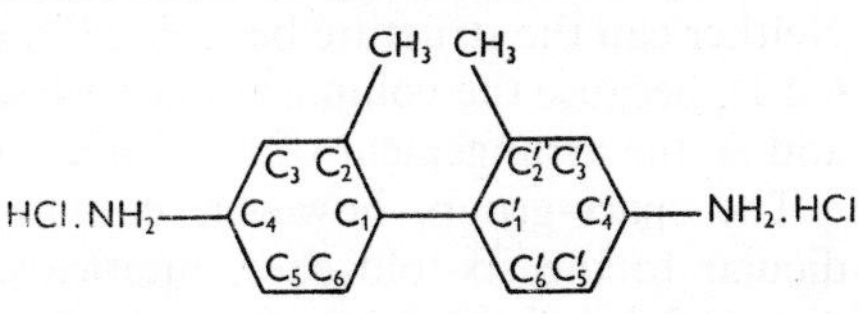

FIG. 115. Schematic form of molecule of metatolidine dihydrochloride (Fowweather and Hargreaves, 1950)

If the unit cell contains a number of molecules sufficient to occupy general positions in the space group, it does not follow that these molecules do not occupy special positions. For example, in stilbene (Robertson and Woodward, 1937*a*) it is found that the four molecules in the unit cell divide into two non-equivalent sets both situated on centres of symmetry. This type of occurrence, though unusual, is by no means unknown, and its possibility should always be borne in mind (Bunn, 1961).

These considerations do not normally apply to screw axes and glide planes, since these symmetry elements do not lead to special positions; or, to look at the matter in another light, molecules cannot possess screw axes or glide planes because these symmetry operations would lead to molecules of infinite size. This distinction, however, is not so clear for high polymers, in which the molecule is made of the same unit indefinitely repeated; such molecules *can* possess screw axes and glide planes. Bunn and Garner (1942) have shown, for example, that rubber hydrochloride has molecules distributed on glide planes of symmetry. Such structures can be quickly solved if it is noted that the distance of translation involved in the symmetry operation is equal to a possible repeat distance in the molecule.

Symmetry elements are not only of importance in dealing with atoms in special positions or with groups of atoms with known symmetry; they can also indicate regions in the unit cell in which atoms cannot be placed. No atom can be at a distance less than its radius from a centre of symmetry, a rotation axis or a mirror plane (unless, of course, it lies *on* the symmetry element) because then it would overlap with a symmetrically related atom. The most productive use made of this principle is undoubtedly the determination of the structure of beryl (Bragg and West, 1926); the space group of this structure is No. 192, P6/*mcc*, and the unit cell, which has $a = 9{\cdot}17$ Å, $c = 9{\cdot}21$ Å, contains $Be_6Al_4Si_{12}O_{36}$. Reference to the space-group data shows that there are so many special positions in the space group that it is unlikely that a systematic survey of the various possibilities would be feasible. Neither can the structure be tackled in the same way as cyanite (section 6.2.1), because the volume associated with each oxygen atom is 18·6 Å^3 and so the arrangement of oxygen atoms is by no means close-packed.

The space-group, however, contains planes of symmetry perpendicular to the six-fold axes, interleaved by systems of two-fold axes distant 2·3 Å from them. Since the diameters of the oxygen atoms are 2·7 Å, and twenty-four of them have to avoid both the planes of symmetry and the two-fold axes, it can readily be appreciated that the possible positions of the atoms are severely limited; in fact, the 24 atoms in general positions are completely fixed, as described in Volume I, and once these positions are determined the positions of the other 12 atoms are immediately indicated. Considerations of the coordination of the remaining atoms allows their positions to be found quite quickly.

It will be seen that, in this structure determination, the opposite principle from the usual one was adopted; the positions of the atoms in general positions were found first, and those in special positions followed. Possibilities such as this should always be borne in mind. While this book is concerned mainly with the laying-down of general principles and methods of procedure, the possibility is always present that, in any particular problem, an unorthodox approach may yield rich dividends; indeed, in one sense, this book aims at being a chronicle of new approaches to the same problem, the intention being to encourage rather than to discourage the introduction of still more new ideas in the future.

2.4. *Pauling's rules.* Packing of atoms, although highly important, is not the only factor in deciding crystal structures and Pauling (1929) has formulated others that enter into consideration. Most of these apply to silicates only, but one is of general importance and can sometimes be used to eliminate certain possibilities of atomic positions in the initial stages of determination of a crystal structure.

This rule is based upon the general principle that high concentration of electric charge is unlikely in a crystal structure and that ions or co-ordination groups of similar charge therefore tend to distribute themselves as uniformly as possible in the space available, producing alternations of positive and negative ions. This rule is so general that its application is not usually of any great importance, but there are occasions when it can help to dismiss some atomic arrangements which are spatially permissible. For example, in the preliminary survey of the possible atomic positions in the structure of analcite (section **2**.7.5), Taylor (1930) points out that the allocation of the sodium and aluminium atoms to the 16-fold sites would be very unlikely; if they were so disposed it would mean that all the positive ions would be placed close together along the three-fold axes, and this would violate Pauling's rule that similar ions should be distributed as evenly as possible over the structure.

2.5. *Use of computer.* Since many of the trial-and-error procedures already described are basically objective, it is possible to use a computer to carry them out more generally and more reliably than a human research worker could do; methods have been described by Milledge (1962). For example, if the relative positions of the atoms in a molecule are known, the computer can evaluate intermolecular distances for all possible positions and orientations, and can reject any dispositions that give unacceptable van der Waals separations (section **6**.2.1). Even a large computer cannot carry out this process completely for a molecule of moderate complexity, and Milledge points out that common sense (which the computer lacks!) must first be used to reduce the problem to tractable dimensions, using the considerations discussed in the preceding sections. She gives examples of structures worked out in this way.

3. Evidence from Physical Properties

3.1. *Detection of centrosymmetry.* It has been pointed out in section **2**.4.2 that, because of Friedel's law, the presence or absence of a centre of symmetry cannot usually be deduced from the symmetry of the X-ray diffraction pattern of a crystal. The deduction may sometimes be made indirectly by the statistical methods introduced by Wilson (Chapter 3) or by the detection of both a glide plane and screw axis as in the space group No. 14, $P2_1/c$. But often there is an ambiguity in space-group determination which can only be removed if direct evidence of the presence or absence of centrosymmetry can be obtained.

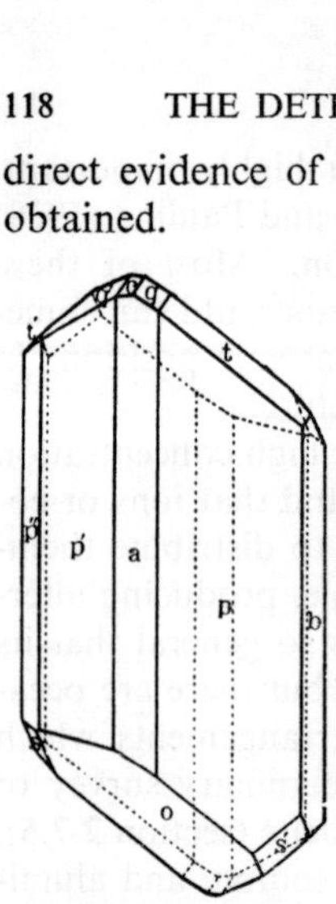

FIG. 118 (i). Drawing of ideal crystal of $CuSO_4 . 5H_2O$

The classical approach to the problem was based upon the study of external morphology; a large number of small crystals, grown under carefully controlled conditions, were measured, and if pole figures of the distribution of face normals showed that each face was accompanied by a parallel face on the other side of the crystal, the presence of a centre of symmetry could be safely inferred. Tutton (1922) in this way showed that $CuSO_4.5H_2O$ had a centre of symmetry. Fig. 118 (i) shows an idealized drawing of a crystal of this substance, and fig. 118 (ii) shows a pole-figure of the face normals (Phillips, 1946).

The method, however, has its drawbacks. It is not always easy to obtain perfect crystals, and accidents of growth may obscure the true symmetry. Moreover, unless faces of a general form are exhibited, the symmetry of the crystal may be higher than the symmetry of the underlying structure; for example, most alum crystals show the forms {100}, {110} and {111} and appear to have the symmetry *m3m*, whereas the true symmetry is *m*3. Many crystals cannot be grown with recognizable faces at all, or grow with insufficient faces for any reliable

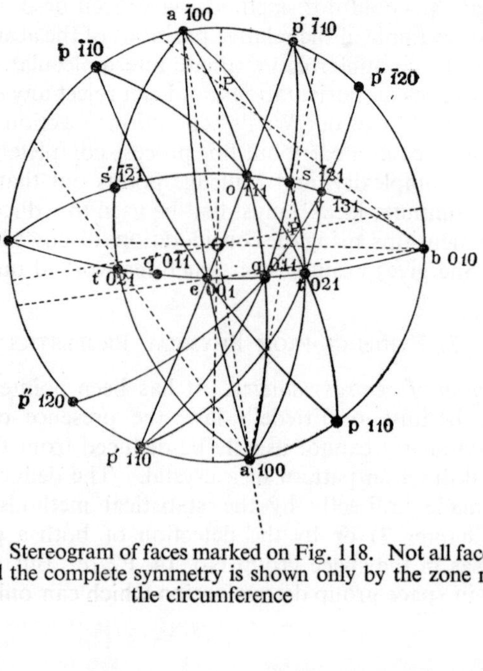

FIG. 118 (ii). Stereogram of faces marked on Fig. 118. Not all faces are marked, and the complete symmetry is shown only by the zone round the circumference

deductions to be made; for such crystals direct tests for centrosymmetry can be very valuable.

Such tests are based upon the detection of some physical property that can exist only in non-centrosymmetrical crystals, and therefore can prove only the absence of centrosymmetry; if no effect is shown it may merely be too small to be detected. This qualification applies to the methods to be described in this section and in Chapter 14.

One property that may be used is optical activity (Henry, Lipson and Wooster, 1951) but the difficulty of detecting this property in crystals has prevented its frequent use. Much more popular are the effects of pyroelectricity and piezoelectricity, which can be observed even in polycrystalline masses. Strong pyroelectricity can be detected by relatively simple methods (Maurice, 1930; Martin, 1931; Robertson, 1935*a*), but in general it is better to use a more sensitive apparatus such as that described by Wood and McCale (1940), since even a slight effect is sufficient to show the absence of centrosymmetry.

Piezoelectric evidence may be used in a similar manner. As Wooster (1938) points out, however, there is one crystal class, 432, which, although non-centrosymmetrical, cannot show the piezoelectric effect. The crystal classes that can show the various effects are shown in a table drawn up by Henry, Lipson and Wooster (1951, p. 161), which also appears in a slightly rearranged form in International Tables (1952, p. 42).

An example of the application of the pyroelectric effect has already been mentioned in section **6**.2.3; Fowweather and Hargreaves (1950) showed that the compound metatolidine dihydrochloride is pyroelectric, and therefore could not belong to the crystal class $2/m$, but must have either of the symmetries 2 or m separately.

3.2. *Optical and magnetic data.* The piezoelectric and pyroelectric effects can help to decide that a crystal does not possess a centre of symmetry, but they have not so far been used to find the positions of the atoms in a crystal structure. For this purpose we must make use of those physical properties which have been found to depend upon atomic arrangement, and the two most important properties so far used are refractivity and magnetic susceptibility.

The relationship between refractive indices and crystal structure has been firmly established by the work of Wasastjerna (1923); and Bragg (1924) has shown that it is possible to calculate the principal refractive indices of calcite from a knowledge of its structure. The problem that we are concerned with, however, is the opposite one—how to deduce, from the observed refractive indices, possible atomic arrangements; this problem is far more difficult and only in special circumstances can useful information be obtained.

Cyanite (section **6**.2.1) provides a simple example. This crystal is pseudo-cubic, and the refractive index is high, 1·720. Bragg (1930) has pointed out that this value is associated with a packing of the oxygen ions in positions which correspond to close packing, and this evidence was used by Taylor and Jackson (1928) in the initial stages of the investigation of the structure of this compound. In general, however, one would not expect to gain much information from a knowledge of the refractive index of a cubic crystal, because it is independent of direction in the crystal.

For other crystal systems, however, the refractive index may not be constant, and its variation with direction may give some indication about the dispositions of certain atoms and ions in crystals. This subject is discussed by Bunn (1961), who gives the following rules:

(1) If a structure is composed of plate-like molecules approximately parallel to each other, then the refractive index for vibrations perpendicular to the plates is lower than in other directions.

(2) If a structure is composed of needle-like molecules approximately parallel to each other, the refractive index for vibrations parallel to the needles is higher than in other directions.

(3) If the crystal is composed of plate-like molecules which are far from parallel, but which have one direction in their planes in common, the refractive index for vibrations parallel to this direction is higher than in other directions, but the difference is less marked than for the second class of crystals.

These rules indicate the weakness of the method; it can be applied only if the crystals are optically very anisotropic. If there are no great differences between the principal refractive indices then the structure may be composed of approximately spherical molecules, or of plate-like or needle-like molecules which are far from parallel to each other. Of course, if the stereochemistry of the molecule is known, such information may be useful, but in general optical methods are more important when the anisotropy is pronounced.

Optical methods were used in this way in the investigation of melamine (Wood and Williams, 1940). The principal refractive indices are $\alpha = 1{\cdot}487$, $\beta = 1{\cdot}846$, $\gamma = 1{\cdot}879$; that is, β and γ are approximately equal and α is much smaller; thus, from the rules stated above, the structure would be expected to contain plate-like molecules whose planes are approximately perpendicular to the direction of α. This was found to be so by Hughes (1941).

Many other examples could be given of the part played by such optical measurements in structure determination and in many laboratories it is customary to begin the study of transparent crystals by optical examination, for obtaining information both about the symmetry (Hartshorne and Stuart, 1950) and about possible molecular dispositions. It is, however, important to realize the limitations of the method. Not only is it of little use for crystals that do not show pronounced anistropy, but also, for inorganic crystals particularly, the results are complicated by the interactions of neighbouring groups of atoms which cannot be neglected in comparison with the interactions of the atoms in single groups.

This latter defect does not apply in so marked a degree to the magnetic method; the paramagnetic or diamagnetic susceptibility of a crystal depends much more simply on the crystal structure than does the refractive index, and thus one would expect to be able to make more precise deductions from such magnetic measurements (Lonsdale and Krishnan, 1936). The reason why the magnetic method has not been used as frequently as the optical is that it requires more specialized apparatus than the microscopes and immersion liquids that can be used for the optical method. It would certainly appear that the method deserves more attention than it has had in the past.

It would have been possible, for example, for the structure of $CuSO_4.5H_2O$ (Beevers and Lipson, 1934) to have been completed without recourse to Fourier methods (section 8.3.2) if measurements of its paramagnetic susceptibility had been taken into account. From measurements of the variation with temperature of the susceptibility of powdered crystals, Jordahl (1934) had been able to deduce that, although the crystals were triclinic, the environments of the copper atoms must have approximately cubic symmetry. Moreover, Krishnan and Mookherji (1936, 1937, 1938) had found that single crystals were magnetically almost uniaxial, the axis being inclined at 156°, 65° and 52° to the *a*, *b* and *c* axes of the crystal. Now the most likely configuration of oxygen atoms around the copper atoms is octahedral; the copper atom is too large for a tetrahedral arrangement to be possible, and it would not be possible for three oxygens of the SO_4 group to form, with the five water molecules, an eight-fold arrangement. If this argument is accepted, Krishnan and Mookherji's data give the orientations of the two octahedra, and there can be little doubt that the structure would have been solved much more quickly than it was had this information been available at the time the structure determination was carried out.

3.3. *Morphology and cleavage.* The external form of a crystal grown under ideal conditions should be that with minimum surface energy (Wells, 1946), and, since the surface energy of each face should be related to the internal structure, it might be expected that a careful study of the morphology of the crystals of a compound would give some indication of the internal structure. This problem has been given a great deal of attention by Donnay (1939), who has shown that it is often possible, by observing the frequency of occurrence of different faces on a large number of crystals of a compound, to deduce the space group. On the other hand, there are some outstanding exceptions to the rules (Donnay and Harker, 1937), and it would be unwise to place reliance upon results obtained in this way; moreover, the amount of work entailed in making the necessary goniometric measurements on a large number of crystals is so great that it would appear to be much simpler to deduce space groups in the manner described in Chapter 2.

It is still more difficult to make any deductions about atomic distributions from the occurrence of faces, although some general rules are given by Bunn (1961). Of rather more utility is the information given by cleavage, which in some crystals is very pronounced. Mica (Jackson and West, 1930) is the most outstanding example, the cleavage indicating a distribution of alkali atoms in (001) planes. Such information proved to be of use in the determination of the structure of sodium sesquicarbonate, which has perfect cleavage parallel to (100) and good cleavage parallel to $(10\bar{1})$ (Brown, Peiser and Turner-Jones, 1949); by analogy with mica, one would expect the sodium atoms to be grouped in planes parallel to these planes and fig. 122 shows that this is so.

Cleavage considerations, however, are rarely so helpful, but the evidence is so simply obtained that, if it exists, it is worth while bearing in mind in the initial stages of a structure determination.

3.4. *Infra-red absorption.* The disadvantage of the use of optical data —that it is difficult to separate intramolecular and intermolecular effects —can be largely overcome by the use of infra-red radiation. On the other hand, the use of this radiation requires special apparatus and large crystals and so has not been very extensive, but some results published by Crookes (1947) and Brown and Corbridge (1948) suggest that the method can be very useful indeed.

The basis of the method is the measurement of the absorption of infra-red radiation as a function of the direction of plane of polarization with respect to the crystal. For visible light such absorption is

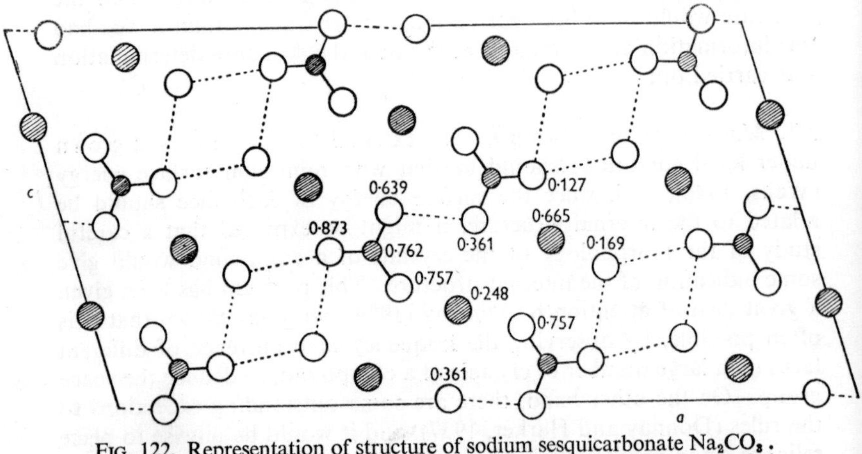

FIG. 122. Representation of structure of sodium sesquicarbonate Na_2CO_3 . $NaHCO_3$. $2H_2O$, showing distribution of sodium atoms (large shaded circles), in 100 and 101 planes (Brown, Peiser and Turner-Jones, 1949)

normally a property of the atomic arrangement as a whole, but for the lower quantum energies of infra-red radiation it is possible to identify the absorption of a particular band of wave-lengths with the presence of a particular detail of structure in the molecule such as a bond of a given nature; the absorption of this bond is greatest when the plane of vibration is parallel to its length. If the particular bonds are all parallel there should be a great variation of absorption with the plane of polarization, and the plane of maximum absorption gives the plane of the bonds; if the bonds are not all parallel, it should be possible to deduce their inclination to the plane of polarization of maximum absorption.

By considering different absorption bands, Brown and Corbridge (1948) were able to obtain information about the orientation of certain bonds in the acetanilide structure, which, supplemented by optical and cleavage data, enabled the complete structure to be so accurately postulated that only little refinement by X-ray methods was required.

4. Algebraic Methods of Solution

4.1. *Crystals with few parameters.* Whatever the methods used for deriving a crystal structure, the final proof of its correctness must lie in the agreement between calculated and observed intensities. It is tempting, therefore, to try to dispense with the various preliminaries already discussed, and to produce, from the intensities themselves, a structure that has this necessary property. Many attempts have been made to solve this problem, but no method of general application has yet been evolved; algebraic methods were first applied only to fairly simple structures.

For instance, if a structure is based on only one variable parameter, all the intensities can be calculated as a function of this parameter, and it is not difficult to find the value that gives the observed intensities. Graphical methods provide the best way of finding the correct solution, as shown in fig. 124, which is taken from a paper by Bradley and Lu (1937).

The material is Cr_2Al, which was found from powder photographs to be tetragonal, with $a = 3{\cdot}00$ Å and $c = 8{\cdot}63$ Å. This unit cell contains two Al and four Cr atoms. Since the only systematic absences observed were those of reflexions with $h+k+l$ odd, the lattice was established as body-centred, but several space groups were possible; that of highest symmetry, No. 139, I4/*mmm*, was tried first and, since an acceptable structure based on this was found, there was no need to try those of lower symmetry (compare section **2**.4.2).

In the space group I4/*mmm*, there are two sets of two-fold positions, (*a*) 0, 0, 0 and $\frac{1}{2}, \frac{1}{2}, \frac{1}{2}$, and (*b*) 0, 0, $\frac{1}{2}$ and $\frac{1}{2}, \frac{1}{2}$, 0; as explained in section **2**.7.1, either of these sets can be chosen, and it is simpler to choose (*a*). There are three sets of four-fold positions, (*c*) $0\,\frac{1}{2}\,0$, $\frac{1}{2}\,0\,0$,

$\frac{1}{2}\,0\,\frac{1}{2}$ and $0\,\frac{1}{2}\,\frac{1}{2}$; (*d*) $0\,\frac{1}{2}\,\frac{1}{4}$, $\frac{1}{2}\,0\,\frac{1}{4}$, $\frac{1}{2}\,0\,\frac{3}{4}$ and $0\,\frac{1}{2}\,\frac{3}{4}$; and (*e*) $0\,0\,z$, $0\,0\,\bar{z}$, $\frac{1}{2}, \frac{1}{2}, \frac{1}{2}+z$, and $\frac{1}{2}, \frac{1}{2}, \frac{1}{2}-z$. Both (*c*) and (*d*) can be immediately rejected; they give unacceptable distances (e.g. 2·1 Å between the chromium atoms) and the calculated intensities do not agree with the observed. For example, (*c*) would give a strong 002 reflexion, and (*d*) would give a strong 004 reflexion, whereas neither of these is observed. The positions (*e*), however, are not so easily dealt with, since a variable parameter, which Bradley and Lu call *u*, is involved.

The formula for the structure factor for the reflexions with $h+k+l$ even is

$$F = 2f_{Al} + 4f_{Cr}\cos 2\pi lu.$$

From this it can be seen that all reflexions with the same index *l* should have the same value of F when allowance is made for changes in scattering factor. As far as lack of resolution of certain powder lines would allow, it was observed that reflexions with *l* equal to a multiple of 3 were strong, those with *l* equal to 1 or 4 were zero, and those with other values of *l* were of intermediate intensities. These facts suggested that *u* was near $\frac{1}{3}$, and fig. 124 shows how F varies with *u* for

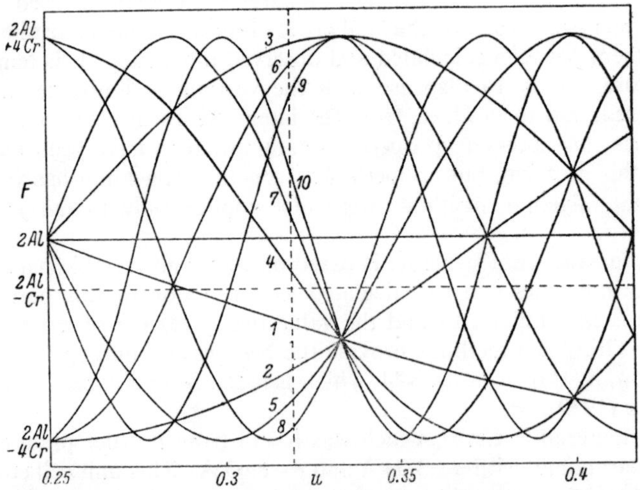

FIG. 124. Determination of parameter in Cr_2Al (Bradley and Lu, 1937)

different values of *l* over a range of values of *u* near to $\frac{1}{3}$, the scattering factors of the two atoms being taken as equal to their atomic numbers (13 for Al and 24 for Cr).

The horizontal dotted line corresponds to zero value for F, and it will be noted that only near 0·32 are the curves for $l=1$ and 4 near to zero. Slightly larger values would be possible, but then the intensities of reflexions with $l=8$ would become too weak, and, taking as much evidence as possible into consideration, Bradley and Lu decided upon the value of 0·319, shown by the vertical dotted line in the diagram.

While this type of method was devised for dealing with structures depending upon only one parameter, it can be applied to structures depending upon more than one parameter if the space group is such that certain intensities depend upon one parameter only. For example, marcasite FeS_2 belongs to the space group No. 58, *Pmnn*, and the unit cell contains two iron atoms and four sulphur atoms (Buerger, 1931). The two iron atoms must be placed on centres of symmetry, and so do not introduce any variable parameters, but the sulphur atoms may be on either two-fold axes or mirror planes; consideration of certain absent reflexions such as 020 and 004 eliminates the possibility of any positions on the two-fold axes, and therefore the mirror planes, involving two variable parameters, must be chosen.

With appropriate choice of origin, the structure-factor formulae are

$$F(hkl) = 2f_{Fe} + 4f_S \cos 2\pi ky \cos 2\pi lz$$

when $h+k+l$ is even,

and $$F(hkl) = -4f_S \sin 2\pi ky \sin 2\pi lz$$

when $h+k+l$ is odd.

For reflexions with l equal to zero, the first expression becomes independent of z, and the second becomes zero; thus the value of y can be found from the $hk0$ reflexions by some such method as that described for Cr_2Al. In a similar way the value of z can be found from the reflexions $h0l$. It will be noted, however, that only reflexions with $h+k+l$ even are used, and for this reason, and also because only the cosine function is involved, the method is unable to distinguish between values such as y, $\bar{y}$, $\frac{1}{2}+y$, and $\frac{1}{2}-y$; the small number of possibilities can nevertheless soon be reduced to the one tenable result by making use of the general reflexions with no zero indices.

4.2. *Crystals with many parameters.* When more than three parameters are involved, graphical methods cannot easily be applied and analytical methods have to be used. Formally, the problem can be quite simply stated; we have a number of equations relating a number of variables, and so long as the former number is greater than the latter, the derivation of a unique solution should be possible. In practice, the problem is so difficult that no general method of solution has yet been found; thus, although the subject is important, we shall not deal with it here as it has not played a major role in any crystal-structure determination.

5. Indirect Methods of Solution

5.1. *Importance of indirect methods.* Since algebraic methods of determining crystal structures would appear to be impracticable, other types of approach have to be resorted to, and the following sections contain what is hoped is a reasonably useful summary of these approaches. One can hardly claim more than this; almost every crystal provides different problems, and hence gives different opportunities for exercise of ingenuity and introduction of new methods. For this reason, the following sections are among the most important in this book. They introduce the various ways that have been used in trying to extract information about a crystal from the way in which it diffracts X-rays, and the use of the word 'indirect' should not be taken as implying any vagueness in the results finally obtained.

5.2. *General survey of intensities.* To begin with, a general survey of intensities, either over the whole reciprocal lattice or over isolated zones, can sometimes be rewarding. Particularly striking examples are given by the work of Bradley and his collaborators in determining the structures of certain alloys from powder photographs. Despite its obvious disadvantages, the powder method does provide an overall view of the diffraction pattern, and the powder photographs of these alloys show obvious relationships to those of the simple structure with atoms at positions (0, 0, 0) and ($\frac{1}{2}$, $\frac{1}{2}$, $\frac{1}{2}$). The similarity implies that the structure approximates to that of the body-centred cube, but that differences in scattering factor and slight displacements of the atoms cause the unit cell to contain an integral number of the body-centred cubes; thus extra lines may appear, and the original lines from the body-centred cubic structure split into several components. The structure of Cr_2Al (section 6.4.1) is an example and would have been worked out by such methods if the direct approach had not proved so fruitful.

The first example, and that which provided the chief inspiration for the work that followed, is given by the alloy Cu_5Zn_8, γ brass (Bradley and Thewlis, 1926), which is cubic with 52 atoms in the unit cell. Analysis of the powder photograph shows that the structure is based upon a body-centred lattice, but no information is given about the symmetry since the reflexions *hkl* and *khl* overlap. Westgren and Phragmen (1925) had obtained some information from Laue photographs of single crystals, and they deduced that the space group was either No. 211, I432; No. 217, $I\bar{4}3m$; or No. 229, *Im*3*m*.

The cell dimension, 8·85 Å, is approximately three times the cell dimension of α iron, which has the body-centred cubic structure with an atomic radius about the same as that of copper and zinc. We may therefore assume that the structure of Cu_5Zn_8 is based upon a unit cell that contains 3^3 body-centred cubes. There are, however, 54 atoms in this collection of unit cells, and the unit cell of Cu_5Zn_8 contains only 52 atoms; two atoms must be removed. The only possible ones are those at (0, 0, 0) and ($\frac{1}{2}$, $\frac{1}{2}$, $\frac{1}{2}$) in the new unit cell, since the removal of these still leaves the lattice body-centred cubic.

The removal of these two atoms, however, leaves 'holes' in the structure, and from consideration of atomic radii Bradley and Thewlis were able to postulate reasonable changes of atomic positions that would tend to fill in these holes. The atomic positions so chosen gave rough agreement with the observed intensities, and the agreement was improved by some further small changes. In this way the complete structure, involving five variable parameters, was determined.

Evidence leading to this type of approach can sometimes be more easily obtained from single-crystal photographs. For example, it may be observed that the odd layer lines on an oscillation photograph are weaker than the even layer lines. This may be taken to infer that the cell dimension about which the crystal is rotating is approximately halved; in other words, the two halves of the unit cell contain approximately similar contents, similarly situated. An illustration is given by the structure of thiophthen, $C_6H_4S_2$, which was worked out by Cox,

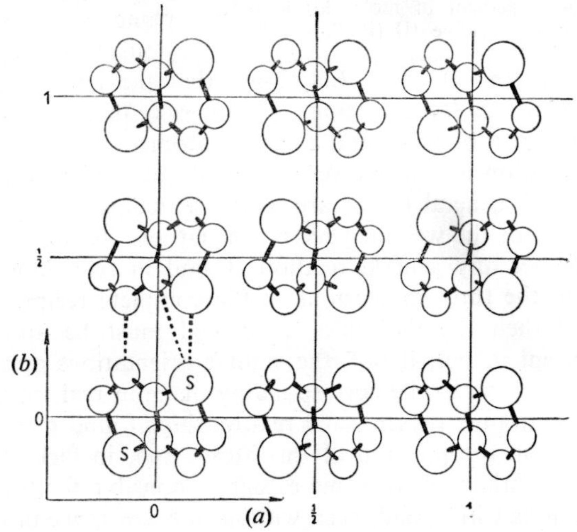

FIG. 127. Projection of structure of thiophthen on (001), showing similarity of contents of unit cell at levels 0 and $b/2$ (Cox, Gillot and Jeffrey, 1949)

Gillott and Jeffrey (1949). It was found that oscillation photographs with [100] as axis showed odd layer lines that are much weaker than the even layer lines, and this fact was of value in determining the final structure, a projection of which on the (001) plane is shown in fig. 127. It will be noted that in this projection the molecule repeats approximately at intervals of $b/2$, as deduced from the general weakness of reflexions with k odd. If it repeated accurately, the reflexions with k odd would be absent; this is so, for the projection, at intervals of $a/2$, and thus reflexions $hk0$ with h odd are completely absent, but this is merely one of the characteristics of the space group, No. 61, Pbca, of the crystal.

Such information is not always obtainable by direct inspection of X-ray photographs, as the general relationships that may exist may not be simply dependent upon the indices. A rather more complicated dependence is shown by acridine (Phillips, 1950), which gives strong reflexions $h0l$ only when $h+l$ is divisible by four; this is explained by the existence of two molecules whose projections on the (010) plane are approximately similar and separated by a distance of $\frac{1}{4}(\mathbf{a}+\mathbf{c})$. Fig. 128 shows that the projection has this feature, the two molecules being different only in the interchange of the positions of a nitrogen and a carbon atom.

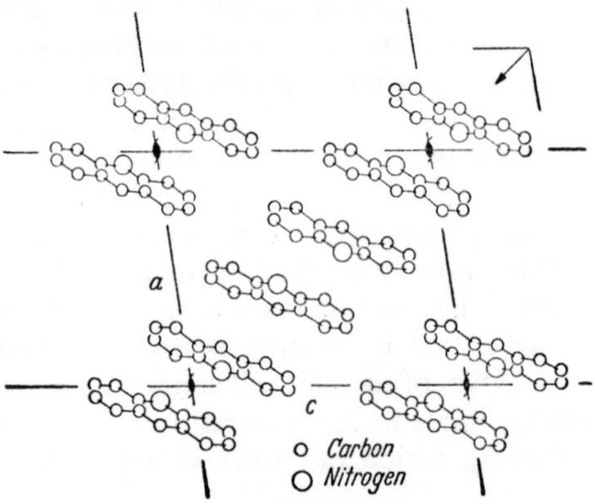

FIG. 128. Arrangement of molecules in (010) projection of acridine III (Phillips, 1950)

This illustration is still not very complicated, but it brings out the point that such general trends are worth searching for by drawing a representation of the weighted reciprocal lattice. It is also important to find whether any general relations found in two dimensions are continued in the three dimensions of the complete reciprocal lattice; if they are, then the molecules concerned must be approximately similarly oriented, but, if not, the similar orientations apply only to their projections on to the corresponding plane in real space.

If a heavy atom is present, any relationships found may be unduly dependent upon the position of this atom, and, in fact, the sulphur atoms in thiophthen are to some extent responsible for the weakness of the reflexions with k odd, even without the assistance of the carbon atoms. Consequently, under these circumstances, information about the lighter atoms is less precise, and may even be quite valueless. For example, general trends were found in the intensities of the reflexions from $CuSO_4.5H_2O$ (section **6**.3.2) which gave the positions of the copper and sulphur atoms, but which gave no direct information about the positions of the oxygen atoms.

A section of the reciprocal lattice of this crystal is shown in table 92, and, in general, it will be seen that the reflexions with $h+k$ even are stronger than those with $h+k$ odd. This tendency is more pronounced at high angles than at low angles, suggesting that it is not due to approximate equality of the two parts of the unit cell separated by $\frac{1}{2}\mathbf{a}+\frac{1}{2}\mathbf{b}$; if this were so, the tendency would be less pronounced at high angles, since any small variations in parameters would have greater effect there. The tendency indicates strongly certain relationships between the parameters of the copper and sulphur atoms, since the oxygen atoms have relatively higher scattering factors at the lower angles, and so become more nearly negligible as the angle increases.

The extra strength of the reflexions with $h+k$ even is shown also by the hkl reflexions, and so there would appear to be a tendency towards C-face centring. There are three ways in which this can arise: the copper atoms, of which there are two in the unit cell, may occupy the positions (0, 0, 0) and $(\frac{1}{2}, \frac{1}{2}, 0)$, which are special positions in the space group No. 2, $P\bar{1}$; the copper atoms may occupy the positions $(\frac{1}{4}, \frac{1}{4}, 0)$ and $(\frac{3}{4}, \frac{3}{4}, 0)$, which are general positions; or the copper atoms may occupy positions (x, y, z) and $(\bar{x}, \bar{y}, \bar{z})$, and the sulphur atoms occupy the positions $(\frac{1}{2}+x, \frac{1}{2}+y, z)$ and $(\frac{1}{2}-x, \frac{1}{2}-y, \bar{z})$. The two former possibilities correspond to a C-face centred arrangement of the copper atoms, and the last corresponds to a C-face centring of the copper atoms by the sulphur atoms.

The second possibility is unlikely. Although the atoms are in general positions, the parameters would have to approximate very closely indeed to the particular values $\frac{1}{4}$, $\frac{1}{4}$ in order to account for the observed trend; the other two possibilities are more likely, and we shall confine our attention to them. If the first explanation is accepted, another general trend can be made use of: the intensities $hk0$ with $h+k$ even tend to be independent of h for a given value of k; for example, when $h+k$ is even, the spots with $k=2$, 5, 9 and 12 tend to be weak or absent, and those with $k=3$, 4, 7 and 10 tend to be strong. These facts would be explained if the x parameter of the sulphur atoms were zero, so that the index h did not enter the expression for the structure factor, and the y parameter had a value of 0·29. (This value can be found by some such method as that described in section 6.4.1.) Thus we may say that the following arrangement of copper and sulphur atoms explains the general tendencies in the intensities:

Cu atoms in special positions (0, 0, 0) and $(\frac{1}{2}, \frac{1}{2}, 0)$,
S atoms in general positions $(0, 0{\cdot}29, z)$,

where z is as yet undetermined.

We still have to consider the third possibility—that the sulphur atoms form a face-centred arrangement with the copper atoms. The structure-factor formulae are then

$$(f_{\mathrm{Cu}}+f_{\mathrm{S}})\cos 2\pi(hx+ky+lz), \text{ when } h+k \text{ is even,}$$

and

$$(f_{\mathrm{Cu}}-f_{\mathrm{S}})\cos 2\pi(hx+ky+lz), \text{ when } h+k \text{ is odd.}$$

These formulae show immediately that the reflexions with $h+k$ even should in general be stronger than those with $h+k$ odd, and the second observation—that the $hk0$ intensities tend to be independent of h—can again be explained by making $x=0$. Methods similar to those described in section 6.4.1, applied to the $hk0$ reflexions, then lead to a value of y of 0·14; thus the general trends in the $hk0$ reflexions can also be explained by the following arrangement of copper and sulphur atoms:

Cu atoms at 0·00, 0·14, z,
S atoms at 0·50, 0·64, z.

Detailed calculations show that these positions give about as good a general agreement with observed intensities as the former positions give, and thus we cannot, on the basis of these intensities alone, distinguish between them. The only two procedures possible for distinguishing between them are, first, to see if either leads to a complete structure that is spatially possible (section 6.2.1) or, secondly, to try to find additional experimental evidence. The former proved to be too difficult to carry out, since little was known about the functions of the water molecules (sections 6.2.2 and 6.3.2), and evidence from the comparison of the reflexions with those from $CuSeO_4.5H_2O$ was used, as described later in section 6.5.7.

A more general application of these methods has been described by Vand (1951). A section of the reciprocal lattice of trilaurin is given in fig. 130; it shows some outstandingly strong spots arranged in a

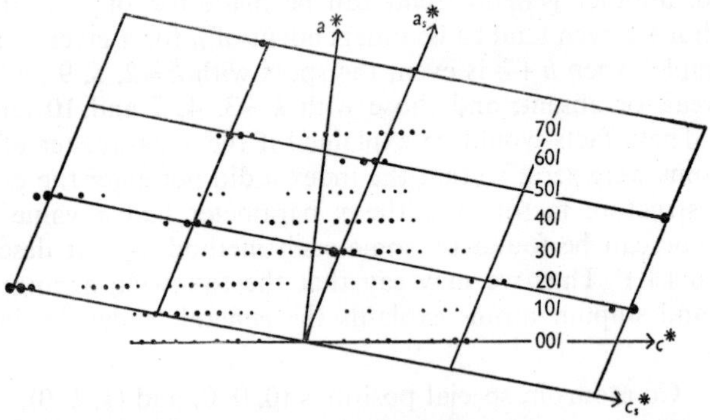

FIG. 130. Reciprocal-lattice section of trilaurin, showing arrangement of stronger reflexions on coarse mesh with axes along a_s* and c_s* (Vand and Bell, 1951)

regular way, and, if all other spots were neglected, a reciprocal lattice with a much coarser mesh is left (Vand and Bell, 1951). This corresponds, in the crystal, to a unit cell containing only two atoms, and so we may deduce that the crystal structure is built up of these 'sub-units' repeated approximately regularly in the unit cell.

To summarize, it may be said that, although a general survey of intensities may not be informative, the method is so simple to try that it is worth considering as a first step; if no help is given, not much time will have been lost, but if some regularity can be noticed, a great deal of time may be saved. The subject will be discussed again in

Chapter 10, when it assumes a greater importance in connexion with the Fourier-transform method.

5.3. *Importance of absolute intensities.* The methods so far described have been based on the observation of relative intensities, and, where these methods produce tangible results, they are of considerable value. But, obviously, if in addition we know the absolute values of the structure amplitudes, we have information of much greater significance; we may know not only that a reflexion is much stronger than any others, but that it is so strong that practically all the atoms must scatter in phase to produce it. The importance of knowledge of absolute intensities in crystal-structure determination was pointed out by Bragg and West (1928), who showed how such considerations had led to the derivation of the crystal structures of some minerals such as diopside (Warren and Bragg, 1928).

For some time after this paper by Bragg and West was published, their insistence on the importance of absolute intensities was largely ignored and almost all published work was based upon relative intensities. This, of course, is understandable; if it is possible to determine a structure on the basis of relative intensities it is not worth while spending effort on absolute measurements. But as more complicated problems have arisen, new methods of solution have had to be found, and, as will be explained in Chapter 9, some of these methods depend critically upon knowledge of absolute values of structure amplitudes. Thus the importance of absolute measurements is now fully realized. Fortunately however the accuracy with which the absolute scale needs to be known is such that statistical methods are usually adequate for this purpose. A complete set of relative measurements contains within itself its own absolute standard. For a given content of a unit cell, any arbitrary arrangement of atoms would give a set of reflexions of the same average value, and this average value would be equal to the average value of the observed intensities.

This, of course, would be a cumbersome method of procedure, and, moreover, would be inaccurate unless the temperature factor (section 1.2.5) were known in advance. If the temperature factor is not known the average of the calculated intensities will exceed the average of the observed intensities by an amount that increases with θ, and Wilson (1942) has shown how this difficulty can be overcome. Harker (1948) has devised an essentially similar method.

Equation *10*.3 states that

$$F(hkl) = \sum_n f_n \exp\{2\pi i(hx_n + ky_n + lz_n)\}$$

and therefore

$$F^*(hkl) = \sum_n f_n \exp\{-2\pi i(hx_n + ky_n + lz_n)\},$$

where F* is the complex conjugate of F. Thus

$$|F(hkl)|^2 = \sum_n f_n \exp\{2\pi i(hx_n + ky_n + lz_n)\}$$
$$\times \sum_n f_n \exp\{-2\pi i(hx_n + ky_n + lz_n)\}.$$

This may be written as

$$|F(hkl)|^2 = \sum_n f_n^2 + \sum_{n \neq m} \sum f_n f_m \exp\{2\pi i[h(x_n - x_m) + k(y_n - y_m) + l(z_n - z_m)]\} \quad (132.1)$$

The first part of the summation, having only positive terms, will be large, whereas the second part, having terms which are as likely to be negative as positive, will have a most probable value of zero. Thus if values of $|F(hkl)|^2$, which we may call the ideal intensity I(hkl), are averaged over a large number of reflexions, we should expect that

$$\overline{I(hkl)} = \sum_n f_n^2, \quad (132.2)$$

where the superior bar represents the average value.

The difficulty that has just been mentioned concerning the lack of knowledge of the temperature factor can be overcome by dividing the reflexions into groups lying between certain values of $\sin^2 \theta$. The mean value of the observed intensities, I′(hkl), may be evaluated over each range, and the constant c found which makes the average equal to the sum of the squares of the scattering factors; theoretical scattering factors should be used. This constant c will be found to increase as the reflexions with higher values of θ are included, and if $\log c$ is plotted against the mean value of $\sin^2 \theta$ for each range of reflexions, a linear relationship should be found, the intercept at $\sin \theta = 0$ being the value of c required.

The method works best for more complicated crystals, and is unsatisfactory if there are atoms in special positions; this probably accounts for the lack of agreement obtained by Wilson for the alums and $CuSO_4.5H_2O$, both of which have atoms in special positions. Moreover, another difficulty also exists, in that these two examples were for single zones of reflexions, whereas the theory strictly applies only when all possible reflexions are considered. This is so because of the requirement that the second part of the summation in equation *132.1* should be zero; this will not be so if, for any one pair of atoms, the quantity $[h(x_n - x_m) + k(y_n - y_m) + l(z_n - z_m)]$ remains near zero for all values of h, k and l. In three dimensions, this difficulty should not arise, because no pair of atoms can be closer together than the sum of their radii, and thus one of the components $x_n - x_m$, $y_n - y_m$ or $z_n - z_m$ must be reasonably large. But in projections on to planes, it is possible that the coordinates of two atoms may almost coincide, and thus the theory will not hold for them.

By comparison with equation *10.3*, it can be seen that the quantity

$2\pi[h(x_n - x_m) + k(y_n - y_m) + l(z_n - z_m)]$ represents the phase difference between the X-rays scattered by the two atoms concerned, and the requirement that the second summation in equation *132.1* should be zero is equivalent to the requirement that this phase difference shall at least have values uniformly distributed between 0 and π. This, in turn, means that the distance between any two atoms shall be greater than half the minimum spacing of the reflexions considered. As already stated, this requirement is easily satisfied for most structures, but may not be so for projections on to planes; the tendency for such projections is for the reflexions to be rather stronger than the simple theory would demand. Nevertheless, projections play such a large part in structure determination that it is usually worth while applying the method to zones of intensities.

The process can be illustrated by means of the data for metatolidine dihydrochloride, already given in table 52. Table 133 shows the various steps needed in the deduction of the conversion constant, and fig. 133

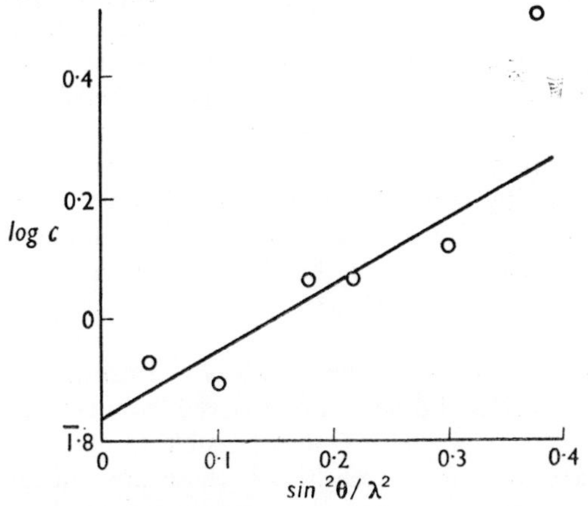

FIG. 133. Determination of absolute values of structure amplitudes of metatolidine dihydrochloride

shows the graph from which the final value of log c is deduced. (The point representing the outermost range of reflexions must obviously be ignored.)

TABLE 133

$\sin^2\theta/\lambda^2$	⟨I⟩	Σf_n^2	c	$\log c$
0·04	875	748	0·85	$\bar{1}$·929
0·10	612	475	0·78	$\bar{1}$·892
0·18	315	358	1·16	0·064
0·24	263	309	1·17	0·068
0·30	204	270	1·32	0·121
0·38	77	244	3·17	0·501

The value of log c extrapolated to $\sin^2 \theta/\lambda^2 = 0$ is $\bar{1}{\cdot}84$, giving a value of c of 0·70. Since the data in table 52 were already on an absolute scale, the value should have been unity, and this degree of error is typical of the method; the error is less than it appears, for it corresponds to only 16 per cent in structure amplitudes.

Other suggestions, based essentially on the same general principles, have also been made. Kasper, Lucht and Harker (1950), for example, have tried equating to zero the minima in a three-dimensional Patterson synthesis computed without the zero-order term; they assumed that these minima corresponded to complete absence of interatomic peaks. The results, however, turned out to be unreliable, and they found that the method just described was more successful.

The choice of method of placing intensities on an absolute scale in any particular problem depends upon a number of considerations. If the crystal contains no atoms heavier than nitrogen, its absorption coefficient will be small, and direct comparison with a standard low-absorption crystal may be used. If the required apparatus is not available, Wilson's method may be used, on the understanding that it is most successful if three-dimensional data are used, and that it tends to give too high a value for the F's from two-dimensional data.

Some of the anomalies found in applying Wilson's method caused him to look more closely into the underlying principles, particularly the effects produced by symmetry. He was able to show that statistical methods could be helpful in establishing the symmetry of a crystal structure; the implications of this discovery have been dealt with in Chapter 3.

5.4. *Information from outstanding reflexions.* In section **6**.5.2 examples were given of structural information derived from general relationships between intensities. Sometimes it is possible to gain important information from only a few intensities if these are outstandingly large, since there are comparatively few ways in which the atoms can be placed to scatter in phase for a given reflexion, whereas there are many ways in which approximately zero scattering can be produced.

For crystals containing planar molecules, the main clue to the structure may be contained in only one reflexion; if a reflexion is found with a structure amplitude near the maximum possible it may be deduced that the molecules are nearly parallel to the crystallographic planes giving this reflexion. The degree of parallelism can be inferred from the strength of the higher orders of reflexion from these planes, since, if all the atoms lay exactly in the planes, the higher orders would also be outstandingly strong amongst reflexions of about the same Bragg angle. This type of deduction may often be made by considering relative intensities only, since, if a reflexion is much stronger than its fellows, it is likely to be significant; but if the intensities are known in absolute measure the deductions are so much the more reliable.

Abrahams and Robertson (1948) made use of considerations of this sort in the determination of the structure of para-nitroaniline,

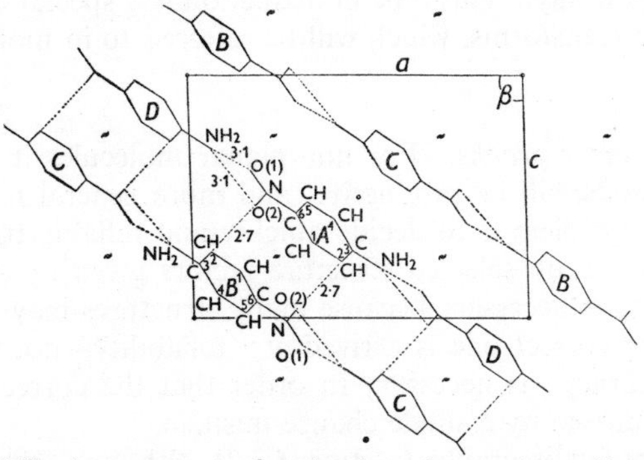

FIG. 135 (i). Arrangement of molecules of para-nitroaniline n the (202) planes. The molecules are arranged in layers *-A-D-A-D-*, and *B-C-B-C-*, the broken lines representing hydrogen bonds (Abrahams and Robertson, 1948)

$NO_2.C_4H_4.NH_2$. They found that the reflexion 202 had a structure amplitude of 119, compared with a maximum possible of 149. They therefore deduced that the molecules lay approximately in the (202) planes, in agreement with the pronounced cleavage of the crystal on the (101) planes. A structure based on these principles was found and is shown in projection in fig. 135 (i). The projection has been verified by Donohue and Trueblood (1956) who have however found that the structure described in Fig. 135 (i) is incorrect.

While such information concerning the general disposition of molecules in a crystal can only be expected to result from consideration of low-order reflexions, the combined information given by *several* outstandingly strong high-order reflexions has sometimes been found to give the structure in almost complete detail. Although one such reflexion by itself would allow of many possibilities for the atomic positions, because of the largeness of the indices, the combination of the information from several reflexions may be quite conclusive.

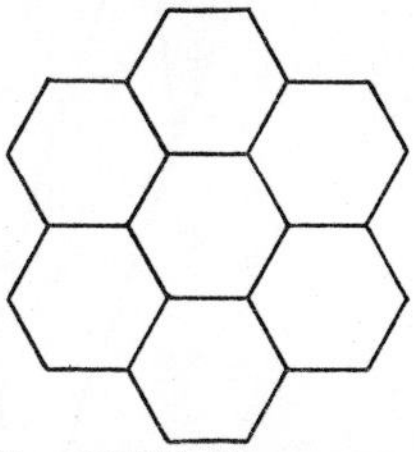

FIG. 135(ii). Representation of the molecule of coronene

One of the earliest applications of this method is the determination of the structure of hexamethylbenzene (Lonsdale, 1929); another example is given by coronene (Robertson and White, 1945). The molecule of coronene (fig. 135(ii)) is, to a first approximation, planar and composed of regular hexagons. Among the reflexions, 16 0 0, 16 0 $\bar{1}$, 14 0 $\bar{8}$, 10 0 $\bar{3}$, 6 0 2, 4 0 $\bar{5}$, and 2 0 7 are found to be outstanding, and fig. 136 shows the traces of the planes in which the atoms should lie in order that they should scatter in phase for each of these reflexions. The molecule can be fitted on to the intersections of these traces in only one way. This type of deduction is a special case of the use of Fourier transforms, which will be referred to in more detail in Chapter 10.

5.5. *Structure-factor graphs.* For non-planar molecules it is unlikely that such methods will be productive, and more general methods are required. The problem is to decide quickly and reliably the approximate values of certain selected structure factors given by a proposed structure: speed is necessary because many structures may have to be tried before the correct one is arrived at; reliability—not to be confused with accuracy—is necessary in order that the correct structure should not be missed by a single chance mistake.

The structure-factor graphs (section 4.3.2), although they were first proposed as a help in dealing with structures of high symmetry, have been found to be of considerable help in dealing with the initial stages of determination of structures of quite low symmetry. For this purpose the graphs need be drawn only roughly, since high accuracy is not

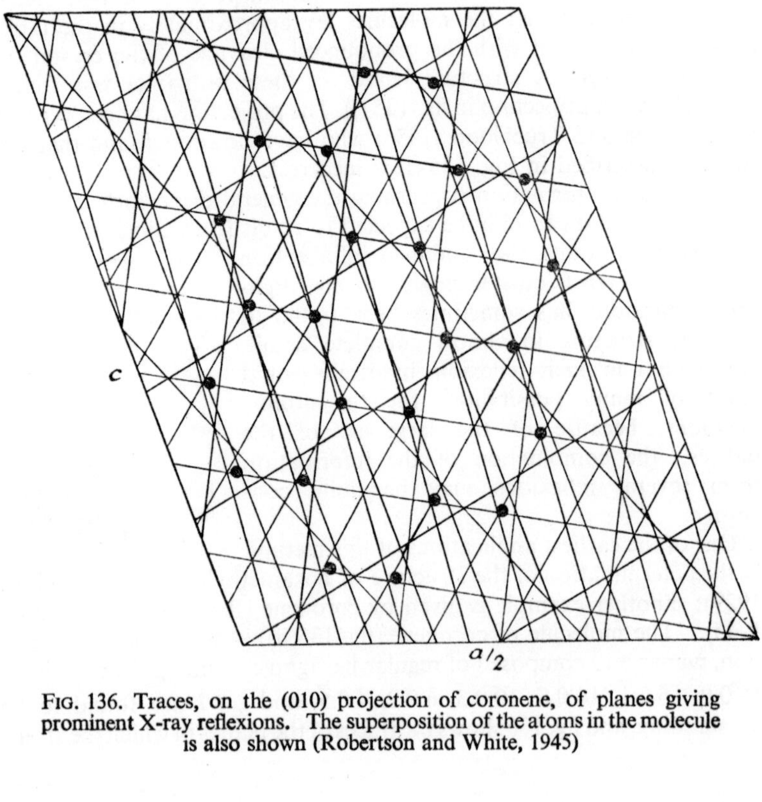

FIG. 136. Traces, on the (010) projection of coronene, of planes giving prominent X-ray reflexions. The superposition of the atoms in the molecule is also shown (Robertson and White, 1945)

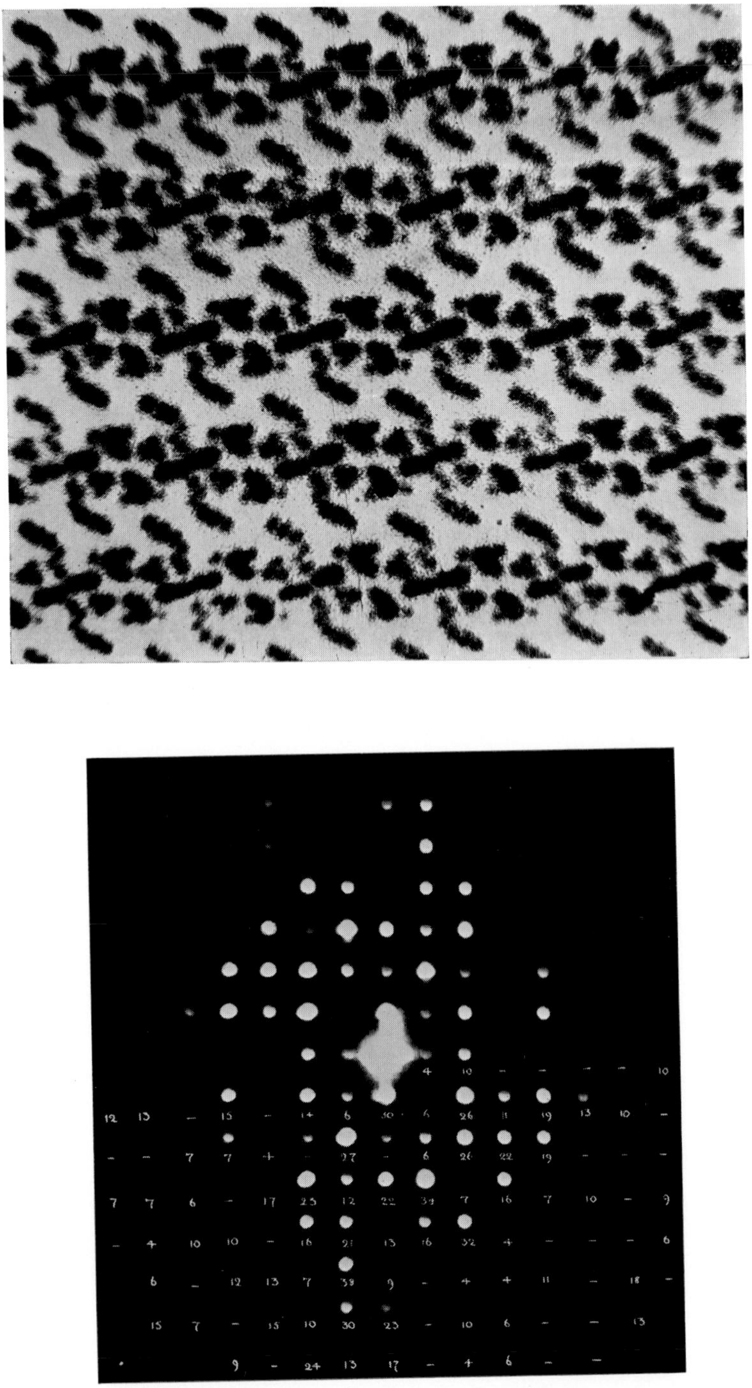

FIG. 137 (*a*). *Above*: Section of 'fly's eye' pattern representing trial structure of sodium benzylpenicillin. (*b*) *Below*: Diffraction pattern of above showing considerable agreement with observed structure factors (Crowfoot et al., 1949)

p. 137

required; with practice, even with only a few contours drawn, it is soon found possible to estimate the contribution of any one atom to a particular reflexion with an error of less than 10 per cent. It is, however, important that the regions of similar sign should be clearly labelled, as a misreading of a sign might lead to non-recognition of a correct structure.

Instead of rough structure-factor graphs drawn to scale, it is possible to use more accurate ones drawn on a square mesh, since these may be used for different structures and so are worth preparing in fair detail.

Structure-factor graphs were used with some success in the determination of the structure of penicillin (Crowfoot, Bunn, Rogers-Low and Turner-Jones, 1949). At first, graphs based upon a square unit cell were used, but since this involved considerable distortion of the projection of the molecule, most of the work was performed with graphs drawn to scale, with only the zero lines drawn in; these were used both as a rapid method for the determination of the signs of particular reflexions and for indication of atomic movements which would improve the intensity agreement.

5.6. *The fly's eye.* The limitations of the structure-factor graphs are that only relatively few reflexions can be considered at once, and that even these represent a tax upon the capabilities of the operator. It would be much better if some method existed whereby all the reflexions in a reciprocal-lattice section could be considered simultaneously, even if the method gave only qualitative estimations of the intensities.

The fly's eye (section **10**.5.4) provides such a method. The mode of use can best be described by means of an actual example. Fig. 137(*a*) shows one of the attempts made by C. W. Bunn (Crowfoot et al., 1949) at the determination of the structure of sodium benzyl penicillin, together with the diffraction pattern (fig. 137 (*b*)). It can be seen that this diffraction pattern shows some degree of correspondence with the observed structure amplitudes, which are given below each spot, and this was actually the first derivation of the approximate structure of the crystal. That the method will work with structures as complicated as this is strong evidence of its power. No claim is made that it will lead to accurate structures, and other methods were brought into play in the determination of the penicillin structure; but the fly's eye certainly helped to overcome the initial obstacles.

5.7. *Changes in scattering factors.* The methods of structure determination based upon intensities will, in general, give either the complete structure or nothing at all; it is not usually possible to determine one particular feature of a structure unless all the others are determined also. This is not so if a heavy atom is present, since, as we have seen in section **6**.5.2, such an atom may be placed without knowledge of the positions of the others; but when the atoms are all approximately of equal weight, then none of the methods so far described can lead to information about only one atom in particular.

Such information would be obtainable, however, if it were possible to vary the scattering factor of a particular atom, and to note the corresponding changes in the intensities of the X-ray reflexions. In certain special cases it is possible to do this: the scattering factor of an atom may be effectively changed by replacing it by another of different atomic weight, or it may be varied by changing the wave-length of the X-rays, or by using other radiations such as electron or neutron beams. None of these methods, however, is likely to be of general application, but they are sometimes worth considering.

The replacement method is possible if a pair of isomorphous compounds can be obtained. Isomorphism is indicated by a similarity of unit-cell dimensions of two compounds which are chemically similar; for example, the crystallographic constants of $CuSO_4.5H_2O$ and $CuSeO_4.5H_2O$ are given in table 138 (Groth, 1908). When such isomorphism occurs, it follows that the atomic positions in the two compounds are almost exactly the same.

TABLE 138

	$a:b$	$c:b$	α	β	γ
$CuSO_4 \cdot 5H_2O$	0·5721	0·5554	82°05′	107°08′	102°41′
$CuSeO_4 \cdot 5H_2O$	0·5675	0·5551	81°58′	106°34′	103°11′

The replacement of the sulphur in $CuSO_4.5H_2O$ by selenium decided the location of both the copper and the sulphur atoms. As shown in section 6.5.2, it was not found possible to decide directly whether the approximate face-centring shown by the intensities was due to the copper atoms alone or to the relative positions of the copper and sulphur atoms; if the copper atoms had a C-face-centred arrangement they would not contribute to the reflexions with $h+k$ odd, whereas if the sulphur atoms formed a C-face-centred arrangement with the copper atoms, the total contribution of these atoms to those reflexions would depend upon the difference between the scattering factors of copper and sulphur. If, then, the sulphur were replaced by selenium, the reflexions with $h+k$ odd would be expected to increase in intensity, since they would be largely due to these atoms if the copper atoms had the centred arrangement; whereas, if the copper atoms oppose the selenium atoms, the intensities of the reflexions with $h+k$ odd would decrease, since the atomic numbers of these atoms are approximately equal.

It was found (Beevers and Lipson, 1934) that with $CuSeO_4.5H_2O$ the reflexions with $h+k$ odd were relatively stronger than with $CuSO_4.5H_2O$, thus proving that the copper atoms were at (0, 0, 0) and

($\frac{1}{2}$, $\frac{1}{2}$, 0), and the sulphur atoms in general positions. It would have been possible to decide on the parameters of the sulphur atoms from the comparison of intensities of reflexions from the two compounds, but as shown in section **6**.5.2, this was not necessary.

6. Proof of Correctness of Structures

6.1. *General considerations.* In view of the absence of general methods for structure determination, and dependence upon methods that are sometimes not classifiable as purely 'objective', the questions may well be asked 'Can we be sure that the structure arrived at in any particular instance is the only possible solution? May there not be others which would satisfy the X-ray data equally well?'

Obviously, no categorical answer can be given to these questions; no proof can be given that there are not two or more arrangements of atoms that would give effectively the same X-ray intensities. But general considerations suggest that it is unlikely. Those who have occupied themselves with structure determination know full well how an incorrect structure manifests itself by lack of agreement between calculated and observed intensities, and how, after many trials and tribulations, a set of atomic positions is found for which an appreciable measure of agreement is obtained. This agreement is improved by small changes, until, when a certain amount of change has been carried out, the calculated structure amplitudes agree in a remarkable way with the observed. One who has been through this process will need no convincing that the structure found is the only one that satisfies the X-ray data!

To those who are unconvinced by these arguments, one can only point out the unlikelihood that, if an approximate structure were wrong, continued work on it would improve the agreement between calculated and observed intensities, finally producing a structure that was plausible, not only in the numbers and types of atoms (which have been assumed anyway) but also in distances of approach and in configuration. So long as one can rely upon the scientific integrity of the individual, there is little chance of an incorrect structure being produced—in fact, less chance than there is of mistakes in other types of scientific work, since there are usually so many experimental facts which must be satisfactorily accounted for.

6.2. *Homometric structures.* This attitude was rather upset by the discovery by Patterson (1944) of certain one-dimensional arrangements of atoms that gave identical sets of interatomic vectors, and thus must give the same X-ray intensities; he called such structures 'homometric'. The number of homometric pairs found was quite large, and since no systematic method of deducing them was found, the suspicion was always present that there might be many more. Furthermore, there are still more pairs of homometric structures in two and three dimensions (section 7.3.4), and these are much more important, since no one relies only upon one-dimensional data as evidence in support of a given structure.

The question has been discussed by Robertson (1945), who decided that, in practice, the chance of finding homometric pairs in two and three dimensions was less, and not greater, than the chance of finding them in one dimension, and that the chance decreases with the complexity of the molecule; moreover, even if a pair were discovered, it is unlikely that both would represent structures that were chemically possible. He therefore concluded that if a structure is proposed that gives reasonable dispositions of atoms and satisfactory agreement between calculated and observed intensities, it is almost certainly correct.

6.3. *Measurement of structure-amplitude agreement.* It may then be asked 'What is meant by satisfactory agreement between calculated and observed intensities?', and much thought has been given to this question. Perfect agreement is never obtained, and the only basis for deciding what extent of disagreement is allowable is an empirical one; certain well-established structures give certain standards of agreement and we therefore expect that any new structures should give about the same.

First of all, therefore, we must decide what quantities to use. Ideally, the intensities should be calculated and compared with those observed, since it is always better to compare theoretical results with direct physical data rather than with deductions from them. On the other hand, tables of structure amplitudes and structure factors are of use to other workers in the same field, and thus it is usual for such tables to appear in papers on crystal-structure determination; the observed structure amplitudes are represented by numbers, and the calculated structure factors by numbers with signs (for centrosymmetric structures) or with phase angles (for non-centrosymmetric structures).

It must be remembered, however, that structure factors involve the square roots of the intensities, and consequently any percentage errors in intensities will be halved in the structure factors; thus the agreement between structure amplitudes appears much better than the agreement between intensities, and this fact should always be allowed for. For example, if we decide to accept no discrepancy greater than 100 per cent in all moderate or stronger intensities, the limit of the discrepancy in structure-amplitude agreement should be about 40 per cent.

It has been found useful to express the overall agreement in terms of the mean discrepancy—the so-called 'residual',

$$R = \frac{\Sigma \left| |F_o| - |F_c| \right|}{\Sigma |F_o|},$$

where $|F_o|$ and $|F_c|$ are the moduli of the observed and calculated structure factors, and the summation is taken over all the reflexions (Booth, 1945*b*). Values of R can be a useful guide in deciding whether any particular change in parameters has produced an improvement in the agreement, but there is a tendency to use it for much more than this. Perhaps the most serious possibility is that R may hide some grave discrepancy; a few poor agreements may not increase the value of R greatly, but they may nevertheless prove that the structure is unacceptable.

In addition, there is a tendency to use the residual as quantity for comparison of the accuracy of the determination of different crystal structures. This also is to be deplored. A complicated crystal structure may give a large number of very weak reflexions, for which the discrepancies may be much greater than 40 per cent; the residual will then be rather large compared with that given by a much simpler structure, but the correctness is not thereby disproved. On the other hand, if the structure contains a single set of heavy atoms, the agreement should be rather better than usual. To take an extreme case, fairly good agreement may result from the heavy atoms alone, and the residual may not change much on insertion of the other atoms. To prove the correctness of the positions of these atoms, it would be necessary to show that the residual decreased when their contributions to the structure factors were inserted.

We must therefore be careful not to read too much from the actual value of the residual; there is no particular figure that must be reached before a structure becomes acceptable, nor does the attainment of a particular figure necessarily prove that the structure is correct. Jaeger, Terpstra and Westenbrink (1927) produced a tetragonal structure for gallium that gave quite good intensity agreement, but Bradley (1935) showed that, for a structure of that simplicity, the agreement was not good enough, and produced an orthorhombic structure that gave better agreement.

The only valid basis for the assessment of the correctness (as distinct from the accuracy) of a structure lies in the agreement for individual reflexions. It is difficult to lay down precise standards, since the nature of the agreement to be expected varies with the magnitude of the structure amplitude. For reflexions which are reasonably strong, and thus reliably estimated, one should expect that calculated and observed values should agree to within 40 per cent, most of them, of course, being much better than this; but for reflexions that are vanishingly small, one would expect the calculated structure amplitudes to be not more than two or three times the minimum that can be observed.

In deriving the value of R, the reflexions which are of vanishingly small structure amplitude are sometimes omitted; because the values of F_o cannot be quantitatively estimated it is not possible to assess accurately the value of the difference $F_o - F_c$. This is hardly satisfactory: to assess the agreement without taking into account the vanishingly small intensities means that an important part of the information is not utilized; moreover, a poor agreement does not influence the value of the residual R. This matter is discussed by Smare (1948), who gives a value of 0·16 for R when all the vanishingly small reflexions from a particular crystal (2-2′dichlorobenzidine) are omitted. If the vanishingly small reflexions are taken as having structure amplitudes which are precisely zero, R becomes 0·32. Smare suggests that these structure amplitudes should be taken as half the minimum value that it has been found possible to observe at the corresponding angle, and on this basis the value of R became 0·24. This would seem to be a reasonable procedure. But, whatever procedure is used, it should be clearly stated when the value of R is given.

Another question that may be asked is 'What value of the residual is necessary in order to demonstrate that a proposed structure is substantially correct, and is worth proceeding with?' This again cannot be answered without qualification, but some results derived by Wilson (1950*b*) and discussed by Phillips, Rogers and Wilson (1950), provide a clue. Wilson shows that if a completely wrong structure, composed of atoms of about equal weight, is postulated, the most probable value for the residual is 0·83 for a centrosymmetric structure and 0·59 for a non-centrosymmetric structure; values near to these therefore indicate that the proposed structure is quite wrong. What values, then, *are* significant? To be on the safe side, about 0·5 and 0·4 for centrosymmetrical and non-centrosymmetrical structures respectively should be demanded. (It is not impossible that even these figures can be exceeded; for example, Furberg (1950) improved the value of R for cytidine from 0·60 down to 0·17. Milledge (1962) says that one might always expect an inordinately high value of R ($\sim$0·8) when all the atomic positions are in error by $\sim$0·5 Å. Sparks (1961) reports a trial structure of anthracene, with errors of 0·10 to 0·55 Å, that gave an R value of 0·89.)

Moderately low values may indicate that the structure is substantially correct, but that comparatively large movements of the atoms are necessary; this, of course, is what one hopes. But it may merely indicate that several of the atoms are in the correct relative positions but are incorrectly placed in the unit cell; some of the interatomic vectors (section **1**.3.2) will thus be correct, and so some measure of intensity agreement will be obtained. It will, however, be found to be impossible to obtain satisfactory agreement for all the reflexions. This apparently was the difficulty in which Dunitz and Robertson (1947) found themselves in the determination of the structure of diacetylenedicarboxylic acid dihydrate. The crystal is centrosymmetrical, and the four molecules in the unit cell must lie on special positions—either two-fold axes or centres of symmetry. The latter seemed more likely, and a structure was devised which had a residual of 0·30, but it was found to be impossible to reduce this further. Another structure based upon the two-fold axes was then tried, and this was more successful; the residual was reduced to less than 0·20, a satisfactory value.

It is probably true to say that, when the agreement for a structure is good but cannot be improved, and a new structure has to be tried, the earlier work is not entirely wasted. Some of the features of the earlier structure must exist in the true one, and it is a test of the ingenuity of the investigator to find a new possibility in which some of these features can be incorporated.

6.4. *Causes of discrepancies.* To the uninitiated it may seem that the latitude allowed is extremely large; acceptance of errors of the order of 20 per cent is happily rare in scientific work. There are, however, several reasons why rather low standards can sometimes be accepted; the interest is frequently in the broad features of the crystal or molecular architecture, rather than in the exact values of bond lengths and bond angles, and such features are already apparent when a value of R of about 0·20 has been obtained.

When careful measurements have been made using a spherical or cylindrical specimen to minimize absorption errors, structure amplitudes whose random errors correspond to a value of R of perhaps 0·02 should be obtained. The lowest values obtained in practice when observed and calculated, rather than observed and 'true' structure amplitudes are compared, are about 0·06. The difference may to some extent be accounted for by undetected systematic errors in the experimental data, such as those associated with secondary extinction and double Bragg reflection (section **2**.4.4), but a sizeable contribution undoubtedly comes from the fact that we cannot usually make an accurate allowance for the redistribution of electrons associated with bonding. This subject is discussed in more detail in Chapter 12.

CHAPTER 7

THE USE OF THE PATTERSON FUNCTION

1. INTRODUCTION

The development of the ideas which led to the discovery of the function now known by his name has been traced back by Patterson to a paper by Zernike and Prins (1927), in which it was shown that the radial distribution of atoms surrounding any given atom of a liquid could be determined by application of Fourier integral analysis to the experimental X-ray diffraction pattern of the liquid. The method was successfully applied in practice by Debye and Mencke (1931) to determine the distribution of atoms in liquid mercury. Warren and Gingrich (1934) pointed out that the same method could be used to determine the radial distribution of atoms in a solid, given only the distribution of intensity in the X-ray powder pattern of the solid. The relevant formula is

$$P(r) = \int_0^\infty 4\pi S^2 i(S) \frac{\sin 2\pi r S}{2\pi r S} \, dS, \qquad (144)$$

where $4\pi r^2 P(r) dr$ is the number of centres of atoms in a shell of radius r and thickness dr drawn about the centre of any one atom, $S = \dfrac{2 \sin \theta}{\lambda}$, and $i(S)$ can be obtained directly from the measured X-ray intensity.

Warren and Gingrich also drew attention to the fact that while the applicability of the Fourier-series method to a crystal is limited because only the magnitudes and not the phases of the coefficients can be measured, an important feature of the above formula is that it involves intensity, not amplitude. Instead of the arrangement of atoms, however, only the radial distribution of atoms about any one atom is obtained. The method was applied to show that in rhombic sulphur each atom has two nearest neighbours at a distance of about 2·35 Å, next nearest neighbours being more than 3·25 Å away. The structure therefore consists of long chains, or chains forming closed rings. The second possibility was regarded as the more probable, and has since been confirmed.

Patterson realized that there must exist a corresponding Fourier relation connecting the distances between atoms, as they occur in the ordered array of a single crystal, with the intensities of the X-ray reflexions. The derivation of this relation has already been given in Chapter 1, and follows closely that given by Patterson (1934, 1935*a*).

2. General Considerations

2.1. *Meaning of the Patterson Function.* We have already seen in Chapter 1 that the Patterson function of an electron-density distribution

$$\rho(x, y, z) = \frac{1}{V} \sum_h \sum_k \sum_l F(hkl) \exp[-2\pi i(hx + ky + lz)]$$

is defined as

$$P(u, v, w) = \int_0^1 \int_0^1 \int_0^1 \rho(x, y, z)\rho(x+u, y+v, z+w) V dx dy dz, \quad (145.1)$$

and can be represented by the Fourier series

$$P(u, v, w) = \frac{1}{V} \sum_h \sum_k \sum_l |F(hkl)|^2 \exp[-2\pi i(hu + kv + lw)]. \quad (145.2)$$

The physical interpretation of this function in terms of interatomic vectors was also mentioned earlier. We now consider some of the properties of this function from a more analytical point of view.

We define

$\mathbf{r} = x\mathbf{a} + y\mathbf{b} + z\mathbf{c}$ as a vector in the crystal,
and $\mathbf{H} = h\mathbf{a}^* + k\mathbf{b}^* + l\mathbf{c}^*$ as a vector to a reciprocal-lattice point.

Consequently $\mathbf{H}\cdot\mathbf{r} = hx + ky + lz$ (compare eqn. *10*.3). We now proceed to show that, just as a crystal may be regarded as built up from N atoms, each of which is repeated on an infinite lattice, so the Patterson function consists of N^2 'Patterson peaks' repeated in the same way. For the crystal itself, we have the relation

$$F(\mathbf{H}) = \sum_{n=1}^{N} f_n(\mathbf{H}) \exp[2\pi i \mathbf{H}\cdot\mathbf{r}_n], \quad (145.3)$$

giving the structure factor in terms of the positions and scattering factors of the N atoms in the unit cell. If the *n*th atom is spherically symmetric, f_n is a function of S only. In the same notation,

$$\rho(\mathbf{r}) = \frac{1}{V} \sum_{\mathbf{H}} F(\mathbf{H}) \exp[-2\pi i \mathbf{H}\cdot\mathbf{r}]. \quad (145.4)$$

Substituting from (*145*.3) in (*145*.4), and changing the order of summation,

$$\rho(\mathbf{r}) = \sum_{n=1}^{N} \left\{ \frac{1}{V} \sum_{\mathbf{H}} f_n(\mathbf{H}) \exp[-2\pi i \mathbf{H}\cdot(\mathbf{r} - \mathbf{r}_n)] \right\}, \quad (145.5)$$

or

$$\rho(\mathbf{r}) = \sum_{n=1}^{N} \rho_n(\mathbf{r} - \mathbf{r}_n), \quad (145.6)$$

where

$$\rho_n(\mathbf{r}) = \frac{1}{V} \sum_{\mathbf{H}} f_n(\mathbf{H}) \exp[-2\pi i \mathbf{H}\cdot\mathbf{r}]. \quad (145.7)$$

Equation *145.6* brings out the point that the periodic distribution $\rho(\mathbf{r})$ is a superposition of N periodic distributions, of which the nth is given by equation *145.7*.

The Patterson function can be considered in the same way. We begin with the fact that, corresponding to (*145.3*),

$$|\mathrm{F}(\mathbf{H})|^2 = \Big(\sum_{n=1}^{N} f_n(\mathbf{H}) \exp[2\pi i\mathbf{H}\cdot\mathbf{r}_n]\Big)\Big(\sum_{n=1}^{N} f_n(\mathbf{H}) \exp[-2\pi i\mathbf{H}\cdot\mathbf{r}_n]\Big)$$
$$= \sum_{n,\,m=1}^{N} f_n(\mathbf{H}) f_m(\mathbf{H}) \exp[2\pi i\mathbf{H}\cdot(\mathbf{r}_n - \mathbf{r}_m)]. \qquad (146.1)$$

We then substitute this value of $|\mathrm{F}(\mathbf{H})|^2$ in the equation for the Patterson function, which in the present notation is

$$\mathrm{P}(\mathbf{r}) = \frac{1}{\mathrm{V}} \sum_{\mathbf{H}} |\mathrm{F}(\mathbf{H})|^2 \exp[-2\pi i\mathbf{H}\cdot\mathbf{r}],$$

obtaining in the same way as before

$$\mathrm{P}(\mathbf{r}) = \sum_{n,\,m=1}^{N} \mathrm{P}_{nm}\{\mathbf{r} - (\mathbf{r}_n - \mathbf{r}_m)\}, \qquad (146.2)$$

where

$$\mathrm{P}_{nm}(\mathbf{r}) = \frac{1}{\mathrm{V}} \sum_{\mathbf{H}} f_n(\mathbf{H}) f_m(\mathbf{H}) \exp[-2\pi i\mathbf{H}\cdot\mathbf{r}]. \qquad (146.3)$$

$\mathrm{P}_{nm}(\mathbf{r})$ is a periodic function, representing a single Patterson peak repeated on a lattice. The form of a Patterson peak, not repeated on a lattice, can be calculated from the integral corresponding to (*146.3*), which, when f_n and f_m are functions of S only, reduces to

$$\mathrm{P}'_{nm}(r) = \int_0^\infty 4\pi \mathrm{S}^2 f_n(\mathrm{S}) f_m(\mathrm{S}) \frac{\sin 2\pi r\mathrm{S}}{2\pi r\mathrm{S}}\, d\mathrm{S}. \qquad (146.4)$$

P'_{nm}, when repeated by the lattice translations **a, b, c,** produces P_{nm}. In practice, lattice translations are usually considerably greater than the distance within which a Patterson peak falls to zero. In such circumstances, repetition of P'_{nm} on a lattice does not result in overlap of adjacent peaks, which consequently retain their spherically-symmetric shape. Either equation *146.3* or equation *146.4* can therefore be used to calculate the shape of an individual Patterson peak, but it must be remembered that in calculating the shape of a peak in a Patterson function derived from a terminated Fourier series, the upper limit of the integral *146.4* has to be taken as S_0, the radius of the sphere in reciprocal space containing those reciprocal-lattice points **H** for which $|\mathrm{F}(\mathbf{H})|^2$ is included in the series.

We also see from equation *146.2* that the Patterson function contains as many peaks as there are values of nm, which is N^2. Of these, N coincide at the origin (those for which $n = m$), and $\frac{1}{2}\mathrm{N}(\mathrm{N}-1)$ are related to the remaining $\frac{1}{2}\mathrm{N}(\mathrm{N}-1)$ by a centre of symmetry. For every pair of atoms at points $\mathbf{r}_n$ and $\mathbf{r}_m$ there is a Patterson peak at $\mathbf{r}_n - \mathbf{r}_m$. This does not necessarily mean that P(**r**) will pass through a maximum at that point, as neighbouring peaks may overlap.

The weight of the *n*th atom we shall define as $\int_V \rho_n(\mathbf{r})dV$, where the integration is over one unit cell. The value of this integral is clearly the atomic number of the atom, Z_n. In the same way, the weight of the *nm*th Patterson peak is $\int_V P_{nm}(\mathbf{r})dV$, which can be shown to be equal to Z_nZ_m. The weight of this peak should not be confused with its height, which is given by

$$P_{nm}(0) = \frac{1}{V}\sum_{\mathbf{H}} f_n(\mathbf{H})f_m(\mathbf{H}) = \int_V \rho_n(\mathbf{r})\rho_m(\mathbf{r})dV. \qquad (147.1)$$

$P_{nm}(0)$ is proportional to Z_nZ_m only to the extent that the electron distributions (or atomic scattering factors) of all atoms are the same, apart from a factor proportional to Z. This is true to a fair approximation, and to a good approximation when the atoms concerned do not differ greatly in atomic number.

Multiple peaks may occur in the Patterson function, apart from purely chance coincidences. For instance, when a structure is centrosymmetric, only $\frac{1}{2}$N of the peaks can be single (section **3**.1.1). Patterson (1935*b*) has tabulated the coordinates, weights and multiplicities of peaks of the Patterson function corresponding to two-dimensional structures having the symmetry of each of the 17 plane groups. Each structure was taken to consist of two atoms in general positions, together with the atoms at equivalent points.

If we now make the assumption that the scattering factor of an atom can be taken to be

$$f_n = \hat{f} Z_n,$$

where $\hat{f}$ is the same for all atoms (section **4**.2.4), $F(\mathbf{H})/\hat{f}$ represents the structure factor of a set of point atoms, occupying the same sites as the atoms whose structure factor is F(**H**). This distribution of points, of which the *n*th has weight Z_n and is situated at $\mathbf{r}_n$, can be represented by a Fourier series,

$$\rho_s(\mathbf{r}) = \frac{1}{V}\sum_{\mathbf{H}} \frac{F(\mathbf{H})}{\hat{f}} \exp[-2\pi i\mathbf{H}\cdot\mathbf{r}], \qquad (147.2)$$

while the corresponding Patterson function is given by

$$P_s(\mathbf{r}) = \frac{1}{V}\sum_{\mathbf{H}} \frac{|F(\mathbf{H})|^2}{\hat{f}^2} \exp[-2\pi i\mathbf{H}\cdot\mathbf{r}]. \qquad (147.3)$$

It is not difficult to show that the latter consists of a set of points of weight Z_nZ_m occurring at $(\mathbf{r}_n - \mathbf{r}_m)$. The points $\mathbf{r}_n$ may be called the fundamental set, and the points $(\mathbf{r}_n - \mathbf{r}_m)$ the vector set. They may also be said to be located in fundamental space and vector space respectively. We shall call ρ_s and P_s the weighted fundamental set and weighted vector set respectively.

2.2. *Symmetry in vector space.* The electron density, or the fundamental set, will usually possess symmetry—that of one of the 230 space groups in fact. The corresponding Patterson function, or the vector set, will not necessarily have the same symmetry. For instance, we have already seen that all Patterson functions have a centre of symmetry. In this connection it will be sufficient to discuss the relation between the symmetry of a fundamental set and that of the corresponding vector set. The fundamental set will consist of a number of points together with the equivalent points related to these by the symmetry of the fundamental set, which we denote by the symbol $\mathscr{F}$. Imagine every pair of points to be joined by a vector, to give a set of vectors in fundamental space, and therefore related by the symmetry $\mathscr{F}$. Now in vector space imagine a vector drawn from the origin to every point of the vector set. These vectors are related by the symmetry of the vector set, which we denote by the symbol $\mathscr{V}$, and are identical in number and orientation with those in fundamental space. They differ from the latter only in the fact that they radiate from a common origin. This corresponds merely to a removal of the translations which separate the ends of the vectors in fundamental space. It follows that the points at the ends of the vectors in vector space, namely the points of the vector set, are related by the 'translation-free residue' of the symmetry element which relates vectors, and points, in fundamental space. For example, if $\mathscr{F}$ contains a two-fold screw axis, $\mathscr{V}$ will contain a parallel two-fold axis through the origin. To derive $\mathscr{V}$ from $\mathscr{F}$ we therefore substitute at the origin (and at all other lattice points of vector space) the translation-free residue of each generating symmetry element in $\mathscr{F}$, complete the group by forming the products of the operations of these elements with the lattice, and add a centre of symmetry at the origin if one is not already present. For example, if $\mathscr{F}$ is P1, $P2_1/c$ or P*bca*, $\mathscr{V}$ is $P\bar{1}$, P2/*m* or P*mmm* respectively. The possible symmetry of a vector set is therefore more restricted than that of a fundamental set; a vector set can in fact have the symmetry of one of only 24 space groups. These have been listed by Buerger (1950*a*, 1959). In two dimensions the plane group of a vector set can be obtained simply by adding a centre of symmetry to the plane group of the corresponding fundamental set.

This discussion of symmetry brings us to another property of the Patterson function which is worthy of note. The one-dimensional Patterson function, for example, is given by

$$P(u) = \int_0^1 \rho(x)\rho(x+u)a\,dx = \frac{1}{a}\sum_h |F(h)|^2 \exp\left[-2\pi i h u\right].$$

There is a second function closely related to P(u) which we define as

$$Q(u)=\int_0^1 \rho(x)\rho(u-x)a\,dx=\int_0^1 \rho(\tfrac{1}{2}u+x)\rho(\tfrac{1}{2}u-x)a\,dx. \qquad (149.1)$$

The Fourier-series representation of Q(u) can be shown to be

$$Q(u)=\frac{1}{a}\sum_h F^2(h)\exp[-2\pi ihu]. \qquad (149.2)$$

Mathematically expressed, Q(u) is the convolution of the electron density with itself, while P(u) is the convolution of the electron density with itself inverted in the origin. The function Q(u), which involves $F^2(h)$ instead of $|F(h)|^2$, can be given a physical interpretation. For a given value of u, the integral *149*.1 measures the extent to which the electron density overlaps itself when inverted in a centre of symmetry at $\frac{1}{2}u$. Q(u) is therefore a measure of the degree to which $\rho(x)$ approximates to centrosymmetry about a point at $\frac{1}{2}u$, or $\frac{1}{2}+\frac{1}{2}u$. If an atom at $\frac{1}{2}u-x$ has a counterpart at or near $\frac{1}{2}u+x$, there will be a contribution to the integral. If there is an atom at $\frac{1}{2}u$ there will be a contribution, because the atom itself closely approximates centrosymmetry. The function Q(u) corresponding to a set of atoms therefore contains two types of peaks: (i) peaks of weight Z_n^2 at $2x_n$ and (ii) peaks of weight $2Z_nZ_m$ at x_n-x_m. In general Q(u) cannot be calculated, since the values of $F^2(h)$ cannot be measured experimentally. However when the crystal is centrosymmetric, there is no distinction between $F^2(h)$ and $|F(h)|^2$, and Q(u) = P(u). Similar results hold, of course, in two or in three dimensions. This suggests a second interpretation of the Patterson function of a centrosymmetric crystal; it can be looked on as a mapping of the centrosymmetric properties of the crystal. If the Patterson function is drawn to one-half its usual linear dimensions, a peak at the point **r** is an indication that the crystal possesses 'some centrosymmetry' at **r**. On this scale, the origin peak recurs at all points where the crystal is truly centrosymmetric. Patterson (1952) has generalized this result, and has shown how the Patterson function can be regarded as indicative of other symmetry elements in the crystal, and the extent to which the asymmetric unit itself possesses the various symmetry elements of the space group.

3. Derivation of a Crystal Structure from the Patterson Function

3.1. *Information contained in the Patterson function.* We have seen that in principle the Patterson function gives the vector distance between every pair of atoms in a crystal. This in itself is valuable information to have when one is trying to solve a crystal structure, but Patterson (1935*a*), in one of the earliest papers on the subject, showed that sometimes it was possible to determine all the main features of a crystal structure from its Patterson function. This proved to be so in the case of KH_2PO_4, where the interpretation was greatly simplified by the occurrence of potassium and phosphorus atoms in special positions in the projection of the structure on (001). In the other examples which Patterson considered (C_6Cl_6 and $CuSO_4.5H_2O$) it was also possible to proceed directly from the Patterson function to at least the main features of the crystal structure. Quite complex structures, having no special features, and in which all atoms were of about the same weight, have since been solved from their two- or three-dimensional Patterson functions, with the help of a few extraneous items of information such as the expected distances between bonded atoms. Experience has shown, therefore, that in particular examples it is possible to make effective use of the Patterson function in determining a crystal structure and we shall consider some practical points of strategy in later sections. In this section, however, we are more concerned with the important theoretical question of whether it is possible, even in principle, to 'recover' the electron density from the Patterson function. We have seen that, given the electron density, it is always possible to calculate the Patterson function, but there was nothing in the derivation to indicate when, if ever, the process can be carried through in the reverse direction. This problem can be regarded as simply another formulation of the phase problem—is it possible to determine a crystal structure knowing the magnitudes, but not the phases, of the Fourier coefficients? The relations between structure factors discovered by Karle and Hauptmann (1950), Goedkoop (1950), and others, showed that this question can be answered in the affirmative. The possibility of practical application of such results will be considered in Chapter 9. Their existence suggests that it is not hopeless to look for a general solution involving the Patterson function.

An obvious objection to the possibility of recovering even a fundamental set from its vector set is that fundamental sets of different symmetries may have vector sets all of the same symmetry. For example, $\mathscr{F}$ may be P222 or P*mmm*, but $\mathscr{V}$ corresponding to both is P*mmm*. Now neither space group results in systematically-absent X-ray reflexions, and consequently not even the symmetry of the fundamental set is determined by the X-ray data. There would therefore appear to be no hope of determining the arrangement of points in the fundamental set, since this includes the symmetry. We know however that there is information in the X-ray data which will distinguish all but a very few pairs of space groups (Chapter 3). Previous to this work, it had in fact been pointed out by Buerger (1946) that information about space-group symmetry $\mathscr{F}$ is carried over into vector space in the form of concentrations of Patterson peaks on certain lines, or on certain planes, of the Patterson function (section **3**.1.1). A study of this subject by Buerger (1950*a*, 1959) has shown that all space groups, except the eleven enantiomorphous pairs, can be distinguished in their vector representations. In practice the statistical methods described in Chapter 3 provide a more certain and convenient method of determining space groups.

3.2. *The Harker section.* The first discovery of a relation between the Patterson function and the electron density was made by Harker (1936). Harker pointed out that in some cases much useful information is concentrated in certain planes of the three-dimensional Patterson function. These are in fact the same planes as were mentioned in the previous paragraph. For example, suppose a crystal to have a two-fold b-axis. Then for every atom at $(x_j y_j z_j)$ in the crystal, there is a peak of weight Z_j^2 in the Patterson function at $(2x_j, 0, 2z_j)$ corresponding to a vector between two equivalent atoms. A section through the Patterson function in the plane $y=0$ is given by

$$P(x0z)=\frac{1}{V}\sum_h\sum_l\{\sum_k|F(hkl)|^2\}\cos 2\pi(hx+lz),$$

or putting $C(hl)=\sum_k|F(hkl)|^2$,

$$P(x0z)=\frac{1}{V}\sum_h\sum_l C(hl)\cos 2\pi(hx+lz). \qquad (151)$$

(We have previously used (uvw) to represent the coordinates of a point in the Patterson function, but since the latter has the same unit cell as the crystal we may equally well use (xyz).) The series *151* can generally be evaluated without too great a computational effort, but it does require the measurement of the intensities of general hkl reflexions. If the crystal has a two-fold screw axis, the plane in which vectors connecting symmetry-related atoms fall is the plane $y=\frac{1}{2}$, and this plane section through the Patterson function is given by *151* with

$$C(hl)=\sum_k(-1)^k|F(hkl)|^2.$$

Such a section is now usually referred to as a Harker section. Sometimes the symmetry results in vectors between equivalent atoms being concentrated on a line in vector space. For instance, if the crystal has a mirror plane perpendicular to b, the Harker section is the line $0y0$. Table 152 gives the Harker sections corresponding to various symmetry elements, as given by Harker (1936) and Buerger (1946).

At first sight it might appear that, for a structure having a two-fold axis for instance, the function $P(x, 0, z)$ should give a projection of the structure down the b-axis, atoms being represented by Patterson peaks, and the scale of presentation being increased by a factor of two. There are two difficulties in the way of such an interpretation, however.

TABLE 152

Symmetry element parallel to b	Harker section
$2, 3, \bar{3}, 4, \bar{4}, 6, \bar{6}$	$P(x0z)$
$6_1, 6_5$	$P(x\frac{1}{6}z)$
$4_1, 4_3$	$P(x\frac{1}{4}z)$
$3_1, 3_2, 6_2, 6_4$	$P(x\frac{1}{3}z)$
$2_1, 4_2, 6_3$	$P(x\frac{1}{2}z)$
Perpendicular to b	
m	$P(0y0)$
Glide $\frac{1}{2}a$	$P(\frac{1}{2}y0)$
,, $\frac{1}{2}(a+c)$	$P(\frac{1}{2}y\frac{1}{2})$
,, $\frac{1}{4}(a+c)$	$P(\frac{1}{4}y\frac{1}{4})$
,, $\frac{1}{4}(3a+c)$	$P(\frac{3}{4}y\frac{1}{4})$

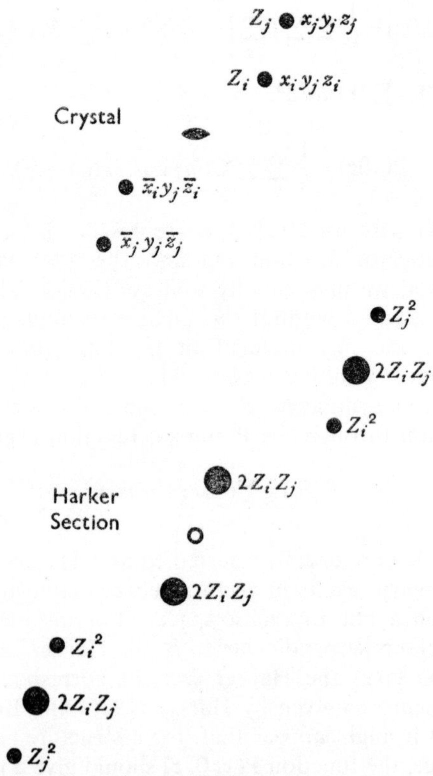

FIG. 152. Atoms related by a two-fold axis are necessarily at the same height. If by chance the unrelated atoms Z_i and Z_j are at the same height, peaks of weight $2Z_iZ_j$ appear in the Harker section, as shown in the lower half of the diagram

The first, usually the less serious, is that there may be a pair of atoms i and j, not related by the two-fold axis, which by chance have the same y-coordinate. Each such pair results in peaks of weight $2Z_iZ_j$ in the Harker section; these peaks do not represent atomic sites, (fig. 152). The more fundamental objection, however, is based on the fact that in this example an atom in any one of the four positions $(x_jy_jz_j)$, $(x_j, y_j, z_j+\frac{1}{2})$, $(x_j+\frac{1}{2}, y_j, z_j)$ and $(x_j+\frac{1}{2}, y_j, z_j+\frac{1}{2})$, together with a symmetry-related atom, results in a Patterson peak at $(2x_j, 0, 2z_j)$. To any one peak of the Harker section there therefore correspond four possible atomic sites in the projection of the crystal.

3.3. *The implication diagram.* These ambiguities of interpretation of Harker sections can be brought out in another way by transforming the coordinate system of the section to give what Buerger (1946) has called an 'implication diagram'. As an example, consider a unit cell of the structure shown in projection in fig. 153*a*, whose only symmetry elements are 2-fold axes. Fig. 153*b* shows the corresponding Harker section. When reduced to one-half its former linear dimensions, it gives (say) the lower left-hand quarter of the implication diagram, fig. 153*c*, while three neighbouring unit cells of the Harker section cover the remaining three-quarters of the unit cell of the implication diagram. The latter clearly includes the original structure, but has a higher symmetry and contains in this instance four times as many 'atoms' as the original. We may say that the ambiguity factor is M = 4. Buerger (1946, 1959) has discussed the implication diagrams of structures containing n-fold axial symmetry elements. The transformation from Harker section to implication diagram usually involves both a shrinkage and a rotation of the former, and the ambiguity factor is generally M = 4, 3, 2 and 1 for n = 2, 3, 4 and 6 respectively. A further complication is the occurrence in certain implication diagrams of 'satellite' peaks which neither correspond to atomic sites nor are related to atomic sites by the symmetry of the implication diagram. For further details the original paper by Buerger (1946) should be consulted. This very complete study of the subject has shown that there are in fact only five space groups whose implication diagrams are free from satellite peaks and for which the ambiguity

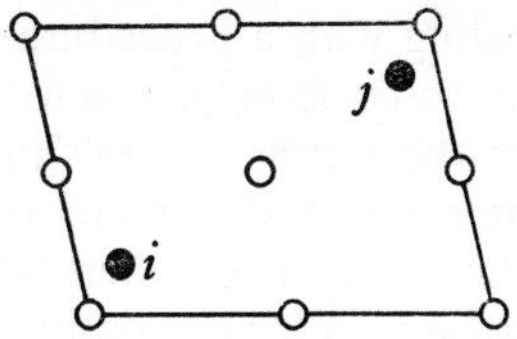

(*a*) Crystal

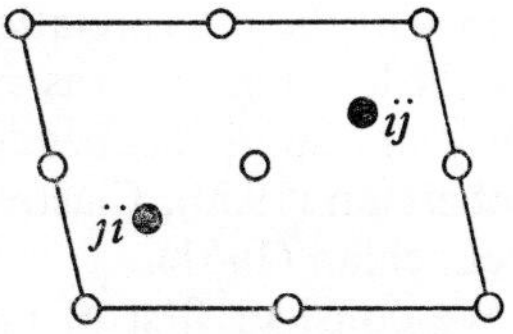

(*b*) Harker Section

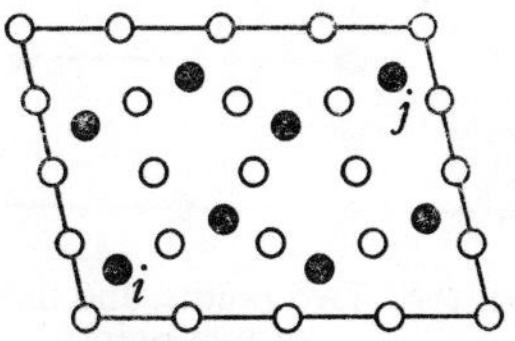

(*c*) Implication Diagram

FIG. 153

factor is unity. In such circumstances the implication diagram is a map of the projected structure, apart possibly from non-Harker peaks whose possible existence we have already noted. The implication method therefore constitutes in principle a limited solution of the phase problem, although it is mainly of academic interest.

3.4. *Image-seeking and superposition methods.* An important paper on the relation between fundamental sets and vector sets was published by Wrinch (1939). It was shown that there exist methods by which the fundamental set, or sets, may be recovered from a vector set. Unlike the Harker-Buerger method, Wrinch's method makes use of all the points of the vector set. Because of the difficulty of illustrating geometrical relations in three dimensions we shall consider two-dimensional sets as examples. It should be emphasized at the outset that we are dealing with a procedure by which a fundamental set of *points* may be recovered from its vector set of *points*. In practice we have available not the vector set, but the Patterson function; the unravelling of the latter is bound to be more difficult and may be impossible. Like many other crystallographers who have discovered new methods of structure analysis, Wrinch optimistically considered the applicability of her method to the determination of the structures of crystalline proteins. In the ensuing controversy, Wrinch's important contribution to the theory of the interpretation of the Patterson function was lost sight of, and little attention was paid to it until parallel results were obtained ten years later, independently by Buerger (1950*b*, 1951), Beevers and Robertson (1950), Clastre and Gay (1950*a*, *b*), Garrido (1950*a*, *b*) and McLachlan (1951).

We consider first of all a fundamental set of two points, 1 and 2, which have weights Z_1 and Z_2 and are situated at $\mathbf{r}_1$ and $\mathbf{r}_2$. Its vector set is also shown in fig. 154 and consists of four points. Two, of weight Z_1^2 and Z_2^2, occur at the origin and points of weight Z_1Z_2 occur at $\pm(\mathbf{r}_1-\mathbf{r}_2)$. The point 12 may be described as the image of point 2 in point 1, and 21 as the image of 1 in 2, etc. The vector set of three points is shown in fig. 155 and may be denoted by the symbol $v(1+2+3)$. Its simplest description is that it consists of a superposition of images of the triangle 123 in each of the points 1, 2 and 3. The centrosymmetrically-related (or enantiomorphous) triangle 1′2′3′ also has $v(1+2+3)$ as its vector set. Similarly we show in fig. 156 four points and their vector set, which can be described as a superposition of images of the quadrilateral 1234 in each of the points 1, 2, 3 and 4. Again the enantiomorphous quadrilateral 1′2′3′4′ (not shown) has the same vector set as 1234.

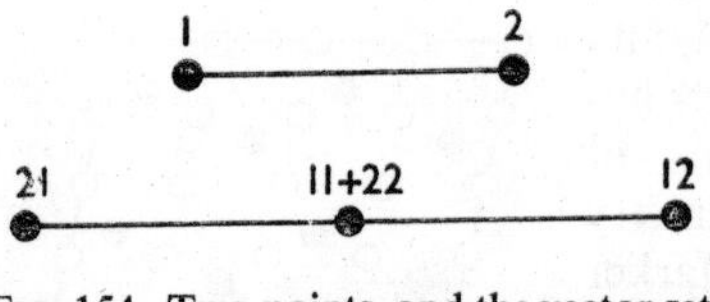

FIG. 154. Two points, and the vector set of two points

We now consider ways in which $1+2+3+4$ can be recovered from $v(1+2+3+4)$. The method proposed by Wrinch will not be given as there is a simpler method based on the same principles which is due to Buerger (1950*b*, 1951, 1959). Let us take any vector from the origin, say 0–12, and move it about in vector space. When the two ends of this vector simultaneously encounter points of the vector set, we record the coincidence by a cross at the centre of the line. This gives six points ABCDEF (fig. 156 (i)*b* which are in fact quadrilaterals 1234 and 1′2′3′4′ superposed on a common line. This 'image-seeking' line has therefore resolved the vector set into the fundamental set, plus the enantiomorphous set. As the 'image-seeking-function' we could use a triangle. This triangle must be one whose vector set is contained in the complete vector set, for example 0–13–23. As we move it over the vector set, we record the coincidences of the vertices of this triangle with the points of the vector set by means of a circle at its centroid. This gives the points *a*,*b*,*c*,*d*, the centroids of the shaded triangles. They are the points of the fundamental set. Other possible choices of triangle would have given the same set, or the enantiomorphous one. It is a remarkable fact that in principle a vector set can be resolved into its fundamental set by means of an appropriate image-seeking triangle, whatever the number of points of the fundamental set. This comes about because any triangle which forms part of the fundamental set is imaged in every point of the set, to appear in the vector set. Indeed when the fundamental set is centrosymmetric the vector set can be recovered by means of an image-seeking *line*, provided it is one from the origin to a single-weight point of the vector set; that is, it must represent a vector from a point to its equivalent point across the centre of symmetry of the fundamental set. This is illustrated in fig. 157.

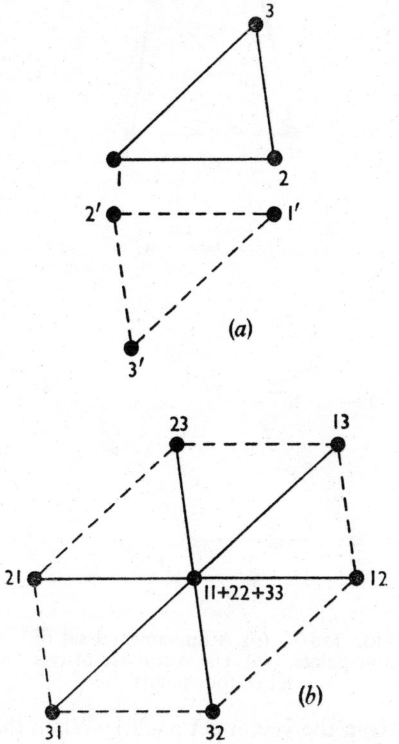

FIG. 155. (*a*) A fundamental set of three points. The three points of the congruent set are joined by dotted lines. (*b*) The vector set of this set of three points, or of its congruent set

The essential feature of the image-seeking function is that it must be *a part of the fundamental set* (or of the enantiomorphous one). If the fundamental set is not centrosymmetric the positions of at least two points relative to a third point must be known; if it is centrosymmetric then the position of at least one point relative to the centre of symmetry must be known. (The required information can of course be deduced

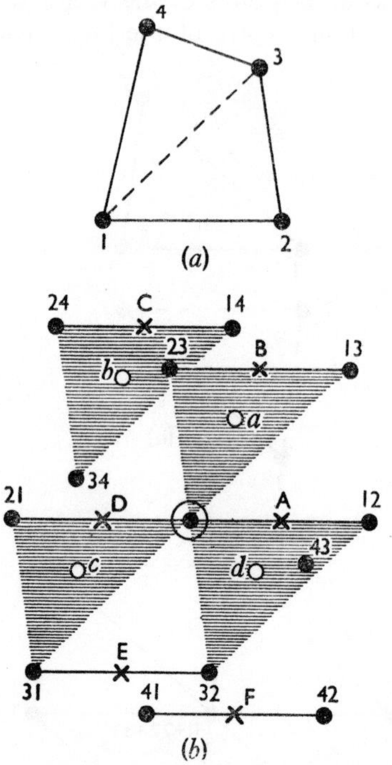

FIG. 156 (i). (*a*) A fundamental set of four points. (*b*) The vector set of this set of four points

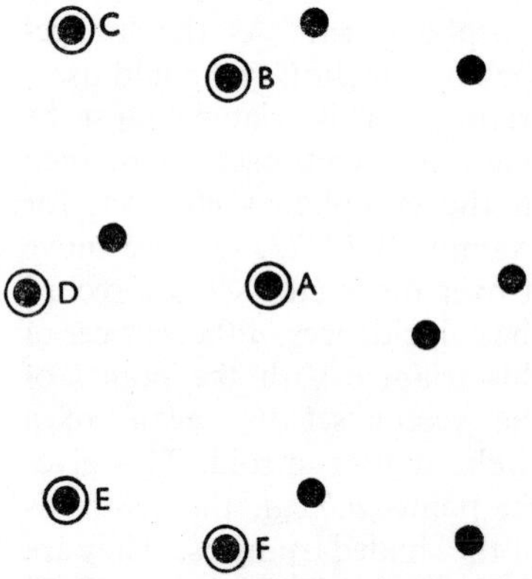

FIG. 156 (ii). When two drawings of Fig. 156(i) (*b*) are made, and the origin of one transferred to the point 21 of the other, the coincidences which occur are denoted by rings in this figure

from the vector set itself.) When the structure is not centrosymmetric and the positions of three points are known in relation to some chosen origin then the relation of the remaining points to this same origin can be deduced. For example suppose the triangle 123 with some attached origin 0 is used as the image-seeking function, and that coincidence of the triangle with three points of the vector set is registered by making a circle at the position then occupied by 0, instead of at the centroid as in our earlier example. The four circles obtained then delineate the enantiomorphous quadrilateral 1′2′3′4′ in its correct position relative to this origin. If the triangle 1′2′3′ with origin attached as marker is used, the quadrilateral 1234 is recovered in its correct position.

It is not difficult to show that the points can be recovered with their correct weights, and, although the discussion so far has been confined to non-periodic sets, it is found that in order to solve a periodic vector set for its periodic fundamental set it is sufficient to consider the eight unit cells of the periodic vector set which surround the origin. In two dimensions four unit cells are needed. Points in this region are then treated just as if they belonged to a non-periodic set (Buerger, 1959). In principle therefore the phase problem is completely soluble. The difficulty in practice has already been mentioned; the Patterson function consists of a set of imperfectly-resolved peaks, and not of weighted points.

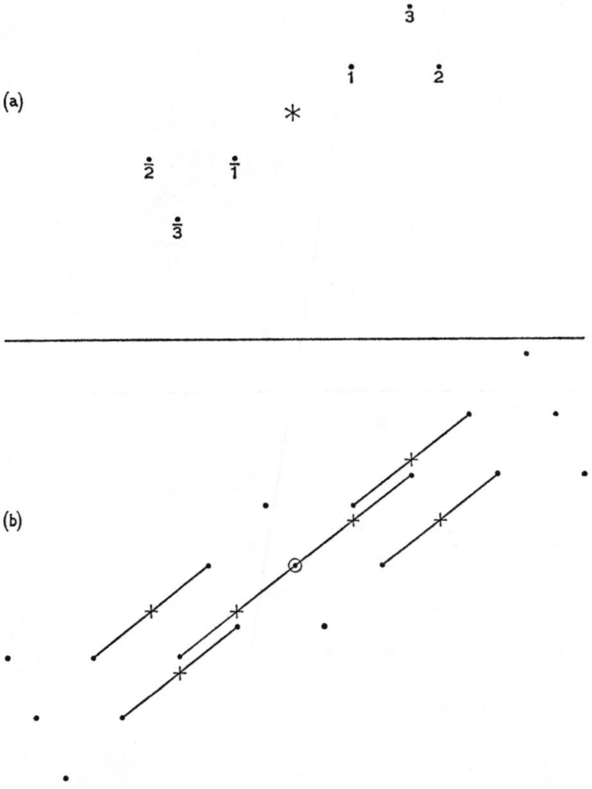

FIG. 157. (*a*) shows a centrosymmetric fundamental set of six points. (*b*) shows the corresponding vector set, and the recovery of the fundamental set from the vector set by means of the image-seeking line $1\bar{1}$

The superposition methods of Beevers and Robertson (1950) and of Clastre and Gay (1950*a*, *b*) are not different in principle from the image-seeking method, although they differ in terminology and in the practical procedures employed. The positions of at least three points of the fundamental set are supposed determined in relation to a chosen origin, say $\mathbf{r}_2$, $\mathbf{r}_3$ and $\mathbf{r}_1$. The vector set is then put down with its origin at each of these points in turn. Triple coincidences of points in the three superposed vector sets then delineate the points of the fundamental set. When the fundamental set is centrosymmetric, superpositions with origins at say $\pm\mathbf{r}_1$ are all that is required. This is illustrated in figs. 158, 159, 160. The advantage of this procedure is that superpositions with origins on a few points of the fundamental set lead to the complete set, and not to the enantiomorphous one.

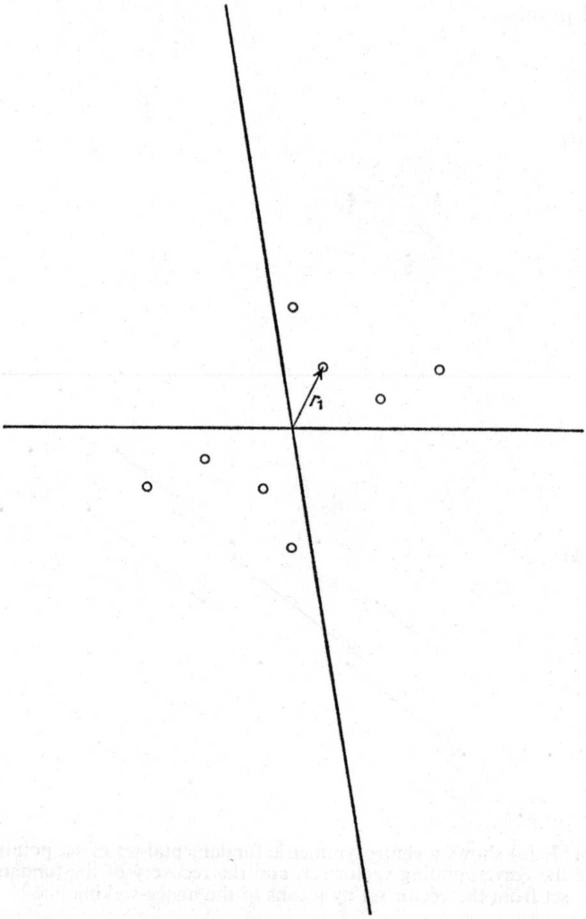

FIG. 158. A centrosymmetric set of eight points, of which one is at $\mathbf{r}_1$

In dealing with the Patterson function P(**r**) rather than a vector set of points we must adopt some numerical measure of the coincidence of peaks, although we may note that in practice Beevers and his colleagues have been successful in determining structures by inspecting superimposed contour maps or photographs only semi-quantitatively for coincidences. Clearly it is also desirable to have an n-fold coincidence to mark out an atomic site, where the number n of atomic coordinates initially known is as large as possible, to discriminate against chance coincidences. In the image-seeking method we might therefore form

$$\mathscr{I}(\mathbf{r}) = \mathscr{F}[\mathrm{P}(\mathbf{r}+\mathbf{r}_1),\ \mathrm{P}(\mathbf{r}+\mathbf{r}_2)\ldots\mathrm{P}(\mathbf{r}+\mathbf{r}_n)]$$

where $\mathscr{F}$ is some function of the values of $\mathrm{P}(\mathbf{r}+\mathbf{r}_1)$, etc.

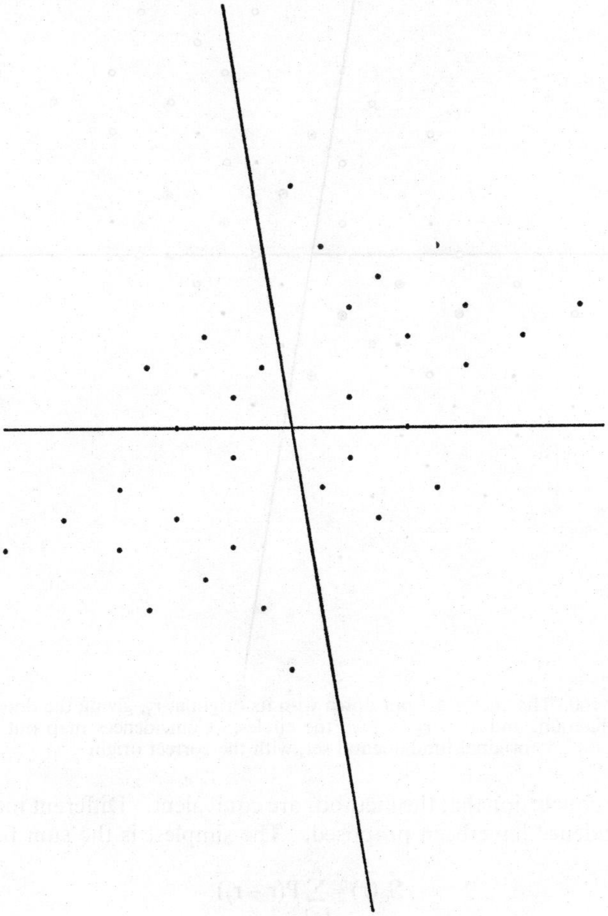

FIG. 159. The corresponding vector set

In the superposition method on the other hand we form

$$\mathscr{J}(\mathbf{r}) = \mathscr{F}[\mathrm{P}(\mathbf{r}-\mathbf{r}_1),\ \mathrm{P}(\mathbf{r}-\mathbf{r}_2)\ldots\mathrm{P}(\mathbf{r}-\mathbf{r}_n)].$$

Comparison of these equations shows that $\mathscr{J}(\mathbf{r}) = \mathscr{I}(-\mathbf{r})$, in agreement

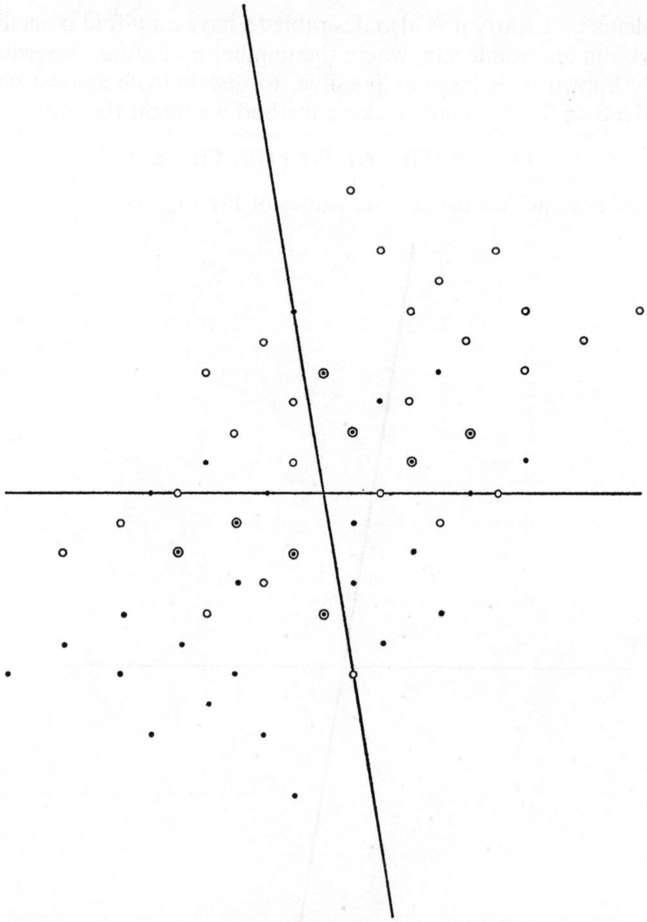

FIG. 160. The vector set put down with its origin at $\mathbf{r}_1$, giving the dots on the diagram, and at $-\mathbf{r}_1$ to give the circles. Coincidences map out the original fundamental set, with the correct origin

with the conclusion that the methods are equivalent. Different measures of coincidence have been proposed. The simplest is the sum function

$$S_n(\mathbf{r}) = \sum_{j=1}^{n} P(\mathbf{r} - \mathbf{r}_j)$$

which can be expressed as a Fourier series

$$S_n(\mathbf{r}) = \frac{1}{V} \sum_{H} \left\{ |F(\mathbf{H})|^2 \sum_{j=1}^{n} \exp(2\pi i \mathbf{H}.\mathbf{r}_j) \right\} \exp(-2\pi i \mathbf{H}.\mathbf{r}).$$

This is the 'mixed series' of McLachlan (1951). A better measure of coincidence is the product function

$$\Pi_n(\mathbf{r}) = \prod_{j=1}^{n} P(\mathbf{r} - \mathbf{r}_j),$$

but Buerger (1950*c*, *d*, 1959) has demonstrated that the function least likely to produce spurious peaks from chance coincidences is the minimum function, $M_n(\mathbf{r})$, by which is meant the value of whichever of $P(\mathbf{r} - \mathbf{r}_1)$, etc. is least. This is symbolized by

$$M_n(\mathbf{r}) = M[P(\mathbf{r} - \mathbf{r}_1), P(\mathbf{r} - \mathbf{r}_2) \ldots P(\mathbf{r} - \mathbf{r}_n)].$$

When the atoms at $\mathbf{r}_1 \ldots \mathbf{r}_n$ on which the superpositions are based have different weights $Z_1 \ldots Z_n$, the minimum function is more correctly defined as

$$M_n(\mathbf{r}) = M\left[\frac{1}{Z_1} P(\mathbf{r} - \mathbf{r}_1), \frac{1}{Z_2} P(\mathbf{r} - \mathbf{r}_2) \ldots \frac{1}{Z_n} P(\mathbf{r} - \mathbf{r}_n)\right].$$

Peaks in $M_n(\mathbf{r})$ then have the same (relative) weights as those in the electron density. The minimum function can be formed in stages; we might form successively

$$M_2(\mathbf{r}) = M\left[\frac{1}{Z_1} P(\mathbf{r} - \mathbf{r}_1), \frac{1}{Z_2} P(\mathbf{r} - \mathbf{r}_2)\right],$$

$$M_2'(\mathbf{r}) = M\left[\frac{1}{Z_3} P(\mathbf{r} - \mathbf{r}_3), \frac{1}{Z_4} P(\mathbf{r} - \mathbf{r}_4)\right]$$

and finally $\quad M_4(\mathbf{r}) = M\,[M_2(\mathbf{r}), M_2'(\mathbf{r})].$

No more than two contour maps need then be superimposed at one time (this is usually referred to as 'a single superposition' in the literature), clearly an advantage in practical work.

Difficulties of course arise in practice from the lack of resolution in the Patterson function and the occurrence of multiple peaks. If for example the image-seeking function is a part of the structure which occurs *m* times with the same orientation, its use will produce *m* overlapping images of the structure. To determine the initial coordinates $\mathbf{r}_1 \ldots \mathbf{r}_n$ the corresponding peaks in the Patterson function must be identifiable, either by being well resolved or by standing out through their greater weight. In certain circumstances, however, particularly for structures containing organic molecules, the configurations of groups of atoms may be known in advance. If their orientations can be determined by inspection of the Patterson function near the origin, they can be used as sites for superpositions, that is, as image-seeking functions. The orientation of a planar group of atoms is likely to be the least difficult to determine in practice. The use of the minimum function to solve structures of some complexity, and in which there are no atoms of comparatively great weight, requires accurate data, since even single-weight peaks in the Patterson function must stand out from the background introduced by errors in the values of $|F|^2$. Indeed, provided that the initial coordinates $\mathbf{r}_1 \ldots \mathbf{r}_n$ correspond to an appreciable part of the whole structure and particularly if one or two of these may be incorrect, it can be advantageous to use the sum function.

More fundamental difficulties arise from the fact that two or more sets which are not enantiomorphous may have the same vector set, although not necessarily the same weighted vector set.

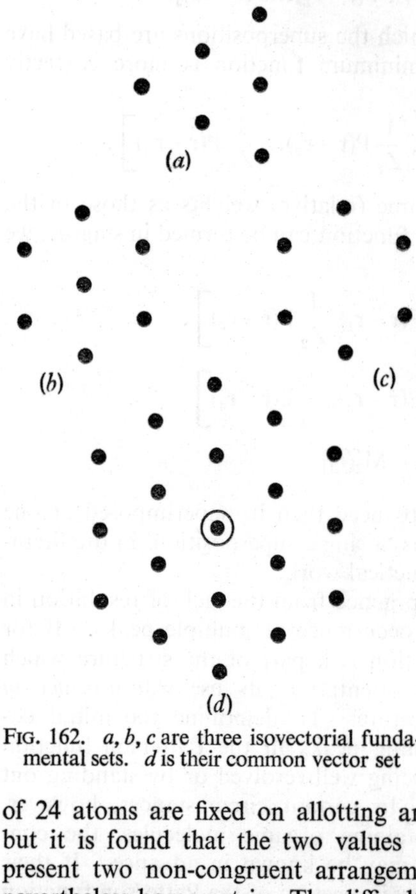

FIG. 162. *a*, *b*, *c* are three isovectorial fundamental sets. *d* is their common vector set

Such fundamental sets have been called 'isovectorial' by Garrido. Three isovectorial sets are shown in fig. 162. Because of the different weighting in the vector sets, the three fundamental sets would not give the same values of $|F|^2$. All three can be derived from the vector set (fig. 162*d*), as has been shown by Wrinch (1939).

Different fundamental sets may not only be isovectorial, but even homometric, that is, give the same *weighted* vector set, and therefore the same values of $|F|^2$ (section 6.6.2). The possible existence of non-congruent homometric structures first became evident from an investigation of the mineral bixbyite by Pauling and Shappell (1930). The space group of this crystal is No. 206, *Ia*3, and a group of atoms occupy the special points 24(*d*) of this space group. The positions of 24 atoms are fixed on allotting an *x*-coordinate to one of them, but it is found that the two values $+x$ and $-x$ of this parameter present two non-congruent arrangements of these atoms which are nevertheless homometric. The difficulty was overcome in this instance by showing that one arrangement of the atoms concerned allowed the remaining atoms of the structure to be fitted into the unit cell in a reasonable stereochemical configuration, while the other did not. The important theoretical point of the uniqueness of the solution obtained by X-ray analysis of a crystal structure was first raised by this observation. Patterson (1944) has discovered many pairs of one-dimensional homometric sets, and has shown that each such pair has its counterpart in two and in three dimensions. We consider a set of N points per repeat distance **a** of a linear lattice, the jth point having a coordinate x_j. The discussion is facilitated by making the coordinate transformation

$$\phi_j = 2\pi \frac{x_j}{a},$$

so that a set of points on a line is replaced by points on the circumference of a circle. Homometric pairs can then be recognized more readily. An example is shown in fig. 163. For the structure shown in fig. 163 (i)a,

$$x_1 = 0 \quad x_2 = \tfrac{1}{8}a \quad x_3 = \tfrac{1}{2}a \quad x_4 = \tfrac{7}{8}a,$$

while for that shown in 163 (i)b,

$$x_1 = 0 \quad x_2 = \tfrac{1}{2}a \quad x_3 = \tfrac{5}{8}a \quad x_4 = \tfrac{7}{8}a.$$

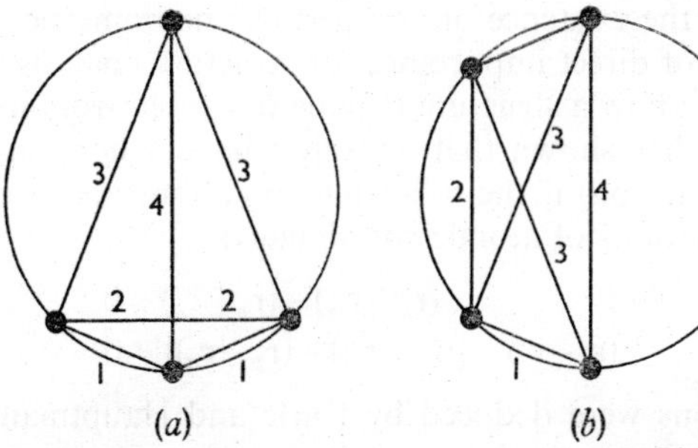

FIG. 163 (i) a, b. Two one-dimensional homometric sets. A coordinate transformation has been made so that points repeated periodically on a straight line appear as points on the circumference of a circle.

The existence of this pair suggested to Patterson that further pairs of the same type might be found by arranging points on a circle at r of the n points of an inscribed regular polygon. Such sets Patterson calls *cyclotomic* sets. An examination of 2664 sets showed the existence

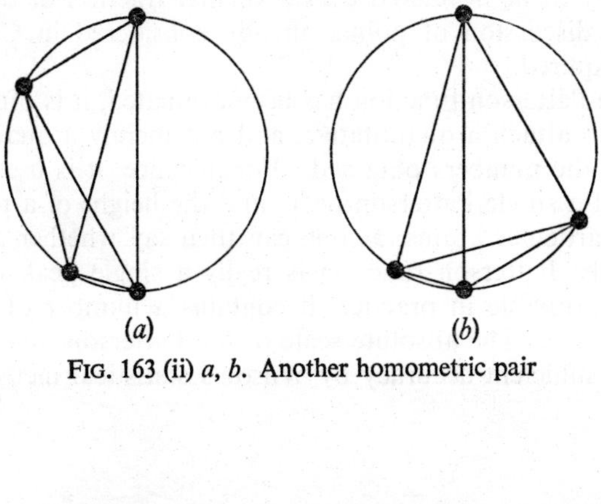

FIG. 163 (ii) a, b. Another homometric pair

among them of 390 homometric pairs, 7 sets of homometric triplets and 3 sets of homometric quadruplets. Non-cyclotomic homometric pairs were also discovered. Those shown in fig. 163 (ii) were obtained by generalization of the pair shown in fig. 163 (i). The theory of the subject has been taken further by Hosemann and Bagchi (1954, 1962), who first of all discuss the classification of homometric structures. They designate as 'pseudo-homometric' those structures which become congruent or enantiomorphic under a suitable affine transformation (a homogeneous distortion of the coordinate system), and also those structures which are homometric only when repeated on an infinite lattice. Patterson's cyclotomic structures belong to this latter category. There remain *finite* homometric structures which are referred to as homomorphs and which do not become congruent or enantiomorphic under any affine transformation. The understanding of the relation between such structures turns out to be an interesting application of the convolution theorem (section **10**.2.5), but we shall not pursue the topic further as the existence of non-periodic homometric structures is not likely to be of direct importance for structure analysis.

By considering how a structure may be recovered from its vector set, Cochran (1958) has shown that it cannot have a homomorph (other than its enantiomorph) if the following conditions are satisfied for all possible combinations of atomic coordinates:

$$(\mathbf{r}_n - \mathbf{r}_m) - (\mathbf{r}_p - \mathbf{r}_q) \neq 0$$

$$(\mathbf{r}_i - \mathbf{r}_j) - \{(\mathbf{r}_n - \mathbf{r}_m) - (\mathbf{r}_p - \mathbf{r}_q)\} \neq 0$$

Similar conditions were deduced by Karle and Hauptmann (1957) in another way.

4. Possible Modifications of the Patterson Function

4.1. *The scale of the Patterson function.* The calculation of the Patterson function from the values of $|F(hkl)|^2$ presents no special difficulties. It is always an easier calculation to make than a corresponding calculation of electron density, since all coefficients of the series representing the Patterson function are positive, and its higher symmetry means that it has generally to be evaluated over a smaller fraction of the unit cell. No further discussion of points already considered in Chapter 5 is therefore required.

When the Patterson function has been evaluated, it is often valuable to be able to attach a quantitative, and not merely a qualitative, significance to the numbers obtained. For instance, it is useful to know the shape of a single Patterson peak, and the height of a peak arising from two particular atoms, as one can then say whether a particular feature of the Patterson function is really a single peak or whether, as is more probable in practice, it contains a number of unresolved Patterson peaks. The absolute scale of the Patterson function can be found with sufficient accuracy by Wilson's statistical method (section

6.5.3), which establishes both the scale of the |F|'s and the value of the constant B in the equation

$$f_j = f_{0j} \exp[-\tfrac{1}{4}BS^2]. \qquad (165.1)$$

The shape of a single Patterson peak arising from atoms i and j may be calculated from equation *146*.3 in the form

$$P_{ij}(xyz) = \frac{1}{V} \sum_h \sum_k \sum_l f_i(hkl) f_j(hkl) \cos 2\pi(hx + ky + lz). \qquad (165.2)$$

A line-section through this peak will give all we want, for instance

$$P_{ij}(x00) = \frac{1}{V} \sum_h \{\sum_k \sum_l f_i(hkl) f_j(hkl)\} \cos 2\pi hx. \qquad (165.3)$$

The tedious calculation of the coefficients of this one-dimensional series can be avoided in the following way. The product $f_i f_j$ as a function of S can always be approximated quite closely by

$$f_i f_j = Z_i Z_j \exp\left[-\frac{\pi^2}{p} S^2\right]. \qquad (165.4)$$

With this assumption, it may be shown that

$$P_{ij}(x00) \simeq \frac{p}{\pi a} \sum_{h=-H}^{+H} \{f_i f_j(h00) - f_i f_j(H00)\} \cos 2\pi hx. \qquad (165.5)$$

H represents the maximum value of h occurring inside the limiting sphere. This one-dimensional series is very easily evaluated. For two dimensions there is no corresponding simple result, but it is not difficult to evaluate directly

$$P_{ij}(x0) = \frac{1}{A} \sum_h \{ \sum_k f_i f_j(hk0)\} \cos 2\pi hx. \qquad (165.6)$$

If equation *165*.5 shows that a Patterson peak has fallen practically to zero in a distance of about 1·4 Å (the minimum separation of atoms), and particularly when the atoms of the structure do not vary greatly in atomic number, a check is provided by the equation

$$\text{Height of Patterson peak } ij \simeq \text{Height of origin peak} \times \frac{Z_i Z_j}{\sum Z_j^2} \qquad (165.7)$$

Equation *165*.7 should be used with caution in a two-dimensional example, as the centre of the origin peak may be overlapped by adjacent peaks.

4.2. *The 'sharpened' Patterson function.* The theoretical considerations outlined in the previous section make it clear that the chances of interpretation of the Patterson function are greatest when individual peaks are resolved to the greatest possible extent. If the weighted vector set, in which each peak is replaced by a point, could be obtained, the determination of the crystal structure would be quite a simple matter. However the coefficients, $|F|^2/\hat{f}^2$, of the series representing the weighted vector set are infinite in number, and cannot be measured beyond some limiting value of S, 1·3 Å^{-1} for instance when CuKα radiation is used. By using radiation of shorter wave-length more coefficients may be obtained, but eventually the values of $|F|^2$ must fall below the limit of experimental measurement. We note, however, that when the crystal is composed of spherically-symmetric atoms the values of $|F|^2$ may be multiplied by *any* function M(S), and the Patterson function will still consist of spherically-symmetric peaks centred at the points of the vector set. These peaks may be modified to such an extent that the word 'peak' is scarcely appropriate any longer. For instance it would be quite possible to choose M(S) so that a section through a Patterson peak was as shown in fig. 166. Clearly this kind of

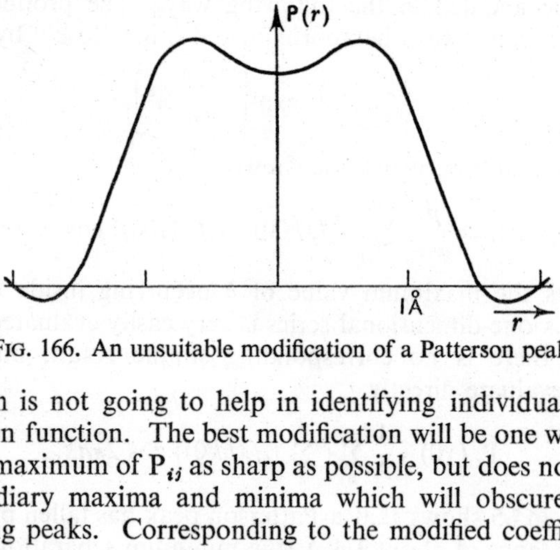

FIG. 166. An unsuitable modification of a Patterson peak

modification is not going to help in identifying individual vectors in the Patterson function. The best modification will be one which makes the central maximum of P_{ij} as sharp as possible, but does not introduce large subsidiary maxima and minima which will obscure or distort neighbouring peaks. Corresponding to the modified coefficients

$$|F_M|^2 = M(s)|F|^2,$$

we introduce modified atomic scattering factors

$$f_{Mj} = \sqrt{M(s)}\, f_j.$$

A single modified Patterson peak P'_{Mij} will then be the Fourier transform of $f_{Mi} f_{Mj}$, and its value when repeated by the lattice, P_{Mij}, can be calculated by replacing $f_i f_j$ by $f_{Mi} f_{Mj}$ in equation *165.3* or equation *165.6*.

A possible modification was suggested by Patterson (1935*a*) and was used by him to increase the resolution of peaks in the two-dimensional Patterson function of $CuSO_4.5H_2O$. This consists in taking

$$\sqrt{M(s)} = \sum_{j=1}^{N} Z_j \Big/ \sum_{j=1}^{N} f_{0j}.$$

We then have, using equation *165.1*,

$$f_{Mj} \simeq Z_j \exp\left[-\tfrac{1}{4}BS^2\right],$$

the approximation again being closest when all atoms of the structure have about the same atomic number. This result is true only for $S<S_0$; for $S>S_0$ we must take $f_{Mj}=0$. There is however no particular reason why the modification should be made so that the constant in the exponent is the actual temperature-factor parameter of the crystal, and we shall consider the shape of P_{Mij} for the general case,

$$f_{Mi}f_{Mj}=Z_i Z_j \exp\left[-\frac{\pi^2}{p}S^2\right] \quad (\text{for } S<S_0).$$

This corresponds to

$$M(S)=\left(\frac{1}{\hat{f}}\right)^2 \exp\left[-\frac{\pi^2}{p}S^2\right].$$

Only if $f_{Mi}f_{Mj}$ has fallen to a small value, say $0{\cdot}01Z_iZ_j$, at $S=S_0$, can the shape of a single Patterson peak be taken to be the Fourier transform of $f_{Mi}f_{Mj}$, which is

$$P'_{Mij}(r)=Z_i Z_j\left(\frac{p}{\pi}\right)^{3/2} \exp[-pr^2] \text{ in three dimensions,}$$

and

$$Z_i Z_j\left(\frac{p}{\pi}\right) \exp[-pr^2] \text{ in two dimensions.}$$

If $f_{Mi}f_{Mj}$ is appreciable at $S=S_0$, equation *165.5* can be used. In table 167*a* values of $P_{Mij}(x00)$, calculated from this equation, are given for a number of values of p, with $S_0=1{\cdot}3$ Å^{-1}, the limit of CuKα radiation;

TABLE 167*a*

I	II	III	$P_{Mij}(x00) \div P_{Mij}(000)$ for $x=$										
p	$\frac{f_{Mi}f_{Mj}(S_0)}{Z_iZ_j}$	$\frac{P_{Mij}(000)}{Z_iZ_j}$	$\frac{0}{6}$	$\frac{1}{6}$	$\frac{2}{6}$	$\frac{3}{6}$	$\frac{4}{6}$	$\frac{5}{6}$	$\frac{6}{6}$	$\frac{7}{6}$	$\frac{8}{6}$	$\frac{9}{6}$	$\frac{10}{6}$ Å
3·64	0·01	1·25	1·00	·90	·67	·41	·20	·08	·03	$\cdot 00_7$	$\cdot 00_2$	—	—
4·77	0·03	1·74	1·00	·89	·63	·35	·14	$\cdot 03_7$	·01	$\cdot 00_3$	$\cdot 00_2$	$\overline{\cdot 00_9}$	$\overline{\cdot 00_9}$
5·57	0·05	2·10	1·00	·88	·61	·30	·10	$\cdot 01_5$	$\cdot 00_4$	$\cdot 01_0$	$\cdot 00_7$	$\overline{\cdot 00_3}$	$\overline{\cdot 00_3}$
7·25	0·10	3·00	1·00	·87	·56	·25	$\cdot 04_5$	0	$\cdot 00_2$	$\cdot 01_6$	$\cdot 00_8$	$\overline{\cdot 00_6}$	$\overline{\cdot 01}$
10·4	0·20	3·85	1·00	·86	·52	·19	$\cdot 00_9$	$\overline{\cdot 03}$	$\cdot 00_3$	$\cdot 01_5$	$\cdot 00_2$	$\overline{\cdot 00_7}$	$\overline{\cdot 00_7}$
∞	1·00	9·20	1·00	·83	·42	·07	$\overline{\cdot 07_5}$	$\overline{\cdot 05}$	·02	·03	0	$\overline{\cdot 02}$	$\overline{\cdot 01}$

TABLE 167*b*

4·15	0·03	0·96	1·00	·82	·44	$\cdot 10_6$	$\overline{\cdot 03_3}$	$\overline{\cdot 05_3}$	$\overline{\cdot 01_7}$	$\overline{\cdot 00_7}$	$\overline{\cdot 00_3}$	—	—
4·15	0·03	0·82	1·00	·85	·51	·16	$\overline{\cdot 03_7}$	$\overline{\cdot 08_7}$	$\overline{\cdot 04_6}$	$\overline{\cdot 01}$	0	·01	$\cdot 00_6$

a was taken as 10 Å, but the shape of P_{Mij} in the range considered is practically independent of a, provided the latter is not too small.

The entry in column II of this table is approximately equal to the ratio of the average value of the modified coefficients $|F_M|^2$ near $S = S_0$, to their average value near $S = 0$. A value of 1% to 3% for this quantity corresponds roughly to what is often obtained in practice, so the entries in the first two rows give an indication of the shape of a peak in an unmodified three-dimensional Patterson function. Again, the temperature factor $\exp[-\frac{1}{2}BS^2]$ for many crystals has a value around 0·20 at $S = 1{\cdot}3$ Å^{-1}, so the figures in the fifth row give an indication of the shape of the peak that would be obtained in this case on making the modification suggested by Patterson. The last row gives the shape of the peak when the coefficients have been modified so that they do not decrease at all with increasing S, that is, $M(S) = (1/\hat{f})^2$, and the modified coefficients are those that would be given by a set of point atoms—until $S = S_0$ is reached when they fall at once to zero. In this case the central maximum of the Patterson peak is confined within a sphere of radius 0·55 Å, but the first minimum is fairly pronounced. The modification corresponding to the entries in row four has been found to be satisfactory in practice. It reduces the radius of a peak to about 0·7 Å, without introducing appreciable subsidiary maxima and minima.

Reliable experimental measurements must be available for the full benefit of the 'sharpening' of peaks to be obtained. The modification corresponding to $p = 10{\cdot}4$ (fifth row) may result in the multiplication of intensities near the limit of Cu radiation by a factor of 10 to 20. If a large proportion of these intensities are not observed experimentally, the series will be effectively terminated at a value of S less than the radius of the limiting sphere, and Patterson peaks will be broader, with larger subsidiary maxima and minima, than an application of equation *165.5* with $H = \dfrac{2a}{\lambda}$ would indicate.

A modification suggested by Schomaker and Shoemaker (unpublished) consists in taking

$$M(S) = \left(\frac{1}{\hat{f}}\right)^2 S^2 \exp\left[-\frac{\pi^2}{p} S^2\right],$$

and therefore

$$f_{Mi} f_{Mj} \simeq Z_i Z_j S^2 \exp\left[-\frac{\pi^2}{p} S^2\right].$$

If $S_0^2 \exp\left[-\dfrac{\pi^2}{p} S_0^2\right]$ is very small, the shape of a single peak is given by

$$P'_{Mij}(r) = \left(\frac{p^5}{\pi^7}\right)^{1/2} (\tfrac{3}{2} - pr^2) \exp[-pr^2].$$

Values are given in the first row of table 167*b*, for $p=4{\cdot}15$. The radius of the central maximum is just over 0·5 Å, and the negative trough is not too pronounced. However, when one takes account of the fact that the value of $f_{Mi}f_{Mj}$ is not negligible at $S=1{\cdot}3$ Å^{-1} in this case, the situation is seen to be somewhat less favourable (last row of table 167*b*). This type of modification reduces greatly the influence of low-order terms on the Patterson function, which is advantageous when they are likely to be in error through extinction.

It has been shown by Jacobson, Wunderlich and Lipscomb (1961) it can be advantageous to use

$$M(S)=(k+S^2)\left(\frac{I}{\hat{f}}\right)^2 \exp\left[\frac{-\pi^2}{p}S^2\right]$$

where k is a constant, chosen empirically to have the value 2/3.

It is perhaps worth reminding the reader that the above calculations refer to peaks in a three-dimensional Patterson function. In the two-dimensional function the height of a central maximum is somewhat smaller, and that of subsidiary maxima and minima, greater, relative to Z_iZ_j.

4.3. *Subtraction of certain peaks.* Another modification which can be made consists in the subtraction from the Patterson function of the peak at the origin, or any other peaks arising from atoms in known positions. From equation *146*.3, the origin peak alone is given by

$$\sum_{j=1}^{N} P_{jj}(r)=\sum_{j=1}^{N}\left\{\frac{1}{V}\sum_{\mathbf{H}} f_j^2(\mathbf{H}) \exp[-2\pi i\mathbf{H}\cdot\mathbf{r}]\right\}.$$

The series

$$\frac{1}{V}\sum_{\mathbf{H}}\left\{|F(\mathbf{H})|^2-\sum_{j=1}^{N} f_j^2(\mathbf{H})\right\} \exp[-2\pi i\mathbf{H}\cdot\mathbf{r}], \qquad (169)$$

therefore represents the Patterson function without the origin peak. The coefficients of this series can be evaluated if measurements have been made on an absolute scale, and if the temperature factor of the atoms in the crystal is known. This is unlikely ever to be so in practice. It is true that scale and temperature factors can be established approximately by Wilson's method (sections **4**.2.3 and **6**.5.3), but the limitations of this method must be kept in mind. For instance, one cannot subtract the origin peak from a two-dimensional Patterson function, with scale and temperature factors established by Wilson's method, and hope to find another peak which in projection was completely obscured. This follows from the fact that we assume, in using Wilson's method, that

$$\sum_{j=1}^{N} f_j^2=\overline{|F|^2}.$$

M

The value of the modified Patterson function at the origin

$$\frac{1}{V}\sum_{\mathbf{H}}\{|F(\mathbf{H})|^2-\overline{|F|^2}\},$$

is therefore bound to be zero. In a three-dimensional Patterson function, on the other hand, peaks representing vectors between nearest-neighbour atoms can always be resolved from the origin peak in any case, if measurements extending to, say, $S_0=1\cdot3$ Å^{-1} are available. There would therefore appear to be little to be gained by subtracting the origin peak.

4.4. *Generalized projections of the Patterson function.* As we have already seen, the Patterson function may be calculated in three dimensions, or we can more readily calculate its projection on a plane. It is also possible to project any section of the function on a plane. The Fourier-series formulation of the function in these various modifications may easily be derived by the processes already described in Chapter 5. In section 8.3.5 it will be shown that it is possible to calculate what is called a 'generalized' projection of the electron density. This can also be done for the Patterson function. For example, when there is a two-fold axis parallel to c,

$$P_L(xy)=\int_0^1 P(xyz)\cos 2\pi Lz\, c dz=\frac{1}{A}\sum_h\sum_k|F(hkL)|^2\cos 2\pi(hx+ky),$$

is the Lth generalized projection of $P(xyz)$ on (001). Every Patterson peak appears in this projection, multiplied by a factor $\cos 2\pi L(z_i-z_j)$, z_i and z_j being the z-coordinates of the two corresponding atoms. The shape of a peak in a generalized projection can be calculated from equation *165.6*, replacing $f_if_j(hk0)$ by $f_if_j(hkL)$. Some examples of the use of these different modifications of the Patterson function will be considered in the next section.

5. Practical Applications of the Patterson Function

The Patterson function of a crystal of even moderate complexity is generally quite difficult to interpret in practice. The volume of the unit cell of a crystal is roughly proportional to N, the number of atoms it contains. The density of peaks in the Patterson function, N^2/V, therefore increases directly with the number of atoms, and for structures which have more than somewhere between 25 and 100 equal atoms per unit cell there is little hope of recognizing individual peaks—a necessary preliminary to systematic application of any known direct methods (Cochran, 1958). However one always has some knowledge of expected interatomic distances and additional items of information such as were discussed in Chapter 6, and one uses all these facts in trying to unravel the Patterson function.

5.1. *The heavy-atom method.* The only important practical case where the Patterson function can be used to solve a structure fairly directly is when the crystal contains a relatively small number of heavy atoms per unit cell. The Patterson peaks due to these atoms then stand out against a background of overlapping smaller peaks, and give immediately the coordinates of the heavy atoms. The remaining atoms can then be located by direct Fourier methods, as described in Chapter 8, or the images of all other atoms in each of the heavy atoms can be brought into coincidence by the superposition method of Beevers and Robertson. An investigation of the structure of cholesteryl iodide by Carlisle and Crowfoot (1945) provides a good example of the first of these methods. The crystals are monoclinic, space group No. 4, $P2_1$, with

$$a = 12{\cdot}5_7, \; b = 9{\cdot}0_4, \; c = 21{\cdot}8_9 \text{ Å}, \; \beta = 149°.$$

The Patterson function projected on (010) is shown in fig. 171(i). From

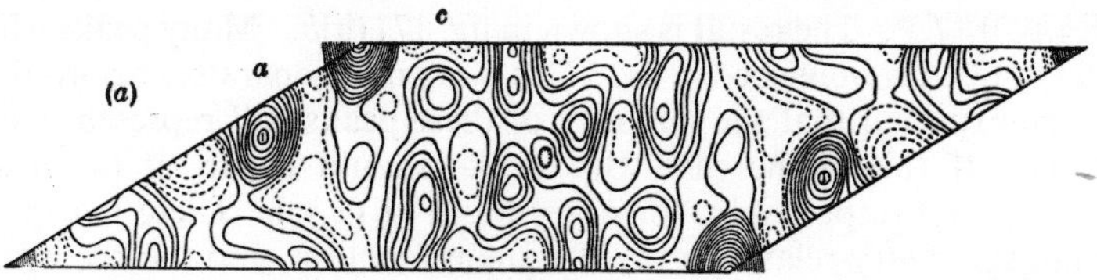

FIG. 171 (i). Patterson function of cholesteryl iodide projected on (010). The large peaks represent vectors between iodine atoms (Carlisle and Crowfoot, 1945)

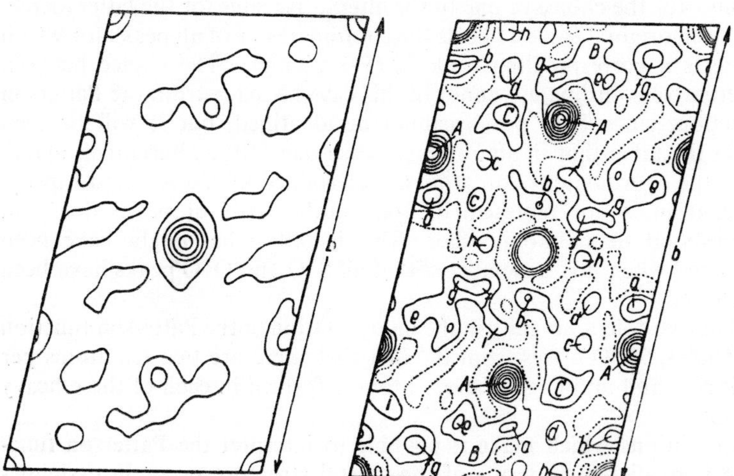

FIG. 171 (ii). (*a*) Patterson function of $CuSO_4.5H_2O$ projected on (001) (Patterson 1935*a*). (*b*) The same function, with the coefficients of the Fourier series modified so as to produce greater resolution of peaks (Patterson, 1935*a*)

it the (xy) coordinates of an iodine atom can be measured as (0·217, 0·042). The remaining atoms were then located as described in section 8.3.2.

One of the earliest applications of the Patterson function was to $CuSO_4.5H_2O$ (Patterson, 1935*a*). The structure of this compound had been solved by Beevers and Lipson (1934) using Fourier methods, so that the Patterson function was used only as a check. The projection of this function on (001) is shown in Fig. 171(ii)*a*. The heavy peak at ($\frac{1}{2}$, $\frac{1}{2}$) shows that some of the atoms occupy a centred lattice. If the Cu atoms were centred by the S atoms we would expect to find larger peaks elsewhere in the function which would correspond to Cu–Cu vectors. Their absence indicates that the Cu atoms occupy special positions of the plane lattice at (0, 0) and ($\frac{1}{2}$, $\frac{1}{2}$). The locations of the next highest peaks give the S coordinates as (·02, ·29)—or (·48, ·21), which corresponds merely to a change of origin. Patterson then calculated a modified function, with Fourier coefficients proportional to $F^2(hk0)/(\bar{f_0})^2$. The result is shown in fig. 171 (ii)*b*. Many peaks which could not be distinguished in fig. 171(ii)*a* are now separately resolved. It is to be expected that the majority of these peaks will represent Cu–O vectors. If this is the case, two peaks should occur, at (x_jy_j) and ($\frac{1}{2}-x_j$, $\frac{1}{2}-y_j$) respectively, for every atom at (x_jy_j). These two peaks are not symmetry-related in the Patterson function, and the occurrence of both serves as a check. Whether a particular pair corresponds to an atom at (x_jy_j) or ($\frac{1}{2}-x_j$, $\frac{1}{2}-y_j$) cannot be decided; two alternative locations are therefore obtained for each atom—apart from the sulphur atom—for the choice of one of the alternative sites for the latter merely fixes the origin. Table 174 lists the coordinates xy of all peaks for which there is a corresponding peak at ($\frac{1}{2}-x$, $\frac{1}{2}-y$). The choice between alternative coordinates cannot in this case be made from the Patterson function, since S–O peaks cannot be identified, but it will be seen from the table that in almost every case one of the alternatives agrees with the coordinates of an atom as determined by Beevers and Lipson. One atom is not represented, and another pair of peaks does not correspond to an atomic site. This is only what might have been expected when it is remembered that all S–O and O–O peaks have been neglected.

The two-fold ambiguity in the interpretation of the Patterson function of $CuSO_4.5H_2O$ arises from the fact that there are two Cu atoms per unit cell, and an image of every atom is formed in each of these heavy atoms.

Conditions which make it possible to interpret the Patterson function immediately in terms of the crystal structure occur in cysteinyl-glycine-sodium iodide (Dyer, 1951*a*). The unit cell is monoclinic, with $a=11{\cdot}1_1$, $b=5{\cdot}12$, $c=16{\cdot}0_4$ Å and $\beta=90°57'$. The space group is No. 5, A2, and the unit cell contains $4(SH.CH_2.CH(NH_2).CO.NH.CH_2.COOH)+2NaI$. The iodine and sodium atoms must therefore

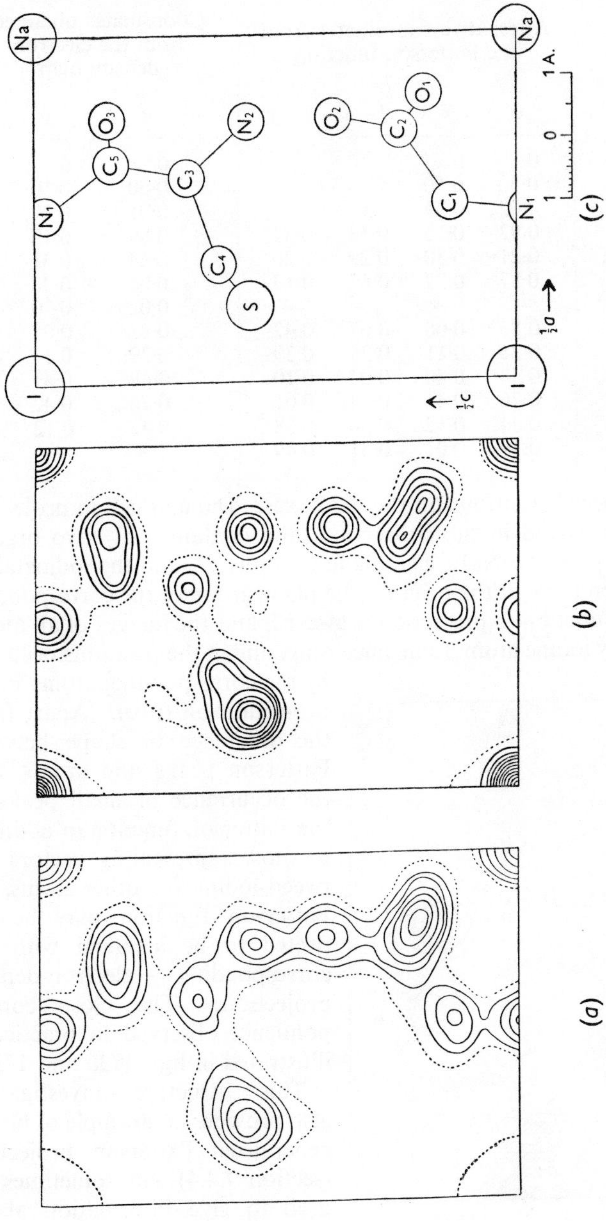

FIG. 173. (*a*) Projection of the Patterson function of cysteinylglycine sodium iodide on (010). (*b*) Corresponding electron-density map. (*c*) Key to (*a*) and (*b*) (Dyer, 1951*a*)

TABLE 174

Atom	Alternative coordinates from the Patterson function				Coordinates obtained from the electron-density map	
	x	y	$\frac{1}{2}-x$	$\frac{1}{2}-y$	x	y
Cu	0	0			0	0
Cu	0·50	0·50			0·50	0·50
S	0·02	0·29			0·01	0·29
O_1	0·92	0·16	0·58	0·34	0·89	0·15
O_2	0·21	0·30	0·29	0·20	0·24	0·31
O_3	0·87	0·37	0·63	0·13	0·86	0·38
O_4	—	—	—	—	0·02	0·30
$(H_2O)_5$	0·83	0·08	0·67	0·42	0·83	0·08
$(H_2O)_6$	0·26	0·11	0·24	0·39	0·29	0·11
$(H_2O)_7$	0·48	0·40	0·02	0·10	0·48	0·41
$(H_2O)_8$	0·76	0·43	0·74	0·07	0·76	0·42
$(H_2O)_9$	0·44	0·12	0·06	0·38	0·43	0·12
—	0·19	0·01	0·31	0·49	—	—

occur in special positions on the diad axes. The unit cell in projection on (010) is halved in the c-direction, and contains only two organic molecules, plus one NaI. The plane group is $p2$, and the iodine atom can be taken to be at the origin. The plane group of the corresponding Patterson function in projection is also $p2$, and the images of all atoms in the heavy iodine atom occur once only, and in the positions occupied by the corresponding atoms in the projection on (010). Apart from the difference in shape between Patterson peaks and atoms, and the occurrence of small peaks in the Patterson function in addition to those representing vectors between iodine and other atoms, the Patterson function may be expected to be identical with the corresponding electron-density projection. The close correspondence observed in practice is illustrated in figs. 173a and 173b.

This structure investigation also provides an example of how a generalized Patterson projection (section 7.4.4) can sometimes be used to give information about the third atomic coordinate, in this case y, which could not readily be obtained other than by cal-

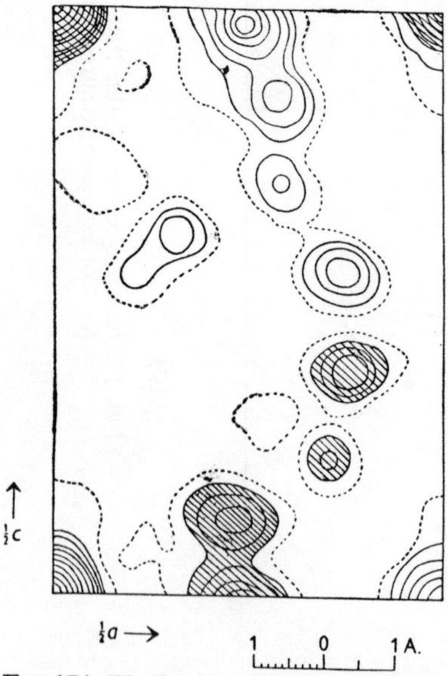

FIG. 174. The function $P_1(xz)$ corresponding to $P_0(xz)$ of Fig. 173a (Dyer, 1951a)

culating the Patterson function in three dimensions. The functions calculated in this case were

$$P_K(xz) = \frac{1}{A} \sum_h \sum_l |F(hKl)|^2 \cos 2\pi(hx + lz),$$

with K = 1 and K = 2. The function $P_1(xz)$ is shown in fig. 174. Shaded areas represent negative regions. We have already seen that every peak in the projection $P_0(xz)$ (fig. 173*a*) will occur with the same (xz) coordinates in $P_1(xz)$, slightly modified in shape as it is the two-dimensional Fourier transform of $f_i f_j(h1l)$ instead of $f_i f_j(h0l)$, and multiplied by a factor $\cos 2\pi(y_i - y_j)$. As in $P_0(xz)$, we can neglect all peaks which do not involve the iodine atom; the height of the peak corresponding to atom j will therefore depend on $\cos 2\pi y_j$, since the y-coordinate of the iodine can be taken to be zero. The non-appearance in fig. 174 of the peaks corresponding to S, O_1 and O_3 (fig. 173*c*) shows at once that these atoms have y-coordinates close to $y = 0{\cdot}25$ or $0{\cdot}75$, and the fact that the peak at $(0, \frac{1}{2})$ in fig. 174 is large and positive indicates that the sodium atom has about the same y-coordinate as the iodine. A misinterpretation of the Patterson function projected on (100) had previously placed the sodium atom at $y = \frac{1}{2}$. The y-coordinates of all atoms were eventually found with fair accuracy by comparing the relative heights of peaks in $P_1(xz)$ and in $P_2(xz)$. This procedure does not distinguish between y and $\bar{y}$, but the information obtained was sufficient to enable the electron-density projection on (100) to be calculated, and refined in the usual way.

5.2. *Use of Harker sections.* We have seen that in certain circumstances a Harker section gives direct information about atomic coordinates, although usually with a certain ambiguity. An example is provided by Harker's (1936) investigation of proustite, Ag_3AsS_3. The hexagonal unit cell has dimensions $a = 10{\cdot}74$, $c = 8{\cdot}64$ Å, and the space group is No. 161, R3*c*. The true unit cell is rhombohedral, but for convenience the hexagonal unit cell was used. This space group provides the equivalent points

$$(2a) \quad (00z) \quad (0, 0, z + \tfrac{1}{2}),$$

and

$$(6b) \quad (xyz) \quad (\bar{y}, x - y, z) \quad (-x + y, \bar{x}, z),$$
$$(x, x - y, z + \tfrac{1}{2}) \quad (\bar{y}, \bar{x}, z + \tfrac{1}{2}) \quad (-x + y, y, z + \tfrac{1}{2}),$$

and positions derived from these by the operation of the rhombohedral lattice. The arsenic atoms are fixed in positions (2*a*) by symmetry, and z_{As} may be taken equal to zero. The silver and sulphur atoms are in general positions (6*b*). By subtracting coordinates of points related to one another by the glide plane perpendicular to y, it is found that $P(xyz)$ will have peaks at $(0, \pm(x - 2y), \frac{1}{2})$, $(0, \pm(-2x + y), \frac{1}{2})$ and $(0, \pm(x + y), \frac{1}{2})$ for each kind of atom, silver or sulphur. The appropriate Harker section is therefore the line $0, y, \frac{1}{2}$. $P(0y\frac{1}{2})$ is shown in fig. 176. The scale is arbitrary. The large peak at $y = 0$ represents an

As–As vector and the peaks at $y = \pm 0{\cdot}17$, $\pm 0{\cdot}33$ and $\pm 0{\cdot}50$ must represent Ag–Ag vectors as silver is so much heavier than sulphur. Since we are dealing with only one atom and its equivalents, there is no ambiguity and we may take

$$(x+y)_{Ag} = \tfrac{1}{2},\ (2y-x)_{Ag} = \tfrac{1}{3} \text{ and } (2x-y)_{Ag} = \tfrac{1}{6},$$

giving $x_{Ag} \approx \frac{4}{18}$, $y_{Ag} \approx \frac{5}{18}$. Any other solution gives an equivalent point. The value of z_{Ag} was fixed by locating the As–Ag peak which occurs along the line $(\frac{4}{18}, \frac{5}{18}, z)$. The sulphur atoms were placed, to complete the structure, from the known bond lengths S–As = 2·25 and S–Ag = 2·40 Å.

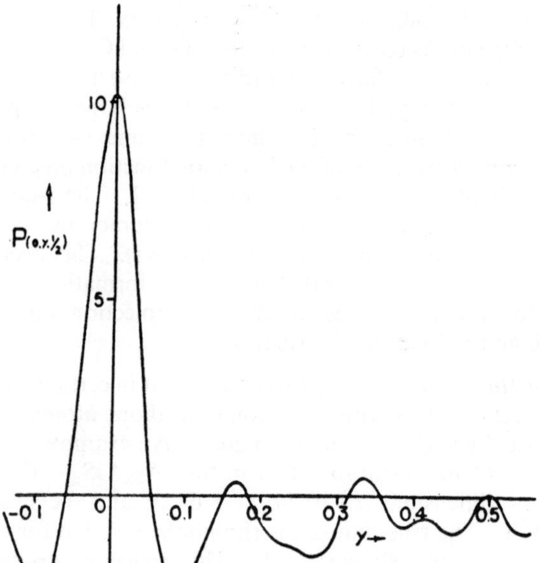

FIG. 176. The Harker section, 0, y, $\frac{1}{2}$ for the mineral proustite (Harker, 1936)

Harker sections have found less application in structures composed of atoms of about the same atomic number. Even when the ambiguity factor is one or two—and it is most commonly four—difficulties arise because of the occurrence of non-Harker peaks. When something of the molecular shape and probable orientation is already known, the occurrence of non-Harker peaks may be a decided advantage, as is shown by the work of Stern and Beevers (1950) on tartaric acid. Crystals of the optically active form of tartaric acid are monoclinic, with $a = 7{\cdot}7_2$, $b = 6{\cdot}0_0$, $c = 6{\cdot}2_0$ Å and $\beta = 100°10'$. The space group is No. 4, $P2_1$. In attempting to solve the crystal structure, sections of the three-dimensional Patterson function at $y=0$ (fig. 177(i)) and $y=\frac{1}{2}$ (fig. 177(ii)) were calculated. We have seen that every atom at (x, z) should result in a peak in the section $y=\frac{1}{2}$ at $(2x, 2z)$, and the ambiguity factor in this case is 4. Attempts to identify the Harker peaks in $P(x, \frac{1}{2}, z)$ proved fruitless. The reason for this can be seen on examining the section $y=0$. This latter strongly suggests that one of the =C.OH. COOH groups of the molecule lies in a plane perpendicular to the b-axis. The group in its correct orientation, together with the peaks

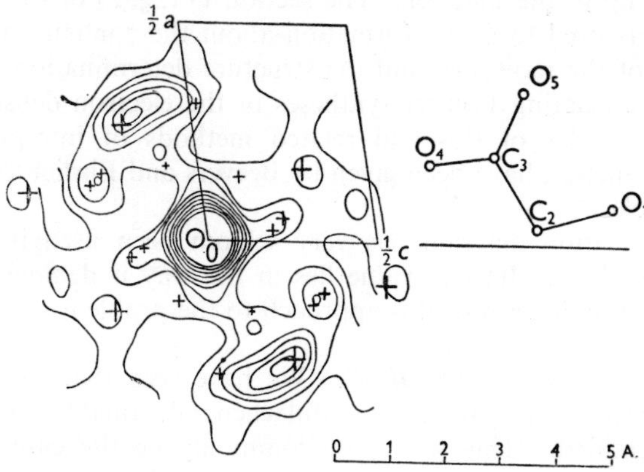

FIG.177 (i). Orientation of one of the C.OH.COOH groups of the tartaric acid molecule compared with the central region of the $y=0$ Patterson section. Peaks due to atoms in this group are marked by crosses in the Patterson section, the sizes of the crosses indicating the relative weights of the peaks (Stern and Beevers, 1950)

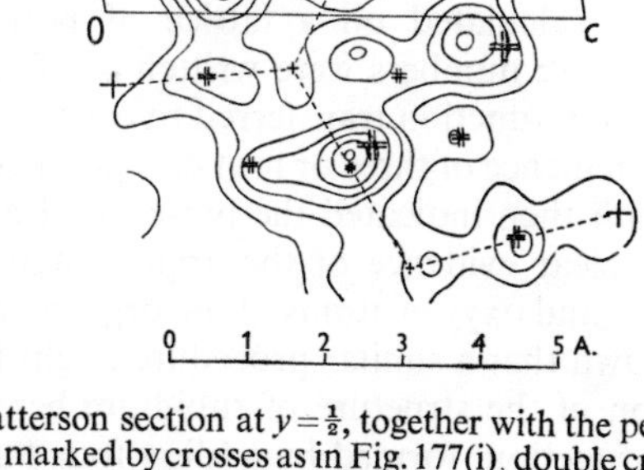

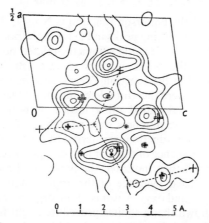

FIG. 177 (ii). Patterson section at $y=\frac{1}{2}$, together with the peaks at $y=\frac{1}{2}$ due to $C_2O_1C_3O_4O_5$, marked by crosses as in Fig. 177(i), double crosses indicating double-weight peaks. To estimate the quality of the agreement all crosses should be imagined as plotted on the asymmetric unit of the Patterson section (Stern and Beevers, 1950)

produced by it in P($x0z$), is shown in fig. 177(i)*a*. The five atoms having the same y-coordinates should produce in the Harker section P(x, $\frac{1}{2}$, z), in addition to five Harker peaks, ten double peaks, each of which falls midway between two single Harker peaks (section 7.3.2). These multiple peaks will account for the main features of the Harker section. When the correct relative positions of these 15 peaks were drawn out, it was found that they could be fitted to P(x, $\frac{1}{2}$, z) in only one way, which is shown in fig. 177(ii). This fixed the position of the =C.OH.COOH group in the unit cell. The section P(x, $\frac{1}{5}$, z) of the Patterson function was used to give information about the configuration of the other half of the molecule, and the structure determination was completed by calculating Fourier syntheses of the electron density.

Other examples of this and related methods of interpreting the Patterson function have been given by Beevers and Ehrlich (1959) in a review article.

The implication diagram has very seldom been used in practical structure analysis. Its real value lies in the way it demonstrates the fundamental difficulties of this approach to the problem.

5.3. *Use of superposition methods.* We have seen that superposition methods are more likely to be successful when individual Patterson peaks can be identified. This will most commonly be the case when the structure contains one, or a few, heavy atoms, as for example strychnine hydrogen bromide, investigated by Robertson and Beevers (1951). This compound has space group No. 19, $P2_12_12_1$, for which the equivalent points are

$$(xyz),\ (\tfrac{1}{2}-x,\ \bar{y},\ \tfrac{1}{2}+z),\ (\tfrac{1}{2}+x,\ \tfrac{1}{2}-y,\ \bar{z})\ \text{and}\ (\bar{x},\ \tfrac{1}{2}+y,\ \tfrac{1}{2}-z).$$

The space group of the Patterson function is No. 47, *Pmmm*, one atom and its equivalents producing peaks in P(xyz) at the points ($\frac{1}{2}+2x$, $2y$, $\frac{1}{2}$) ($\frac{1}{2}$, $\frac{1}{2}+2y$, $2z$), ($2x$, $\frac{1}{2}$, $\frac{1}{2}+2z$), and symmetry-related points. In the case of strychnine–HBr the peaks corresponding to Br–Br vectors could easily be recognized in the function P(xyz), and the coordinates of the four bromine atoms were therefore determined. Values of the Patterson function had been calculated on a lattice of points with spacings $a/15$, $b/15$, $c/60$. These numbers were written out four times, with the origin of the Patterson function transferred to each of the four bromine positions. The coincidence of three or four comparatively large numbers at a particular point then indicated the presence of an atom near that point. This gave clear evidence of the approximate positions of the 27 carbon, nitrogen and oxygen atoms of the organic molecule. Robertson (1951) has shown that a similar procedure might have been helpful in the investigation of the structure of rubidium benzyl penicillin. In this case the sum function, formed by adding four Patterson functions with their origins transferred to the known sites of the rubidium atoms, has planes of symmetry at $z=0$ and $z=\frac{1}{2}$. The structure itself does not possess these symmetry planes—the space group is No. 19, $P2_12_12_1$; they arise from the fact that the rubidium atoms occur in pairs at $z=0$ and $z=\frac{1}{2}$. There is therefore a two-fold ambiguity in the interpretation of the sum function, the coincidence of Patterson peaks at (xyz) and again at $(xy\bar{z})$ corresponding to an atom in only one of these positions. In fact the symmetry of the sum function is always the same as that of the approximation to the electron density that is obtained when the phase angles are calculated from the known positions of the heavy atoms alone.

The structure of thiamine hydrochloride, which has four molecules per unit cell of space group $P2_1/c$ and includes two chlorine, one sulphur and eighteen carbon, nitrogen or oxygen atoms per molecule, was determined by superposition methods (Kraut and Reed, 1962), using a sharpened three-dimensional Patterson function. The co-ordinates of the three heavier atoms were determined by inspection of the positions of the largest peaks in the Patterson function, and each set of individual heavy-atom positions was used to compute a separate four-term minimum function. All three were quite similar, and when they were combined the correct structure stood out clearly.

When all the atoms of a structure are of about the same atomic number, and the number of atoms is not so small that individual peaks are resolved in the Patterson function, the superposition method may lead to a false structure which is, however, nearly isovectorial with the correct structure, and therefore gives structure factors which show some agreement with observed values. An example is provided by the investigation of $NaOH.4H_2O$ by Hemily (1952). Crystals of this substance belong to the space group No. 12, $C2/m$, with $a=15{\cdot}4_9$, $b=4{\cdot}0_4$, $c=9{\cdot}4_5$ Å and $\beta=117°16'$. The atoms are confined to the two planes $y=0$ and $y=\frac{1}{2}$, and since the b-axis is very short this should be a favourable case for utilizing the Patterson function in projection on (010). There are 1·11 peaks per Å^2, so one scarcely expects to find isolated peaks in this projection, which is shown in fig. 179. The average height of a Patterson peak was determined approximately by dividing the

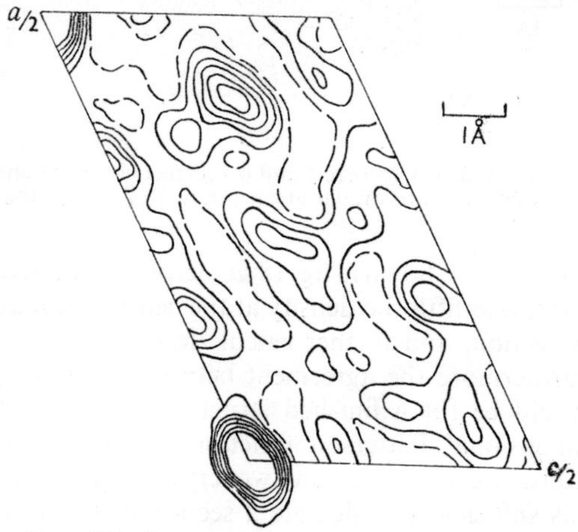

FIG. 179. Patterson function of $NaOH.4H_2O$, projected on (010)

origin peak by the number of atoms; this showed that peaks can occur only within areas bounded by the first solid line of fig. 179. A modified function was constructed which had the value unity wherever the Patterson function was higher than the height of a single peak, but was zero elsewhere. In other words it was simply the function shown in fig. 179, with only the first solid line as an indication of its value. With this modified projection of the Patterson function, several superpositions were made. This was done by choosing a well-defined peak in one modified function and transferring the origin of another to this peak. Non-zero regions common to both then represented possible atomic sites. A series of superpositions using different peaks as starting points appeared to indicate clearly an ensemble of atomic coordinates. The agreement between F_o and F_c was satisfactory. After several successive approximations, the electron

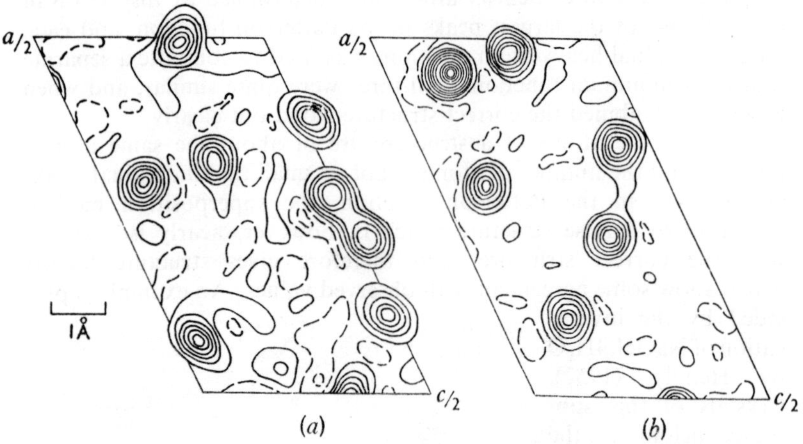

FIG. 180. (*a*) incorrect and (*b*) correct electron density maps of $NaOH.4H_2O$. Contours are drawn at an interval of $2e/Å^2$; the zero contour is broken

density map shown in fig. 180*a* was obtained. Irregularities of magnitude about one-fifth the density at the centre of an atom are apparent in this projection, and further calculation did not lead to any improvement. Furthermore the agreement between F_o and F_c was not as good as it should be for a finished structure. Following this impasse, a three-dimensional Patterson function was calculated, or rather, since all atoms are contained in two crystallographically-equivalent planes, it was sufficient to calculate a section of this function, shown in fig. 181.

Special consideration was given to

(1) Determination of the absolute scale by Wilson's method.
(2) Modification of the function to obtain sharp peaks.
(3) Subtraction of the origin peak.

(4) Calculation of the exact form of the Patterson peak corresponding to any pair of atoms.

The heights of an Na–Na single peak and an Na–O double peak are approximately the same, and such peaks can occur only inside the area bounded by the first solid line ($300e^2/\text{Å}^2$). This information was

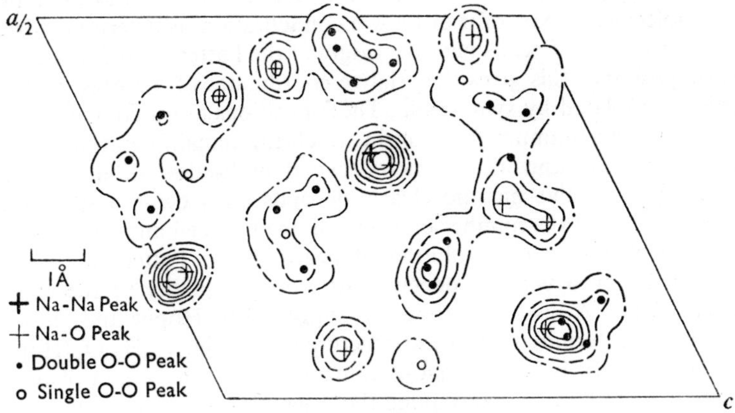

FIG. 181. Section in the plane $y=0$ of the Patterson function of $NaOH,4H_2O$, Contours at $100e^2/\text{Å}^2$

sufficient to lead to the structure determination. Double O–O peaks lie within the broken line ($200e^2/\text{Å}^2$), and single O–O peaks within the remaining line of fig. 181. The positions of Patterson peaks as predicted by the final structure are indicated by the labelled crosses and dots of fig. 181. The true structure is shown by the electron-density projection of fig. 180*b*, and is very different from that determined by the superposition method.

Striking examples of the power of superposition techniques are provided by the structure determinations of sucrose (Beevers, McDonald, Robertson and Stern, 1952) and of cellobiose (Jacobson, Wunderlich and Lipscomb, 1961) which have the same empirical formula $C_{12}H_{22}O_{11}$ and contain no heavy atoms. Both have space group $P2_1$ with two molecules in the unit cell. The orientation of a group of three atoms in cellobiose was found, and their coordinates relative to the 2_1 axis were determined by inspection of the Harker section. A six-term minimum function then showed two recognizable puckered six-membered rings related by the 2_1 axis, with some of their attached hydroxyl groups. These atoms, comprising about half the structure, were used to calculate phases for a projection down the shortest axis, 5·1 Å in length. The procedure was not as straightforward as this brief outline would suggest; there were several false starts and graphical methods of obtaining the minimum function failed to yield the structure.

A fast computer is almost essential for this type of work, although in the investigation of sucrose a photographic method was used to produce approximations for the sum function.

A promising method applicable to molecular crystals has been developed by Nordman and Nakatsu (1963) and also requires a fast computer with sufficient storage for something like 10^5 numbers representing the three-dimensional Patterson function. The orientation of a molecule, or part of it of known configuration, is determined from the distribution of peaks near the origin of the Patterson function. Let us suppose that this gives the relative coordinates of n atoms, none of which are related by symmetry. These positions are used as the basis of an n-term minimum function in which the remaining atoms of the same molecule, and all symmetry-related molecules, should appear. The success of this method clearly depends on n being a sufficiently large fraction of the number of atoms in one unit cell and, as usual, on a sufficient degree of resolution of peaks in the Patterson function (section 7.4.2), which will depend partly on the quality of the experimental data. A related method was suggested by Hoppe and played a part in the determination of the structure of biflorin, $C_{20}H_{20}O_3$ (Hoppe, 1957). When it is known that n atoms of a molecule lie in a plane, an analytical method of determining the orientation of this group can be used (Tollin and Cochran, 1964). A superposition method can then be used to determine the coordinates of the remaining atoms. This procedure proved successful in determining the structure of deoxyadenosine, which has two molecules of $C_{10}H_{13}N_5O_3.H_2O$ in a unit cell of space group $P2_1$, with eleven atoms of a molecule in one plane (Watson, Sutor and Tollin, 1965).

The practical scope of superposition methods, and of other methods of deriving the structure when a part of it is known, has been reviewed by Fridrichsons and Mathieson (1962), with many references. Their conclusions are based partly on experience gained in determining the structure of *p*-tosyl-L-prolyl-L-hydroxyproline monohydrate, $C_{17}H_{22}N_2O_6S.H_2O$, space group $P2_1$. They made use of two-dimensional data for their comparisons, and since there are no fewer than 23·5 peaks per Å² in the *b*-axis projection, some of their conclusions, for example that the sum function is to be preferred to the minimum function, are the outcome of this unfavourable circumstance.

5.4. *Use of known interatomic distances.* Particularly in the investigation of organic compounds, a good deal is known in advance about the distances between atoms in the same molecule, and the probable separation of atoms in different molecules can usually be predicted within fairly narrow limits. Good use of this information can sometimes be made in interpreting the Patterson function. An investigation of the structure of salicylic acid (Cochran, 1951*c*) provides a simple example. The space group of the crystals is No. 14, $P2_1/a$, with

$a=11{\cdot}5_2$, $b=11{\cdot}2_1$, $c=4{\cdot}90$ Å and $\beta=91°$. The positions of the atoms in one molecule are as shown in fig. 183(i)*a*, and the corresponding weighted

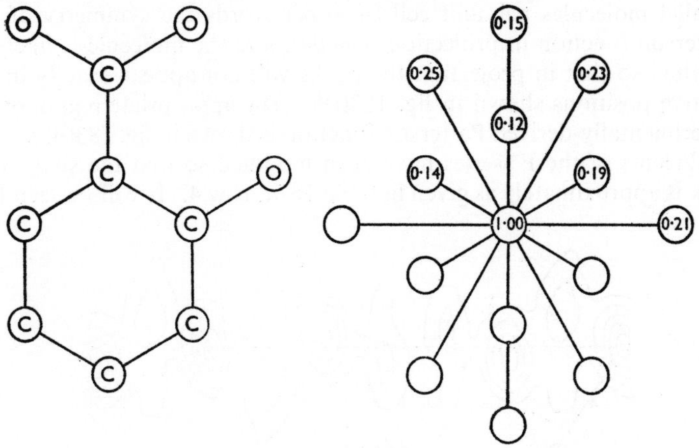

FIG. 183 (i). (*a*) A molecule of salicylic acid. (*b*) The relative positions and weights of peaks which will occur near the origin of the Patterson function of salicylic acid

vector set is shown in fig. 183(i)*b*. Only points within 2·8 Å of the origin have been considered, and the heights of CC, CO and OO Patterson

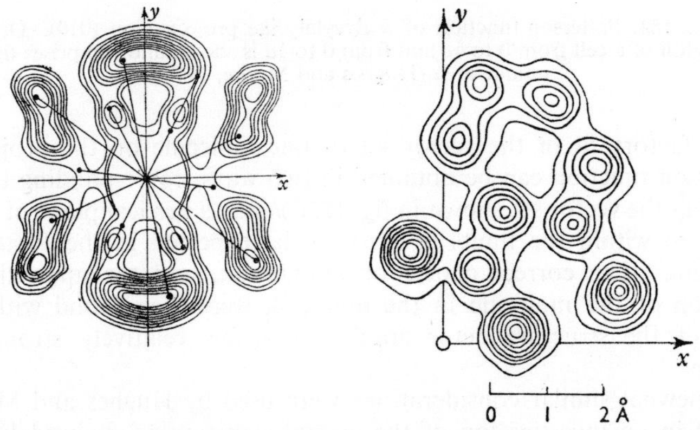

FIG. 183 (ii). (*a*) Peaks near the origin in the experimental Patterson function of salicylic acid projected on (001). Contours in the origin peak are omitted. (*b*) A single molecule of salicylic acid projected on (001), for comparison with (*a*)

peaks are assumed to be in the ratio 36 : 48 : 64. Because of the shortness of the *c*-axis, one would expect atoms belonging to different molecules to be separated by at least 2·6 Å in projection on (001). The distribution of peaks near the origin of the Patterson function projected on (001) should therefore correspond to that shown in fig. 183(i)*b*. There will be two overlapping sets of vectors as there are two pairs of non-parallel molecules per unit cell (in other words the symmetry of the Patterson function in projection is *pmm*), and the molecule is likely to be tilted so that in projection the peaks will not appear exactly in the relative positions shown in fig. 183(i)*b*. The appropriate region of the experimentally-derived Patterson function is shown in fig. 183(ii)*a*. The coefficients of the F^2-series have been modified so that the shape of a peak is approximately as given in table 167*a*, row 4. It will be seen that

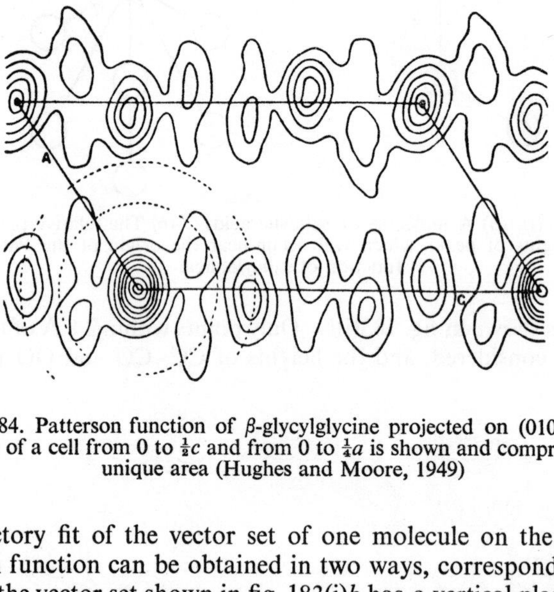

FIG. 184. Patterson function of β-glycylglycine projected on (010). One eighth of a cell from 0 to $\frac{1}{2}c$ and from 0 to $\frac{1}{4}a$ is shown and comprises the unique area (Hughes and Moore, 1949)

a satisfactory fit of the vector set of one molecule on the projected Patterson function can be obtained in two ways, corresponding to the fact that the vector set shown in fig. 183(i)*b* has a vertical plane of symmetry to within the limits of error to be expected in the Patterson function. The correct choice of orientation, and the approximate position of the molecule in the unit cell, were then found with the help of the structure-factor graphs of a few relatively strong reflexions.

Somewhat similar considerations were used by Hughes and Moore (1949) in an investigation of the crystal structure of β-glycylglycine. In this example the space group is No. 15, A2/*a*, and the unit-cell dimensions are $a = 17{\cdot}8_9$, $b = 4{\cdot}6_2$, $c = 17{\cdot}0_6$ Å, $\beta = 125°10'$. The Patterson function projected on (010) is shown in fig. 184. The smaller dotted circle about the origin shows the area outside which all peaks which correspond to vectors between hydrogen-bonded atoms must lie, while peaks corresponding to vectors between atoms separated by the van der Waals distance must lie outside the larger circle. The distribution of peaks along the lines $x=0$ and $x=\frac{1}{4}$, together with the optical properties of the crystal, suggest that the length of the molecule (shown in fig. 185) lies along the c-axis, and indeed one can see in the arrangement of peaks along $x=0$ the suggestion of an extended zig-zag chain molecule. It therefore appears fairly certain that all the peaks along $x=0$ represent vectors between atoms of one molecule. The length of the b-axis and the optical properties of the crystals suggest that the plane of the molecule is inclined at about 45° to (010). Trials were therefore made with an extended planar model of the molecule (fig. 185), tilted at 45° to (010). From the projection of the model in (010), the pattern of peaks along $x=0$ was calculated and showed a reasonable fit with the observed Patterson function. A second possible model failed to pass this test. The array of peaks to be expected between two molecules related by a centre of symmetry, which is the only

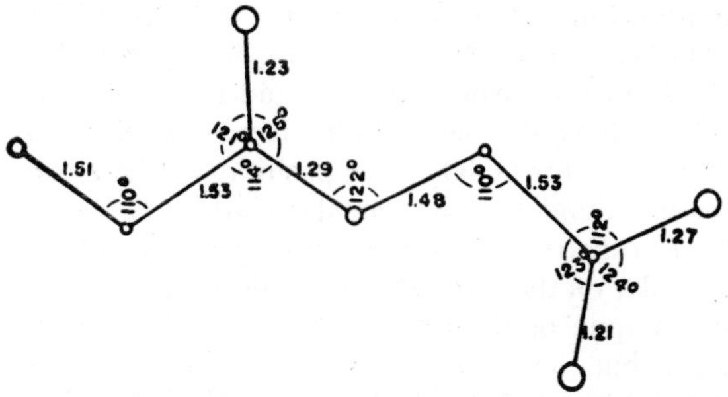

FIG. 185. A molecule of β-glycylglycine. Small circles represent carbons, intermediate circles nitrogens and large circles, oxygens (Hughes and Moore, 1949)

symmetry element in the b-axis projection of the space group A2/a, was plotted in duplicate on two sheets of tracing paper and these were superimposed with correct orientation on fig. 184. They were then moved about in such a way as to maintain the centres of symmetry in the Patterson function at $(\frac{1}{4}, 0)$ and $(\frac{1}{4}, \frac{1}{4})$, and an arrangement was found which accounted for the peaks along $x=\frac{1}{4}$. The structure found in this way proved to be substantially correct.

In the examples considered in detail so far, it proved possible to interpret the Patterson function in projection. For more complex structures there is little hope of success unless the three-dimensional Patterson function is used. Shoemaker, Donohue, Schomaker and Corey (1950) made extensive use of the three-dimensional Patterson function of l-threonine in determining its crystal structure. Crystals of threonine have the space group No. 19, $P2_12_12_1$, with $a=13{\cdot}6$, $b=7{\cdot}7_4$ and $c=5{\cdot}14$ Å.

The molecular formula is:—

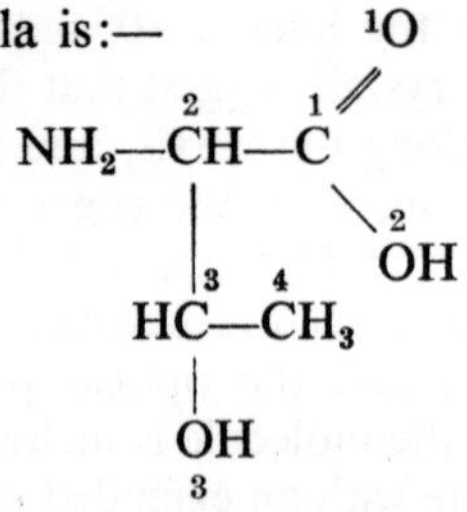

The coefficients of the three-dimensional Patterson function were modified in the way suggested by Schomaker and Shoemaker (see section 7.4.2). The Harker sections could not be interpreted because of the large number of non-Harker peaks, and it did not prove possible to find the molecular orientation from a study of the peaks near the origin as they were mostly unresolved. A well-resolved peak was found in the section $y=0$ at a distance of 2·25 Å from the origin. This is exactly the distance to be expected between the two oxygen atoms of the carboxyl group, and no other pair of atoms can be expected to have this separation. It was concluded that this peak represented the vector O_1–O_2. The positions of these two atoms in the unit cell were found by studying the Harker sections at $x=\frac{1}{2}$, $y=\frac{1}{2}$ and $z=\frac{1}{2}$. For a structure of this complexity it is difficult to correlate unambiguously, on the three Harker sections, the Harker peaks due to one atom, in spite of the restrictions imposed by symmetry on their coordinates; but once the relative positions of two atoms were known, it proved possible to identify the six Harker peaks corresponding to O_1 and O_2, and three additional non-Harker peaks were also found in the predicted places. In the section $y=0$ two other peaks were observed, separated by a vector equal to the O_1O_2 vector. This suggests that, in Wrinch's terminology, this pair is the image of O_1O_2 in some third atom, which is thereby located relative to O_1 and O_2. This was proved by the success with which peaks were found in positions required by vectors between this new atom and all those already located (O_1, O_2 and symmetry-related atoms). A fourth atom was found in approximately the same way, and from its position it was identified as C_2. The third atom could be identified as C_3 or N, with the former choice best satisfying stereochemical requirements. It is probable that the remaining atoms could now have been located by the Patterson-superposition or vector-coincidence method, but this method had not been developed at the time of the investigation of threonine. The remaining possibilities were in fact tested by trial-and-error procedures, using a model of the molecule and structure-factor graphs. Some features of the Patterson function of threonine are shown in fig. 187(i).

5.5. *Use of the Patterson functions of related compounds*. A comparison of the Patterson functions of two substances may, in favourable cir-

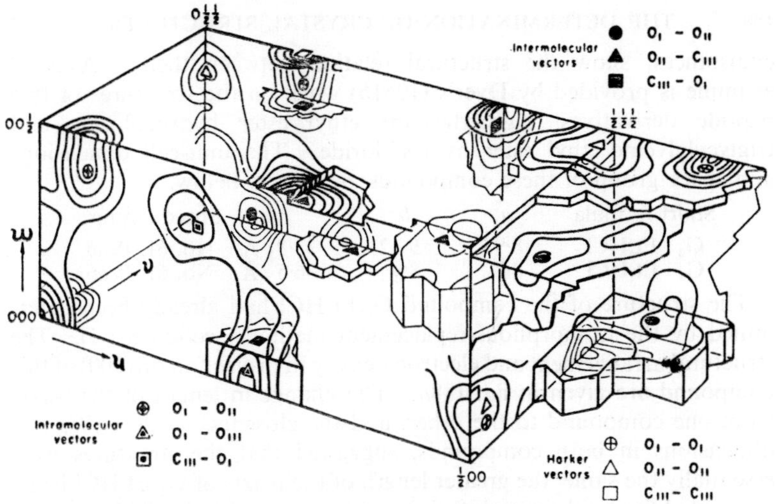

FIG. 187 (i). A representation of the three-dimensional Patterson function of threonine. Since the Patterson function has symmetry *Pmmm*, only one octant of the Patterson unit cell is shown. Only the peaks which correspond to interactions among the atoms O_1O_2 and C_3 are shown; other peaks were omitted for clarity (Shoemaker, Donohue, Schomaker and Corey, 1950)

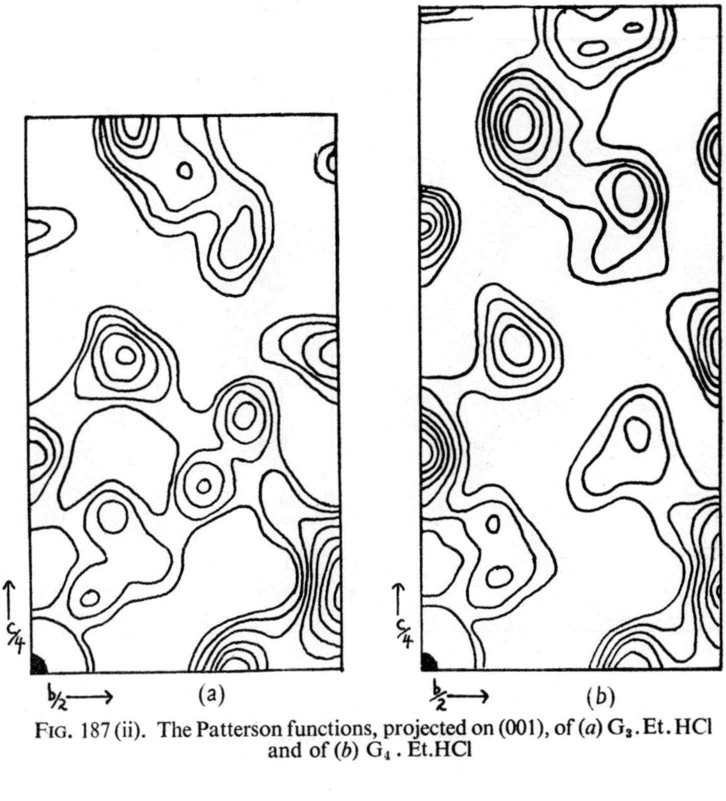

FIG. 187 (ii). The Patterson functions, projected on (001), of (*a*) G_3.Et.HCl and of (*b*) G_4.Et.HCl cumstances, show the structural relation between them. A good example is provided by Dyer's (1951*b*) work on the structures of two peptide derivatives, diglycylglycine ethyl ester hydrochloride and triglycylglycine ethyl ester hydrochloride. The unit-cell dimensions and space group of these compounds are shown below.

Short formula	*a*	*b*	*c*	Space Group
G_3 . Et.HCl	8·95	9·12	31·8$_5$ Å	No. 61, P*cab*
G_4 . Et.HCl	8·7	8·9	36·5 Å	No. 61, P*cab*

The structure of the compound G_3.Et.HCl had already been determined by the isomorphous-replacement method (section **8**.3.3). The structural arrangement and electron density in projection on (100) of this compound are given in fig. 188*a*. The change in length of the *c*-axis from one compound to the other, and the closeness of the other two dimensions in both compounds, suggested that the structures were essentially the same, the greater length of the *c*-axis of G_4.Et.HCl being accounted for by the extra glycine residue per molecule. This assump-

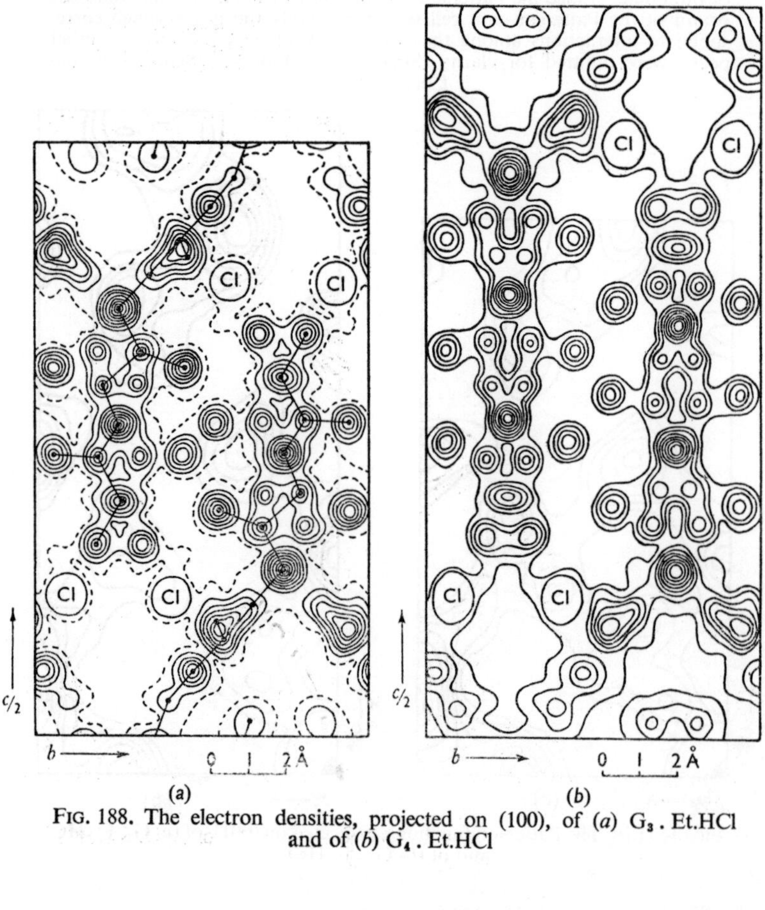

(a) (*b*)

FIG. 188. The electron densities, projected on (100), of (*a*) G_3 . Et.HCl and of (*b*) G_4 . Et.HCl tion received strong support from a comparison of the projections on (100) of the Patterson functions of the two compounds, shown in figs. 187(ii)*a* and *b*. These showed clearly that the majority of atoms occupy the same relative positions in the two compounds, and enabled the correct structure for G_4.Et.HCl to be postulated, and verified without much difficulty. Corresponding electron-density projections are shown in figs. 188*a* and *b*.

5.6. *The Patterson function in protein crystallography.* In determining the structure of a crystalline protein by the methods of isomorphous replacement, at least two heavy-atom derivatives of the protein must be available for phase-angle determination (section **8**.4.7). A number of methods based on the Patterson function have been developed for the determination of the positions of the heavy atoms. Earlier methods proposed by Harker (1956) and by Bragg (1958) have been less used in practice.

Two-dimensional data can sometimes give information about heavy-atom positions. In their investigation of the centrosymmetric *b*-axis projection of paramercuribenzoate haemoglobin, Green, Ingram and Perutz (1954) calculated the difference Patterson function, whose Fourier coefficients are $F_1^2 - F^2$, F_1 being a structure factor of the heavy atom derivative while F refers to the native protein. Peaks in this function correspond to vectors between the heavy atoms and all atoms, and in practice the peak which corresponded to a vector between symmetry-related mercury atoms could be identified. In an investigation of the non-centrosymmetric *a*-axis projections of these and other isomorphous crystals Blow (1958) found the difference Patterson function to be of no value, since the mercury-mercury peak was not greater in height than peaks which corresponded to vectors between mercury and projected chains of light atoms. Blow made use instead of the Patterson function whose coefficients are $(|F_1| - |F|)^2$, the properties of which we shall consider shortly.

Perutz (1956) discussed certain 'correlation functions' which can be used to give the relative coordinates of the heavy atoms in two different but isomorphous, derivatives and these have been used in practice to find the relative *y*-coordinates of the heavy atoms in monoclinic crystals, for example in the investigation of myoglobin (Bodo, Dintzis, Kendrew and Wyckoff, 1959). These functions will not however be described in detail since the required information can apparently be found more reliably in the following way, which is due to Rossmann (1960).

Let F_1 and F_2 (fig. 190) be structure factors of the two isomorphous heavy-atom derivatives, and f_1 and f_2 the contributions of the heavy atoms. Consider the difference electron density, whose Fourier coefficients are the values of $F_1 - F_2$, which equals $f_1 - f_2$. Atoms of the protein are cancelled out from this distribution; positive peaks occur at the positions of heavy atoms of type 1 and negative peaks at the

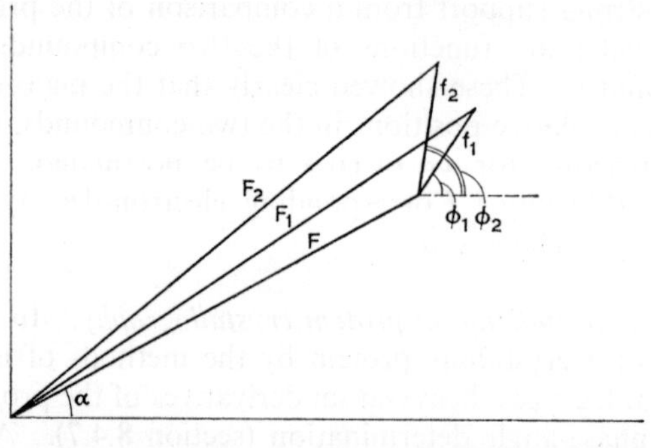

FIG. 190. Addition of the heavy-atom contribution f_1 to the structure factor F of a protein crystal gives the structure factor F_1 of the isomorphous derivative. F_2 is the structure factor of a second isomorphous derivative and the contribution f_2 results from heavy atoms with different coordinates

positions of heavy atoms of type 2. The Patterson function of this distribution is given by

$$D_{12}(\mathbf{r}) = \frac{1}{V}\sum_H |F_1(\mathbf{H}) - F_2(\mathbf{H})|^2 \cos 2\pi\mathbf{H}\cdot\mathbf{r}.$$

It consists entirely of positive peaks between heavy atoms of type 1, positive peaks between heavy atoms of type 2 and *negative* peaks between heavy atoms of type 1 and type 2. This function cannot however be calculated since it involves unknown phase angles. We note from fig. 190 however that

$$|F_1| - |F_2| \simeq |f_1| \cos(\phi_1 - \alpha) - |f_2| \cos(\phi_2 - \alpha)$$

where ϕ_1 is defined by $f_1 = |f_1| \exp(i\phi_1)$, etc., (see also fig. 190). Hence we find that

$$(|F_1| - |F_2|)^2 = \tfrac{1}{2}(|f_1|^2 + |f_2|^2 - 2|f_1|\,|f_2| \cos(\phi_1 - \phi_2))$$
$$+ \tfrac{1}{2}(|f_1|^2 \cos 2(\phi_1 - \alpha) + |f_2|^2 \cos 2(\phi_2 - \alpha) - 2|f_1|\,|f_2| \cos(\phi_1 + \phi_2 - 2\alpha).$$

The first term on the right-hand side is equal to $\frac{1}{2}|f_1 - f_2|^2$, that is, to $\frac{1}{2}|F_1 - F_2|^2$. It follows that a Patterson function whose coefficients are the values of $(|F_1| - |F_2|)^2$ will be equal to $\frac{1}{2}D_{12}$, plus a contribution coming from the second term on the right-hand side of the equation, which may be expected to produce some unwanted background peaks. (This conclusion differs from Rossmann's, who deduced that D_{12}, not $\frac{1}{2}D_{12}$, would be obtained.) Rossmann made calculations using three-dimensional data for three different haemoglobin derivatives;

No. 1, one mercury atom per asymmetric unit at $x = 0{\cdot}16$, $y = 0$, $z = 0{\cdot}18$.

No. 2, one mercury atom per asymmetric unit at $x = 0{\cdot}07$, $y = 0{\cdot}16$, $z = 0{\cdot}29$.

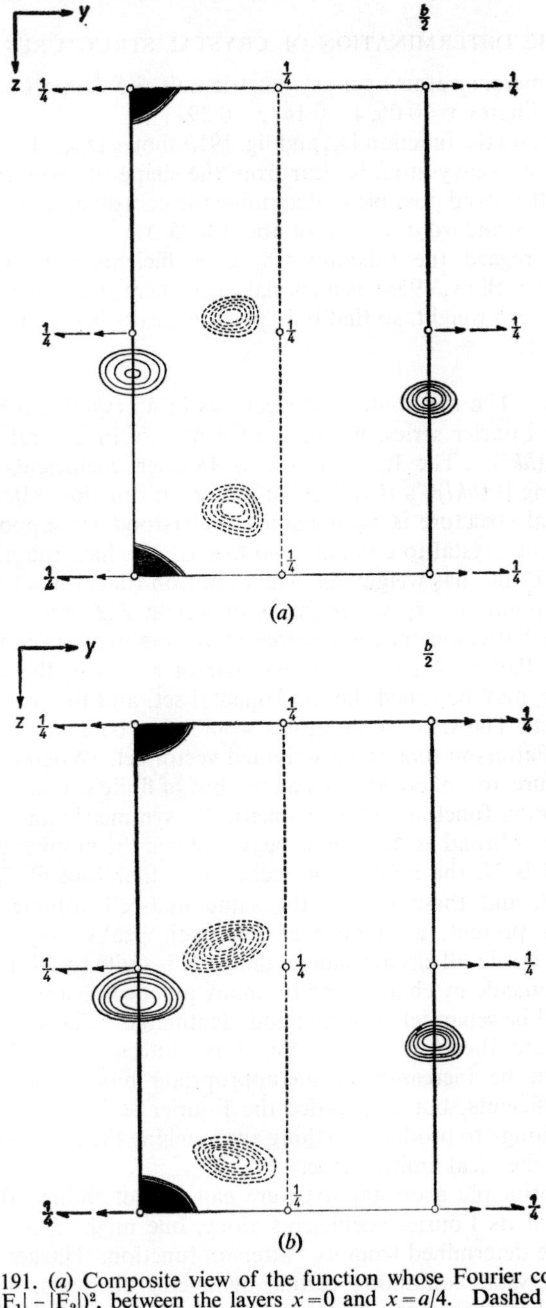

FIG. 191. (*a*) Composite view of the function whose Fourier coefficients are $(|F_1| - |F_2|)^2$, between the layers $x=0$ and $x=a/4$. Dashed contours denote negative values. The scale is arbitrary. (*b*) Composite view of the function whose Fourier coefficients are $(|F_1| - |F_3|)^2$ between the layers $x=0$ and $x=a/4$. The derivative whose structure factors are F_3 differs from that whose structure factors are F_2 in that it has two mercury atoms in close proximity, instead of only a single one in about the same position. (See also text)

No. 3, two mercury atoms per asymmetric unit, 3·5 Å apart with mean coordinates $x=0{\cdot}06$, $y=0{\cdot}14$, $z=0{\cdot}29$.

Fig. 191*a* shows the function D_{12} and fig. 191*b* shows D_{13}. The presence of a composite heavy atom is clear from the shape of certain peaks in the latter. It proved possible to determine the coordinates of the heavy atoms with a standard deviation of about 0·25 Å.

We may regard the function whose coefficients are $(|F_1|-|F|)^2$ (Perutz, 1956; Blow, 1958) as a special case where the heavy atoms of type 2 have zero weight, so that only positive peaks between the heavy atoms appear.

6. *Summary.* The distribution of electrons in a crystal can be represented by a Fourier series, whose coefficients are in general complex numbers, F(*hkl*). The function whose Fourier coefficients are the corresponding $|F(hkl)|^2$'s is called the Patterson function. Its relation to the crystal structure is most readily understood by supposing the unit cell of the crystal to contain *point* atoms, of which the *j*th occurs at the point $\mathbf{r}_j$ and has weight Z_j. The Patterson function is then finite only at the points $\mathbf{r}_i-\mathbf{r}_j$, where peaks of weight Z_iZ_j occur; that is, peaks of the Patterson function represent vectors between atoms, and there is one Patterson peak for every pair of atoms in the unit cell. The points $\mathbf{r}_j$ may be called the fundamental set, and the points $\mathbf{r}_i-\mathbf{r}_j$ the vector set. The set of point atoms would then be a weighted point set, and its Patterson function a weighted vector set. When the atoms of the structure are spherically symmetric but of finite extent, the peaks of the Patterson function are also spherically symmetric and approximately twice as broad as the atomic peaks. When the number of atoms per unit cell is N, the number of vectors and therefore of Patterson peaks is N^2, and these occupy the same unit-cell volume. When symmetry is present, a number of Patterson peaks may occur in coincidence, but in all circumstances, unless N is quite small, Patterson peaks will coincide by chance, and (in many practical instances) few or no peaks will be separately resolved and identifiable. The sharpness of the peaks, and therefore the degree of resolution of the Patterson function, can be increased by an appropriate modification of the Fourier coefficients, but in practice the Fourier series cannot be extended far enough to produce anything approaching the weighted vector set, which is the ideal limiting case.

Since in principle a crystal structure can be determined from the magnitudes of its Fourier coefficients alone, one might expect that it could also be determined from its Patterson function. Harker showed that for a crystal containing certain symmetry elements, a section along a line or in a plane through the three-dimensional Patterson function is related to a projection of the crystal structure on this line or plane. The peaks which occur in this 'Harker section' correspond to vectors between equivalent atoms of the structure. This work was given a firmer theoretical basis by Buerger, who showed that a transformation of coordinates of the Harker section, to produce what was called an implication diagram, made the structural and symmetry relations between the section through the Patterson function and the corresponding electron-density projection much clearer. In the great majority of cases the symmetry of the implication diagram is higher than that of the corresponding projection, although for a few space groups they are the same. The practical application of these results is limited by the higher symmetry of the Harker section, and the fact that peaks may occur in the Harker section which do not represent vectors between symmetry-related atoms. In crystal-structure analysis the Harker section is generally used in conjunction with other information, such as the expected shape of a molecule.

Wrinch was the first to show that a fundamental set of points could be recovered completely from its vector set of points. In some cases the method showed that more than one fundamental set may correspond to a given vector set. Such fundamental sets are called 'isovectorial'. It is possible for two or more fundamental sets to have the same weighted vector set; the corresponding crystal structures would give the same X-ray diffraction pattern, and Patterson has called them 'homometric'. A structure which has a homometric counterpart is not likely to occur in practice at all frequently. All methods for the systematic recovery of the crystal structure from its Patterson function depend on the possibility of recognising individual Patterson peaks. It is therefore always possible to recover a fundamental set of points from the corresponding vector set of points, but the Patterson function does not consist of a set of points. When the number of atoms in the unit cell is small, so that individual peaks are separately resolved in the Patterson function, or when the structure contains a few relatively heavy atoms so that the peaks corresponding to vectors between these and other atoms stand out in the Patterson function, the latter can lead directly to the crystal structure. Also when the positions of a number of atoms are already known, those of the remainder may be found directly from the Patterson function.

In the practical use of the Patterson function in other circumstances one is always able to make use of additional items of information, such as the expected distances between atoms or the known configuration of a particular group of atoms. Methods based on the Patterson function, such as the superposition method, and particularly the evaluation of a minimum or sum function with the help of an automatic computer, are probably the most powerful methods of crystal structure analysis at the present stage of development of the subject, apart of course from the heavy-atom method and the method of isomorphous replacement, which however cannot always be used.

CHAPTER 8

FOURIER METHODS

1. Introduction

Although the basic principles of the application of Fourier series to the representation of crystal structures had been pointed out by W. H. Bragg in 1915, practical use was not made of these principles until 1925, when Duane (1925) and Havighurst (1925) used them to derive, from the results of Bragg, James and Bosanquet (1922), the electron distribution in the sodium and chlorine atoms in rock salt. It was not until 1929 that W. L. Bragg suggested that Fourier methods could be used in crystal-structure determination; he showed that clear representations of projections on to three planes of the structure of diopside, $CaMg(SiO_3)_2$, could be obtained, and showed that knowledge of the positions of the calcium and magnesium atoms was sufficient to determine the relative phases of the structure factors for one of these projections.

Despite this work, however, the Fourier method was for some time largely adopted as a method of 'refining' structures—that is, of obtaining the best possible atomic positions in structures which had been derived by trial-and-error methods (Booth, 1945*a*). This subject, in which the work of Robertson (1937) was particularly prominent, will be discussed in more detail in Chapter 12. The present chapter is concerned only with methods that have been used for determining atomic positions *ab initio*.

In this connexion, a distinction must be made between centrosymmetric and non-centrosymmetric structures. For the latter, the reflexions have relative phase angles which may assume any values between 0 and 2π; thus slight errors in any postulated atomic position will lead to slight errors in the phase angles as well as in the structure amplitudes, and Fourier syntheses computed with these values of phase angles will tend to reproduce the atomic positions from which they were derived (Section **12**.2.2). For centrosymmetric structures, however, only the values 0 or π are possible for the phase angle, and if these values can be correctly allotted to the various structure factors, a Fourier synthesis should give a close approximation to the correct structure. In other words, it is possible to envisage absolute correctness in the phase angles of a centrosymmetric structure, but not in those of a non-centrosymmetric structure.

These considerations also apply to a centrosymmetric projection, even if the structure itself is non-centrosymmetric. Such projections occur when they are perpendicular to two-fold, four-fold or six-fold rotation or screw axes (compare section **4**.1.4). For example, the space group No. 3, P2 gives *hkl* reflexions whose phase angles are arbitrary, but the reflexions *h*0*l* must have relative phase angle sof 0 or π, if the origin is taken as a point on the two-fold axis, since projections on the (010) plane are centrosymmetric. The space group No. 19, $P2_12_12_1$, which is exceedingly common (Nowacki, 1942), is non-centrosymmetric, but has three centrosymmetric projections perpendicular to the screw axes; the structure of $NiSO_4.7H_2O$, which has this space group, was determined by Beevers and Schwartz (1935) by means of the Fourier projection method.

Some practical difficulties arise in dealing with this type of space group. In the commonly accepted set up for $P2_12_12_1$ (International Tables, vol. I) none of the screw axes passes through the origin, and consequently none of the projections has a centre of symmetry at the origin; the relative phase angles are then limited to 0 or π for certain reflexions only, the others being limited to $\pi/2$ or $3\pi/2$. While in principle there is no difficulty in handling a Fourier series with these properties, in practice it is found to be rather confusing, and the common practice is therefore to treat each projection separately with the origin lying on the screw axis perpendicular to it. In plotting the results finally, the fact that the origins of the three different projections are not identical must be borne in mind, and it is best to shift all the projections so that they refer to the usual origin for the space group.

2. Uses of Fourier Synthesis

2.1. *Completion of partially known structures.* In general, when an approximation to a correct structure has been derived, the method of Fourier refinement should lead to a more accurate result. If, however, there is some doubt about the stereochemistry, and the structure is still not accurately enough known, the Fourier method may not be adequate, since it necessarily involves the assumption that certain peaks in the Fourier synthesis correspond to certain atoms. For example, at one stage in the determination of the structure of sodium benzyl penicillin (Crowfoot et al., 1949), a certain peak was assumed to correspond to sulphur, whereas the structure as finally deduced showed that it corresponded to two unresolved carbon atoms.

In this work Bunn made use of an elegant device which showed quite clearly which details of the postulated structure were incorrect. The principle of this device is as follows. In accepting the signs for the structure factors given by a postulated structure we are biasing the Fourier synthesis towards the pattern of that structure, for if we adopted both the signs *and* the magnitudes of the structure factors we should reproduce the postulated structure completely. Since, however, we use the signs given by the postulated structure and the magnitudes given by the true structure, we obtain a compromise between the two.

Thus it should be possible to decide which detail in the postulated structure is wrong by finding which atoms are least well represented in the Fourier synthesis.

In view, however, of the deficiencies that are inevitably present in any Fourier synthesis, it is not always easy to decide which atoms are least well represented, and it may be still less easy to decide what changes are suggested. Bunn therefore suggests plotting directly the difference between the syntheses given by the observed and calculated structure factors, a result that can be arrived at by using the differences between the observed and calculated structure factors, F_o and F_c respectively, as Fourier coefficients.

A difficulty exists, however, in carrying out this suggestion; the signs of the observed structure factors may not be known with any certainty. For example, if $|F_o| = 24$ and $F_c = +3$, the value of $F_o - F_c$ is $+21$ if $F_o = +24$, and is -27 if $F_o = -24$. If, however, $|F_o| = 3$ and $F_c = +24$, the value of $F_o - F_c$ is -21 if $F_o = +3$ and is -27 if $F_o = -3$; there is little difference between these two values, and the probability that F_o has the same sign as F_c is so high that the value of -21 for $F_o - F_c$ may be confidently used, with the knowledge that if the sign of F_o is wrong no great error will result. The terms for which F_o is small and F_c is large may thus be used as Fourier coefficients with values $F_o - F_c$.

The resulting synthesis is named by Bunn the 'error synthesis', and, as can be seen from the last paragraph, it makes particular use of the

TABLE 196

Comparison of some observed and calculated F's for an incorrect structure of durene

hkl	F_o	F_c	$F_o - F_c$
001	38·5	7·6	—
202	5·5	15·5	$\overline{10\cdot0}$
$20\bar{4}$	8·0	$\overline{28\cdot1}$	20·1
$20\bar{5}$	0·0	7·5	$\overline{7\cdot5}$
400	9·0	0·0	—
402	2·5	$\overline{8\cdot9}$	6·4
$40\bar{2}$	6·0	$\overline{27\cdot3}$	21·3
404	9·0	17·5	$\overline{8\cdot5}$
$60\bar{1}$	1·5	15·6	$\overline{14\cdot1}$
$60\bar{6}$	3·5	12·6	$\bar{9}\cdot\bar{1}$

The value in the last column is obtained by assuming that F_o has the same sign as F_c.
For 001 and 400, the sign of F_o is doubtful.

reflexions that are of negligible observed intensity—a rather rare procedure in Fourier methods. Strongly negative regions in the synthesis indicate that, in the postulated structure, too much scattering matter has been assumed there, and positive regions indicate that too little matter has been assumed; a steep gradient at an assumed atomic position implies that the atom has been incorrectly placed.

The method can best be illustrated by an example. In table 196 are given observed and calculated values of F(*h*0*l*) for certain reflexions from durene (Robertson, 1933), together with values calculated for an incorrect structure. In this structure the molecules are so oriented that the atoms in the benzene rings have the same coordinates as in the correct structure; but one pair of CH_3 groups is slightly displaced, and the other pair is completely wrong. (The impossibility of fitting the molecules into the unit cell in these orientations is ignored.) For brevity, only those terms showing pronounced disagreement are included in the table; in the complete table sufficient correspondence is found to indicate a certain measure of correctness.

Of the terms in the table, all but two (001 and 400) have large calculated values and small observed values, and these are used for the error synthesis. The result, shown in fig. 203, with the postulated atomic positions superposed, shows clearly that one pair of CH_3 groups is completely misplaced; fig. 197 also shows that the other pair of CH_3 groups is somewhat misplaced, and indicates the direction of movement which would improve the agreement. There is no definite suggestion of movement of any of the atoms in the benzene ring.

From this example it can be seen that the uses of the error synthesis are two-fold. First, it indicates which atoms are in the wrong places,

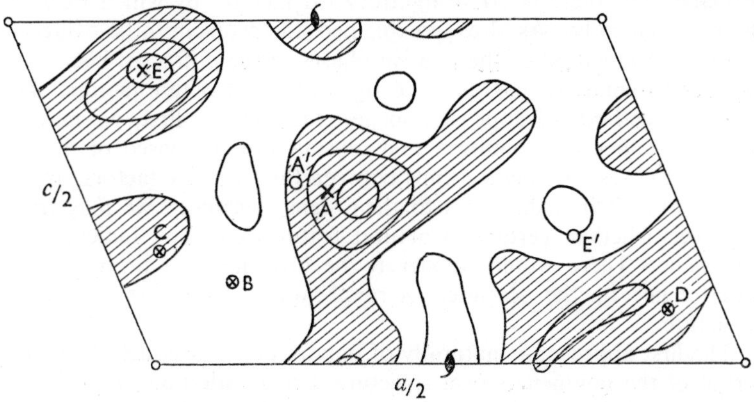

FIG. 197. Error synthesis for incorrect structure of durene. The negative areas are shaded. The assumed atomic positions are *A*, *B*, *C*, *D* and *E*, and the fact that *A* and *E* lie in strongly negative regions suggests that their positions are incorrect. The correct positions are *A′* (which lies up a steep slope from *A*) and *E′* (which is a completely different position from *E*, as suggested by the occurrence of a deep minimum at *E*)

and gives some indication—which knowledge of interatomic distances and stereochemistry can usually supplement—where they should be moved to; and secondly, it indicates which atoms are only slightly displaced, and the directions in which they should be moved. If all the errors are of the second kind, then it is likely that practically all the signs of the structure factors will be known, and thus all the terms can be included in the error synthesis. The result, called the 'difference synthesis' (Cochran, 1951*a*), is of considerable use in improving the accuracy of atomic positions, and will be discussed in more detail in section **12**.2.5.

Fig. 199 shows the error synthesis which helped in the determination of the structure of sodium benzyl penicillin. The postulated positions of the sodium atoms lie on gradients which indicate that some movement of these atoms is required. But the most striking indication is the strongly negative region around the position of the sulphur atom, flanked by two fairly large peaks; these details indicate that what was thought to be a sulphur atom was really two carbon atoms partly resolved. The synthesis hinted at other changes also, and altogether gave most useful evidence of the correct nature of the molecule.

Ramachandran and his school in Madras have made attempts to systematize Fourier methods of completing partially known structures by modifying the coefficients according to the knowledge available. Full details of the methods are contained in a book edited by Ramachandran (1964).

2.2. *Determination of unknown structures.* As an aid to the determination of unknown structures, Fourier methods have proved invaluable, but there is no straightforward method by which they can be used generally. As already explained, the problem to be overcome is the determination of the relative phases of the diffracted beams, or, for centrosymmetric crystals, the signs of the structure factors. Two possible methods of approach suggest themselves: first, we may try to see whether the condition that crystals are composed of discrete atoms imposes any relationships between the structure factors, and so leads from their magnitudes to their signs; secondly, we may try to discover whether certain structural features give any indication of the signs. There would appear to be little hope of producing, by interference of the scattered X-ray beams, a direct image of the structure.

The first approach is naturally of importance in producing a logical proof of the uniqueness of a structure, but, in addition, it has led to several methods which have been successfully used for determining new structures. Because of their importance, these methods will be described in Chapter 9, although it must be emphasized that they should always be explored before the methods described in this present chapter are brought into play.

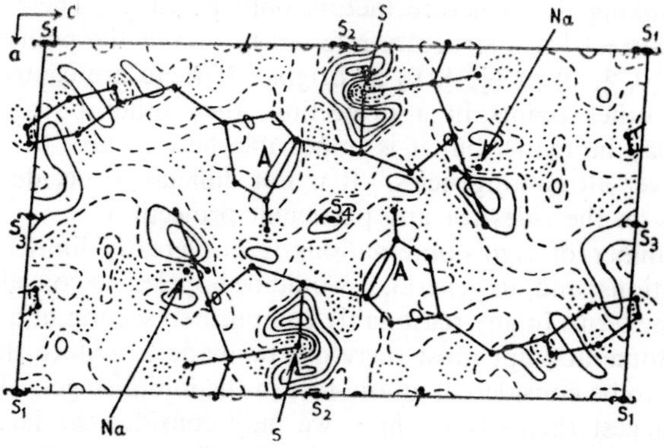

FIG. 199. Error synthesis used in the determination of the structure of sodium benzylpenicillin. The most striking feature is that which shows that the peak thought to be *S* is really two unresolved peaks. Also, the Na positions lie on steep gradients (Crowfoot et al., 1949)

3. METHODS FOR CENTROSYMMETRIC STRUCTURES AND PROJECTIONS

3.1. *Trials of different sign combinations.* It might be thought that a trial-and-error process of sign selection would be possible for centrosymmetric crystals; since there are only two possibilities for each term, different combinations could be tried until one was found that gave an interpretable representation of the projection of the given structure. Errors in a few signs should not make a great difference, and so it should be possible to recognize when the correct structure was being approached. The difficulty, however, lies in the enormous number of combinations possible with even a few terms, and if any success is to be gained by such methods some degree of systematization must be introduced.

One useful fact is that not all the signs of the structure factors are absolute; some can be chosen arbitrarily. This arises from the number of different centres of symmetry that exist in the unit cell; in the (001) projection of space group $P\bar{1}$, for example, there are centres of symmetry at the points (0, 0, 0), ($\frac{1}{2}$, 0, 0), (0, $\frac{1}{2}$, 0) and ($\frac{1}{2}$, $\frac{1}{2}$, 0), and any of these can be chosen as origin. A shift of origin from (0, 0, 0) to ($\frac{1}{2}$, 0, 0) merely corresponds to change of sign of all terms with *h* odd, and thus we can choose the positive sign for any *one* of these terms; once this term has been fixed, however, the other terms with *h* odd are fixed relatively to it: the terms with *h* even do not change at all. Similar considerations apply to the choice of sign for one term with *k* odd; the two possibilities correspond to origins at (000) and (0$\frac{1}{2}$0).

We can make use of both these considerations simultaneously, if we choose as two arbitrary terms one with *h* odd and the other with

k odd, making the structure factors both positive. These two signs must be correct for a structure referred to one of the points (0, 0, 0), ($\frac{1}{2}$, 0, 0), (0, $\frac{1}{2}$, 0) or ($\frac{1}{2}$, $\frac{1}{2}$, 0) as origin. If there are centres of symmetry at other points in a projection, then other possible choices of sign may be made, but it is impossible here to give the rules that would cover all contingencies. It is not difficult to decide from first principles on the rules for any particular projection.

The number of sign combinations is not greatly limited by these considerations, and, in general, it would be hopeless to consider dealing with all the terms in any reasonably complicated section of a reciprocal lattice. Some attempt must therefore be made to reduce the number that have to be considered, at any rate in the initial stages. Two possibilities suggest themselves: first, we may consider the largest terms first, choosing a small enough number to allow systematic consideration; and secondly, we may include only the terms within a small range of Bragg angle. The first method does not lend itself to systematic treatment, as even twelve terms, including two with arbitrary signs, would give over one thousand combinations; and it is doubtful whether twelve terms only would give a recognizable approximation to a moderately complicated structure.

The second method would appear to be more promising. The inclusion of only a small number of terms within a given range of Bragg angle would correspond to the decrease of the numerical aperture of an optical instrument (Bragg and West, 1930), and thus we should expect to see the structure with a lower degree of resolution, and so should have some idea of what to expect. An arbitrary cut-off at a given Bragg angle would however introduce unwanted diffraction effects, and it would probably be advisable to introduce an artificial temperature factor to eliminate these.

Not all combinations of sign are equally likely: for example, if a structure contains atoms of approximately equal weight, it is impossible for all the structure factors to be positive, since this would imply an excessive concentration of electron density at the origin. Thus not all the thousand possibilities need be considered. In fact, the absence of a heavy atom at the origin demands that positive and negative structure factors should be present in about equal numbers, and such combinations of signs should therefore be tried. The existence of other centres of symmetry in structure projections suggests further limitations on the possible combinations of signs; thus it is impossible for all the structure factors with h even to be positive and all those with h odd to be negative, although this distribution would give approximately equal numbers of positive and negative signs. The number of combinations can thus be further reduced by eliminating such possibilities.

No success has yet been reported with methods such as these, although Hanson and Lipson (1952*b*) have shown that, by means of the optical method of Fourier synthesis described in section 5.5.2, the structure of hexamethylbenzene (Lonsdale, 1929) could have been derived in this way. Also, Boyes-Watson and Perutz (1943) have used computational methods to produce, with poor resolution, a representation of the projection of a protein molecule. This was possible because the crystal used gave very few reflexions, but as the number of reflexions that one wishes to include increases, so the computational work increases, and rapid methods of summation become more desirable.

Woolfson (1954) has examined the problem quantitatively, and has derived a system of choice of signs that ensures that in a given collection one combination will contain not more than one wrong sign. He applied his method successfully to a known structure, evaluating 256 syntheses photographically (section 5.5.1) with 16 terms; a complete survey would require 2^{14}, or 16,000 syntheses. The method is, of course, not very elegant, but it may be worth trying if all others fail. A computer enables large numbers of syntheses to be carried out reasonably expeditiously.

3.2. *'Heavy-atom' method.* The failure of the sign-permutation method to produce a general solution to the problem of crystal-structure determination makes it necessary to consider whether less direct methods can be used. Direct determination of phase angles, for example by means of the double-reflexion phenomena described in section 2.4.4, does not appear to be promising (Lipscomb, 1949), but the indirect approach has been extraordinarily fruitful and most of the triumphs of the subject have been achieved in this way. Crystal structures with hundreds of variable parameters have been solved, and these would obviously have been far too difficult for the trial-and-error methods described in Chapter 6.

The term 'indirect' is applied to the methods in which the phase angles are inferred from certain structural features. The simplest of such features are atoms which have predominant scattering factors; their positions can be located fairly easily by Patterson methods (section 7.5.1), and thence the phase angles that would result from these atoms alone can be deduced. The assumption that these phase angles are those of the various reflexions should then give a Fourier synthesis which is a close approximation to the complete structure.

Formally, this result can be shown by writing the structure factor for a crystal with one heavy atom in the unit cell as

$$F(hkl) = f_H \exp 2\pi i(hx_H + ky_H + lz_H) + \sum_n f_n \exp 2\pi i(hx_n + ky_n + lz_n),$$

where f_H is the scattering factor of the heavy atom, whose parameters are x_H, y_H and z_H. If f_H is much greater than f_n, then the first term will tend to be much greater than the second, since the summation, being due to several atoms, will usually be relatively small.

It is therefore unnecessary, and indeed inadvisable, that f_H should be greater than $\sum f_n$—that is, that the heavy atom should scatter more than all the other atoms together. If f_H is too large, the Fourier synthesis will tend to show only this atom, the lighter atoms being seen only with difficulty; at the best, their positions would be highly inaccurate. For example, Perutz and Weiss (1946) found that a projection of the structure of tribromo-trimethylphosphine-gold showed only the gold and bromine atoms, and the remaining features had to be inferred from spatial considerations. The work of Robertson and Woodward (1940) on platinum phthalocyanine, on the other hand, did show all the structural features expected, but the peaks representing the lighter atoms were more distorted (fig. 205) than would be expected for a structure containing only light atoms.

As a rough guide, for successful use of the method the sum of the squares of the atomic numbers of the heavy atoms and of the light atoms should be approximately equal. This may be seen by considering equation *132.2*,

$$\overline{\mathrm{I}(hkl)} = \sum_j f_j^2,$$

which shows that, on the average, the contribution of any one atom to the diffracted intensity depends upon the square of its scattering factor. If we require that the average contribution of the heavy atoms should be about equal to the average contribution of the light atoms, the signs of about three-quarters of the structure factors will be correct; half will be correct because the two contributions have the same sign, and half of the remainder will be correct because the contributions of the light atoms are opposite in sign to, but less than, the contributions of the heavy atoms.

That the rule works well is indicated by some practical examples. For metatolidine dihydrochloride, $C_{14}H_{18}N_2Cl_2$ (Fowweather and Hargreaves, 1950), the sum of the squares of the atomic numbers of the chlorine atoms is 578, and the sum of the squares of the atomic numbers of the carbon and nitrogen atoms is 602. For determining the structure of strychnine, $C_{21}H_{22}N_2O_2$, an element of atomic number near to 31 would be required; Robertson and Beevers (1950) made use of bromine (35) and Bokhoven, Schoone and Bijvoet (1948, 1949, 1951) made use of selenium (34).

Sim (1961) has made a more precise study of this approach and gives a graph (fig. 203) showing the proportion of correct signs in terms of a function r, defined as

$$r = \frac{f_H^2}{\sum f_L^2};$$

f_H and f_L are the scattering factors of the heavy and light atoms respectively, and for this purpose must be taken as proportional to the atomic numbers. For $r=1$, the proportion of correct signs is rather greater than that given by the simplified theory outlined above.

The signs of those structure factors to which the heavy atom makes only a small contribution are uncertain and should be omitted from the first Fourier synthesis. The precise condition for omission is however rather arbitrary and Woolfson (1956) has suggested that it is better to

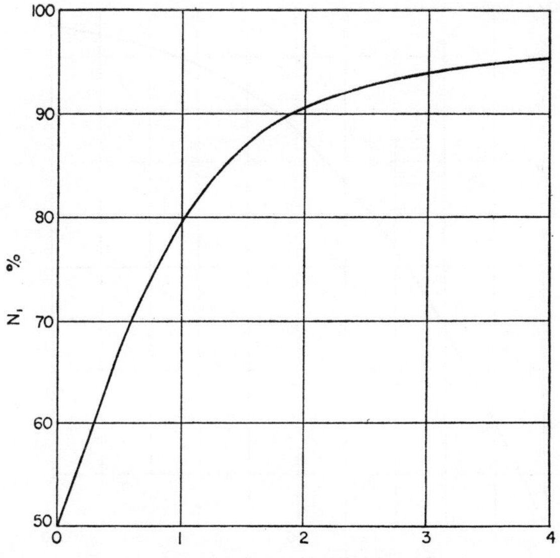

FIG. 203. The fraction N of structure factors whose signs are determined by a heavy atom

weight each term according to the value of F_H, the contribution of the heavy atom to the structure factor; the weighting factor he proposes is

$$\tanh |F| \frac{|F_H|}{\Sigma f_L^2},$$

the form of which is shown in fig. 204. In addition to removing the arbitrariness in deciding which reflexions to omit, the method also improves the clarity of the result. Woolfson shows that, in an application to an artificial structure, some atoms are shown more clearly if weighting rather than a simple cut-off is used. The method becomes of less use as the weight of the heavy atom increases.

The determination of the structure of phthalocyanine by Robertson and Woodward (1940) was the first *direct* application of the heavy-atom method. The molecule has a large space at the centre; into this space various metal atoms can be introduced. It has been shown already that platinum should be heavy enough to decide the phase angles of the reflexions, and this turned out to be so in a particularly simple way. The space group is No. 14, $P2_1/a$, and the unit cell contains two molecules; thus the molecules must have their centres on centres of symmetry and the platinum atoms must lie on these centres. The occupation of special positions by the heavy atoms, despite the advantage previously mentioned, can, however, lead to difficulties:

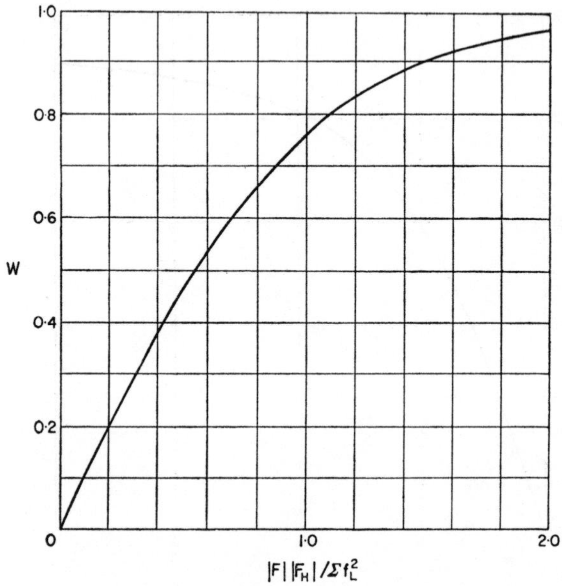

FIG. 204. Woolfson's weighting factor for centrosymmetric structures

usually, atoms in such positions do not contribute to certain reflexions, and thus do not help to fix the phases of the structure factors of these reflexions. In this space group, however, the *h*0*l* reflexions to which the platinum atoms do not contribute are those that are forbidden by the space group; thus a projection of the structure on to the (010) plane can be computed as though the crystal had one molecule in a cell with dimensions $a/2$ and c, with a platinum atom at the origin—the most favourable circumstances for application of the heavy-atom method.

The structure factors of the *h*0*l* reflexions should all be positive, and the resulting Fourier synthesis is shown in fig. 205; it will be seen that all the details of the molecule are clearly shown. The molecule is tilted somewhat from the plane of projection, and so is foreshortened in one direction, but when this foreshortening is allowed for the molecular dimensions show good agreement with those found in other structures.

Results such as this can be obtained only if the experimental data are accurate. The electron density at the peak of the platinum atom is $160e/\text{Å}^2$, whereas that at the peaks of the carbon atoms is only

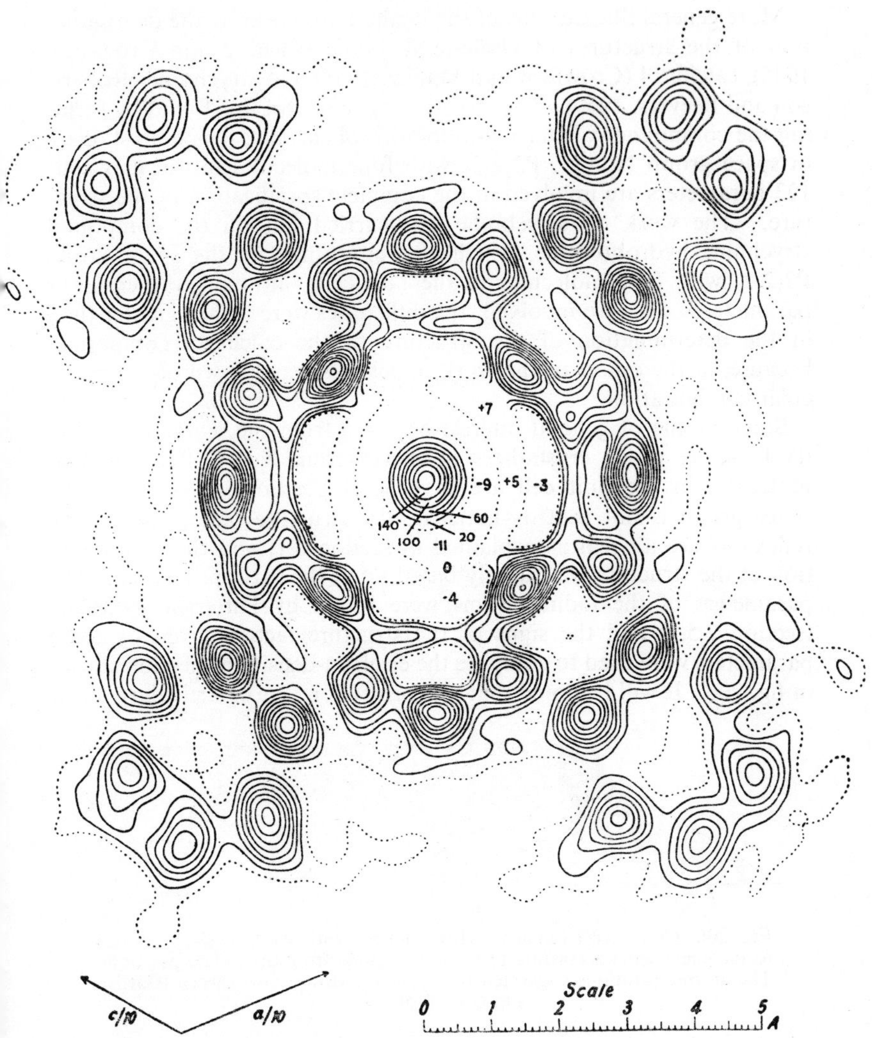

FIG. 205. Platinum phthalocyanine: (010) electron-density projection, with contours at intervals of $1e/\text{Å}^2$, except in centre (Robertson and Woodward, 1940)

$8e/\text{Å}^2$; thus small errors in the structure amplitudes, which would affect the platinum atoms only slightly, would make much greater proportionate differences to the lighter atoms. It will be noted, as stated earlier in this section, that the carbon-atom peaks are rather distorted, and this effect must always exist to some extent if the heavy-atom method is used.

More general illustrations of the method are given by the determination of the structures of cholesteryl iodide (Carlisle and Crowfoot, 1945), calciferol (Crowfoot and Dunitz, 1948) and strychnine (Robertson and Beevers, 1950). The structure of calciferol was found by forming the compound calciferol-4-iodo-5-nitrobenzoate, which crystallizes in space group No. 19, $P2_12_12_1$ with four molecules in the unit cell; 123 parameters are involved in the complete specification of the structure. The work on strychnine was carried out on the compound strychnine hydrobromide, which also crystallizes in the space group $P2_12_12_1$ with four molecules in the unit cell; although rather fewer parameters—84—are involved, the difficulties were rather greater than in the determination of the structure of the calciferol compound, because, at the outset of the work, much less was known of the molecular configuration.

Some points of general interest emerged from the work on cholesteryl iodide, which crystallizes in space group No. 4, $P2_1$; the two molecules in the unit cell are in general positions. Although the space group is not centrosymmetric, the structure factors of the $h0l$ reflexions are all real as explained in section 8.1, and the determination of the structure was largely based upon the (010) projection. The parameters of the iodine atoms were found by Patterson synthesis (section 7.5.1) and the signs of the structure factors given by these parameters were used to compute the electron-density projection shown in fig. 206. It will be noted that this projection is not particularly clear

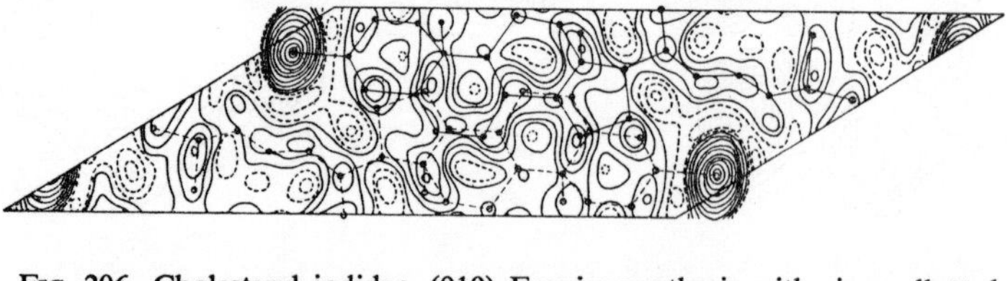

FIG. 206. Cholesteryl iodide: (010) Fourier synthesis with signs allotted to the coefficients according to the calculations from the iodine positions. The atomic positions suggested by the synthesis are also shown (Carlisle and Crowfoot, 1945)

and would not, by itself, be sufficient to establish the structure; stereochemical evidence had to be used to enable the projection to be interpreted, and the signs of the structure factors were recalculated with all the atoms taken into account.

The first successful use of Fourier series in crystal-structure determination was the determination of the structure of $CuSO_4.5H_2O$ (Beevers and Lipson, 1934). The starting point was the knowledge of the positions of the copper and sulphur atoms (section 6.5.2). The copper atoms, being in the special positions (0, 0, 0) and ($\frac{1}{2}$, $\frac{1}{2}$, 0), are not sufficient to establish enough signs to enable the Fourier method to be applied, although they contain nearly twenty-five per cent of the electron content; they do not contribute to those reflexions with $h+k$ odd, and if these reflexions are omitted from the Fourier synthesis the correct projection would be combined with another related to it by a C-face-centring. It might have been possible to determine the structure from such a result, by means of methods similar to those used for cholesteryl iodide, but since the sulphur positions were known, the correct projection was found by making use of these positions to give the signs of the structure factors with $h+k$ odd. It is interesting to note, however, that traces of the related projection are shown in the published result (fig. 207); the computations were made before systematic methods had been developed and, in order to economize in effort, the smaller structure factors were omitted; since there were more of these small ones with $h+k$ odd than with $h+k$ even, traces of face-centring remained, and are shown by a 'ghost' peak related to that of the sulphur atom.

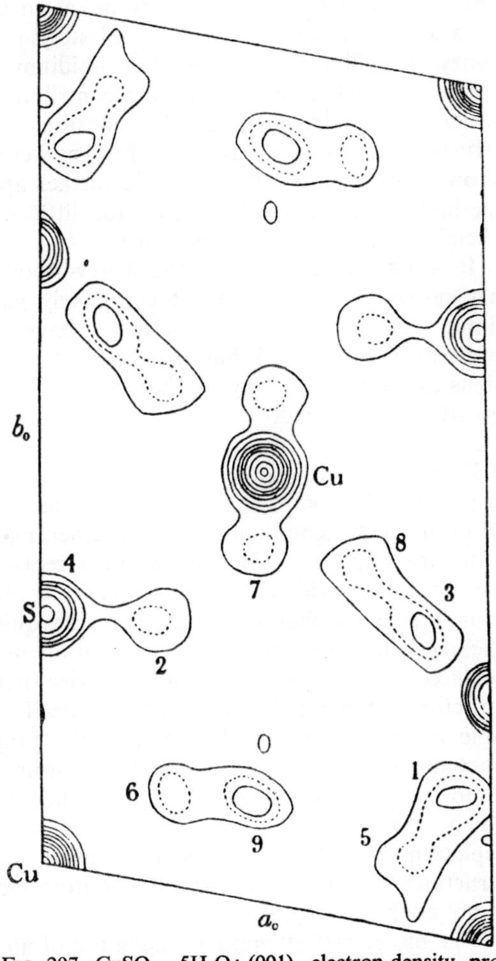

FIG. 207. $CuSO_4 . 5H_2O$: (001) electron-density projection. The small peak near the water molecule 9 is a 'ghost' related to the peak S (Beevers and Lipson, 1934)

The indeterminacy of the phase angles of certain structure factors may arise in other problems, and is worth special consideration. It must occur when the heavy atoms are related by symmetry elements that are not present in the complete structure, since the phase angles given by the heavy atoms must give a structure that has this same symmetry. Although the effect will, in general, occur only when the heavy atoms are in special positions, as in $CuSO_4.5H_2O$, this is not always so, as the experience with cholesteryl iodide shows. In rubidium benzyl penicillin, for example, the rubidium atoms have $z=0$ (Crowfoot et al., 1949), and thus do not contribute to the $h0l$ reflexions for which $h+l$ is odd, nor to the $0kl$ reflexions for which k is odd. If the structure factors with indeterminate signs were omitted, the projections showed too high a symmetry, and further application of the Fourier method was not possible because too little was known of the stereochemistry of the penicillin molecule.

It will thus be seen that the heavy-atom method, powerful as it has proved to be, is still not completely general. It is, of course, limited to those structures in which a heavy atom exists or into which one can be introduced, but also there may be many reflexions whose signs are not affected by the heavy atoms. Thus further evidence is greatly to be desired.

3.3. *Isomorphous replacement.* One method of obtaining this evidence is provided by comparing the X-ray intensities from a pair or a series of isomorphous compounds; we can then make use of the changes in structure amplitude when one atom is replaced by another, since, if the position of this atom is known, its contribution to a particular structure factor may determine the sign quite definitely. In effect, the method is similar to the heavy-atom method, since one of the replaceable atoms is usually much heavier than the other atoms in the structure, but it enables problems to be dealt with in which the replaceable atom contains much less than the proportion of the electron content that is required for the heavy-atom method. On the other hand, the changes in structure amplitude are difficult to interpret when variable phase angles are involved, and thus the isomorphous-replacement method is usually applied only to centrosymmetric structures or projections; the heavy-atom method, as we have seen, is not confined to these cases.

One of the first attempts to make use of an isomorphous series was that of Cork (1927), who made extensive measurements of intensities from what is probably the best-known isomorphous series—the alums. This series is typified by the compound $KAl(SO_4)_2.12H_2O$, the potassium being replaceable by certain monovalent atoms or radicals, the aluminium by other tervalent atoms, and the sulphur by selenium. Cork measured the intensities of reflexions of the types $h00$, $hh0$ and hhh from crystals containing ammonium, rubidium, caesium and thallium in place of potassium, and chromium in place of aluminium, but the sulphur atom was left undisturbed. It has already been shown (section

2.7.1) that in the unit cell the metal atoms are fixed and that the sulphur atoms are situated on the three-fold axes; Cork's first problem therefore was to find the parameter of the sulphur atoms. Of the intensities measured, only the *hhh* reflexions can fix this uniquely, since neither the *h*00 or the *hh*0 reflexions can distinguish between parameters u and $\frac{1}{2}-u$, and thus Cork used these reflexions to compute the projection of the electron density on to the cube diagonal.

TABLE 209

Structure amplitudes of the *hhh* reflexions from various alums, $R'Al(SO_4)_2.12H_2O$

hkl	NH_4(11)	K(19)	Rb(37)	Tl(81)
111	86	38	29	113
222	0	19	79	195
333	111	125	158	236
444	25	6	55	125
555	24	49	64	131
666	86	86	122	164
777	53	34	0	18
888	0	16	22	56
999	25	0	0	25

Table 209 gives some of the measurements used, and it can be clearly seen how the structure factors change as the substitution proceeds. Thallium, of atomic number 81, is heavy enough to cause all the *hhh* reflexions to have positive structure factors, but as lighter atoms are substituted the value for 111, for example, decreases until for potassium it obviously becomes negative. The signs can all be fixed in this way, and the resulting Fourier syntheses are shown in fig. 210; only one half of the diagonal need be considered because the structure is centrosymmetric. The synthesis shows clearly the peaks due to the metal atoms, and, in between them, a complex mass of sulphate ions and water molecules. (Actually caesium alum has a different structure from the other compounds used (Lipson, 1935), and the coincidence of its electron-density curve with the others is accidental. The data for caesium alum are not included in table 209.)

From these results it seems a reasonable guess that the sulphur atoms have a parameter of about 0·36, but Cork was not able to deduce a structure based on spatial considerations that gave acceptable agreement, and he had to abandon the determination. The reason for the impasse became apparent when measurements were made of the corresponding reflexions from potassium aluminium selenium alum (Beevers and Lipson, 1935); these measurements are shown in table 210 and, if appropriate signs are allotted, the resultant Fourier synthesis (fig. 211) shows an increase of the peak at $u=0{\cdot}19$, not that at 0·36. It

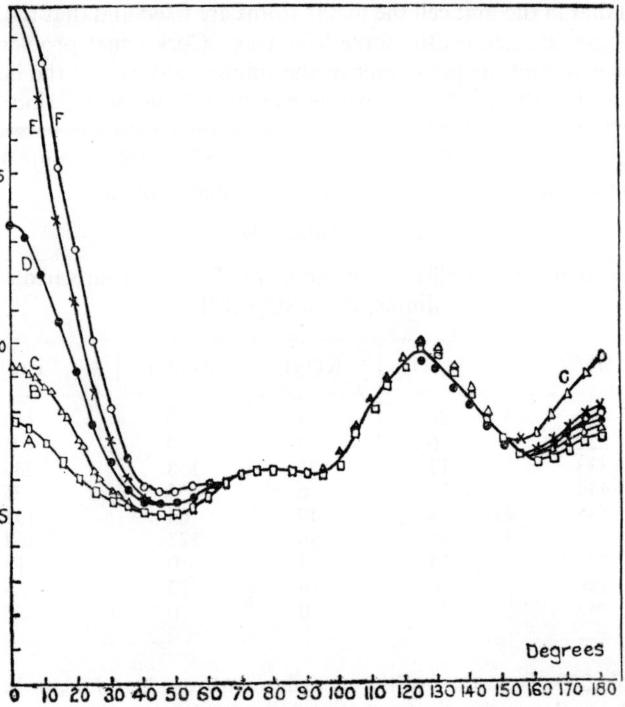

FIG. 210. Electron densities, in arbitrary units, between the (111) planes of various alums (Cork, 1927)

TABLE 210

Structure factors of *hhh* reflexions from $KAl(SO_4)_2.12H_2O$ and $KAl(SeO_4)_2.12H_2O$

Indices	111	222	333	444	555	666	777	888
Sulphate	$\overline{38}$	19	125	6	49	86	$\overline{34}$	16
Selenate	$\overline{48}$	$\overline{52}$	64	0	116	100	$\overline{16}$	0

The values for the selenate were given the same signs as for the sulphate (deduced from table 209); only for 222 did the assignment prove wrong. The incorrectness of the parameter 0·36 is evident from the decrease in structure amplitude of the reflexion 333.

was proved therefore that the apparently reasonable deduction that the sulphur lay in the high peak of fig. 210 was wrong, and that the much smaller peak at $u = 0{\cdot}19$ was the correct one. This result indicates the danger of relying only upon projections on to lines, as these can be deceptive because of the possibility of overlapping of several lighter atoms. In fact, since the space group contains three-fold axes, three atoms in general positions *must* project on to the same point on the axis; three oxygen atoms, which are heavier than one sulphur atom, would therefore give a larger peak in the Fourier synthesis.

This difficulty was increased inadvertently by the adoption of an artificial temperature factor in the computation of the curves shown in fig. 210, as false detail due to the arbitrary termination of the series was feared; the curves shown in fig. 211 are derived from data that do

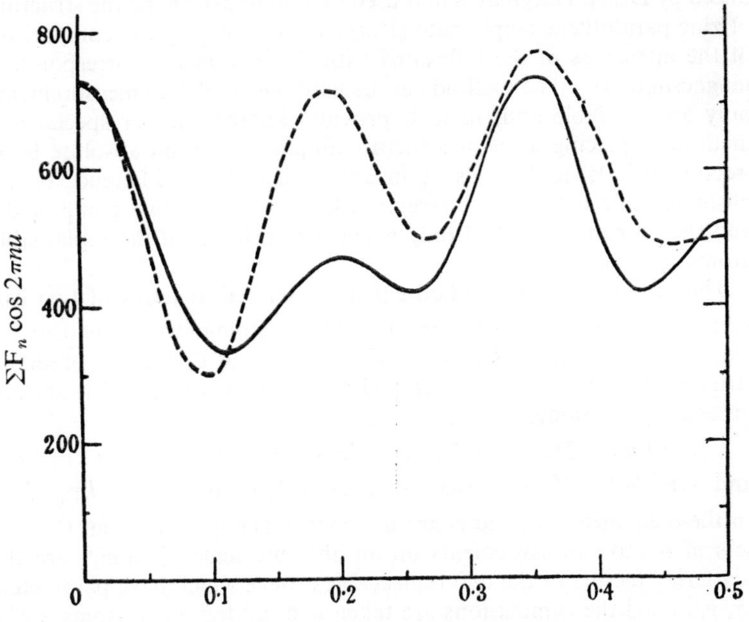

FIG. 211. Electron densities, in arbitrary units, between the (111) planes in KAl $(SO_4)_2 12H_2O$ (full line) and KAl $(SeO_4)_2 12H_2O$ (broken line). The enhancement of the peak at 0·20 shows that the S and Se parameters are in this vicinity (Beevers and Lipson, 1935)

not include this factor, and it will be seen that the sulphur peak is more pronounced: but whether this fact would have helped to locate the sulphur atoms is doubtful. This experience does, however, suggest that the adoption of an artificial temperature factor is rather dangerous; even if it is considered essential, the computations without the factor should also be carried out to see if any significant detail has been lost.

When the three heavy atoms had been located, the determination of the remaining atoms, by two-dimensional Fourier methods, was straightforward.

Despite its lack of complete success, Cork's work illustrates well the principles of the isomorphous-replacement method, and it also illustrates some of the difficulties that are met with when only a pair of compounds is available. Thus the change of sign for 111 on passing from rubidium to potassium would not have been evident. Similar difficulties arose in the change from rubidium to potassium benzyl penicillin (Crowfoot et al., 1949); for example, the two structure amplitudes for the reflexion 004 were 7 and 5, but nevertheless there was a large contribution from the alkali atoms, since it ultimately turned out that the structure factors were +7 and −5.

Such difficulties can be avoided by a more general method introduced by Dr. A. Hargreaves and used by him to determine the structure of zinc paratoluene sulphonate (Hargreaves, 1946), by the comparison of the intensities of the reflexions with those from the corresponding magnesium salt. The method can be used when relative measurements only are available and, in fact, provides another, rather specialized, method of placing a set of structure amplitudes on an absolute basis (section 6.5.3); it depends upon knowledge of the difference on an absolute scale between the structure factors for the two compounds, and thus it can be applied only when the positions of the replaceable atoms are known.

The principle of the method can be described in terms of two isomorphous crystals of space group $P\bar{1}$, containing two equivalent replaceable atoms in the unit cell. Then, if F'_a and F'_b are the observed structure factors for the two crystals, on relative scales which are not necessarily the same,

$$c_a F'_a(hkl) = 2f_a \cos 2\pi(hx+ky+lz) + 2\sum f_n \cos 2\pi(hx_n+ky_n+lz_n)$$

and $$c_b F'_b(hkl) = 2f_b \cos 2\pi(hx+ky+lz) + 2\sum f_n \cos 2\pi(hx_n+ky_n+lz_n).$$

In these equations, c_a and c_b are the constants required to put the two sets of relative measurements on an absolute scale, f_a and f_b are the scattering factors of the two replaceable atoms, which have parameters (x, y, z) and the summations are taken over all the other atoms in the cell, which are supposed to have the same parameters in the two crystals. Thus, since the value of the summation is the same for the two crystals

$$c_a F'_a(hkl) - 2f_a \cos 2\pi(hx+ky+lz) = c_b F'_a(hkl) - 2f_b \cos 2\pi(hx+ky+lz),$$

or $$c_a F'_a(hkl) - c_b F'_b(hkl) - 2(f_a - f_b) \cos 2\pi(hx+ky+lz) = 0. \quad (212.1)$$

The basis of the method is the graphical plotting of a relationship between the two sets of structure amplitudes, and in order to put this in its simplest form, we may rewrite equation *212*.1 as

$$c_a \frac{F'_a(hkl)}{\cos 2\pi(hx+ky+lz)} - c_b \frac{F'_b(hkl)}{\cos 2\pi(hx+ky+lz)} - 2(f_a - f_b) = 0, \quad (212.2)$$

in which all the quantities are known except c_a and c_b. The quantity $f_a - f_b$ is not, however, a constant, and although this fact could be allowed for by multiplying each equation by the appropriate factor to make $f_a - f_b$ constant, this cannot be carried out unless the temperature factor is known. Hargreaves found it simpler to consider only those reflexions within a small range of Bragg angle, for which the scattering factors can be considered as constant. Since the scattering factors of lighter atoms tend to fall off more rapidly than do those of heavier ones, the difference may tend to be reasonably constant.

Difficulties will be met for those reflexions for which $\cos 2\pi(hx+ky+lz)$ is small, as then the quantities in equation *212.2* will be large and will not plot accurately; this corresponds, of course, to the fact that the signs of the structure factors cannot be determined from those reflexions for which the replaceable atoms have zero or only small contributions. In Hargreaves' work this difficulty did not arise, because the zinc and magnesium atoms lay in special positions at the origin of the projection (compare section **8**.3.2); thus $f_a - f_b$ was always a maximum—the most favourable case.

Values of the two sets of relative structure amplitudes for reflexions with $\sin\theta < 0{\cdot}25$ are given in table 213.

TABLE 213

Values of F($h0l$) for Zn and Mg paratoluene sulphonate

hkl	200	400	600	800	101	301	501	701
F'_a	13·1	9·9	14·8	11·5	3·4	20·2	22·4	22·5
F'_b	5·3	2·5	12·1	10·5	6·3	9·0	11·1	11·5
hkl	$\bar{1}01$	$\bar{3}01$	$\bar{5}01$	$\bar{7}01$	002	202	402	$\bar{2}02$
F'_a	3·3	21·7	22·6	14·1	28·5	8·1	4·7	9·0
F'_b	5·9	10·9	12·4	7·1	15·8	8·1	—	9·5

A graph showing the relationship between these values is shown in fig. 214, and it will be seen that most of them lie reasonably well upon a straight line; some of them, however, appear to lie upon another parallel straight line, but this is so only because no account has been taken of the possibility of change of sign, and if five of the values are plotted with negative signs, as shown in fig. 214, all lie quite well upon the same straight line. Thus the signs of all the structure factors of the two crystals were established.

If a change of sign occurred on replacement, as was mentioned earlier in the penicillin work, the corresponding point would lie in the upper left-hand quadrant of fig. 214, and one example of such a point was found when reflexions at higher values of θ were examined. Such values, however, are found only rarely, as both reflexions must be weak when the replacement of one atom is sufficient to change the sign. The intercepts of the straight line on the axes of the graph give the values of c_a and c_b required to put the measurements on an absolute basis. Thus when $F'_b = 0$, $F'_a = 5{\cdot}4$, and thus $c_a = 2(f_a - f_b)/5{\cdot}4$. The mean value of $f_a - f_b$ over the range considered can be derived from tables of scattering factors, and so c_a can be derived. For zinc paratoluene sulphonate, there are two metal atoms in the true unit cell (as distinct from the unit cell of the projection), and thus if $f_a - f_b$ is taken as 16, values of structure factors corresponding to the complete unit cell are obtained if c_a is taken as $2 \times 16/5{\cdot}4 = 5{\cdot}9$.

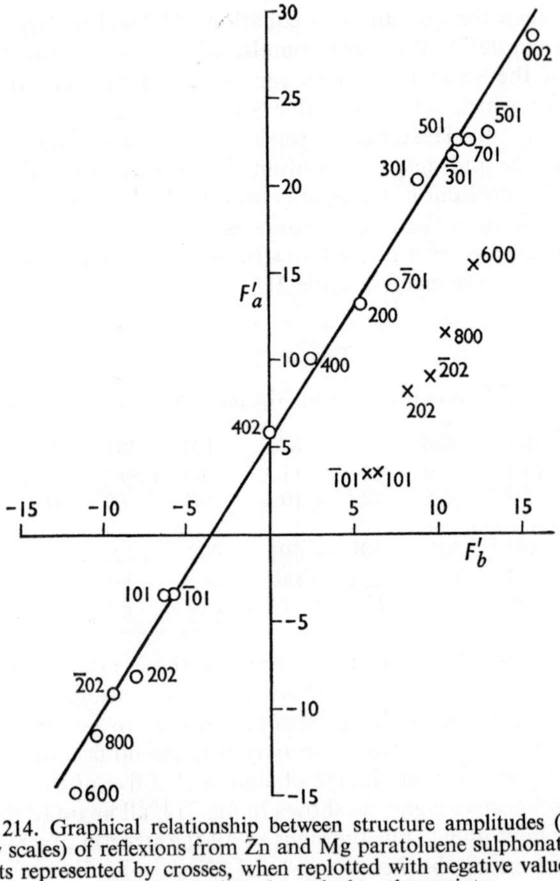

FIG. 214. Graphical relationship between structure amplitudes (on arbitrary scales) of reflexions from Zn and Mg paratoluene sulphonates. The points represented by crosses, when replotted with negative values, lie on the straight line through the other points

By these means, the signs of all the structure factors in the $h0l$ zone were derived correctly, giving the projection of the structure shown in fig. 215. The methods are similar to those used by Robertson and Woodward (1937*b*) to find the signs of the $h0l$ structure factors of phthalocyanine; these authors observed the changes that occurred when a nickel atom was placed in the molecule. They made use, however, of absolute values of the structure amplitudes, so that signs could be allotted almost by inspection. Hargreaves' work is therefore more general.

The isomorphous-replacement method has proved to be extremely fruitful, one of its outstanding triumphs being the determination of the structure of the strychnine molecule, which had baffled the chemist

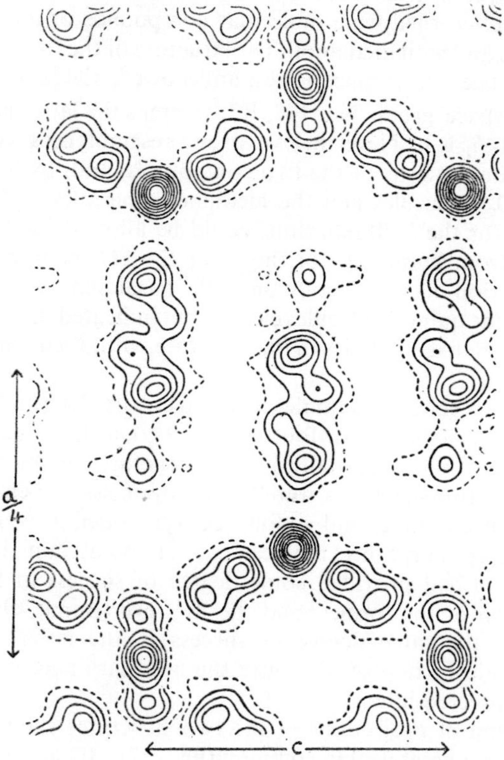

FIG. 215. Zinc paratoluene sulphonate: (010) electron-density projection (Hargreaves, 1946)

for some considerable time. Containing only carbon, nitrogen, oxygen and hydrogen atoms, the molecule itself cannot easily be dealt with by trial-and-error methods, and success was achieved by forming compounds with acid molecules. Bokhoven, Schoone and Bijvoet (1948, 1949, 1951) used compounds with sulphuric and selenic acid, and found a molecular structure in excellent agreement with that finally decided upon by chemical considerations (Robinson and Stephen, 1948).

3.4. *Comparison of related structures.* Methods similar to those involving isomorphous replacement can sometimes be applied to substances that are related to each other but which are not isomorphous. No general rules governing the application of these methods can be laid down, and recognition of opportunities of using them depends to a considerable degree upon the intuition and background knowledge of the investigator; all that can be done at this stage is to provide examples for guidance of those who may wish to explore the possibilities of such methods.

One example is that given by Palin and Powell (1948). The two compounds concerned were molecular compounds of quinol with sulphur dioxide and with methanol. The structure of the former compound had already been determined (Palin and Powell, 1947), and was found to have the space group No. 148, $R\bar{3}$, whereas the latter had the space group No. 146, R3. Nevertheless, strong resemblances were found in the diffraction patterns of the two compounds, and, by assuming that both the SO_2 molecules and the methanol molecules scatter as single units, signs for the *hki*0 reflexions could be allotted for the methanol compound from knowledge of those for the SO_2 compound; in this way a projection of the structure on to the basal plane was derived, and this showed the quinol molecules clearly, but indicated that the methanol molecules were fixed in holes in the structure, with their lengths parallel to the *c* axis.

A still more general example occurred in the determination of the structure of penicillin (Crowfoot et al., 1949), as here the comparison of the results for two partially known structures enabled both to be derived. The two structures were those of potassium benzyl penicillin which is orthorhombic, and sodium benzyl penicillin which is monoclinic; the isomorphous replacement of potassium by rubidium (section 6.5.7) had provided some degree of success in the structure determination of the former, and the fly's eye (Bunn, 1961) had provided about the same degree of success in the latter: but neither structure could be improved to give the necessary agreement of calculated and observed intensities.

Comparison of projections of the two structures showed, however, that they had a great deal in common (fig. 217). By adopting the common features and rejecting the others, a new type of molecular configuration was found to fit fairly well, and refinement produced the correct structure.

The investigation was of far-reaching importance. At the beginning little was known of the stereochemistry of the penicillin molecule, although enough was known to provide a start. In the later stages, however, the proposed chemical configurations tended to hinder progress, and the final success was due to the purely physical considerations just described. In the variety of methods used to determine the structure, this investigation stands supreme.

3.5. *Generalized crystal-structure projections.* Sometimes a crystal is found for which all the atoms are well resolved in one projection, making possible the assignment of, say, *x* and *y* coordinates, but for which there is no other clear projection. The evaluation of the electron density in three dimensions, or of a projected section, would require the measurement of general *hkl* structure amplitudes. Sometimes it may not be possible to avoid this, but unless very accurate coordinates are required a generalized projection or 'higher-layer-line synthesis' may be used to provide approximate z-coordinates, without requiring a great deal of experimental measurement or calculation.

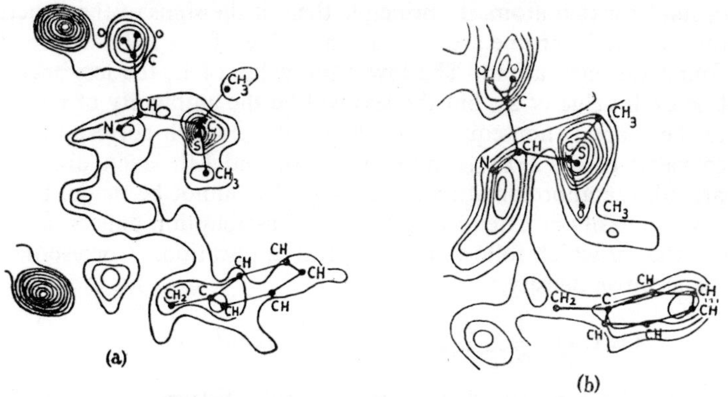

Fig. 217. Rubidium benzylpenicillin and sodium benzylpenicillin; comparison of approximate electron-density projections, showing similar groupings of atoms (Crowfoot et al., 1949)

The principle of the generalized projection may be made clear by considering first of all a crystal whose space group is No. 10, P112/*m*. The structure factor F(*hk*0) is given by

$$F(hk0) = 4 \sum_{n=1}^{N/4} f_n(hk0) \cos 2\pi(hx_n + ky_n), \qquad (217.1)$$

where $f_n(hk0)$ is the value of f_n for the reflexion *hk*0; and the electron density projected on (001) is given by

$$\rho(x, y) = \frac{1}{A} \sum_h \sum_k F(hk0) \cos 2\pi(hx + ky). \qquad (217.2)$$

The corresponding formula for a structure factor which belongs to the Lth layer, is

$$F(hkL) = 4 \sum_{n=1}^{N/4} [f_n(hkL) \cos 2\pi L z_n] \cos 2\pi(hx_n + ky_n). \qquad (217.3)$$

The contribution of the *n*th atom to F(*hk*L) is the same as if this were an (*hk*0) structure factor, but the atomic scattering factor had been changed from $f_n(hk0)$ to $f_n(hkL) \cos 2\pi L z_n$. By analogy with equations *10*.3 and *12*.2, the function

$$C_L(x, y) = \frac{1}{A} \sum \sum F(hkL) \cos 2\pi(hx + ky)$$

will contain projected 'atoms' at all the points $(x_n y_n)$, the shape of each atom being such that its scattering factor at the point (hk) is $f_n(hk\mathrm{L}) \cos 2\pi \mathrm{L} z_n$. This is a function of h and k only; if the real atom is spherically symmetric its 'generalized projection' will have circular symmetry. If the difference between $f_n(hk\mathrm{L})$ and $f_n(hk0)$ is small, to a good approximation $\mathrm{C}_L(xy)$ represents a projection of the structure on (001), with the electron density in the nth atom multiplied by $\cos 2\pi \mathrm{L} z_n$, a constant for that atom. In principle then, if the signs of the structure factors of one layer line are known, the value of $\cos 2\pi \mathrm{L} z$ can readily be found for each atom. The lower the value of L, the less accurate will be each value of z_n, but the less will be the ambiguity of position, since there are L non-equivalent values of z_n which correspond to a given value of $\cos 2\pi \mathrm{L} z_n$. When the zero and Lth layers are widely separated, the approximation $f(hk0) = f(hk\mathrm{L})$ cannot be made, but the theory can easily be extended to make this assumption unnecessary.

The theory which follows is of general application. Corresponding to the electron density,

$$\rho(x, y, z) = \frac{1}{\mathrm{V}} \sum_h \sum_k \sum_l \mathrm{F}(hkl) \exp\{-2\pi i(hx + ky + lz)\},$$

we define the generalized projection of this distribution on a plane perpendicular to the c-axis as

$$\rho_L(x, y) = c \int_0^1 \rho(x, y, z) \exp[2\pi i \mathrm{L} z] dz. \qquad (218.1)$$

Substituting for $\rho(xyz)$ from *12.2* and using the fact that

$$\int_0^1 \exp[2\pi i(\mathrm{L} - l)z] dz = 1 \text{ when } l = \mathrm{L}$$
$$= 0 \text{ when } l \neq \mathrm{L},$$

we find that

$$\rho_L(x, y) = \frac{1}{\mathrm{A}} \sum_h \sum_k \mathrm{F}(hk\mathrm{L}) \exp[-2\pi i(hx + ky)]. \qquad (218.2)$$

If we let $\mathrm{F}(hk\mathrm{L}) = \mathrm{A}(hk\mathrm{L}) + i\mathrm{B}(hk\mathrm{L})$ as usual, and

$$\rho_L(x, y) = \mathrm{C}_L(x, y) + i\mathrm{S}_L(x, y), \qquad (218.3)$$

we have from *218.2*,

$$\left.\begin{aligned} \mathrm{C}_L(x, y) &= \frac{1}{\mathrm{A}} \sum_h \sum_k \{\mathrm{A}(hk\mathrm{L}) \cos 2\pi(hx + ky) + \mathrm{B}(hk\mathrm{L}) \sin 2\pi(hx + ky)\} \\ &\text{and} \\ \mathrm{S}_L(x, y) &= \frac{1}{\mathrm{A}} \sum_h \sum_k \{\mathrm{B}(hk\mathrm{L}) \cos 2\pi(hx + ky) - \mathrm{A}(hk\mathrm{L}) \sin 2\pi(hx + ky)\}. \end{aligned}\right\} \qquad (218.4)$$

These functions assume simpler forms when the structure possesses symmetry. For example, for space group No. 10, P112/m, $\mathrm{C}_L(x, y) = \frac{1}{\mathrm{A}} \sum_h \sum_k \mathrm{F}(hk\mathrm{L}) \cos 2\pi(hx + ky)$ as we have already seen, and $\mathrm{S}_L(xy) = 0$.

We now make use of the fact that when the structure is composed of spherically-symmetric atoms,

$$\mathrm{F}(hk\mathrm{L}) = \sum_{n=1}^{N} f_n(hk\mathrm{L}) \exp\{2\pi i(hx_n + ky_n + \mathrm{L}z_n)\}. \qquad (219.1)$$

Substituting in equation *218*.2 and using equation *218*.3 we find

$$\left.\begin{aligned} \mathrm{C}_L(x, y) &= \sum_{n=1}^{N} \sigma_{nL}(x - x_n, y - y_n) \cos 2\pi \mathrm{L}z_n \\ \text{and} \quad \mathrm{S}_L(x, y) &= \sum_{n=1}^{N} \sigma_{nL}(x - x_n, y - y_n) \sin 2\pi \mathrm{L}z_n, \end{aligned}\right\} \qquad (219.2)$$

where $$\sigma_{nL}(x, y) = \frac{1}{\mathrm{A}} \sum_h \sum_k f_n(hk\mathrm{L}) \exp\{-2\pi i(hx + ky)\}. \qquad (219.3)$$

These results express the fact that $\mathrm{C}_L(x, y)$, for instance, can be built up by multiplying each $\sigma_{nL}(x, y)$ by a factor $\cos 2\pi\mathrm{L}z_n$ and centring it at the point (x_n, y_n). The function $\sigma_{nL}(x, y)$ corresponds to the electron distribution of the nth atom in an ordinary projection. It can readily be evaluated from equation *219*.3, in which $\exp\{-2\pi i(hx + ky)\}$ can be replaced by $\cos 2\pi(hx + ky)$, since $f_n(hk\mathrm{L}) = f_n(\overline{hk}\mathrm{L})$. In fact, since $\sigma_{nL}(x, y)$ is circularly symmetric, it will be sufficient to evaluate

$$\sigma_{nL}(x, 0) = \frac{1}{\mathrm{A}} \sum_h \{\sum_k f_n(hk\mathrm{L})\} \, . \cos 2\pi hx.$$

Comparison of the heights of the peaks in $\mathrm{C}_L(x, y)$ or $\mathrm{S}_L(x, y)$ with the corresponding $\sigma_{nL}(x, y)$ then gives $\cos 2\pi\mathrm{L}z_n$ or $\sin 2\pi\mathrm{L}z_n$.

It is clear that in practice only a very inaccurate value of z_n can be obtained if $\mathrm{C}_1(x, y)$ is being used, and $z_n = 0$, for instance. Nevertheless the generalized projection has been found to be useful in practical crystal-structure analysis, as the following example will show. Crystals of diglycylglycine ethyl ester hydrochloride and the corresponding hydrobromide are isomorphous (Dyer, 1951*b*). The unit-cell dimensions of the two compounds differ very little, and the space group is No. 61, P*cab*. The projection of the electron density on (100), shown in fig. 220, was obtained by the isomorphous-replacement method (section 8.3.3). In this projection the unit cell is halved in the direction of the *c*-axis. Two molecules related by a glide plane at $y = \frac{1}{4}$, which appears as a plane of symmetry in projection, overlap in projection. In the diagram one molecule is distinguished by lines representing bonds, but at first, of course, there was no way of telling which atom belonged to which molecule. The projection on (010) does not resolve this ambiguity, and in any case this projection could not be obtained by the isomorphous-replacement method; the replaceable atom has an x-coordinate of zero and therefore does not contribute to one half of the $\mathrm{F}(h0l)$'s. The difficulties were overcome by evaluating the function $\mathrm{C}_1(y, z)$.

Since the structure is centrosymmetric, we have from equation *218.4*,

$$C_1(y, z) = \frac{1}{A} \sum_k \sum_l F(1kl) \cos 2\pi(ky + lz). \qquad (220.1)$$

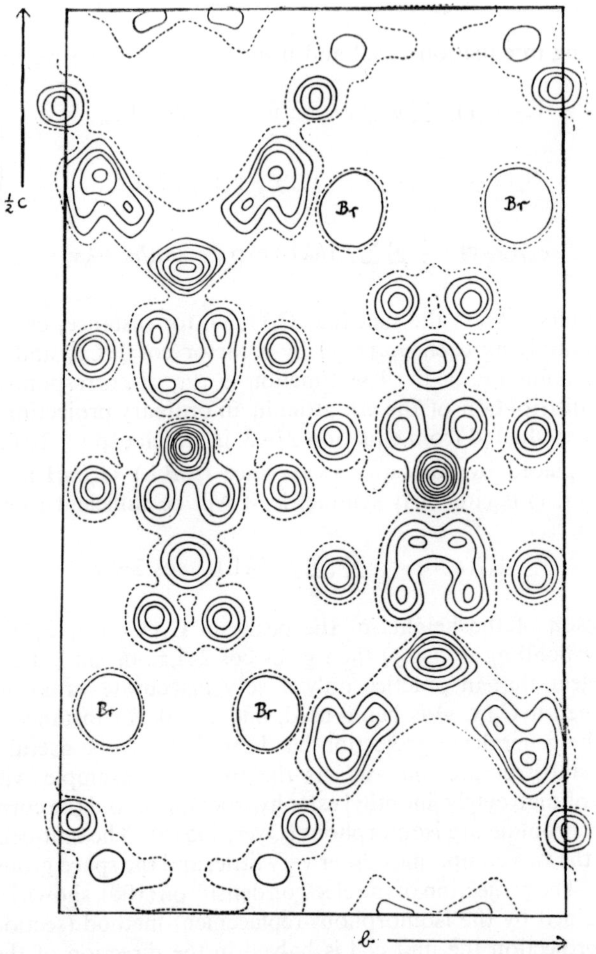

FIG. 220. Projection of electron density in diglycylglycine ethyl-ester hydrobromide on (100)

From the relations between F(1*kl*), F(1$\bar{k}\bar{l}$), etc., which are given by Lonsdale (1936) for this space group, we find

$$C(yz) = \frac{4}{A}\left\{\sum_{k=1}^{\infty} \sum_{l=1}^{\infty} F(1kl) \cos 2\pi ky \cos 2\pi lz\right\} \quad k \text{ odd}, l \text{ odd}$$

$$-\frac{4}{A}\left\{\sum_{k=2}^{\infty} \sum_{l=1}^{\infty} F(1kl) \sin 2\pi ky \sin 2\pi lz\right\} \quad k \text{ even}, l \text{ odd} \qquad (220.2)$$

Only $F(1kl)$'s for which l is odd are involved, and their signs can be determined by the isomorphous-replacement method. $C_1(y, z)$ was

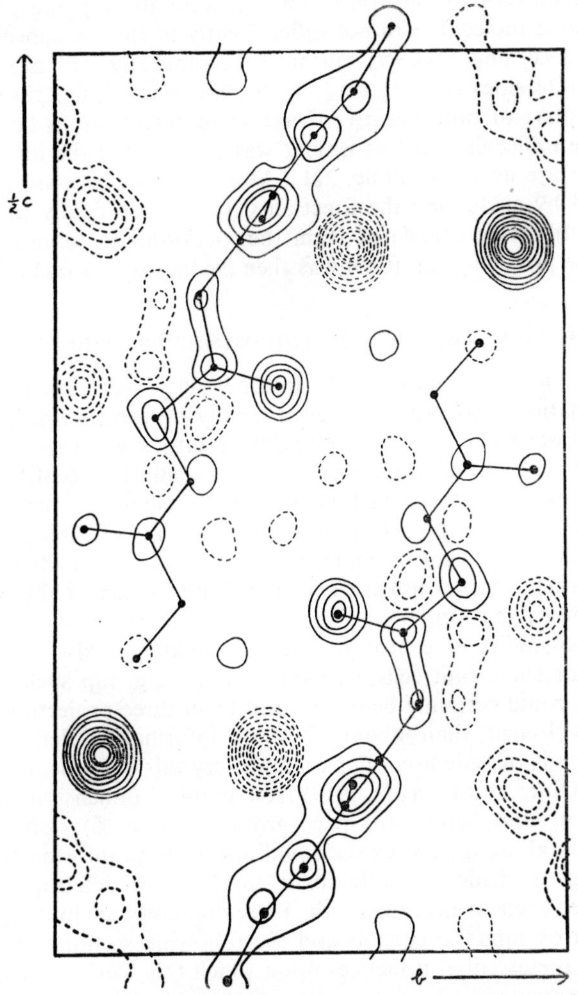

FIG. 221. Generalised projection of diglycylglycine ethyl-ester hydrobromide obtained from the structure factors $F(1kl)$. The separate molecules can be easily recognized from this projection although they overlap in Fig. 220

evaluated for the compound diglycylglycine ethyl ester hydrobromide; the result is shown in fig. 221. The plane of symmetry at $y = \frac{1}{4}$ in fig. 220 is now replaced by a plane of antisymmetry. This follows from the fact that two atoms related by the glide plane at $y = \frac{1}{4}$ have coordinates (xyz) and $(\frac{1}{2} + x, \frac{1}{2} - y, z)$. The heights of the corresponding peaks in $C_1(y, z)$ therefore depend on $\cos 2\pi x$ and $\cos 2\pi(\frac{1}{2} + x)$; that is, they are equal in magnitude but opposite in sign. A comparison of the heights of the peaks in fig. 220 with those in fig. 221 gave approximate x-coordinates for all the atoms. Two adjacent atoms p and q belonging to the same molecule will not differ greatly in their x-coordinates, so that $\cos 2\pi x_p$ and $\cos 2\pi x_q$ will have the same sign unless p and q lie on opposite sides of $x=\frac{1}{4}$ or $\frac{3}{4}$. Adjacent peaks in fig. 221 which are both positive or both negative therefore represent atoms belonging to the same molecule. In this way, it was proved that the atoms of one molecule are as shown in fig. 221. More accurate x-coordinates were obtained by evaluating the function $C_3(y, z)$, and finally the signs of the $F(h0l)$'s were calculated from the x-coordinates obtained in this way; the projection on (010) was then evaluated and refined.

4. Methods for Non-centrosymmetric Structures

4.1. *Need for a general method.* In the early years of crystal-structure determination emphasis was placed largely on centrosymmetric structures. It was sometimes said that most structures were centrosymmetric and that any non-centrosymmetric ones usually had centrosymmetric projections. Whatever justification this statement ever had, it is certainly not true now; in particular, structures of biological importance cannot be centrosymmetric because an asymmetric molecule could form a centrosymmetric crystal only if it is partnered by one of an enantiomorphic form.

The possibility of centrosymmetric projection is also now of little help. For small unit cells, structures of space group such as $P2_12_12_1$ (No. 19) could certainly be determined from three projections, but for any axis longer than about 12 Å the information derived from a projection is of little use. For example, crystals of horse haemoglobin (Cullis, Dintzis and Perutz, 1957) have unit-cell dimensions of 109, 63 and 55 Å, and belong to space group C2 (No. 5); obviously the projection along the 63 Å axis would not be at all informative.

The great strides recently made in structure determination have therefore been concerned with three-dimensional investigation of non-centrosymmetric crystals and the following sections are designed to show the essential principles upon which this work has been based.

4.2. *Heavy-atom method.* In principle, the heavy-atom method may be used in the same way as for centrosymmetric structures; the heavy atom may be found, for example, by Patterson methods and may then be used to give a first approximation to the phase of each X-ray reflexion.

The success of the method depends upon the relative weight of the heavy atom (section 8.3.2). Sim (1961) has introduced the quantity $r\ (=\Sigma f_H^2/\Sigma f_L^2)$ where f_H and f_L are the atomic numbers of the heavy atoms and light atoms respectively; he gives a diagram (fig. 223) which shows the proportion, $N(\xi)$ of various errors ξ—20°, 60°, 100°—if the phase angle is assumed to be that due to the heavy atom alone. For $r=1$, about a third of the reflexions will have errors less than 20°, and four-fifths will have errors less than 60°. One would therefore expect this value of r to give a reasonable Fourier synthesis.

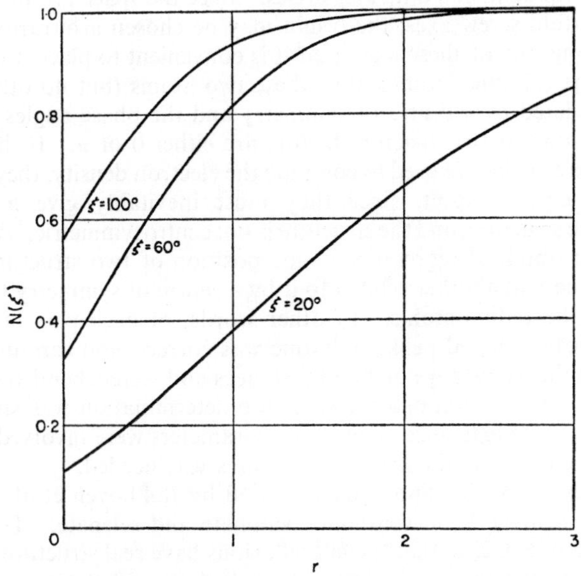

FIG. 223. N(ξ) as a function of r. The curves shown are for $\xi=20°$, 60° and 100°

It has already been pointed out in section **8**.3.2 that the success of these methods does not necessarily depend upon the accuracy with which the phase angles deduced from the heavy atom alone reproduce the true phase angles; with $r=3$ over four-fifths of the reflexions will have errors less than 20°. But with such a large value of r, the lighter atoms would not be easily seen since they would be obscured by the irregularities caused by experimental errors. Success therefore depends considerably on accurate measurement; the higher the value of r, the more accurate the measurements must be to produce significant results.

4.3. *Heavy-atom symmetry and pseudosymmetry.* Before discussing the method further, and giving examples of its use, it is necessary to describe another difficulty that arises surprisingly often—the problem of pseudosymmetry. In other words, the positions of the heavy atom may simulate the symmetry of a higher space group and the phases deduced from them may therefore necessarily give false information about the structure.

One of the earliest examples of this difficulty was provided by cholesteryl iodide (section 8.3.2). The space group is $P2_1$ (No. 4) and therefore only the projection along *b* is centrosymmetric; from fig. 206 we can see that this is not particularly clear. Three-dimensional work had therefore to be undertaken.

Here a fundamental difficulty arises. Since the space group contains only two-fold screw axes, the origin may be chosen arbitrarily at any point along one of these axes, and it is convenient to place it half-way between two iodine atoms; thus these two atoms (but no others) are exactly related by a centre of symmetry and the phase angles of their contributions to the structure factors are either 0 or π. If, however, these phase angles are used to compute the electron density, they cannot give the correct result, since they must inevitably give a centrosymmetric structure, and the structure is not centrosymmetric. Actually, the result obtained represents a superposition of two structures—the correct one and another related to it by a centre of symmetry half-way between the iodine atoms. In other words, of each pair of centrosymmetrically related peaks only one was correct, and careful choice, based on the knowledge of bond distances and stereochemistry had to be made. Thus, although the structure determination was successful —a remarkable feat since eighty-four parameters were involved—prior knowledge of the main structural features was needed.

Another interesting approach was used by Bokhoven et al. (section 8.3.3) in their work on strychnine sulphate and selenate. The space group is No. 5, C2, so that the *h*0*l* reflexions have real structure factors, but all the others are complex. The calculation of the projection of the electron density upon the (010) plane, followed the general lines already described, the sulphur and selenium atoms, since they lie upon the two-fold axes, being at the origin of the projection. With a molecule as complicated as strychnine, however, the details cannot be firmly established from one projection alone, and other projections had to be considered. For these projections the isomorphous-replacement method does not produce unique values for the phase angles.

This can be seen by drawing a diagram representing the vectors F_S and F_{Se}, which are structure factors for the sulphate and selenate respectively. Now, since the space group C2 has no absolute origin, a sulphur atom may be taken as defining the origin, and consequently the contribution of the sulphur atoms will be the maximum possible for the real parts of the structure factors, and zero for the imaginary parts. Thus when sulphur is replaced by selenium, the real parts of the structure factors will be increased by an amount Δf—the difference between the scattering factors of selenium and sulphur—and the imaginary parts will be unchanged. These facts are represented in fig. 225, and it will be seen that if α_S is the phase angle for the sulphate,

$$\cos \alpha_S = \frac{|F_{Se}|^2 - |F_S|^2 - (\Delta f)^2}{2|F_S|\Delta f}$$

Since all the quantities on the right-hand side are known, α_S can be evaluated, but there is no indication of its sign.

The method of overcoming this difficulty was as follows. Suppose we perform a summation with terms corresponding to both signs; that is, in addition to the term

$$F(hk0)\cos\{2\pi(hx+ky)+\alpha(h,k)\}$$

we include another,

$$F(hk0)\cos\{2\pi(hx+ky)-\alpha(h,k)\}.$$

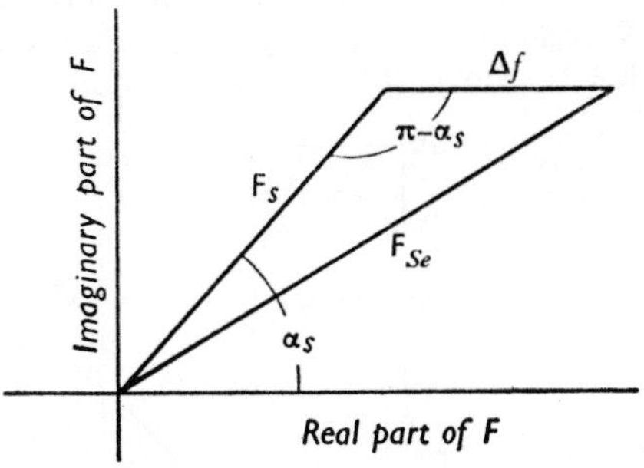

FIG. 225. Derivation of phase angles α_S for strychnine sulphate

The summation is then of the form

$$\sum_h \sum_k F(hk0)\cos\alpha(h,k)\cos 2\pi(hx+ky),$$

and, since this corresponds to a summation with real coefficients, the result is centrosymmetric. Obviously, it corresponds to a superposition of the true structure on to its symmetrically related counterpart, and, as with the investigation of cholesteryl iodide, each atom is represented by a pair of peaks, one of which has to be discarded. The choice was made from knowledge of the projection on (010), and of interatomic distances.

In the orthorhombic system the same sort of trouble can arise accidentally if one of the coordinates of the heavy atom happens to approximate to a special value. Thus Norton, Kartha and Lu (1964) investigated the structure of 4-bromoestradiol-methanol, $C_{19}H_{27}O_3Br$ and found the space group to be $P2_12_12_1$ (No. 19); by three-dimensional Patterson methods the parameters of the bromine atoms were found to be 0·205, 0·190 and 0·233. This last parameter is uncomfortably close to $\frac{1}{4}$ so that, to a first approximation, the arrangement of bromine atoms has mirror-plane symmetry; the coordinates become $x, y, \frac{1}{4}$; $\frac{1}{2}-x, \bar{y}, \frac{3}{4}$; $\frac{1}{2}+x, \frac{1}{2}-y, \frac{3}{4}$; $\bar{x}, \frac{1}{2}+y, \frac{1}{4}$. This arrangement has a centre of symmetry at $(\frac{1}{4}, 0, 0)$, and thus all the phase angles must be either $0, \pi/2, \pi$ or $3\pi/2$.

A Fourier synthesis based upon the phases given by the bromine positions therefore showed a mirror plane, and thus each of the light atoms was represented by two peaks of which only one was correct. In the same way as for cholesteryl iodide, stereochemical considerations helped to decide upon the positions of the light atoms and 16 out of 21 were located successfully. These were sufficient to give the right symmetry, and the rest of the atoms were then found from further Fourier syntheses.

4.4. *Weighting of structure factors.* Since some of the phase angles of moderately strong reflexions will be almost independent of the positions of the heavy atoms, a weighting procedure similar to that proposed by Woolfson for centrosymmetric structures can again be used (section 8.3.2). Sim (1961) suggests the quantity W shown graphically in fig. 226.

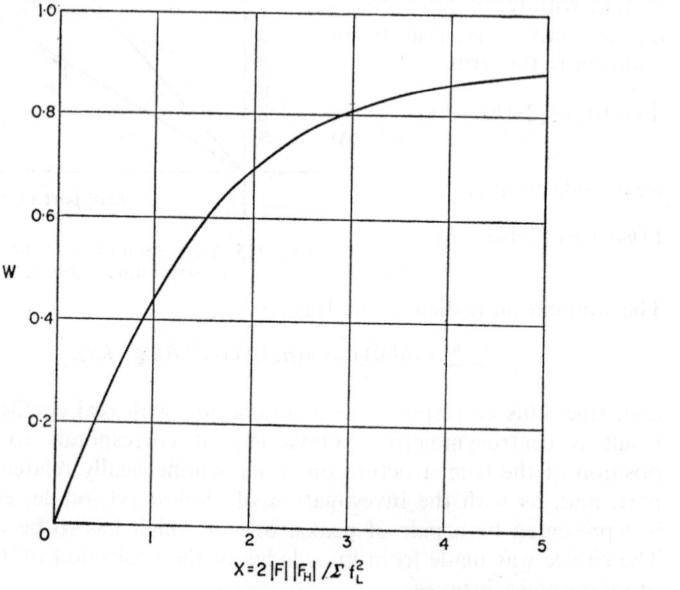

FIG. 226. The weighting function which minimizes for the noncentrosymmetric case the mean-square error in electron density due to the phase-angle errors ($\alpha - \alpha_H$)

4.5. *Some examples.* The structure described in section 8.4.3, $C_{19}H_{27}O_3Br$, has a value of r of 1·4, and therefore contains an atom of about the right weight for the heavy-atom method to work. The work on dihydro-β-erythroidine hydrobromide, $C_{16}H_{22}NO_3Br$ (Hanson, 1962) followed a very similar course. For this molecule $r = 1{\cdot}5$. The space group was $P2_12_12_1$, and both the x and z coordinates of the bromine atoms were near to $\frac{1}{4}$. Hanson found that a marked improvement of the Fourier synthesis occurred if the bromine atoms were assumed to lie exactly on mirror planes; the symmetry of the Fourier synthesis was then exact and the other peaks easier to interpret.

The heavy-atom method can work with values of r much smaller than unity. One reason for this is that the method of computing r from atomic numbers is artificial; a more realistic value would be that obtained from the average relative scattering factors, but the work of obtaining these is hardly justified for this rather trivial purpose. Nevertheless, it is known that the scattering factors of the heavier atoms relative to those of the lighter atoms increases with angle, and so the value of r for higher angles for the compounds just described should be greater than the values given. In particular, for assessing r it is certainly better to ignore hydrogen than to include it.

This may explain the success obtained in the investigation of vitamin B_{12} (Hodgkin, Kamper, Lindsey, Mackay, Pickworth, Robertson, Shoemaker, White, Prosen and Trueblood, 1957). The formula was found to be $C_{62}H_{88}O_{14}N_{14}PCo$ and at first sight it seems unlikely that the cobalt atom could be heavy enough to enable the heavy-atom method to be used; the value of r is only 0·15. If however we compute r with scattering factors at $\sin\theta/\lambda = 0{\cdot}30$, with values taken from the International Tables, Vol. III (table 3.3.1A) it becomes 0·37—a value still small but not quite so unhopeful as that computed from atomic numbers.

FIG. 227. Section at $x = \frac{1}{2}$ of Patterson synthesis of vitamin B_{12}

The positions of the cobalt atoms were clearly indicated in the Patterson synthesis computed with sharpened coefficients (section 7.4.2). In addition, knowledge of the expected environment around the cobalt atom enabled certain other deductions to be made. Fig. 227 shows part of the section of the Patterson synthesis at $x = \frac{1}{2}$ for the air-dried crystal; this gives a clear idea of the boldness that is necessary in order to make progress. One cannot expect precise information; peaks are not clear and well defined and there may be much confusion caused by diffraction effects and false symmetry (section **8**.4.3).

The important fact is that a start *can* be made: an electron-density calculation showed the positions of the phosphorous atoms and confirmed the orientation of the planar groups around the cobalt atoms (fig. 228). Here again the boldness in interpretation is well illustrated. It will be seen that it is not necessary at this stage that atoms should be indicated by peaks; it is sufficient that the postulated atomic positions should lie on positive regions of electron density. Then the agreement residual is bound to improve by inclusion of these postulated atoms and, for this reason, decrease of the residual is not adequate proof that the postulations are correct.

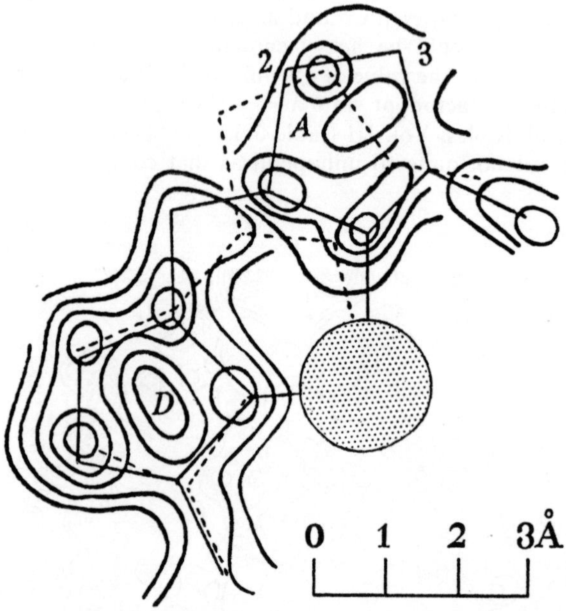

FIG. 228. Deduction of some of the atomic positions around Co (shaded spot). The broken lines show the ultimate correct positions

The real proof is that further information is also produced. At each stage, calculation will always confirm any step taken, but wrong steps will not give clear indication of any further atoms. It is obvious that extensive work of this sort is possible only by means of digital computers; without them the successful outcome of the work would not have been possible. As the investigation proceeded, more and more atoms were found, the earlier ones at the same time becoming more clearly delineated. The information spread outwards from the position of the cobalt atom, presumably because structural knowledge with respect to this atom and its environment was being used. Finally, clear fairly undistorted representations of all the atoms were found (fig. 229).

4.6. *Isomorphous replacement*. Although the heavy-atom method is adequate for structures of moderate or even considerable complexity, it still may require expert judgement and a degree of speculation that

FIG. 229. Final Fourier synthesis of part of the structure of vitamin B_{12}

make the method rather a subjective one. For those who seek a more objective method by which the phase angles would be directly determined, some further information must be obtained. The isomorphous-replacement method satisfies this condition, and, for structures containing hundreds of light atoms, it is the only method possible.

The basis for the method can be explained in terms of the Argand diagram, in which the real part of the structure factor is plotted horizontally and the imaginary part vertically. All we know about the structure factor of a single reflexion is that the resultant of the two parts lies on a circle—called the phase circle—whose radius is the structure amplitude. If we investigate another isomorphously-related compound, we have the same information about each reflexion, and also the knowledge of the difference in the scattering factors of the two replaceable atoms.

To use this information, these atoms must first be located, usually by Patterson methods. Then we know the vector contribution F_P of the atoms to the structures; we also know that the contribution F_R of the other atoms is the same, if we neglect any slight changes in parameters caused by introducing atoms of different sizes. How do we combine this information?

The information is presented in graphical form in fig. 230. F_P and $F_{P'}$ are the contributions of the replaceable atoms, and F_R is the contribution of the rest of the atoms. We can see then that if we draw two phase circles, the centre of one displaced with respect to the other by the vector distance $F_P - F_{P'}$, they must intersect in a point that gives the complete structure factor. Unfortunately they also intersect in another point which gives the same amplitude of contribution of the light atoms, but a completely different phase angle. Some further information is therefore needed.

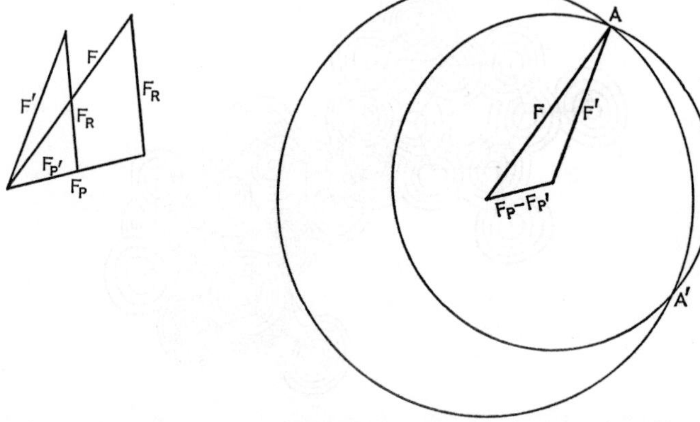

FIG. 230. Use of phase circles to determine phase angles. The two circles intersect in A, giving the correct result, but they also intersect in A′, which is incorrect

4.7. *Double isomorphous replacement.* The further information can be provided if another isomorphous compound is available with *different* replaceable atoms, Q and Q′. Then the same procedure carried through with atoms Q and Q′ produces two more intersections only one of which should coincide with one of the earlier intersections; this then is correct.

The method was first suggested by Bokhoven, Schoone and Bijvoet (1951) who gave as a possible example the compounds α-chlorine strychnine sulphate, α-chlorine strychnine selenate, and α-bromine strychnine sulphate. The method was further elaborated by Harker (1956), who suggested its application to the structure of proteins. Here it has been successful and has produced the greatest triumphs in the subject of crystal-structure analysis.

4.8. *Some practical difficulties.* The isomorphous-replacement method can be very sensitive to experimental errors in determination of the structure amplitudes. This does not matter greatly when the phase circles intersect at a large angle; but if they intersect at a small angle (fig. 230) the value of the phase angle is critically dependent upon the accuracy of the measurements and of the absolute scales upon which they are based.

Bokhoven et al. (1951) placed their results upon an absolute basis by comparison of the intensities with those obtained from the organic crystal resorcinol. Harker (1956) however points out that comparison with a standard crystal is not necessary; from the dimensions of the crystals and their absorption coefficients the structure amplitudes can be put on the same *relative* scale, and then put on to an absolute scale when the positions of the replaceable atoms have been found. Wilson's method (section 6.5.3) may also be used; although it is not very accurate for absolute standards it should be much better for relative standards since the error-producing factors are likely to be the same for both crystals.

Measurements should obviously be as accurate as possible and the development of counter diffractometers has helped greatly in this direction. Even so, it is unlikely that in the double isomorphous-replacement method the three phase circles will intersect accurately and some estimate must be made of the best value of phase angle to be used in the Fourier synthesis. It is helpful, of course, if more phase circles can be brought into play by other isomorphous replacements. Where this is not possible, the best use must be made of the data available; some general principles have been laid down by Blow and Crick (1959).

These authors discuss the problem in general terms. As we have seen, single isomorphous replacement gives two values of the phase angle, and a probability curve can be drawn showing maxima exactly at these values (fig. 232*a*). A second isomorphous replacement gives another probability curve (fig. 232*b*), and the total probability is then given by the product of the two curves (fig. 232*c*). In the example shown, the result is clear: two of the peaks coincide fairly well and so their product is large; the other two are well separated and so produce practically no effect. But it can well happen that two reasonably well-defined peaks are produced (fig. 232*d*) and it might be thought that the larger should be taken as correct. In fact, Blow and Crick show that the best result is obtained if the centroid of the two distributions is taken.

It should be noted that the centroid is that obtained from the Argand diagram, not from the probability distributions of phase angles themselves. Although these distributions have to be obtained from the formulae given by Crick and Blow, effectively the same results are given if the maxima of the distributions are taken.

4.9. *Summary*. Although in principle these methods seem to be completely satisfactory, and have proved themselves to be so in structures of immense complexity, it is obvious that they can be considered for use only in very special circumstances. The work involved is considerable. Several derivatives—about five is a reasonable number—must be used, and therefore the gathering of the data is itself a large task, requiring automatic equipment (Arndt and Phillips, 1961).

When the positions of the heavy atoms have been found they must be refined as far as possible since the success of later operations depends upon accuracy at this stage. Then each reflexion must be considered separately and since there is necessarily a very large number of them the evaluations of their phases involves use of a digital computer. Then the Fourier synthesis must be carried out and only then will it be known whether the work has been worth while.

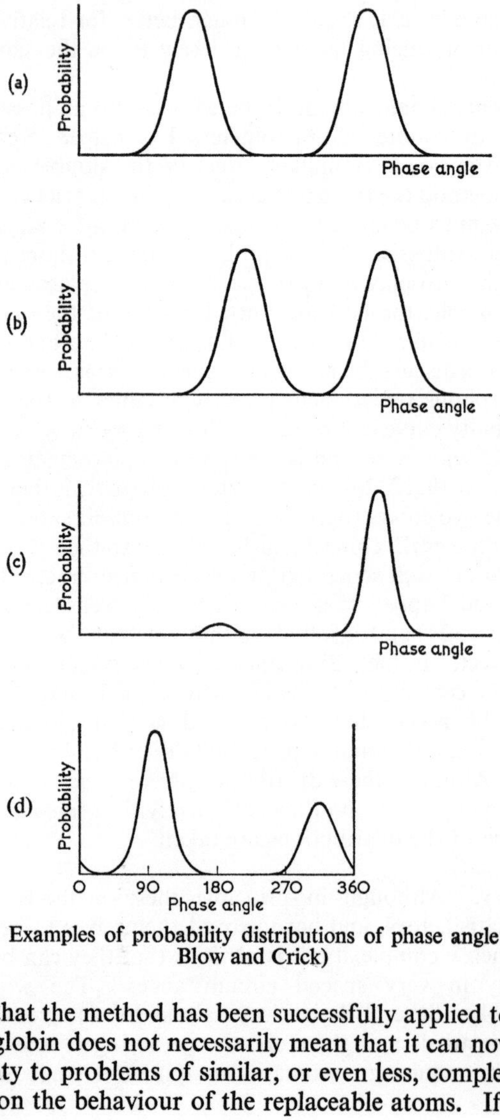

FIG. 232. Examples of probability distributions of phase angle ((d) after Blow and Crick)

The fact that the method has been successfully applied to myoglobin and haemoglobin does not necessarily mean that it can now be applied with certainty to problems of similar, or even less, complexity. Much depends upon the behaviour of the replaceable atoms. If they always choose the same locations the method is straightforward. But with very large molecules there must obviously be an element of chance, and if several locations are possible the heavy atoms may choose to place themselves at random upon them. There the method becomes much more difficult to apply and may even be impossible. Thus even with the enormous success so far obtained, there can still be no guarantee of success in dealing with any specific problem.

CHAPTER 9

DIRECT METHODS

1. Introduction

There are a number of ways of attempting to solve the crystal-structure problem which may be regarded as direct methods in the sense of offering a mathematically objective procedure for passing from the observed X-ray data to a complete knowledge of the crystal structure. There is, for example the heavy-atom method described in section **8**.3.2, or one could attempt to solve the complete set of equations

$$|F_{hkl}|^2 = \sum_{i=1}^{N} \sum_{j=1}^{N} f_i f_j \cos 2\pi[h(x_i - x_j) + k(y_i - y_j) + l(z_i - z_j)]$$

for the quantities $x_i - x_j$, etc., from which the atomic coordinates could be recovered. Attempts to derive a general procedure to do this have been made by Ott (1927) and Avrami (1938) but their methods cannot cope with non-trivial problems.

However the term 'direct-methods' is usually taken to imply that class of methods (Woolfson, 1961) in which one attempts to derive the phases of the structure factors without previously having postulated any atomic positions. These methods first made an appearance in the form of inequality relationships between the structure factors, given notably by Harker and Kasper (1948) and Karle and Hauptman (1950). These inequalities depended only on the positivity of the electron density but Goedkoop (1950) showed that the fact that the electron density consists of a superposition of atoms of approximately the same shape results in equality relationships between the structure factors. A particular case of such relationships had also been considered by Banerjee (1933) but in both cases the equations are far too unwieldy to be of any practical use.

A notable landmark in the development of direct methods was the derivation of a simple form of equality relation between structure factors by Sayre (1952). Although the equations themselves were difficult to handle (even so, Sayre solved a structure by their use) they led Cochran (1952) and Zachariasen (1952) to the discovery of a simple probability relationship between structure factors which is both convenient to handle and sufficiently powerful to have solved many fairly complicated structures.

Other probability relationships were soon discovered by Karle and Hauptman (1953) and these latter workers have also described in a series of papers detailed procedures for determining signs for the centrosymmetric space groups.

Although Karle and Hauptman derived their formulae by purely analytical methods, some of these formulae can be given a physical interpretation in terms of the Patterson function. Hauptman and Karle (1962) have also used the Patterson function more directly as a means of determining phases, and properties of the Patterson function have also been used to this end by Anzenhofer and Hoppe (1962) and by Main and Woolfson (1963).

The greatest stimulus to direct methods has been given by the widespread availability of fast electronic computers. Many proposed methods, particularly those of recent origin, are quite impracticable without the aid of a computer. However it is interesting to note that the advent of computers has enabled Diamond (1963) to explore the possibility of extending the range of application of one of the earliest direct methods, the inequality relationships of Karle and Hauptman.

2. Inequality Relations Between Structure Factors

2.1. *Harker-Kasper Inequalities.* In considering inequality relationships we shall find it convenient to introduce the idea of the unitary structure factor. This is defined as

$$\mathrm{U}_{\mathbf{h}} = F_{\mathbf{h}} \Big/ \sum_{j=1}^{N} f_j = \sum_{j=1}^{N} n_j \cos 2\pi \mathbf{h}\cdot\mathbf{r}_j \qquad (235.1)$$

where n_j, the unitary scattering factor, is given by

$$n_j = f_j \Big/ \sum_{j=1}^{N} f_j \qquad (235.2)$$

and where

$$\mathrm{U}_0 = \sum_{j=1}^{N} n_j = 1. \qquad (235.3)$$

It is convenient to assume that all the atoms in the structure have unitary scattering factors (section **1**.2.4), which are constant throughout reciprocal space.

We can now make use of the Cauchy inequality

$$\left|\sum_{j=1}^{N} a_j b_j\right|^2 \leqslant \left(\sum_{j=1}^{N} |a_j|^2\right)\left(\sum_{j=1}^{N} |b_j|^2\right). \qquad (235.4)$$

In (235.1) we take

$$a_j = \sqrt{n_j} \quad \text{and} \quad b_j = \sqrt{n_j} \exp 2\pi i \mathbf{h}\cdot\mathbf{r}_j$$

and we find

$$|\mathrm{U}_{\mathbf{h}}|^2 \leqslant \left(\sum_{-1}^{N} n_j\right)\left(\sum_{j=1}^{N} n_j\, |\exp 2\pi i \mathbf{h}\cdot\mathbf{r}_j|^2\right).$$

Since $|\exp 2\pi i\mathbf{h}\cdot\mathbf{r}|^2 = 1$, from (*235.3*) we have $|U_\mathbf{h}|^2 \leqslant 1$.

This result is neither novel nor useful although we might note in passing one point of interest. While $a_j^2 = n_j$ by definition, $|a_j|^2 = n_j$ only if n_j is positive, that is to say that the atoms are positive scatterers. This result does not necessarily hold in neutron diffraction (section **13**.1.2) for instance.

When the structure contains symmetry, more-interesting results are found. With a centre for instance we have

$$U_\mathbf{h} = \sum_{j=1}^{N} n_j \cos 2\pi\mathbf{h}\cdot\mathbf{r}_j \tag{236.1}$$

whence from Cauchy's inequality

$$U_\mathbf{h}^2 \leqslant \left(\sum_{j=1}^{N} n_j\right)\left(\sum_{j=1}^{N} n_j \cos^2 2\pi\mathbf{h}\cdot\mathbf{r}_j\right)$$

or

$$U_\mathbf{h}^2 \leqslant \tfrac{1}{2}\left(\sum_{j=1}^{N} n_j(1 + \cos 2\pi.2\mathbf{h}\cdot\mathbf{r}_j)\right)$$

whence

$$U_\mathbf{h}^2 \leqslant \tfrac{1}{2}(1 + U_{2\mathbf{h}}). \tag{236.2}$$

This inequality can be used to show that an invariant structure factor—that is to say, one whose indices are all even so that its sign does not depend on the choice of origin—must be positive.

For example with $|U_\mathbf{h}| = 0{\cdot}6$ and $|U_{2\mathbf{h}}| = 0{\cdot}5$ the left-hand side of (*236.2*) is 0·36 and the right-hand side is $\frac{1}{2}(1 + 0{\cdot}5s(2\mathbf{h}))$ where $s(2\mathbf{h})$ is the sign of $U_{2\mathbf{h}}$. Unless $s(2\mathbf{h})$ is positive the inequality cannot be satisfied.

For other symmetry elements other inequality relations may be found. If the crystal has a two-fold axis so that atoms occur in pairs with coordinates x, y, z; $\bar{x}, y, \bar{z}$ the unitary-structure-factor equation becomes

$$U_{hkl} = 2\sum_{j=1}^{N/2} n_j \exp 2\pi iky_j \cos 2\pi(hx_j + lz_j).$$

By taking $a_j = \sqrt{n_l} \exp 2\pi iky_j$ and $b_j = \sqrt{2n_j} \cos 2\pi(hx_j + lz_j)$ we find

$$U_{hkl}^2 \leqslant \tfrac{1}{2}(1 + U_{2h,0,2l}). \tag{236.3}$$

Similarly a two-fold screw axis will give

$$U_{hkl}^2 \leqslant \tfrac{1}{2}(1 + (-1)^k U_{2h,0,2l}). \tag{236.4}$$

Equations (*236.2*) and (*236.3*) can only be used to find a sign positive while (*236.4*) may find a sign either positive or negative, but all three of these equations have in common that they can only determine signs for a structure invariant.

To bring other structure factors into consideration one has to derive new inequalities. One of these may be derived from

$$U_{\mathbf{h}}+U_{\mathbf{h}'}=2\sum_{j=1}^{N} n_j \cos 2\pi\frac{\mathbf{h}+\mathbf{h}'}{2}\cdot\mathbf{r}_j \cos 2\pi\frac{\mathbf{h}-\mathbf{h}'}{2}\cdot\mathbf{r}_j \qquad (237.1)$$

which by taking

$$a_j=\sqrt{2n_j}\cos 2\pi\frac{\mathbf{h}+\mathbf{h}'}{2}\cdot\mathbf{r}_j \quad \text{and} \quad b_j=\sqrt{2n_j}\cos 2\pi\frac{\mathbf{h}-\mathbf{h}'}{2}\cdot\mathbf{r}_j$$

gives

$$(U_{\mathbf{h}}+U_{\mathbf{h}'})^2\leqslant(1+U_{\mathbf{h}+\mathbf{h}'})(1+U_{\mathbf{h}-\mathbf{h}'}). \qquad (237.2)$$

Alternatively by starting from

$$U_{\mathbf{h}}-U_{\mathbf{h}'}=-2\sum_{j=1}^{N} n_j \sin 2\pi\frac{\mathbf{h}+\mathbf{h}'}{2}\cdot\mathbf{r}_j \sin 2\pi\frac{\mathbf{h}-\mathbf{h}'}{2}\cdot\mathbf{r}_j$$

we obtain

$$(U_{\mathbf{h}}-U_{\mathbf{h}'})^2\leqslant(1-U_{\mathbf{h}+\mathbf{h}'})(1-U_{\mathbf{h}-\mathbf{h}'}). \qquad (237.3)$$

It is possible to combine (*237*.2) and (*237*.3) into the useful form

$$(|U_{\mathbf{h}}|+|U_{\mathbf{h}'}|)^2\leqslant(1+s(\mathbf{h})s(\mathbf{h}')s(\mathbf{h}+\mathbf{h}')|U_{\mathbf{h}+\mathbf{h}'}|)$$
$$\times(1+s(\mathbf{h})s(\mathbf{h}')s(\mathbf{h}-\mathbf{h}')|U_{\mathbf{h}-\mathbf{h}'}|). \qquad (237.4)$$

Relation (237.4) may be used to prove that one or both of the two triple products is positive.

For example with $|U_{\mathbf{h}}|=0{\cdot}4$, $|U_{\mathbf{h}'}|=0{\cdot}4$,

$$|U_{\mathbf{h}+\mathbf{h}'}|=0{\cdot}5, \quad |U_{\mathbf{h}-\mathbf{h}'}|=0{\cdot}2,$$

the left-hand side equals 0·64 while the right-hand side cannot exceed this unless $s(\mathbf{h})s(\mathbf{h}')s(\mathbf{h}+\mathbf{h}')$ is positive. No information is gained in this case about $s(\mathbf{h})s(\mathbf{h}')s(\mathbf{h}-\mathbf{h}')$. It should be noted that one does not obtain information about a single sign from (*237*.4) but about a product of signs which is a structure invariant.

While the inequality relationships (*236*.2), (*237*.2), (*237*.3) and (*237*.4) are the most generally useful basic relationships, since they can be applied to any centrosymmetric space group, the presence of higher symmetry can lead to stronger and sometimes very useful inequality relationships. As an example we shall take the space group No. 10, P2/*m*. The simplified unitary-structure-factor equation for this space group leads to

$$U_{hkl}=4\sum_{j=1}^{N/4} n_j \cos 2\pi k y_j \cos 2\pi(hx_j+ky_j). \qquad (237.5)$$

We may now apply Cauchy's inequality to this equation and also to the equations involving the sum or difference of U's. The a_j's and b_j's for the inequality may be selected in any way as long as they are *real* and the list of inequalities shown in table 238 results.

TABLE 238

$$U_{hkl}^2 \leqslant \tfrac{1}{4}(1 + U_{0,2k,0} + U_{2h,0,2l} + U_{2h,2k,2l})$$
$$U_{hkl}^2 \leqslant \tfrac{1}{4}(1 + U_{0,2k,0})(1 + U_{2h,0,2l})$$
$$(U_{h0l} \pm U_{hkl})^2 \leqslant \tfrac{1}{2}(1 + U_{0k0})\{1 + U_{2h,0,2l} \pm (U_{0k0} + U_{2h,k,2l})\}$$
$$(U_{hkl} \pm U_{h'kl'})^2 \leqslant \tfrac{1}{2}(1 + U_{h+h',0,l+l'})\{1 + U_{0,2k,0} \pm (U_{h-h',0,l-l'} + U_{h-h',2k,l-l'})\}$$
$$(U_{hkl} \pm U_{h'k'l'})^2 \leqslant \tfrac{1}{4}\{2 + U_{0,2k,0} + U_{2h,0,2l} + U_{2h,2k,2l} + U_{0,2k',0} + U_{2h',0,2l'} + U_{2h',2k',2l'} \pm 2(U_{h-h',k-k',l-l'} + U_{h-h',k+k,'l-l'} + U_{h+h',k-k',l+l'} + U_{h+h',k+k',l+l'})\}$$

These relationships are more powerful than those which depend on the presence of a centre of symmetry, two-fold axis or mirror plane alone but in addition the relationships (*236*.2), (*236*.3), (*237*.2), (*237*.3) and (*237*.4) still hold since they depend on symmetry elements present in the space group P2/*m*.

The number of inequality relationships which may be found for the various space groups is extremely large and an exhaustive list cannot be given here. Many inequality relationships of the simple type with which we are concerned have been published, some derived by the Harker and Kasper technique which has just been discussed, and some by using other inequality theorems. However, in using inequalities for a particular space group the first step is usually to work out the appropriate inequality relationships by the methods outlined in this section.

It will be noticed that for the space group P$\bar{1}$ the inequalities (*236*.2) or (*237*.4) can show that a structure invariant, which is either a single sign or a product of three signs, is positive. There is no possibility by means of these inequalities alone of establishing any negative relationships between structure factors. Negative signs will certainly occur unless the structure is dominated by a heavy atom at the origin of the unit cell. Such negative relationships can be established by the special application of (*237*.2) and (*237*.3) taken together. To illustrate this let us consider the numerical example

$$|U_{\mathbf{h}}| = 0{\cdot}6, \quad |U_{\mathbf{h}'}| = 0, \quad |U_{\mathbf{h}+\mathbf{h}'}| = |U_{\mathbf{h}-\mathbf{h}'}| = 0{\cdot}5.$$

For either the inequality (*237*.2) or (*237*.3) the magnitude of the left-hand side is now 0·36. Now let us assume that $U_{\mathbf{h}+\mathbf{h}'}$ and $U_{\mathbf{h}-\mathbf{h}'}$ have both the same sign and are positive. In this case the right-hand side of inequality (*237*.3) will be (1 − 0·5) (1 − 0·5), which is less than the left-hand side, showing that $U_{\mathbf{h}+\mathbf{h}'}$ and $U_{\mathbf{h}-\mathbf{h}'}$ cannot both be positive. Similarly the assumption that $U_{\mathbf{h}+\mathbf{h}'}$ and $U_{\mathbf{h}-\mathbf{h}'}$ are both negative can be disposed of by use of inequality (*237*.2). The only tenable solution is that $U_{\mathbf{h}+\mathbf{h}'}$ and $U_{\mathbf{h}-\mathbf{h}'}$ have opposite signs, or in other words that $s(\mathbf{h}+\mathbf{h}') \times s(\mathbf{h}-\mathbf{h}')$ is negative, when both (*237*.2) and (*237*.3) are valid.

The use of (*237*.2) and (*237*.3) together in this way is only rarely possible but it is certainly worth looking for the circumstances which lead to it; unless there is a heavy atom at the origin in the space group

$P\bar{1}$ there are bound to be some negative structure factors and none of the other inequalities introduces negative relationships into the sign-determining process.

2.2. *Practical application of Harker-Kasper Inequalities.* The first step in applying inequalities to structure determination is the derivation of the unitary structure amplitudes from the measured X-ray intensities, which will generally be on a relative scale and involve an unknown temperature factor. Methods of establishing an approximately absolute scale have been described in Section **6**.5.3 and the $|U|$'s could be obtained from the absolute $|F|$'s derived in this way. It is simpler however to avoid the intermediate steps and make use of the fact that

$$\overline{U^2} = \sum_{j=1}^{N} n_j^2 \tag{239.1}$$

the result corresponding to equation (*132*.2). This quantity can be evaluated from the known n_j values. Then if I_{hkl} represents the measured intensity of a particular reflexion and $\bar{I}$ the local average intensity of reflexions in that range of $\sin\theta$,

$$\frac{U_{hkl}^2}{\overline{U^2}} = \frac{I_{hkl}}{\bar{I}} \tag{239.2}$$

whence

$$|U_{hkl}| = \left\{ \sum_{j=1}^{N} n_j^2 \Big/ \bar{I} \right\}^{1/2} I_{hkl}^{\frac{1}{2}}. \tag{239.3}$$

We shall illustrate the practical application of Harker-Kasper inequalities by solving the *b*-axis projection of baddeleyite (McCullough and Trueblood, 1959). This crystal has space group $P2_1/c$ with $4\{ZrO_2\}$ in each unit cell. The unit cell parameters are $a = 5{\cdot}169$, $b = 5{\cdot}232$, $c = 5{\cdot}341$ Å and $\beta = 99°\ 15'$. In the *b*-axis projection there is an effective halving of the *c*-dimension and the projection with $a' = a$ and $c' = c/2$ has plane group *p*2.

The unitary structure amplitudes have been determined from the published observed structure amplitudes by the method which has been described and the values of 100 $|U|$ are shown plotted in fig. 240.

The first step is to search the data for structure factors satisfying the relationship (*236*.2) which will show that $U_{2\mathbf{h}}$ is positive if

$$|U_{2\mathbf{h}}| > 1 - 2U_{\mathbf{h}}^2.$$

We find

$|U_{604}| = 0{\cdot}35$ $\quad 1 - 2U_{30\bar{2}}^2 = -0{\cdot}28$ $\quad$ whence $s(60\bar{4}) = +1$.
$|U_{400}| = 0{\cdot}60$ $\quad 1 - 2U_{200}^2 = 0{\cdot}44$ $\quad$ whence $s(400) = +1$.
$|U_{404}| = 0{\cdot}63$ $\quad 1 - 2U_{202}^2 = -0{\cdot}41$ $\quad$ whence $s(404) = +1$.

At this stage we may add to our known signs by choosing two signs

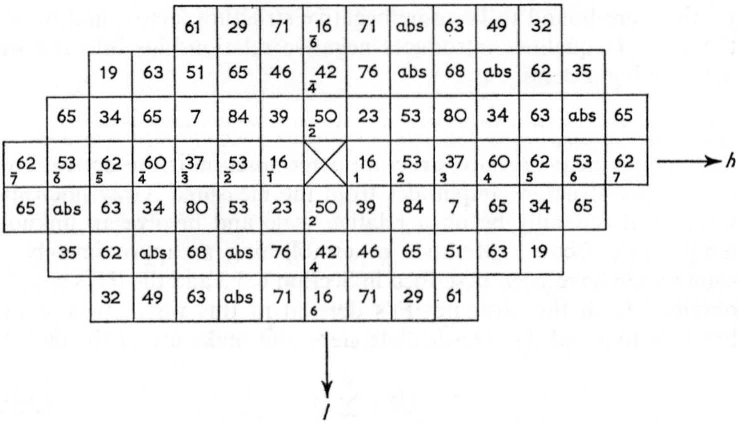

FIG. 240. Values of $100|U_{h0l}|$ for baddeleyite

arbitrarily (section **8**.3.1). It is an advantage for these to be large $|U|$'s and we choose $s(202) = +1$* and $s(10\bar{4}) = +1$.

We now search for unitary structure factors of large magnitude whose indices are related as are those in (*237*.4). As an aid to doing this we can prepare a copy of fig. 240 on transparent material. When the origin of this copy is placed over the point **h** of fig. 240, under the points **h**′ and −**h**′ of the overlay we find the points **h**+**h**′ and **h**−**h**′.

We shall now show in some detail the first few steps of using (*237*.4) to extend our knowledge of signs.

$$|U_{\mathbf{h}}| = |U_{400}| = 0{\cdot}60 \qquad |U_{\mathbf{h}'}| = |U_{202}| = 0{\cdot}84$$
$$|U_{\mathbf{h}+\mathbf{h}'}| = |U_{602}| = 0{\cdot}65 \qquad |U_{\mathbf{h}-\mathbf{h}'}| = |U_{20\bar{2}}| = 0{\cdot}53.$$

Inequality

$$(0{\cdot}60 + 0{\cdot}84)^2 \leqslant \{1 + s(400)s(202)s(602)0{\cdot}65\}\{1 + s(400)s(202)s(20\bar{2})0{\cdot}53\}.$$

$$\text{Conclusion } s(602) = s(400)s(202) = +1$$
$$\text{and } s(20\bar{2}) = s(400)s(202) = +1.$$

The next few steps are briefly indicated

h	**h**′	**h**+**h**′	**h**−**h**′	*Conclusion*
$U_{400} = 0{\cdot}60$	$\lvert U_{004}\rvert = 0{\cdot}42$	$U_{404} = 0{\cdot}63$	$U_{40\bar{4}}$ (absent)	$s(004) = s(400)s(404) = +1$
$U_{10\bar{4}} = 0{\cdot}76$	$U_{20\bar{2}} = 0{\cdot}53$	$\lvert U_{30\bar{6}}\rvert = 0{\cdot}63$	$\lvert U_{102}\rvert = 0{\cdot}39$	$s(30\bar{6}) = s(10\bar{4})s(20\bar{2}) = +1$ and $s(102) = s(10\bar{4})s(20\bar{2}) = +1$
$U_{404} = 0{\cdot}63$	$U_{20\bar{2}} = 0{\cdot}53$	$U_{602} = 0{\cdot}65$	$\lvert U_{206}\rvert = 0{\cdot}29$	$s(206) = s(404)s(20\bar{2}) = +1$

* Usually a structure factor whose indices are all even is a structure invariant and cannot arbitarily be given a sign, but for this projection the indexing corresponds to a non-primitive cell.

This process can be continued but can lead only to a knowledge of new positive signs. However as mentioned earlier, we can introduce negative relationships by the use of (*237*.2) and (*237*.3) together.

Thus from

$$|U_{30\bar{2}}| = 0{\cdot}80 \quad U_{20\bar{4}}(\text{absent}) \quad |U_{50\bar{6}}| = 0{\cdot}32 \quad \text{and} \quad U_{102} = 0{\cdot}39$$

we may deduce that $s(50\bar{6})s(102) = -1$

or that $$s(50\bar{6}) = -1.$$

From this point the repeated use of (*237*.4) leads to the complete set of signs for the projection of baddeleyite.

2.3. *Matrix inequalities.* In 1950 Karle and Hauptman showed that, from some results given by Toeplitz (1911) and Herglotz (1911), a necessary and sufficient condition that the electron density is everywhere non-negative is

$$D = \begin{vmatrix} F_0 & F_{-\mathbf{h}_1} & F_{-\mathbf{h}_2} & \cdots & F_{-\mathbf{h}_n} \\ F_{\mathbf{h}_1} & F_0 & F_{\mathbf{h}_1-\mathbf{h}_2} & & F_{\mathbf{h}_1-\mathbf{h}_n} \\ \vdots & & & & \\ F_{\mathbf{h}_n} & F_{\mathbf{h}_n-\mathbf{h}_1} & & & F_0 \end{vmatrix} \geqslant 0. \qquad (241.1)$$

The indices **h** are different from each other and from zero but otherwise can have quite arbitary positive and negative values. The rank of the determinant is not restricted in any way. For example, we have

$$\begin{vmatrix} F_0 & F_{\mathbf{h}} \\ F_{-\mathbf{h}} & F_0 \end{vmatrix} \geqslant 0 \quad \text{and} \quad \begin{vmatrix} F_{000} & F_{320} & F_{110} \\ F_{\bar{3}\bar{2}0} & F_{000} & F_{\bar{2}\bar{1}0} \\ F_{\bar{1}\bar{1}0} & F_{210} & F_{000} \end{vmatrix} \geqslant 0.$$

By expanding the determinant D and making use of the fact that certain minors of the determinant are also non-negative, Karle and Hauptman found

$$\left| F_{\mathbf{h}_n} - \frac{\Delta'}{\Delta} \right| \leqslant \frac{\Delta_1^{\frac{1}{2}} \Delta_2^{\frac{1}{2}}}{\Delta}, \qquad (241.2)$$

where Δ, Δ', Δ_1 and Δ_2 are determinants of rank lower than D; Δ_1 for example is obtained from D by omission of the last row and last column. To express (*241*.2) in words the coefficient $F_{\mathbf{h}_n}$ lies within a circle in the complex plane whose centre is at $\delta = \frac{\Delta'}{\Delta}$ and whose radius is $r = \frac{\Delta_1^{\frac{1}{2}} \Delta_2^{\frac{1}{2}}}{\Delta}$ (fig. 242). The vector $\mathbf{F} = A + iB$ representing $F(\mathbf{h}_n)$ in magnitude and phase must end somewhere in the circle. If the value of $|F|$ is known, the phase angle is further limited, as **F** must end somewhere on the heavy line. Generally speaking, the greater the rank of the determinant D (that is the more structure factors that are known in magnitude and phase) the more closely will the magnitude and phase of an additional one be limited.

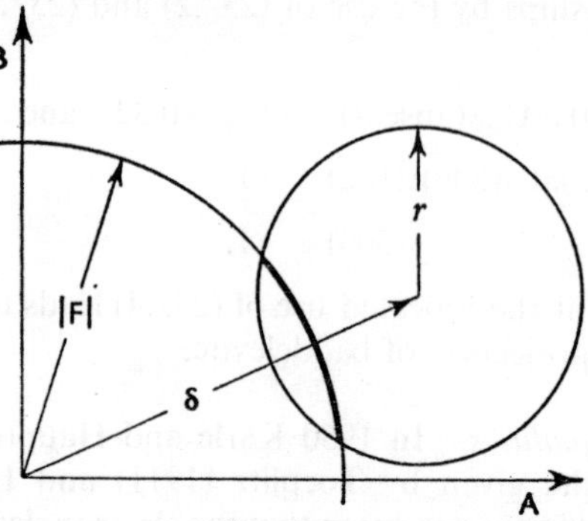

FIG. 242

It is possible to insert unitary structure factors into the determinants, as these are the structure factors for a structure consisting of point atoms. Three inequalities of increasing complexity which can be obtained from (*241*.1) and (*241*.2) are :

(i) $n=0$. Then $U_0 \geqslant 0$, from (*241*.1). (*242*.1)

(ii) $n=1$. Substituting $U_0=1$ then

$$\begin{vmatrix} 1 & U_{-h} \\ U_h & 1 \end{vmatrix} \geqslant 0 \quad \text{or} \quad |U_h| \leqslant 1. \qquad (242.2)$$

(iii) $n=2$.

$$\begin{vmatrix} 1 & U_{-h_1} & U_{-h_1-h_2} \\ U_{h_1} & 1 & U_{-h_2} \\ U_{h_1+h_2} & U_{h_2} & 1 \end{vmatrix} \geqslant 0 \qquad (242.3)$$

or from (*241*.2)

$$\left| U_{h_1+h_2} - \frac{U_{h_1}U_{h_2}}{1} \right| \leqslant \left| \begin{matrix} 1 & U_{-h_1} \\ U_{h_1} & 1 \end{matrix} \right|^{1/2} \times \left| \begin{matrix} 1 & U_{-h_2} \\ U_{h_2} & 1 \end{matrix} \right|^{1/2} \Big/ 1 \qquad (242.4)$$

Symmetry considerations were not used to derive any of these general inequalities. If the origin is a centre of symmetry, $U_h = U_{-h}$ and (*242*.4) becomes, for the special case $h = h_1 = h_2$.

$$|U_{2h} - U_h^2| \leqslant 1 - U_h^2$$

from which it can be shown that

$$U_h^2 \leqslant \tfrac{1}{2}(1 + U_{2h}), \qquad (242.5)$$

which will be recognized as one of the Harker-Kasper inequalities.

The inequalities of higher order become increasingly more difficult to handle although VonEller (1955*b*, 1960, 1961, 1962), Kitaygorodsky

(1961) and Diamond (1963) have given some attention to the problem.

Kitaygorodsky's contribution has been to show that the higher-order inequalities become increasingly more powerful as n increases in the sense that, if only one knew how to handle such complex inequality expressions, they would inevitably lead to the solution of more complicated problems. Von Eller has transformed the inequalities by writing

$$U_{\mathbf{h}} = \cos \phi_{\mathbf{h}}, \tag{243.1}$$

a convenient step since, like $U_{\mathbf{h}}$, $\cos \phi_{\mathbf{h}}$ can take up values between $+1$ and -1. The inequalities are studied by making use of the geometrical relationships which exist between the values of ϕ.

Diamond has mainly considered the problem of using a computer to derive information from the inequalities with $n=3$, although his approach can be generalized to deal with larger n.

The general inequality with $n=3$ can be written

$$\begin{vmatrix} 1 & U_{\mathbf{h}_1} & U_{\mathbf{h}_2} & U_{\mathbf{h}_3} \\ U_{-\mathbf{h}_1} & 1 & U_{\mathbf{h}_2-\mathbf{h}_1} & U_{\mathbf{h}_3-\mathbf{h}_1} \\ U_{-\mathbf{h}_2} & U_{\mathbf{h}_1-\mathbf{h}_2} & 1 & U_{\mathbf{h}_3-\mathbf{h}_2} \\ U_{-\mathbf{h}_3} & U_{\mathbf{h}_1-\mathbf{h}_3} & U_{\mathbf{h}_2-\mathbf{h}_3} & 1 \end{vmatrix} \geqslant 0. \tag{243.2}$$

We shall use the terminology of Diamond and write

$$u_{ij} = |U_{\mathbf{h}_i-\mathbf{h}_j}|, \quad s_{ij} = U_{\mathbf{h}_i-\mathbf{h}_j}/U_{ij} \tag{243.3}$$

so that each s is either $+1$ or -1.

The inequality now becomes

$$\begin{vmatrix} 1 & s_{10}u_{10} & s_{20}u_{20} & s_{30}u_{30} \\ s_{01}u_{01} & 1 & s_{21}u_{21} & s_{31}u_{31} \\ s_{02}u_{02} & s_{12}u_{12} & 1 & s_{32}u_{32} \\ s_{03}u_{03} & s_{13}u_{13} & s_{23}u_{23} & 1 \end{vmatrix} \geqslant 0. \tag{243.4}$$

If the four columns are multiplied by 1, s_{10}, s_{20} and s_{30} respectively and the four rows by 1, s_{01}, s_{02} and s_{03} respectively then we have not changed the value of the determinant since we have multiplied it by $s_{10}s_{20}s_{30}\ s_{01}s_{02}s_{03}$ which, since $s_{ij}=s_{ji}$ etc., equals unity.

The inequality now appears as

$$\begin{vmatrix} 1 & u_{10} & u_{20} & u_{30} \\ u_{01} & 1 & s_{01}s_{20}s_{21}u_{21} & s_{01}s_{30}s_{31}u_{31} \\ u_{02} & s_{02}s_{10}s_{12}u_{12} & 1 & s_{02}s_{30}s_{32}u_{32} \\ u_{03} & s_{03}s_{10}s_{13}u_{13} & s_{03}s_{20}s_{23}u_{23} & 1 \end{vmatrix} \geqslant 0. \tag{243.5}$$

Diamond considers the restraints placed by the inequalities on the triple-sign products (triproducts)

$$\alpha = s_{01}s_{20}s_{21} = s_{10}s_{02}s_{12}$$
$$\beta = s_{01}s_{30}s_{31} = s_{10}s_{03}s_{13} \tag{244.1}$$
$$\text{and } \gamma = s_{02}s_{30}s_{32} = s_{20}s_{03}s_{23}.$$

These three triproducts may have eight possible combinations of sign and the effect of each combination is tried on the inequality. From this it may be found for example that α must be positive and at least one of β and γ must be positive. This information is stored in the computer in the form of logical 'statements' and when all such statements regarding all the triproducts have been found they are analysed by the processes of logical algebra to extract the maximum of information.

It seems possible that the usefulness of inequality relationship may be extended by applying them in this fashion although no application to the solution of an unknown structure has yet been attempted.

2.4. *Other inequality relationships.* It is possible to derive many simple types of inequality relationship between a small number of unitary structure factors although it will normally be found in practice that, for any structure which can be solved by inequalities, the Harker-Kasper inequalities will be adequate.

As an example we may consider the so-called linear inequalities which were developed by Okaya and Nitta (1952). The basic inequality relationship which they used was

$$\sum_{i=1}^{N} n_i a_j^2 + \sum_{i=1}^{N} n_i b_j^2 \geqslant 2\,|\sum_{i=1}^{N} n_i a_i b_i| \tag{244.2}$$

where the n's were taken as the unitary scattering factors. Substituting $a_i = \cos 2\pi\mathbf{h}\cdot\mathbf{r}_i$ and $b_i = 1/m$ one finds

$$2 + m^2 + m^2\mathrm{U}_{2\mathbf{h}} \geqslant 4m|\mathrm{U}_{\mathbf{h}}|. \tag{244.3}$$

With $m = 1$, $\sqrt{2}$ and 2, for example, we have

$$3 + \mathrm{U}_{2\mathbf{h}} \geqslant 4|\mathrm{U}_{\mathbf{h}}|$$
$$2 + \mathrm{U}_{2\mathbf{h}} \geqslant 2\sqrt{2}|\mathrm{U}_{\mathbf{h}}|$$
$$3 + 2\mathrm{U}_{2\mathbf{h}} \geqslant 4|\mathrm{U}_{\mathbf{h}}|. \tag{244.4}$$

However it can be shown that, while it is possible to choose a value of m such that (244.3) is as powerful as (236.2) to determine the sign of $\mathrm{U}_{2\mathbf{h}}$, it can never be *more* powerful. The same is almost certainly true for the other inequalities given by Okaya and Nitta and also those given by other workers (e.g. Gillis, 1948).

3. Equality Relations Between Structure Factors

3.1. *Sayre's equation.* A special equality relationship between structure factors exists when the structure is composed of identical atoms which are fully resolved from one another.

The electron density is given by

$$\rho(\mathbf{r}) = \frac{1}{V}\sum_{\mathbf{h}} F_{\mathbf{h}} \exp(-2\pi i \mathbf{h}\cdot\mathbf{r}) \tag{245.1}$$

and the square of the electron density may be expressed as

$$\rho^2(\mathbf{r}) = \frac{1}{V}\sum_{\mathbf{h}} G_{\mathbf{h}} \exp(-2\pi i \mathbf{h}\cdot\mathbf{r}) \tag{245.2}$$

where $G_{\mathbf{h}}$ is the **h**th Fourier coefficient of the squared structure.

From equation (*245*.1)

$$\rho^2(\mathbf{r}) = \frac{1}{V^2}\sum_{\mathbf{h}'}\sum_{\mathbf{h}''} F_{\mathbf{h}'}F_{\mathbf{h}''} \exp[-2\pi i(\mathbf{h}'+\mathbf{h}'')\cdot\mathbf{r}].$$

If terms for which $\mathbf{h}'+\mathbf{h}''=\mathbf{h}$ are collected together this gives

$$\rho^2(\mathbf{r}) = \frac{1}{V^2}\sum_{\mathbf{h}}\left\{\sum_{\mathbf{h}'} F_{\mathbf{h}'}F_{\mathbf{h}-\mathbf{h}'} \exp(-2\pi i \mathbf{h}\cdot\mathbf{r})\right\}. \tag{245.3}$$

Comparing (*245*.2) and (*245*.3) we find

$$G_{\mathbf{h}} = \frac{1}{V}\sum_{\mathbf{h}'} F_{\mathbf{h}'}F_{\mathbf{h}-\mathbf{h}'}. \tag{245.4}$$

This is a perfectly general equation relating the Fourier coefficients of the square of a periodic function to those of the function itself. It may also be obtained directly from certain results in the theory of Fourier transforms which connect the operation of squaring in direct space with self-convolution in reciprocal space (section **10.2.5**).

If we now consider a structure consisting of equal resolved atoms then the process of squaring maintains the condition of equal resolved atoms but with atoms of different shape. If f is the atomic scattering factor of an atom and g that of the 'squared atom' we have

$$F_{\mathbf{h}} = \sum_{j=1}^{N} f \exp(2\pi i \mathbf{h}\cdot\mathbf{r}_j)$$

and

$$G_{\mathbf{h}} = \sum_{j=1}^{N} g \exp(2\pi i \mathbf{h}\cdot\mathbf{r}_j) = \frac{g}{f}F_{\mathbf{h}}. \tag{245.5}$$

Combining (*245*.4) and (*245*.5) we find

$$\frac{g}{f}F_{\mathbf{h}} = \frac{1}{V}\sum F_{\mathbf{h}'}F_{\mathbf{h}-\mathbf{h}'}. \tag{245.6}$$

This equation was derived by Sayre (1952) who illustrated its value by the solution of a (to him) unknown crystal structure, hydroxyproline:

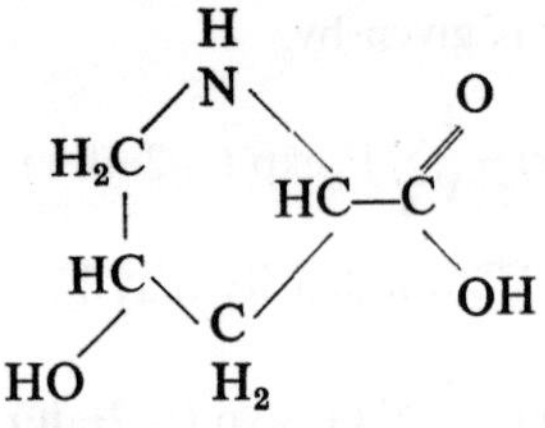

The structure was considered in projection on (100) as it was expected that due to the short *a*-axis, 5·0 Å, the atoms would all be resolved. The equation which was used, corresponding to (*245.6*), was

$$\frac{g}{f}F_{hk0} = \frac{1}{A}\sum_{h'}\sum_{k'} F_{h'k'0}F_{h-h',\,k-k',\,0}. \tag{246}$$

There is little point in following Sayre's derivation of signs in great detail; the application is of historical interest only and nowadays nobody would contemplate trying to solve a crystal structure in this way. The technique he used was to find a consistent set of signs for some of the larger structure factors which satisfied the set of equations (246) as well as possible.

The first 19 signs found by Sayre were all correct, of the next 12 one was incorrect, while for the last 22, 8 were incorrect. A Fourier synthesis involving the first 19 terms only showed the molecule fairly clearly (fig. 246) and there seems little doubt that the structure could have been refined from this point.

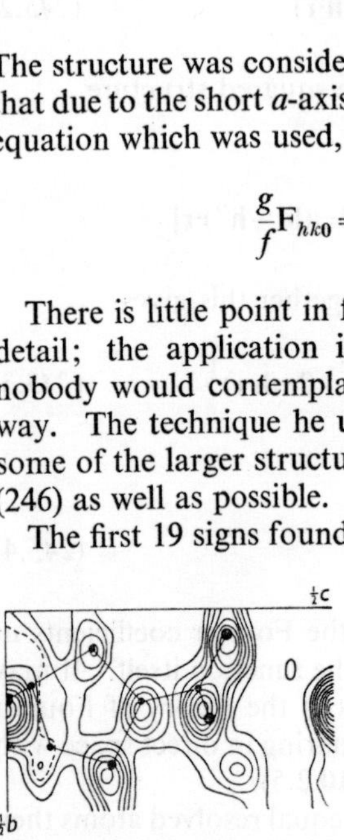

FIG. 246. An approximation to the projected electron density in hydroxyproline. The Fourier series contained only the 19 terms whose signs were determined by Sayre's equations. The correct atomic positions are indicated (Sayre, 1952).

Although Sayre's equation is not very useful for determining signs directly it can be valuable when used in conjunction with other sign-determining techniques (section 9.5.3).

3.2. *A Sayre-type equation for structures containing non-equal atoms.* The Sayre equations will only be valid for a structure containing equal resolved atoms although it may hold approximately when a structure contains a number of nearly equivalent atoms (e.g. C, N, O) or a number of atoms whose contribution can be ignored for both the original and squared structures (e.g. H in presence of heavier atoms).

It was shown by Woolfson (1958*b*) that it is possible to derive a precise equation between structure factors for structures which contain two types of resolved atoms. Let us denote the two types of atom by the symbols P and Q and for a particular structure-factor index **h** let the scattering factors for the original, squared and cubed atoms be f_P, f_Q; ${}_2f_P$, ${}_2f_Q$ and ${}_3f_P$, ${}_3f_Q$ respectively. It is always possible to find two numbers $A_{\mathbf{h}}$ and $B_{\mathbf{h}}$ such that

$$f_P = A_{\mathbf{h}}\, {}_2f_P + B_{\mathbf{h}}\, {}_3f_P$$

and

$$f_Q = A_{\mathbf{h}}\, {}_2f_Q + B_{\mathbf{h}}\, {}_3f_Q, \tag{247.1}$$

these numbers being

$$A_{\mathbf{h}} = \frac{f_P\, {}_3f_Q - f_Q\, {}_3f_P}{{}_2f_P\, {}_3f_Q - {}_2f_Q\, {}_3f_P}$$

and

$$B_{\mathbf{h}} = \frac{f_P\, {}_2f_Q - f_Q\, {}_2f_P}{{}_3f_P\, {}_2f_Q - {}_3f_Q\, {}_2f_P}. \tag{247.2}$$

Thus for any particular **h**, $A_{\mathbf{h}}$ and $B_{\mathbf{h}}$ may be determined from the known shapes of the atoms P and Q.

Since

$$F_{\mathbf{h}} = \sum_{j=1}^{N} f_j \cos 2\pi \mathbf{h}\cdot\mathbf{r}_j$$

and for each of the atoms in the structure

$$f_j = A_{\mathbf{h}}\, {}_2f_j + B_{\mathbf{h}}\, {}_3f_j$$

then

$$F_{\mathbf{h}} = A_{\mathbf{h}} \sum_{j=1}^{N} {}_2f_j \cos 2\pi\mathbf{h}\cdot\mathbf{r}_j + B_{\mathbf{h}} \sum_{j=1}^{N} {}_3f_j \cos 2\pi\mathbf{h}\cdot\mathbf{r}_j. \tag{247.3}$$

If $G_{\mathbf{h}}$ and $H_{\mathbf{h}}$ are the structure factors for the squared and cubed electron densities then

$$F_{\mathbf{h}} = A_{\mathbf{h}} G_{\mathbf{h}} + B_{\mathbf{h}} H_{\mathbf{h}}. \tag{247.4}$$

$G_{\mathbf{h}}$ and $H_{\mathbf{h}}$ can be expressed in terms of the F's to give

$$F_{\mathbf{h}} = \frac{A_{\mathbf{h}}}{V} \sum_{\mathbf{h}'} F_{\mathbf{h}'} F_{\mathbf{h}+\mathbf{h}'} + \frac{B_{\mathbf{h}}}{V^2} \sum_{\mathbf{h}'} \sum_{\mathbf{h}''} F_{\mathbf{h}'} F_{\mathbf{h}''} F_{\mathbf{h}+\mathbf{h}'+\mathbf{h}''} \tag{247.5}$$

This equation will hold precisely when there are two types of atom in the structure and can hold fairly well under a variety of other conditions. For example if an equal-atom structure is being considered in projection and there is the possibility of overlap to the extent of the complete overlap of not more than two atoms, then, by setting $A_{\mathbf{h}}$ and $B_{\mathbf{h}}$ to the values corresponding to a single and double-weight atom, a reasonable equality of the two sides of (*247.5*) is obtained. If there are three or more types of atom it is sometimes possible to choose $A_{\mathbf{h}}$ and $B_{\mathbf{h}}$ in such a way that the equation will hold fairly well. Examples of such cases have been given by Woolfson (1961).

The possibility of using (*247.5*) directly is even more remote than that of using (*245.6*). However (*247.5*) has been applied as an aid to structure determination (section **9.5.4**).

3.3. *Other equations between structure factors.* In section **1** reference was made to the equality relationship between structure factors given by Banerjee (1933) and Goedkoop (1950). These relationships, while of theoretical interest, are not of very great practical value and will therefore not be considered any further.

Other types of equality relationships, which are useful in practice, have been given by Hauptman and Karle (1957, 1962), Anzenhofer and Hoppe (1962) and Main and Woolfson (1963).

A description of these equations and their use will be given in later sections; it is better from both the logical and historical standpoints to consider now what are probably the most important and useful of the direct methods—those which involve probability relationships between the structure factors.

4. Probability Relations Between Structure Factors

4.1. *The triple-product sign relationship.* If the structure factors involved are sufficiently large then equations (*237*.4) or (*245*.6) can show that the product $F_{\mathbf{h}}F_{\mathbf{h}'}F_{\mathbf{h}+\mathbf{h}'}$ is certainly positive or

$$s(\mathbf{h})s(\mathbf{h}')s(\mathbf{h}+\mathbf{h}') = +1. \qquad (248.1)$$

However even where the structure factors are not large enough to prove (*248*.1) there may be a strong probability that the relationship is true. Such a relationship may be written as

$$s(\mathbf{h})s(\mathbf{h}')s(\mathbf{h}+\mathbf{h}') \approx +1 \qquad (248.2)$$

where $\approx$ means 'probably equals'. Various estimates of the probability of (*248*.1) have been given. The most accurate analysis of this problem has been made by Klug (1958) but a simpler expression, which is good enough for most practical purposes, has been given by Cochran and Woolfson (1955). This is

$$P_+(\mathbf{h}, \mathbf{h}') = \tfrac{1}{2} + \tfrac{1}{2} \tanh\left[(\epsilon_3/\epsilon^{3/2})|U_{\mathbf{h}}U_{\mathbf{h}'}U_{\mathbf{h}+\mathbf{h}'}|\right] \qquad (248.3)$$

where

$$\epsilon_3 = \sum_{j=1}^{N} n_j^3 \quad \text{and} \quad \epsilon = \sum_{j=1}^{N} n_j^2. \qquad (248.4)$$

For a structure containing N equal atoms in the unit cell the expression becomes

$$P_+(\mathbf{h}, \mathbf{h}') = \tfrac{1}{2} + \tfrac{1}{2} \tanh\left(N|U_{\mathbf{h}}U_{\mathbf{h}'}U_{\mathbf{h}+\mathbf{h}'}|\right). \qquad (248.5)$$

We can get some idea of the probabilities involved by showing the values of $P_+(\mathbf{h}, \mathbf{h}')$ for various values of N and of $|U_{\mathbf{h}}U_{\mathbf{h}'}U_{\mathbf{h}+\mathbf{h}'}|^{1/3}$.

	$\lvert U_h U_{h'} U_{h+h'} \rvert^{1/3}$			
N	0·2	0·3	0·4	0·5
20	0·579	0·746	0·928	0·993
40	0·655	0·897	0·994	1·000
60	0·723	0·962	1·000	1·000
80	0·782	0·987	1·000	1·000

It can be shown that when $U_h = U_{h'} = U_{h+h'} = 0{\cdot}5$ then $P_+(\mathbf{h}, \mathbf{h}')$ is unity for all values of N. In this case (*248*.5) gives an underestimate of the probability and it was shown by Klug that the probability given by (*248*.5) is always too low, although as N increases the discrepancy becomes less. Most applications of the triple-product sign relationship do not require a precise knowledge of the probabilities involved and where probabilities are subsequently quoted they will have been computed from (*248*.3) or (*248*.5).

4.2. *Sign relationships used with inequalities.* It was shown by Zachariasen (1952) that when some signs, or relative signs, have been determined by inequalities it is possible to extend greatly the sign information by using sign relationships. In fact Zachariasen used not relationship (*248*.2) but effectively a modified form of Sayre's equation. For a centrosymmetric structure containing equal point atoms and with an infinite amount of data one may write

$$U_{\mathbf{h}} = N\overline{U_{\mathbf{h}'}U_{\mathbf{h}+\mathbf{h}'}}^{\,\mathbf{h}'} \qquad (249.1)$$

(Cochran and Woolfson, 1955) and this implies that

$$s(\mathbf{h}) = s\{\sum_{\mathbf{h}'} U_{\mathbf{h}'}U_{\mathbf{h}+\mathbf{h}'}\}. \qquad (249.2)$$

If the summation on the right-hand side of (*249*.2) does not include all the data then the equality symbol may be replaced by 'probably equals'. Zachariasen used a simpler form of relationship

$$s(\mathbf{h}) \approx s(\overline{s(\mathbf{h}')s(\mathbf{h}+\mathbf{h}')}) \qquad (249.3)$$

which will be statistically true when the signs of the larger structure factors are being used.

Zachariasen applied this equation to determine the structure of metaboric acid HBO_2. For this compound, $a = 7{\cdot}13$, $b = 8{\cdot}85$, $c = 6{\cdot}67$ Å and $\beta = 93{\cdot}25°$. The space group is No. 14, $P2_1/a$ and the asymmetric unit consists of three molecules of HBO_2. Zachariasen considered only those structure factors for which $U > 1{\cdot}5(\overline{U^2})^{1/2}$ and for this structure there were 138 U's which satisfied this condition ($>0{\cdot}25$). The signs of three structure factors were chosen arbitarily as positive and those of an additional 14 were determined by inequality relations. When the signs of five further structure factors were expressed by symbols *b*, *c*,

k, x, y, those of 18 more could be obtained in terms of these symbols. The signs of 40 structure factors were therefore determined in terms of five unknowns. Among these 40 there are five pairs of indices $\mathbf{h}'$ and $\mathbf{h}+\mathbf{h}'$ corresponding to $\mathbf{h}=(1\ 5\ 4)$. For each pair one finds $s(\mathbf{h}')s(\mathbf{h}+\mathbf{h}')=+1$, whence $s(1\ 5\ 4)=+1$ with almost complete certainty. Again there are nine pairs of this type among the 40 structure factors corresponding to $\mathbf{h}=(1\ 3\ 3)$. For five of these $s(\mathbf{h}')s(\mathbf{h}+\mathbf{h}')=b$, and for the remaining four, $s(\mathbf{h}')s(\mathbf{h}+\mathbf{h}')=kb$. The implication of this information is that $s(1\ 3\ 3)\simeq b$ and $k=+1$. The list of structure factors of known sign was gradually expanded in this way until it included all for which $\mathrm{U}>0{\cdot}25$, and eventually all the symbols were eliminated. The signs of a number of relatively small structure factors were also determined. For example, corresponding to $\mathbf{h}=(0\ 0\ 1)$, for which $|\mathrm{U}|=0{\cdot}11$ there are 21 pairs of $\mathrm{U}_{\mathbf{h}'}$ and $\mathrm{U}_{\mathbf{h}+\mathbf{h}'}$ of large structure factors. The quantity $s(\mathbf{h}')s(\mathbf{h}+\mathbf{h}')$, averaged over these 21 pairs, has a value of $-0{\cdot}90$, and hence $s(0\ 0\ 1)\approx -1$. When the signs of some 200 of the largest F's had been determined, a three-dimensional Fourier synthesis was evaluated, and showed clearly the positions of all oxygen and boron atoms.

Although Zachariasen relied on some information from inequalities before using (*249*.3) it is sometimes possible to use sign relationships without the initial help of inequalities. Cochran and Penfold (1952) solved the structure of glutamine by first using inequalities and then sign relationships but when the structure was solved it became apparent that, due to an incorrect estimate of the scale of the unitary structure amplitudes, none of the inequalities which had been used was really valid. What Cochran and Penfold had done, effectively, was to assume that some of the most probable sign relationships of type (*248*.2) would not fail.

It is very often worth while, for a structure which leads to a number of 'near-inequality' situations, to assume that some small number of the strongest sign relationships must hold and to attempt to deduce other signs in the way proposed by Zachariasen. Even if this process does not lead to the correct solution it is usually rapid to apply and does not involve a heavy loss of time or effort.

4.3. *The coincidence method.* It is possible to relate the signs of pairs of structure factors by suitable combinations of triple-product sign relationships. For example the following pair of sign relationships

and
$$\left.\begin{aligned} s(\mathbf{h})s(\mathbf{h}')&\approx s(\mathbf{h}+\mathbf{h}') \text{ with probability } \mathrm{P}_1 \\ s(\mathbf{h})s(\mathbf{h}')&\approx s(\mathbf{h}-\mathbf{h}') \text{ with probability } \mathrm{P}_2 \end{aligned}\right\} \qquad (250.1)$$

imply that

$$s(\mathbf{h}+\mathbf{h}')\approx s(\mathbf{h}-\mathbf{h}') \qquad (250.2)$$

with probability $2P_1P_2 - P_1 - P_2 + 1$. For the probability of (*250*.2) to be reasonably high all the structure factors involved must be large.

The derivation of (*250*.2) from (*250*.1) may be shown graphically in fig. 251(*a*) where the relative positions of the reflexions with indices $\mathbf{h}+\mathbf{h}'$ and $\mathbf{h}-\mathbf{h}'$ may be seen; it is clear that the basis of (*250*.2) is the fact that $s(\mathbf{h}) = s(-\mathbf{h})$.

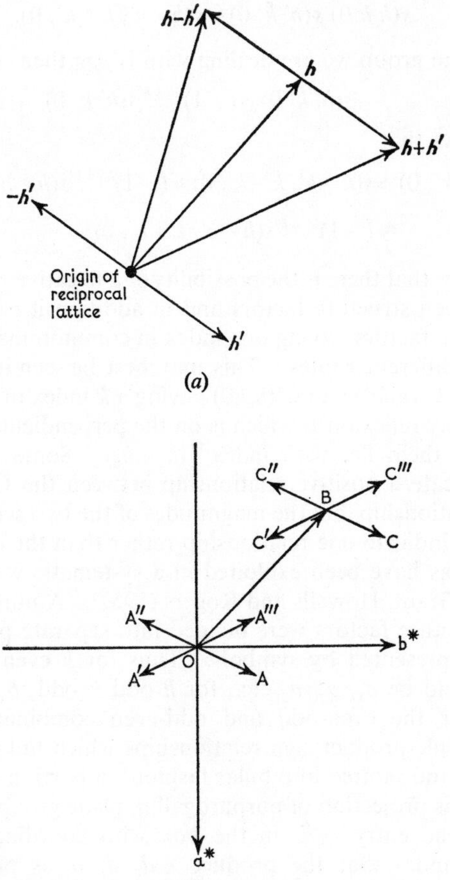

FIG. 251. (*a*) A graphical representation of the coincidence $s(\mathbf{h}+\mathbf{h}') = s(\mathbf{h}-\mathbf{h}')$. (*b*) A graphical representation of the coincidences formed for a rectangular space group

For the space group $P\bar{1}$ a pair of reflexions, which must of course be of the same parity group, may only be linked in one way but for higher space groups new possibilities arise. This is most easily shown in fig. 251(*b*) which shows the situation for a rectangular two-dimensional space group. Since the signs of the reflexions at A, A′, A″ and A‴ are related, then the signs of the reflexions at C, C′, C″ and C‴ may be related through the reflexion at B.

Let us see what this looks like in terms of indices.

$$\begin{aligned} s(h\,k\,0)\,s(h'\,k'\,0) &\approx s(h+h', k+k', 0)\\ s(h\,k\,0)\,s(h'\,k'\,0) &\approx s(h-h', k-k', 0)\\ s(h\,k\,0)\,s(h'\,\bar{k}'\,0) &\approx s(h+h', k-k', 0)\\ s(h\,k\,0)\,s(h'\,\bar{k}'\,0) &\approx s(h-h', k+k', 0). \end{aligned} \tag{252.1}$$

If the plane group we are dealing with is *pgg* then

$$s(h'\,\bar{k}'\,0) = (-1)^{h'+k'} s(h'\,k'\,0)$$

and it follows that

$$\begin{aligned} s(h+h', k+k', 0) &\approx s(h-h', k-k', 0) \approx (-1)^{h'+k'} s(h+h', k-k', 0)\\ &\approx (-1)^{h'+k'} s(h-h', k+k', 0). \end{aligned} \tag{252.2}$$

We first see that there is the possibility of a negative relationship being found between structure factors and in addition it can be shown that two structure factors having one index in common may be related by a number of different routes. This may best be seen in fig. 251(*b*); the reflexions at C′(h_1k0) and C′(h_2k0) having a k index in common may be related by any reflexion B which is on the perpendicular bisector of the line joining them i.e. with index $\frac{1}{2}(h_1+h_2)$. Some of the reflexions B may indicate a positive relationship between the C′'s and others a negative relationship, but the magnitudes of the two sets of probabilities will usually indicate one relationship rather than the other.

These ideas have been exploited in a systematic way by Rumanova (1954) and Grant, Howells and Rogers (1957). A number of the larger unitary structure factors were divided into separate parity groups and the signs represented by symbols. Thus for h even k even the sign symbols could be a_1, a_2, a_3 etc., for h odd k odd, b_1, b_2, b_3 etc., and similarly for the even-odd and odd-even combinations of indices. Then the triple-product sign relationships which linked these symbols were found and plotted in tabular fashion; a portion of a typical table (for the *c*-axis projection of purpurogallin, plane group *pgg*) is shown in fig. 253. The entry $-d_7$ in the box with coordinates (d_6, a_5), for example, implies that the product $-d_7\,d_6\,a_5$ is probably positive. Wherever two symbols appear in a single square we have what Grant et al. call a 'coincidence' and sometimes there may be a number of 'coincidences' involving the same sign symbols. Thus in the section of table in fig. 253 there are four 'coincidences' between d_4 and d_{11} which indicate that $d_4\,d_{11} \approx -1$ and two indicating that $d_5 d_{12} \approx -1$.

Grant et al. have shown how these relationships can give rise to the determination of the signs of a large number of structure factors and some quite elegant structure determinations have been made using this method.

Another way of using the triple-product sign relationship together with symmetry relationships to determine the probable signs of certain structure invariants has been given by Woolfson (1954) but there have been no practical applications of these ideas.

	c_4	c_5	c_6	c_7	c_8	c_9	c_{10}	c_{11}	c_{12}	c_{13}	d_1	d_2	d_3	d_4	d_5	d_6	d_7	d_8	d_9	d_{10}	d_{11}	d_{12}	d_{13}	d_{14}
a_1		c_6	c_5		c_9	c_8								d_5	d_4					$-d_{11}$	d_{12} $-d_{10}$	d_{11}		
a_2																d_7	d_6			$-d_{12}$		$-d_{10}$		
a_3				$-c_8$ c_9	$-c_7$	c_7									$-d_6$	$-d_5$					$-d_{13}$		$-d_{11}$	
a_4															$-d_7$		$-d_5$							
a_5																$-d_7$	$-d_6$							
a_6			c_2			c_{11}	c_4	c_9	c_{13}	c_{12}		d_6				d_2 d_9			d_6					
a_7					$-c_{11}$			$-c_8$	$-c_{13}$	$-c_{12}$	$-d_6$		d_4	d_3		$-d_1$		$-d_{13}$	d_{10}	d_9			$-d_8$	
a_8				c_{13}	c_2		c_3	c_4		c_7		$-d_3$	d_9 $-d_2$	d_{10}		d_{12}			d_3	$-d_{14}$ d_4	d_{14} d_6			$-d_{10}$ d_{11}
a_9				c_1	$-c_1$ $-c_3$		$-c_2$				$-d_4$ d_{11}	d_{13}		$-d_1$				$-d_{14}$			d_1		d_2	$-d_8$
a_{10}				c_2			$-c_1$				$-d_{11}$ d_4	$-d_5$ d_{12}	$-d_6$	d_1	$-d_2$	$-d_3$					$-d_1$	d_2		
a_{11}								$-c_2$			$-d_{12}$ d_5	d_{11} $-d_4$		$-d_2$	d_1						d_2	$-d_1$		
a_{12}						c_1				$-c_5$	$-d_{13}$	d_4 $-d_{11}$	$-d_{10}$	d_2						$-d_3$	$-d_2$		$-d_1$	
a_{13}							$-c_6$		$-c_2$					$-d_{14}$										$-d_4$
a_{14}								$-c_2$	$-c_3$					$-d_6$	d_{14}	$-d_4$								d_5
a_{15}									$-c_1$	c_1	$-d_9$			d_5	d_4 $-d_7$	d_{14}	$-d_5$		$-d_1$					d_6
a_{16}															$-d_8$			$-d_5$						
b_1										$-d_{11}$					c_8	c_7	c_6	c_8	c_8	$-c_{11}$	$-c_{13}$			
b_2											$-c_1$		c_1	$-c_8$ c_{10}	c_5 c_6					$-c_{12}$			$-c_{13}$	
b_3													c_7			$-c_2$				$-c_{10}$	$-c_9$	$-c_8$		
b_4													$-c_4$	c_2		c_1		c_3	c_1			$-c_4$		
b_5																					c_5	c_6		$-c_{12}$
b_6																		c_1		$-c_2$		$-c_1$		
b_7																		$-c_3$			$-c_2$	c_3		$-c_8$

FIG. 253. Part of coincidence array for purpurogallin

4.4. *The structure invariant method.* Another technique for determining signs from the triple-product sign relationship has been given by Woolfson (1957). The method is best explained by means of tables similar to those described for the coincidence method. Fig. 254(a) represents sign relationships of the type *abb* where the sign symbols of type 'a' apply to the structure-invariant reflexions (those whose indices are all even) while those of type 'b' are all members of some other single parity group. If the signs of the a's are known, for example in this case if $a_1 = -1$, $a_2 = -1$, $a_3 = +1$, $a_4 = +1$, $a_5 = -1$ and $a_6 = +1$, then these signs can be substituted in fig. 254(a) to give fig. 254(b).

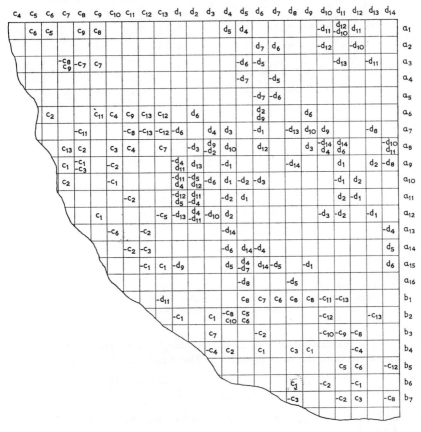

	b_1	b_2	b_3	b_4	b_5	b_6	b_7
b_1		a_1		a_6	a_4		a_3
b_2	a_1		a_4	a_4			
b_3		a_4		a_2			a_1
b_4	a_6	a_4	a_2		a_5		
b_5	a_4			a_5		a_6	
b_6					a_6		a_3
b_7	a_3		a_1			a_3	

(*a*)

	b_1	b_2	b_3	b_4	b_5	b_6	b_7
b_1		−		+	+		+
b_2	−		+	+			
b_3		+		−			−
b_4	+	+	−		−		
b_5	+			−		+	
b_6					+		+
b_7	+		−			+	

(*b*)

	b_1	b_2	b_3	b_4	b_5	b_6	b_7
$b_1 - b_3$		− −		+ +	+		+ +
b_2	−		+	+			
b_4	+	+	−		−		
b_5	+			−		+	
b_6					+		+
b_7	+		−			+	

(*c*)

FIG. 254. (*a*) Table of *abb* sign relationships. (*b*) Table of *abb* sign relationships with signs of *a*'s entered. (*c*) Table of *abb* sign relationships with rows b_1 and b_3 combined as $b_1 - b_3$

An examination of fig. 254(*b*) reveals three columns which have entries in both the rows b_1 and b_3. These entries indicate that

$$\left.\begin{matrix} b_1 b_2 = -1 \\ b_3 b_2 = +1 \end{matrix}\right\} \quad \left.\begin{matrix} b_1 b_4 = +1 \\ b_3 b_4 = -1 \end{matrix}\right\} \quad \left.\begin{matrix} b_1 b_7 = +1 \\ b_3 b_7 = -1 \end{matrix}\right\}$$

and each bracketed pair of probability relationships indicates that $b_1 = -b_3$.

If this conclusion is accepted, and in view of the multiple indications it will have a high probability, then b_1 may be arbitrarily chosen as positive, b_3 accepted as negative and rows b_1 and b_3 combined together as the row $b_1 - b_3$ in fig. 254(*c*). This row may then be compared with the other rows to deduce further signs.

The way in which this technique is used in practice is outlined below:

(i) All sets of signs for the structure invariants are found which satisfy a sufficient number of the *aaa* relationships. For the example we have used there may be three *aaa* relationships $a_1 a_2 a_3 = +1$, $a_2 a_4 a_5 = +1$ and $a_2 a_5 a_6 = +1$. If all these relationships hold then there are eight possible sets of signs for the *a*'s.

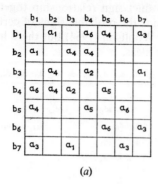

(ii) For each set of '*a*' signs, tables as in fig. 254(*a*) are constructed for each of the other parity groups '*b*' '*c*' and '*d*' (assuming two-dimensional data) and sets of signs determined for these. In general the correct set of '*a*' signs should give a consistent development of other signs and the majority of the other '*a*' sets should lead to a number of inconsistencies.

(iii) From the signs deduced the sign-relationship products of the type *bcd* are computed. In step (ii) an arbitary sign must be chosen for each of groups '*b*' '*c*' and '*d*' although only two arbitary signs are allowed to fix the origin. If the majority of the *bcd* sign relationships are found to be positive this indicates that, by chance, the three arbitarily chosen signs are consistent with respect to a particular origin—assuming that the set of signs is the correct one. If the majority of the *bcd* relationships are negative then this indicates that the signs for one parity group must be completely reversed. When there is a rough balance between positive and negative *bcd* products it may be taken as an indication that the set of signs is implausible.

This method can be applied by hand for not too complex structures; otherwise it is amenable to being programmed for a computer (Woolfson, 1960).

4.5. *Interdependencies of sign relationships.* The triple products of signs which form the basic sign relationships are often related to each other. To explain this we shall introduce the notation of representing a triple product by a symbol S which has the property that it is most probably equal to +1 but might possibly equal −1.

Consider the following reflexions and sign symbols corresponding to large unitary structure factors.

$$\begin{aligned} a_1 &= s(2\,0\,0) \\ a_2 &= s(2\,2\,0) \\ b_1 &= s(1\,3\,0) \\ b_2 &= s(3\,3\,0) \\ b_3 &= s(1\,1\,0) \\ b_4 &= s(1\,\bar{1}\,0). \end{aligned}$$

They are related by the sign relationships

$$\begin{aligned} a_1 b_1 b_2 &= \mathrm{S}_1 \\ a_1 b_3 b_4 &= \mathrm{S}_2 \\ a_2 b_1 b_4 &= \mathrm{S}_3 \\ a_2 b_2 b_3 &= \mathrm{S}_4 \end{aligned} \qquad (255.1)$$

and, since the square of any sign symbol equals +1, we find by multiplying together the four equations that

$$\mathrm{S}_1\mathrm{S}_2\mathrm{S}_3\mathrm{S}_4 = +1. \qquad (255.2)$$

Thus if any one of the four sign relationships fails then one or all of the remainder must fail and equation (*255*.2) strengthens the probability for each of the individual sign relationships. If a particular S occurs in many equations of type (*255*.2) so that its failure indicates an unacceptable number of other failures then we may accept that this S equals +1 with a great degree of confidence (Woolfson, 1958*a*).

A systematic and quantitative technique for using equations of type (*255*.2) has been given by de Vries (1965). We may rewrite (*255*.2) as

$$S_1 = S_2S_3S_4 \qquad (256.1)$$

and one estimate of the probability that S_1 is positive is the probability that the right-hand side of (*256*.1) is positive. This will be so if S_2, S_3 and S_4 are all positive or if any two are negative. If we denote the probability that S_r is positive by P_r then the probability that S_1 is positive based on the right-hand side of (*256*.1) is

$$\begin{aligned} {}_1\phi^+_{2,3,4} &= P_2P_3P_4 + P_2(1-P_3)(1-P_4) + P_3(1-P_2)(1-P_4) + P_4(1-P_2)(1-P_3) \\ &= 4P_2P_3P_4 - 2(P_2P_3 + P_2P_4 + P_3P_4) + P_2 + P_3 + P_4. \end{aligned} \qquad (256.2)$$

If S_1 takes part in a number of equations of the type (*256*.1) then the probability that S_1 is positive is given independently by (*248*.3) and by a number of expressions such as (*256*.2). The overall probability that S_1 is positive, divided by the overall probability that it is negative, is then given by

$$\frac{\Phi_1^+}{\Phi_1^-} = \frac{P_1 \prod\limits_{r,s,t} {}_1\phi^+_{r,s,t}}{(1-P_1)\prod\limits_{r,s,t}(1-{}_1\phi^+_{r,s,t})}. \qquad (256.3)$$

This expression requires modification if some S's occur in more than one of the right-hand-side products of (*256*.1), for the various ϕ's are not then independent, as assumed in (*256*.3).

If for the single equation (*255*.2) all the P's equal 0·8 then from (*256*.2) we find ${}_1\phi_{2,3,4} = 0{\cdot}608$ and (*256*.3) gives

$$\frac{\Phi_1^+}{\Phi_1^-} = \frac{0{\cdot}8 \times 0{\cdot}608}{0{\cdot}2 \times 0{\cdot}392} = 6{\cdot}2.$$

Since $\Phi_1^- = 1 - \Phi_1^+$ this gives $\Phi_1^+ = 0{\cdot}861$.

If S_1 occurred in four independent equations of type (*255*.2) then the final value of Φ_1^+ would be 0·955, a much stronger indication than that derived from (*248*.3) alone.

These ideas were used successfully by de Vries to derive signs for the *a*-axis projection of L-asparagine monohydrate, a structure which had resisted many attempts at solution by other techniques of applying the triple-product sign relationship.

4.6. *The matrix-inversion method.* Consider the signs of a number of structure factors represented by the symbols $x_1, x_2, \ldots, x_n$ with m triple-product sign relationships linking them. These sign relationships may be written in the form

$$\begin{aligned} S_1 &= \pm x_{r_1} x_{s_1} x_{t_1} \\ S_2 &= \pm x_{r_2} x_{s_2} x_{t_2} \\ &\vdots \\ S_m &= \pm x_{r_m} x_{s_m} x_{t_m} \end{aligned} \qquad (257.1)$$

where each of the S's has magnitude unity and is more probably $+1$ than -1. The choice of signs on the right-hand side of the equations (*257*.1) may arise from space-group considerations.

If $m \geqslant n$ it is usually possible to select a subset of (*257*.1) from which the x's may be found in terms of the S's. A simple example will illustrate this point. With $n = 6$ and $m = 8$ we could have

$$\begin{aligned} S_1 &= x_1 x_2 x_3 \\ S_2 &= x_1 x_2 x_5 \\ S_3 &= x_1 x_3 x_5 \\ S_4 &= -x_1 x_5 x_6 \\ S_5 &= x_2 x_3 x_5 \\ S_6 &= x_2 x_4 x_6 \\ S_7 &= x_3 x_4 x_6 \\ S_8 &= x_4 x_5 x_6 \end{aligned} \qquad (257.2)$$

From the subset S_1 to S_6 it may be found that

$$\begin{aligned} x_1 &= S_1 S_2 S_3 \\ x_2 &= S_1 S_2 S_5 \\ x_3 &= S_1 S_3 S_5 \\ x_4 &= -S_2 S_4 S_6 \\ x_5 &= S_2 S_3 S_5 \\ x_6 &= -S_1 S_4 S_5 \end{aligned} \qquad (257.3)$$

and, by substituting these values of x in the final two equations of (*257*.2) we also find

$$\begin{aligned} S_7 &= S_2 S_3 S_6 \\ S_8 &= S_1 S_3 S_6. \end{aligned} \qquad (257.4)$$

If all the sign relationships S_1 to S_6 held, that is to say that all these S's were positive, then from equations (*257*.3) one could derive the signs for the x's i.e. $+ + + - + -$. In addition, from (*257*.4) S_7 and S_8 are also found to be positive and this set of signs for the x's satisfies all the sign relationships. However, there may be other acceptable sets of signs; the probabilities calculated from equation (*248*.3) may indicate that the most probable situation is that up to one of the set S_1 to S_6 and up to two of the complete set S_1 to S_8 may fail. Now, in addition to the case already considered where all the S's were positive, one investigates the six possible ways in which one of the set S_1 to S_6 may be negative. For example, with S_1 negative we find as signs for the x's, $- - - - + +$, $S_7 = +1$ and $S_8 = -1$. Thus this set of signs for the x's satisfies the condition that not more than one of the primary set S_1 to S_6 and not more than two of the complete set S_1 to S_8 should be negative. In fact by looking at the equations (*257.3*) and (*257.4*) we see that S_2, S_4 and S_5 are permitted failures of the primary set and S_3 and S_6 are not. Thus the investigation shows five sets of signs for the x's which satisfy the specified conditions.

In the general case if it is permitted to have δ_1 failures in the primary set S_1 to S_n then the number of combinations which must be examined is

$$M = \sum_{r=0}^{\delta_1} \frac{n!}{r!(n-r)!}$$

For example with $n = 16$ and $\delta_1 = 3$, $M = 697$ and the problem can only be handled satisfactorily in a computer. Cochran and Douglas (1955) have described how to make full use of logical operations in a computer to handle efficiently this type of problem. In the programme which they designed for the EDSAC computer each of the M combinations for the primary set of S's was examined and if it led to less than some specified number of failures δ_2 for the complete set S_1 to S_m then the appropriate x's were computed and printed out.

This is, of course, a multisolution method and, indeed, it may lead to an embarrassingly large number of possible sets of signs. Cochran and Douglas were thus led to design a test for the sets of signs, the zero check, which helps to distinguish the correct set of signs. This and other tests are described in the following section.

Vand and Pepinsky (1956) have described a variant of the Cochran and Douglas method which, at the expense of possibly losing some plausible sets of signs, enables quite large values of n and δ_1 to be managed by hand operations.

4.7. *Phase-determining formulae.* A great deal of work has been done, particularly by Hauptman and Karle, on the development of phase-determining formulae in which phase information is deduced from the magnitudes of the structure factors.

Hauptman and Karle have expressed these results in terms of the normalized structure factor defined as

$$E_{\mathbf{h}} = \frac{U_{\mathbf{h}}}{(\overline{U^2})^{1/2}}$$

The first results, which are applicable to the space group $P\bar{1}$, were given by Hauptman and Karle in a monograph (1953) and may be expressed as

$$\begin{aligned}
\Sigma_1 &= s(E_{2h}) \approx s(E_h^2 - 1)\\
\Sigma_2 &= s(E_h) \approx s\langle E_{h'} E_{h-h'}\rangle_{h'}\\
\Sigma_3 &= s(E_h) \approx s\langle E_{h'}(E^2_{\frac{1}{2}(h-h')} - 1)\rangle_{h'}\\
\Sigma_4 &= s(E_{2h}) \approx s\langle (E_{h'}^2 - 1)(E_{h-h'}^2 - 1)\rangle_{h'}
\end{aligned} \quad (259.1)$$

The formulae Σ_1 and Σ_4 require only a knowledge of the magnitudes of the E's to compute the right-hand side and hence these may be used from the very beginning of a structure determination. However, Σ_1 can only give the sign of E_{2h} with high probability when E_{2h} is positive and this is similar to using (*248.2*) with $\mathbf{h}' = \mathbf{h}$, when $s(2\mathbf{h}) = +1$ with a high probability if the structure factors of indices **h** and **2h** both have large magnitudes.

It was shown by Cochran and Woolfson (1954) that, despite the fact that Σ_4 involves averaging over a large number of terms and would seem to be statistically more significant than Σ_1, it is actually less useful than Σ_1 for determining the sign of E_{2h}. This was shown by a simple argument which also gives a physical picture of the meaning of Σ_1 and Σ_4.

For an equal-atom structure, a Fourier synthesis with coefficients $E_h^2 - 1$ would be the Patterson function for point atoms of weight $N^{1/2}$ with the origin-peak removed. This would consist of N inversion peaks of weight N and coordinates of the type $2\mathbf{r}_j$ and $\frac{1}{2}N(N-2)$ general peaks of weight 2N and coordinates of the type $\mathbf{r}_i - \mathbf{r}_j$. Hence we may write

$$E_h^2 - 1 = \sum_{j=1}^{N} N.\cos 2\pi\mathbf{h}.\,2\mathbf{r}_j + \sum_{\substack{i=1\\ \mathbf{r}_i \neq \pm\mathbf{r}_j}}^{N} \sum_{j=1}^{N/2} 2N\cos 2\pi\mathbf{h}(\mathbf{r}_i - \mathbf{r}_j)$$

or $$N^{1/2}E_{2h} = (E_h^2 - 1) + \text{double summation.} \quad (259.2)$$

The double summation contains a large number of terms but is regarded as having a probable value zero, whence E_{2h} probably has the same sign as $E_h^2 - 1$. We may picture this by saying that the inversion peaks of weight N are a 'signal' indicating the sign of E_{2h} while the general peaks of weight 2N are a 'noise' tending to swamp the signal. Now when we think of Σ_4 in the same light we find that the right-hand-side expression is the Fourier coefficient of the *squared* Patterson function. This would have inversion peaks of weight N^2 and general peaks of weight $4N^2$; the signal-to-noise ratio is reduced and the indication of sign is therefore less reliable.

Cochran (1954) has shown that an exact equation can be derived from Σ_1 and Σ_4; a weighted sum of the two associated Patterson functions can yield a function which contains only inversion peaks, the coefficient of which will be proportional to E_{2h}.

The equation is

$$E_{2h} = 2N^{1/2}(E_h^2 - 1) - N^{3/2}\langle (E_{h'}^2 - 1)(E_{h-h'}^2 - 1)\rangle_{h'}. \quad (259.3)$$

This equation depends on the unrealizable condition that the Patterson function consists of resolved peaks and in practice it is not useful.

The formula Σ_2 is similar to Sayre's equation and Σ_3 can be interpreted physically as the **h**th Fourier coefficient of the product of the electron density and a half-scale Patterson function (Vand and Pepinsky, 1953; Cochran and Woolfson, 1954).

If symmetry other than a centre is also present then stronger sign-determining formulae result. As an example, for the space group $P2_1/c$ one finds

$$s(E_{2h02l}) = s\langle(-1)^{h+l}(E^2_{hkl}-1)\rangle_k, \qquad (260.1)$$

an equation which can be interpreted physically in terms of the Patterson-Harker section.

Hauptman and Karle (1957*a*), by purely algebraic processes, and Vaughan (1958), by consideration of the Patterson function, have developed similar interesting formulae of the type

$$\begin{aligned} E_{\mathbf{h}}E_{\mathbf{h}'}E_{\mathbf{h}+\mathbf{h}'} = {} & \tfrac{1}{8}N^{3/2}\langle(E^2_{\mathbf{H}}-1)(E^2_{\mathbf{h}'+\mathbf{h}}-1)(E^2_{\mathbf{h}+\mathbf{h}'+\mathbf{H}}-1)\rangle_{\mathbf{H}} \\ & +\frac{1}{N^{1/2}}(E^2_{\mathbf{h}}+E^2_{\mathbf{h}'}+E^2_{\mathbf{h}+\mathbf{h}'}-2) \\ & +\frac{1}{2N^{1/2}}(E_{\mathbf{h}}E_{2\mathbf{h}+\mathbf{h}'}+E_{\mathbf{h}'}E_{2\mathbf{h}+\mathbf{h}'}+E_{\mathbf{h}+\mathbf{h}'}E_{\mathbf{h}-\mathbf{h}'}) \\ & -\frac{1}{N}(E_{2\mathbf{h}}+E_{2\mathbf{h}'}+E_{2\mathbf{h}+2\mathbf{h}'}). \end{aligned} \qquad (260.2)$$

Equation (*260*.2) applies only to the equal-atom case; Hauptman and Karle (1959) have derived more general formulae for structures with unequal atoms.

These equations, when applied to the data for real structures, seem to give useful indications of the signs of triple products of structure factors. These triple products are of the same type as occur in the Sayre relationship, and it is interesting that (*260*.2) and related equations often correctly give as negative the triple products of large structure factors.

5. Tests for Sets of Signs

5.1. *Single-solution and multiple-solution methods.* Some of the methods which have been described in the preceding sections lead to a single set of signs whereas other methods often give many plausible sets. In the latter case it is necessary to use some test to select the correct set of signs. If the number of plausible sets is not too large then it is possible to compute the corresponding Fourier syntheses and to examine them for expected features. However, the number is often too large to do this and other objective tests have been devised to narrow the possibilities to a few or even to a single set of signs.

5.2. *Electron-density tests.* A number of simple objective tests have been devised which depend on features of the electron-density map which corresponds to the set of signs. One such is the 'origin check'. If it is known from chemical or other evidence that there can be no atom at or near the origin then one can simply add the Fourier coefficients together to find what their contribution would be there. For the three-dimensional case there are eight origins which can be so treated while for two dimensions there are four. Such a test can eliminate a number of sets of signs which grossly violate the origin-check criterion. However, some allowance must be made for the fact that one is dealing only with partial data so that the Fourier synthesis corresponding to the correct set of signs may show some false features.

The same limitation is imposed on a negativity check, an examination of computed Fourier syntheses and the elimination of those showing negative regions. Even the correct partial set of signs may give appreciable negativity and the test can only be used to eliminate those sets of signs showing negative regions of large magnitude.

5.3. *The zero-check.* This test was designed by Cochran and Douglas (1957) and is applicable under the same conditions as Sayre's equations, that there should be equal resolved atoms.

The equation which was used was the statistical form of Sayre's relationship (*249*.1). Unitary structures of index **h** were chosen such that $U_{\mathbf{h}}$ was zero or very small in magnitude. For each such $U_{\mathbf{h}}$ the sum

$$\sum_{\mathbf{h}'} U_{\mathbf{h}'} U_{\mathbf{h}-\mathbf{h}'}$$

was found for the particular set of signs to be tested, the summation including all available products of U's. The zero-check test function was taken as

$$\psi_0 = \sum_{\mathbf{h}} \Big| \sum_{\mathbf{h}'} U_{\mathbf{h}'} U_{\mathbf{h}-\mathbf{h}'} \Big| . \qquad (261.1)$$

Since each $U_{\mathbf{h}}$ is zero, or nearly so, then ψ_0 should be small for the correct set of signs.

This test has been found to be quite efficient and usually gives the correct set of signs with the lowest or nearly the lowest value of ψ_0.

5.4. *The Z-test.* When the atoms of a structure are unequal or overlap in projection then the zero-check becomes less efficient and, when atoms greatly differing in weight are present, can even be misleading. Under these circumstances Woolfson (1958*c*) has recommended a test function derived from equation (*247*.5). This involves computing

$$Z = \frac{\sum_{\mathbf{h}} \big| (|F_{\mathbf{h}}| - |A_{\mathbf{h}} G'_{\mathbf{h}} + B_{\mathbf{h}} H'_{\mathbf{h}}|) \big|}{\sum_{\mathbf{h}} |F_{\mathbf{h}}|} \qquad (261.2)$$

where

$$G'_{\mathbf{h}} = \frac{1}{V}\sum_{\mathbf{h}'} F_{\mathbf{h}'}F_{\mathbf{h}-\mathbf{h}'}$$

$$H'_{\mathbf{h}} = \frac{1}{V^2}\sum_{\mathbf{h}'}\sum_{\mathbf{h}''} F_{\mathbf{h}'}F_{\mathbf{h}''}F_{\mathbf{h}-\mathbf{h}'-\mathbf{h}''}$$

The summations over $\mathbf{h}'$ and $\mathbf{h}''$ are carried out with all the available data; the summation over $\mathbf{h}$ is usually restricted to reflexions with not too high a Bragg angle, say with $\sin\theta/\lambda$ up to about 0·3–0·4.

The Z-test is more complicated than the zero-check and hence takes longer to apply. However, with a modern computer both tests may be applied to as many as hundreds of trial sets of signs in a moderate time and so greatly restrict the number of sets of signs which need be considered in any detail.

6. The Patterson Function and Sign Determination

6.1. *The vector-interaction formula of Hauptman and Karle.* As has already been noted some of the early sign-determining formulae of Hauptman and Karle can be related to the Patterson function. In fact Hauptman and Karle derived their formulae by purely analytical methods but they did note that there were certain restrictions on the atomic positions if the equations were to be valid. For example, one such restriction was of the form

$$(\mathbf{r}_i - \mathbf{r}_j) \neq (\mathbf{r}_k - \mathbf{r}_l) \qquad (262.1)$$

which is another way of saying that no two Patterson peaks should overlap.

Hauptman and Karle (1962) have subsequently developed sign-determining formulae which use the actual calculated values of the Patterson function, $P(\mathbf{r})$. One such formula, which applies to a structure having equal resolved atoms and a perfectly resolved Patterson function is

$$\begin{aligned}|E_{\mathbf{h}}E_{\mathbf{h}'}E_{\mathbf{h}+\mathbf{h}'}| \cos(\phi_{\mathbf{h}} + \phi_{\mathbf{h}'} + \phi_{\mathbf{h}+\mathbf{h}'})\\ \approx N(|E_{\mathbf{h}}|^2 + |E_{\mathbf{h}'}|^2 + |E_{\mathbf{h}+\mathbf{h}'}|^2 - 2)\\ + \tfrac{1}{2}\sum_{\mathbf{r}}\sum_{\mathbf{r}'} \{P(\mathbf{r})P(\mathbf{r}')P(\mathbf{r}+\mathbf{r}')\}^{1/2} [\cos 2\pi(\mathbf{h}\cdot\mathbf{r} - \mathbf{h}'\cdot\mathbf{r}')\\ + \cos 2\pi(\mathbf{h}\cdot\mathbf{r}' - \mathbf{h}'\cdot\mathbf{r}) + \cos 2\pi\{\mathbf{h}'\cdot\mathbf{r} - (\mathbf{h}+\mathbf{h}')\cdot\mathbf{r}'\}\\ + \cos 2\pi\{(\mathbf{h}+\mathbf{h}')\cdot\mathbf{r} - \mathbf{h}'\cdot\mathbf{r}'\} + \cos 2\pi\{\mathbf{h}\cdot\mathbf{r} - (\mathbf{h}+\mathbf{h}')\cdot\mathbf{r}'\}\\ + \cos 2\pi\{(\mathbf{h}+\mathbf{h}')\cdot\mathbf{r} - \mathbf{h}\cdot\mathbf{r}'\}]. \qquad (262.2)\end{aligned}$$

The summation is to be taken over all Patterson peaks $\mathbf{r}$ and $\mathbf{r}'$ such that there is another Patterson peak at $\mathbf{r}+\mathbf{r}'$, which would be the case, for example, when

$$\mathbf{r} = \mathbf{r}_i - \mathbf{r}_j$$
$$\mathbf{r}' = \mathbf{r}_j - \mathbf{r}_k$$
$$\mathbf{r} + \mathbf{r}' = \mathbf{r}_i - \mathbf{r}_k. \qquad (263)$$

When there is overlap of peaks in the Patterson function Karle and Hauptman suggest that in place of $P(\mathbf{r})P(\mathbf{r}')P(\mathbf{r}+\mathbf{r}')$ there should be used $m(\mathbf{r}, \mathbf{r}')^{3/2}$ where $m(\mathbf{r}, \mathbf{r}')$ is the minimum of $P(\mathbf{r})$, $P(\mathbf{r}')$ and $P(\mathbf{r}+\mathbf{r}')$.

No practical application of this or similar formulae appears to have been made although tests of the equations with known model structures have been encouraging.

6.2. *The method of Anzenhofer and Hoppe*. Anzenhofer and Hoppe (1962) have described a method which makes use of the zero points of the Patterson function. If at the point $\mathbf{u}$ in the Patterson function $P(\mathbf{u}) = 0$ then we know that no interatomic vector $\mathbf{u}$ exists. We can generalize this statement by saying that for all points $\mathbf{r}$ in the unit cell the product $\rho(\mathbf{r})\rho(\mathbf{r}+\mathbf{u}) = 0$, otherwise $P(\mathbf{u}) \neq 0$. This is illustrated in fig. 263 where a structure is shown and also the effect of displacements $\mathbf{u}$ and $-\mathbf{u}$ such that no displaced atom falls on any original atomic position.

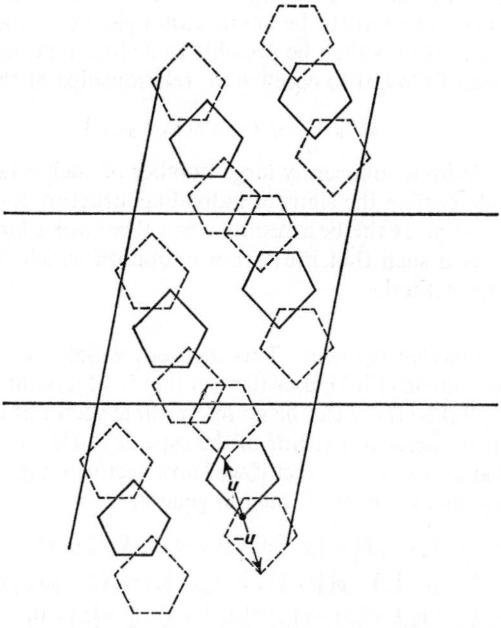

FIG. 263. When the structure (solid lines) is displaced by a vector **u** or $-\mathbf{u}$ (dashed lines) no displaced atom falls on an undisplaced atom

In such a case we may write

$$\phi(\mathbf{r}) = \rho(\mathbf{r})\{\rho(\mathbf{r}+\mathbf{u}) + \rho(\mathbf{r}-\mathbf{u})\} = 0 \text{ for all } \mathbf{r}.$$

The Fourier coefficients of $\phi(\mathbf{r})$ will be given by the convolution of the Fourier coefficients of $\rho(\mathbf{r})$ and $\rho(\mathbf{r}+\mathbf{u})+\rho(\mathbf{r}-\mathbf{u})$; the Fourier coefficients of these are $F_{\mathbf{h}}$ and $2F_{\mathbf{h}}\cos 2\pi\mathbf{h}\cdot\mathbf{u}$ respectively.

Hence the **h**th Fourier coefficient of $\phi(\mathbf{r})$ is given by

$$\mathscr{F}_{\mathbf{h}}=\frac{2}{V}\sum_{\mathbf{h}'} F_{\mathbf{h}'}F_{\mathbf{h}-\mathbf{h}'}\cos 2\pi\mathbf{h}'\cdot\mathbf{u}. \qquad (264.1)$$

Since $\phi(\mathbf{r})=0$ for all **r** then $\mathscr{F}_{\mathbf{h}}=0$ for all **h** and we may write

$$\sum_{\mathbf{h}'} F_{\mathbf{h}'}F_{\mathbf{h}-\mathbf{h}'}\cos 2\pi\mathbf{h}'\cdot\mathbf{u}=0 \qquad (264.2)$$

for all **h** and for all **u** for which $P(\mathbf{u})=0$.

For a particular **h** there will be several values of **u** giving equations of type (*264*.2) and we may take any linear combination of such equations to give

$$\sum_{\mathbf{h}'} F_{\mathbf{h}'}F_{\mathbf{h}-\mathbf{h}'}\Big(\sum_{s} a_s\cos 2\pi\mathbf{h}'\cdot\mathbf{u}_s\Big)=0. \qquad (264.3)$$

We may now build up a large coefficient for a particular $F_{\mathbf{h}'}F_{\mathbf{h}-\mathbf{h}'}$ in (*264*.3) by suitably choosing the coefficients a_s, i.e. $a_s=s(\cos 2\pi\mathbf{h}'\cdot\mathbf{u}_s)$ or, better, $a_s=\cos 2\pi\mathbf{h}'\cdot\mathbf{u}_s$. The coefficients of the remaining terms of the summation will mostly be small although, by chance, some may be quite large. It may then be possible to deduce that, in order for the left-hand side of (*264*.3) to equal zero, relationships of the form

$$s(F_{\mathbf{h}''}F_{\mathbf{h}-\mathbf{h}''})=\pm s(F_{\mathbf{h}'}F_{\mathbf{h}-\mathbf{h}'}) \qquad (264.4)$$

must exist. With a sufficiently large number of such relationships it is possible to determine the signs of individual structure factors.

This method gives the best results when there are a large number of distinct points **u** such that $P(\mathbf{u})=0$, a limitation which also applies to the following method.

6.3. *The M-function method.* This method, which was developed by Main and Woolfson (1963), uses the fact that if, at a point **u** in Patterson space, $P(\mathbf{u})=0$ then there can be no interatomic vector at that point and in particular no inversion vector of the type $2\mathbf{r}_j$. Hence where $P(\mathbf{u})=0$ we know that $\rho(\tfrac{1}{2}\mathbf{u})=0$. In fact if we leave vector notation and express the condition as $P(x, y, z)=0$ then in general

$$\begin{aligned}&\rho(\tfrac{1}{2}x,\tfrac{1}{2}y,\tfrac{1}{2}z)=\rho(\tfrac{1}{2}+\tfrac{1}{2}x,\tfrac{1}{2}y,\tfrac{1}{2}z)=\rho(\tfrac{1}{2}x,\tfrac{1}{2}+\tfrac{1}{2}y,\tfrac{1}{2}z)\\&=\rho(\tfrac{1}{2}x,\tfrac{1}{2}y,\tfrac{1}{2}+\tfrac{1}{2}z)=\rho(\tfrac{1}{2}+\tfrac{1}{2}x,\tfrac{1}{2}+\tfrac{1}{2}y,\tfrac{1}{2}z)=\rho(\tfrac{1}{2}+\tfrac{1}{2}x,\tfrac{1}{2}y,\tfrac{1}{2}+\tfrac{1}{2}z)\\&=\rho(\tfrac{1}{2}x,\tfrac{1}{2}+\tfrac{1}{2}y,\tfrac{1}{2}+\tfrac{1}{2}z)=\rho(\tfrac{1}{2}+\tfrac{1}{2}x,\tfrac{1}{2}+\tfrac{1}{2}y,\tfrac{1}{2}+\tfrac{1}{2}z)=0.\end{aligned}$$

Thus it is possible to find regions of the unit cell where there *cannot* be any electron density, while other regions may or may not have finite electron density. From this information a function $M(\mathbf{r})$ is defined such that

$M(\mathbf{r}) = 0$ where there can be no electron density
$M(\mathbf{r}) = 1$ elsewhere.

It is clear that $M(\mathbf{r})$ has the property that

$$\rho(\mathbf{r}) = M(\mathbf{r})\rho(\mathbf{r}) \tag{265.1}$$

for all **r**. Hence, from the convolution theorem we may write

$$F_{\mathbf{h}} = \frac{1}{V}\sum_{\mathbf{h}'} X_{\mathbf{h}'} F_{\mathbf{h}-\mathbf{h}'} \tag{265.2}$$

where the F's are the structure factors and the X's the Fourier coefficients of $M(\mathbf{r})$. The X's can be determined and hence (*265*.2) is a linear equation in the F's. Since there are as many equations as unknowns (more if one takes account of accidental absences) it is possible to solve this set of equations for the F's both in sign and magnitude.

This idea has been tried on trial model structures and it has been found that the quality of the Patterson function is of great importance. In one application to a real three-dimensional structure it was possible to solve the structure using the calculated $|F|$'s but not using the observed. It is also necessary for the Patterson function to contain a large proportion of regions for which $P(\mathbf{u}) = 0$, otherwise the equations (*265*.2) are ill-conditioned and the solutions not very reliable. This limits the application of the method to three dimensions and hence involves the use of fast modern computers.

7. Phase Determination for Non-centrosymmetric Structures

7.1. *General comments.* The problem of determining phases for non-centrosymmetric structures has not received as much attention as has the centrosymmetric problem. One can easily see why this is so and why this field of study has seemed to offer so little prospect. Let us suppose that for a structure of given complexity a knowledge of the phases of a number n of the largest structure factors would serve to determine the structure. In the centrosymmetric case each phase is 0 or π and so, *ab initio*, we are confronted with 2^n possible sets of signs (less if we take account of arbitrary signs for fixing an origin). In the non-centrosymmetric case each phase can be anywhere in the range 0–2π; if, say, we decide that determining such phase to within $\pm\frac{1}{8}\pi$ is satisfactory then we may stipulate that there are eight possible phases—$0, \frac{1}{4}\pi, \frac{1}{2}\pi, \frac{3}{4}\pi, \pi, \frac{5}{4}\pi, \frac{3}{2}\pi, \frac{7}{4}\pi$ and consequently 8^n possible combinations of phase.

When one has experienced the problems associated with *sign* determination one realizes how bleak is the outlook with the much more complex general phase-determining problem. While some theoretical studies have been carried out, no great progress has been made in a practical direction.

7.2. *Phase relationships.* Cochran (1955) showed that if one has three structure factors of indices **h**, **h**′ and **h** − **h**′ the expected value of the phase $\phi_{\mathbf{h}}$ is given by

$$\langle\phi_{\mathbf{h}}\rangle = \phi_{\mathbf{h}'} + \phi_{\mathbf{h}-\mathbf{h}'}. \qquad (266.1)$$

The distribution about the mean value can be calculated; the larger the product $|U_{\mathbf{h}}U_{\mathbf{h}'}U_{\mathbf{h}-\mathbf{h}'}|$ the less the variance of the distribution.

Karle and Hauptman (1956, 1958) deduced expressions

$$|E_{\mathbf{h}}| \cos \phi_{\mathbf{h}} \simeq \frac{\delta_2^{3/2}}{\delta_3} \langle |E_{\mathbf{h}'}E_{\mathbf{h}-\mathbf{h}'}| \cos (\phi_{\mathbf{h}'} + \phi_{\mathbf{h}-\mathbf{h}'})\rangle_{\mathbf{h}'} \qquad (266.2)$$

and

$$|E_{\mathbf{h}}| \sin \phi_{\mathbf{h}} \simeq \frac{\delta_2^{3/2}}{\delta_3} \langle |E_{\mathbf{h}'}E_{\mathbf{h}-\mathbf{h}'}| \sin (\phi_{\mathbf{h}'} + \phi_{\mathbf{h}-\mathbf{h}'})\rangle_{\mathbf{h}'}. \qquad (266.3)$$

For an equal-atom structure the $\simeq$ is replaced by =. Karle and Hauptman have shown that if one knows the phases of a number of the larger E's then one can calculate approximate phases for additional E's by the expression

$$\tan \phi_{\mathbf{h}} = \frac{\text{right-hand side of } (266.3)}{\text{right-hand side of } (266.2)}. \qquad (266.4)$$

This offers the possibility of building up a larger body of phase information if the phases of a basic set are given—but no practical way of choosing a basic set is known for the general space group P1. However, Karle and Karle (1964) demonstrated an elegant procedure for determining phases for a structure of space group $P2_12_12_1$, which relied on the fact that symbols chosen to represent phases in the centro-symmetric projections were known to be 0, $\pi/2$, π or $3\pi/2$. An initial set of phases for general reflexions was found and then refined by an iterative process using equation *226*.4.

A phase-relating formula for P1, similar to (*260*.2) has also been given by Karle and Hauptman (1957*b*). This is

$$|E_{\mathbf{h}}E_{\mathbf{h}'}E_{-\mathbf{h}-\mathbf{h}'}| \cos (\phi_{\mathbf{h}} + \phi_{\mathbf{h}'} + \phi_{-\mathbf{h}-\mathbf{h}'})$$
$$= \frac{N^{3/2}}{2} \langle (|E_{\mathbf{H}}|^2 - 1)(|E_{\mathbf{h}+\mathbf{H}}|^2 - 1)(|E_{\mathbf{h}+\mathbf{h}'+\mathbf{H}}|^2 - 1)\rangle_{\mathbf{H}}$$
$$+ \frac{1}{N^{1/2}}(|E_{\mathbf{h}}|^2 + |E_{\mathbf{h}'}|^2 + |E_{-\mathbf{h}-\mathbf{h}'}|^2 - 2). \qquad (266.5)$$

Equation (*262*.2) also applies to P1 but the stringent conditions the Patterson function must satisfy in order for this equation to apply make its utility very dubious.

CHAPTER 10

FOURIER TRANSFORMS AND OPTICAL METHODS

1. General Outline

1.1. *Diffraction by a non-periodic distribution.* In this book we are chiefly concerned with X-ray diffraction by crystals. This is however only a special case of the theory of scattering, in which a *periodic* electron distribution happens to be involved. The general theory of scattering (of light, X-rays, electrons, neutrons) is intimately related to the theory of Fourier transforms, and it is illuminating to approach our special problem from this point of view. Furthermore the calculation of Fourier transforms by an optical analogue method has turned out to be an important method of crystal structure analysis, and is described later in this chapter. The Fourier-transform approach also helps one to see crystallography in perspective in its relation to physical optics and solid state physics.

The following discussion of diffraction by a continuous distribution $\sigma(\mathbf{r})$ follows closely that already given for diffraction by a lattice (section **1**.2.1). The path difference between radiation scattered from P (fig. 267) and from the origin, is $ON - MP = \lambda\mathbf{r}\cdot\mathbf{S}$, so that the phase

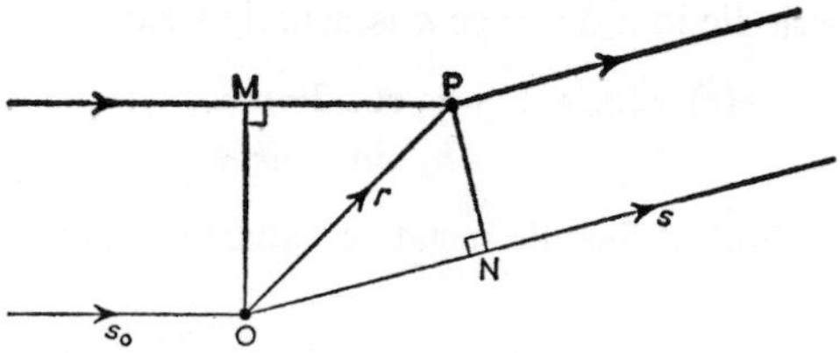

FIG. 267. The scattering vector $\mathbf{S}$ is the difference, $\mathbf{s}-\mathbf{s}_0$, between the wave-vectors of the scattered and incident beams

difference is $2\pi\mathbf{r}\cdot\mathbf{S}$, where, as in section **1**.2.1, $\mathbf{S}$ is the difference between the wave-vectors of the scattered and incident radiations—the scattering vector (section **1**.2.1). If the scattered amplitude from a volume element dV at $\mathbf{r}$ is measured simply by $\sigma(\mathbf{r})\, dV$ (possibly after allowance for a polarization factor, depending on the nature of the scattering process), the resultant scattered amplitude is given in amplitude and phase by

$$F(\mathbf{S}) = \int_V \sigma(\mathbf{r}) \exp(2\pi i\mathbf{r}\cdot\mathbf{S})\, dV. \qquad (267)$$

As we shall see shortly, this result expresses the fact that the scattered amplitude is the Fourier transform of the scattering distribution. The change of momentum of a scattered photon is $2\pi\hbar\mathbf{S}$, and the same result applies when material particles are involved, so that **S** is a measure of the momentum transfer.

S may also be thought of as a vector in reciprocal space (section 1.2.3). Let us refer the distribution $\sigma(\mathbf{r})$ to a coordinate system specified by three non-coplanar vectors **a**, **b**, **c** so that

$$\mathbf{r} = x\mathbf{a} + y\mathbf{b} + z\mathbf{c}. \tag{268.1}$$

It is then convenient to refer **S** to axes **a***, **b***, **c*** such that

$$\mathbf{S} = \xi\mathbf{a}^* + \eta\mathbf{b}^* + \zeta\mathbf{c}^* \tag{268.2}$$

and if one chooses these axes to be reciprocal to the original ones, as defined by equation (7.2), with $V = \mathbf{a}.\mathbf{b} \times \mathbf{c}$, one arrives at the simple expression

$$\mathbf{r}.\mathbf{S} = x\xi + y\eta + z\zeta. \tag{268.3}$$

Notice that **a**, **b**, **c** do not define a lattice since $\sigma(\mathbf{r})$ is not periodic; nevertheless reciprocal axes can be defined and it is convenient to use them. Volume elements in the two spaces can now be written $V\,dx\,dy\,dz$ and $V^*\,d\xi\,d\eta\,d\zeta$ respectively, where $V^* = \mathbf{a}^*.\mathbf{b}^* \times \mathbf{c}^* = 1/V$.

1.2. *The Fourier transform.* The theory of Fourier transforms, which is quite independent of their appearance in scattering theory, can be approached via the theory of Fourier series, which we now briefly recapitulate. The Fourier expansion of a *one-dimensional* function $\rho(r)$ which is periodic in a distance a is usually written

$$\rho(r) = \tfrac{1}{2}a_0 + \ldots + a_n \cos 2\pi nr/a + \ldots$$
$$\ldots + b_n \sin 2\pi nr/a + \ldots$$

It is however helpful to include negative values of n, and a factor $1/a$; we then write

$$\rho(r) = \frac{1}{a}\sum_{n=-\infty}^{+\infty} (A_n \cos 2\pi nr/a + B_n \sin 2\pi nr/a) \tag{268.4}$$

where $A_{-n} = A_n$ and $B_{-n} = -B_n$. From the orthogonality of cosine and sine waves of different wavelength, there then follow the well-known results

$$A_n = \int_{-a/2}^{+a/2} \rho(r) \cos 2\pi nr/a\, dr$$
$$B_n = \int_{-a/2}^{+a/2} \rho(r) \sin 2\pi nr/a\, dr. \tag{268.5}$$

We now introduce complex coefficients

$$F_n = A_n + iB_n \tag{268.6}$$

and it is easily shown that equation (*268*.4) becomes

$$\rho(r) = \frac{1}{a} \sum_{n=-\infty}^{+\infty} F_n \exp(-2\pi i n r/a) \tag{269.1}$$

while the result corresponding to (*268*.5) is

$$F_n = \int_{-a/2}^{+a/2} \rho(r) \exp(2\pi i n r/a)\, dr. \tag{269.2}$$

Notice that there is a certain symmetry between equations (*269*.1) and (*269*.2) but where one has a minus sign in the exponent the other has plus. (The choice is arbitrary but the signs cannot be identical.) We might draw a diagram showing the values of the coefficients A_n and B_n as a function of n/a for a given $\rho(r)$, and this may be called a wave-number analysis of ρ, since n/a is the wave-number of the nth Fourier component.

Now let us consider how we might make a wave-number analysis of a function $\sigma(r)$ (fig. (269(*a*)) which is not periodic but falls to zero in some finite range. We can pretend that the function is periodic by repeating

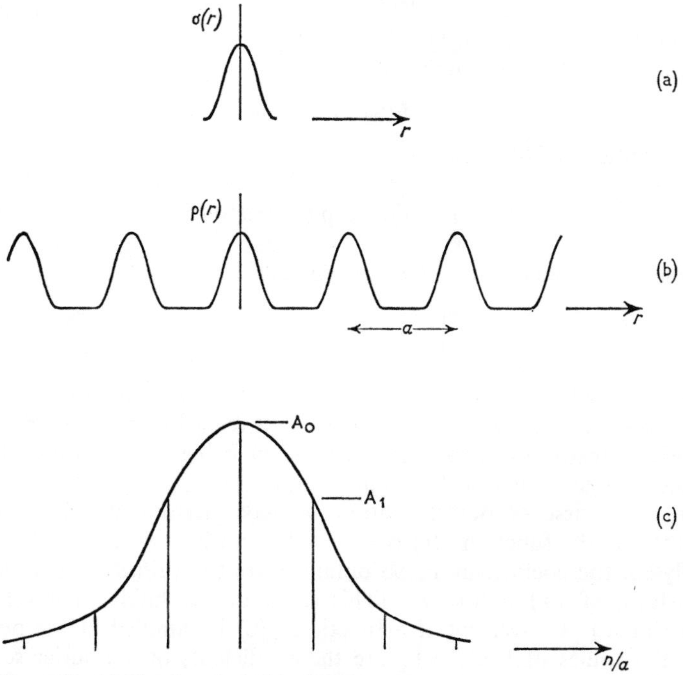

FIG. 269. (*a*) The function $\sigma(r)$. (*b*) The periodic function $\rho(r)$ obtained by repeating $\sigma(r)$ with interval a. (*c*) The ordinates are successive coefficients of the Fourier series for $\rho(r)$. The continuous curve is the Fourier transform of $\sigma(r)$

it indefinitely with a spacing a which is greater than its range so that adjacent blocks do not overlap; this gives a periodic function $\rho(r)$, equal to $\sigma(r)$ in the range $\pm a/2$. A wave-number analysis may then be made in the usual way (fig. 269(*c*)); only A's appear because we have chosen an even function (figs. 269(*a*), (*b*)). If now a is doubled, A_{2n} has the magnitude and position of the previous A_n (see equation (*268*.5)); in fact the pattern of A's is the same, but twice as many appear. If we continue the process of increasing a, the ordinates come sufficiently close to trace out a continuous curve $F(n/a)$ which is in fact the Fourier transform of $\sigma(r)$, (fig. 269(*c*)).

To put this more quantitatively, write the wave-number $n/a = S$. Then in the limit $a \to \infty$, S becomes a continuous (one-dimensional) variable, despite the fact that n increases in steps of $\Delta n = 1$, and we put $dS = \Delta n/a$. The sum in equation (*269*.1) can now be replaced by an integral, and inside the range $\pm a/2$ we can interchange $\rho(r)$ and $\sigma(r)$, so that

$$\sigma(r) = \frac{1}{a}\int_{n=-\infty}^{+\infty} F_n \exp(-2\pi i n r/a)\, \Delta n. \qquad (270.1)$$

As $a \to \infty$, F_n maintains the same value for a given value of n/a, as can be verified from equation (*269*.2), remembering that $\rho(r) = \sigma(r)$ inside the range of integration and has fallen to zero before the limits are reached. We therefore write

$$F_n = F(S) \quad \text{for } S = n/a$$

and equation (*270*.1) becomes

$$\sigma(r) = \int_{-\infty}^{+\infty} F(S) \exp(-2\pi i r S)\, dS. \qquad (270.2)$$

At the same time equation (*269*.2) becomes

$$F(S) = \int_{-\infty}^{+\infty} \sigma(r) \exp(2\pi i r S)\, dr. \qquad (270.3)$$

F(S) is called the Fourier transform of $\sigma(r)$, and equation (*270*.2) expresses the fact that we may equally well regard $\sigma(r)$ as the (inverse) Fourier transform of F(S), the word inverse being put in to remind us of the change in sign of the complex exponent.

In the course of our derivation we have arrived at other useful results. If the function $\sigma(r)$ is repeated at an interval a, and Fourier analysed, the coefficients F_n so obtained are the values of the Fourier transform of $\sigma(r)$ at $S = n/a$. (This result in fact holds whatever the value of a.) Conversely, if a function F(S) is sampled at the points n/a, the values of $F(n/a) = F_n$ are the coefficients of a Fourier series, equation (*269*.1). Provided $1/a$ is sufficiently small, this series within the interval $\pm a/2$ gives the (inverse) Fourier transform of F(S). A Fourier transform may therefore be calculated by any of the usual methods of Fourier analysis or Fourier synthesis, the latter being usually the more convenient in practice.

All of these results can be extended to apply to three dimensions, but detailed derivations will be left as an exercise to the reader. The one-dimensional variable r is replaced by a vector $\mathbf{r}$, and a wave-vector analysis of a distribution $\sigma(\mathbf{r})$ can be made by first repeating it on a three-dimensional lattice to give, in the notation used elsewhere (section **1**.2.3)

$$\rho(r)=\frac{1}{V}\sum_{\mathbf{h}} F_{\mathbf{h}} \exp(-2\pi i\mathbf{h}\cdot\mathbf{r}). \qquad (271.1)$$

The wave-vector $\mathbf{h}$ is thus the analogue of n/a above. By proceeding to the limit where the lattice translations are infinite we find a continuous function F(S) related to $\sigma(\mathbf{r})$ by

$$F(S)=\int_V \sigma(\mathbf{r}) \exp(2\pi i\mathbf{r}\cdot S)\, dV \qquad (271.2)$$

and

$$\sigma(\mathbf{r})=\int_{V*} F(S) \exp(-2\pi i\mathbf{r}\cdot S)\, dV^* \qquad (271.3)$$

where dV^* is a volume element at the end of the wave-vector S. We have of course already seen equation (*271*.2) as equation (*267*.1), but whereas (*271*.2) is the formal definition of the Fourier transform of $\sigma(\mathbf{r})$, (*267*.1) expressed a physical result. From equation (*271*.3) we see that if the scattered amplitude, as defined in (*267*.1), could be measured over a sufficient range of S, in magnitude and in phase, the scattering distribution could immediately be derived.

Although for simplicity we have chosen to derive the one-dimensional analogues of equations (*271*.2) and (*271*.3) from the properties of Fourier series, it is quite possible to discuss transforms without reference to series, by making use of Fourier's integral theorem (see for example, Titchmarsh, 1948). We have not hedged our derivation about with any of the qualifications such as are to be found in the reference just given, as we have not tried to be mathematically rigorous in this discussion.

2. Examples of Fourier Transforms, and some of Their Properties

2.1. *Examples.* The Fourier transforms of many functions have been tabulated (see for example International Tables, Vol. 2), and we shall quote here a few results which are particularly useful in crystallography.

If $\sigma(\mathbf{r})$ is spherically symmetric, so is its transform, and is given by

$$F(S)=\int_0^\infty 4\pi r^2\sigma(r)\,\frac{\sin 2\pi rS}{2\pi rS}\,dr. \qquad (271.4)$$

This formula will be recognized as that giving the atomic scattering factor of an atom having a spherically symmetric electron distribution (section **1**.3.3). If for example

$$\sigma(r) = (p/\pi)^{3/2} \exp(-pr^2) \tag{272.1}$$

then

$$F(S) = \exp\left(-\frac{\pi^2}{p}S^2\right) \tag{272.2}$$

Thus the Fourier transform of a Gaussian is also a Gaussian, and their widths are inversely proportional to one another.

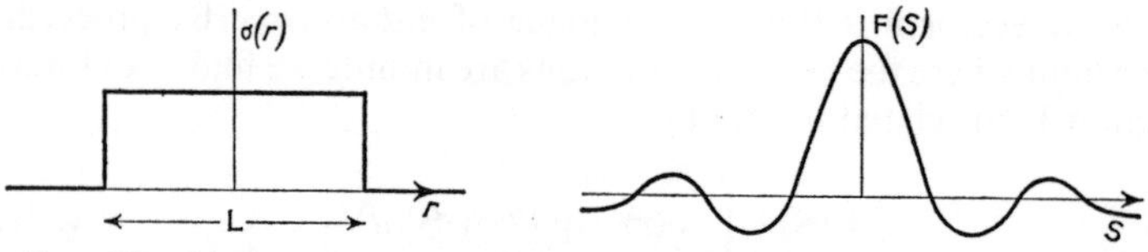

FIG. 272. (*a*) A unit step function of width L. (*b*) The corresponding Fourier transform

To take now a simple one-dimensional example, suppose $\sigma(r)$ is a unit step function centred on the origin and of length L (fig. 272(*a*)). Its transform (fig. 272(*b*)) is given by

$$F(S) = L\,\frac{\sin \pi LS}{\pi LS}\,. \tag{272.3}$$

Once again, the widths of $\sigma(r)$ and of its transform are inversely proportional. Equation (*272*.3) will be recognized as giving the Fraunhofer diffraction amplitude for a slit of width L (section **1**.4.2). This result can readily be generalized. Let $\sigma(\mathbf{r})$ be unity inside a parallelepiped which is centred at the origin and has sides $x_0\mathbf{a}$, $y_0\mathbf{b}$, $z_0\mathbf{c}$. Then, with **S** given by equation (*268*.2),

$$F(\mathbf{S}) = V\,\frac{\sin \pi x_0\xi}{\pi x_0\xi}\,\frac{\sin \pi y_0\eta}{\pi y_0\eta}\,\frac{\sin \pi z_0\zeta}{\pi z_0\zeta} \tag{272.4}$$

where V is the volume of the parallelepiped. The extension of F(**S**) along any reciprocal axis is thus inversely proportional to the extension of $\sigma(\mathbf{r})$ along the corresponding axis. These examples also illustrate another general result, readily derived from equation (*271*.2), which is that the weight of a function, defined as $\int \sigma(\mathbf{r})\, dV$, is the value of its transform at the origin, F(0).

Consider the situation when p of equation (*272*.1) tends to infinity. $\sigma(\mathbf{r})$ in this equation is so defined that its weight remains equal to unity, although it is infinite at the origin and zero elsewhere. This defines Dirac's δ-function. We see from equation (*272*.2) that its transform is $F(S)=1$. Physically this result expresses the fact that a scattering centre whose dimensions are much smaller than a wave-length scatters isotropically—for example a classical electron scattering X-rays, or a nucleus scattering slow neutrons.

2.2. *Addition and translation of functions.* It is easily shown that if F_1 and F_2 are the transforms of σ_1 and σ_2 respectively, then the transform of $\sigma_1+\sigma_2$ is F_1+F_2. The operation of addition in space corresponds to the same operation in reciprocal space.

Suppose the distribution $\sigma(\mathbf{r})$ is moved to give a new distribution $\sigma(\mathbf{r}-\mathbf{r}_0)$. The new transform is

$$\begin{aligned} F'(S) &= \int \sigma(\mathbf{r}-\mathbf{r}_0) \exp(2\pi i \mathbf{r}\cdot S)\, dV^* \\ &= \exp(2\pi i \mathbf{r}_0\cdot S) \int \sigma(\mathbf{r}-\mathbf{r}_0) \exp(2\pi i(\mathbf{r}-\mathbf{r}_0)\cdot S)\, dV^* \\ &= \exp(2\pi i \mathbf{r}_0\cdot S)\, F(S). \qquad (273.1) \end{aligned}$$

In words, the effect of translating $\sigma(\mathbf{r})$ is to multiply its transform by a fringe function. While $|F(S)|$ is not affected, the real and imaginary parts of $F(S)$ are multiplied by $\cos 2\pi\mathbf{r}_0\cdot S$ and $\sin 2\pi\mathbf{r}_0\cdot S$ respectively.

In crystallography we frequently have to deal with scattering distributions composed of a number of individual distributions $\sigma_j(\mathbf{r}-\mathbf{r}_j)$, the atoms comprising one molecule or perhaps one unit cell. Let $f_j(S)$ be the transform (or scattering factor) of one atom. Then the integral for $F(S)$ can be expressed as a sum of separate integrals taken over the individual atoms, so that

$$F(S) = \sum_{j=1}^{N} f_j(S) \exp(2\pi i \mathbf{r}_j\cdot S). \qquad (273.2)$$

Usually $f_j(S)$ is taken to be spherically symmetric.

2.3. *Symmetry and homogeneous distortion of functions.* If we invert $\sigma(\mathbf{r})$ through the origin to give $\sigma(-\mathbf{r})$, it is easy to show that the same operation must be made on $F(S)$. Also if $\sigma(\mathbf{r})$ has a centre of symmetry at the origin, so has $F(S)$.

Again, suppose $\sigma(xyz)=\sigma(x\bar{y}z)$. Then using the notation of equations (*268*.1), (*268*.2) and (*268*.3),

$$F(\xi\eta\zeta) = \int \sigma(xyz) \exp 2\pi i(x\xi+y\eta+z\zeta)\, V\, dx\, dy\, dz \qquad (273.3)$$

$$\begin{aligned} &= \int \sigma(x\bar{y}z) \exp 2\pi i(x\xi+y\eta+z\zeta)\, V\, dx\, dy\, dz \\ &= \int \sigma(xyz) \exp 2\pi i(x\xi-y\eta+z\zeta)\, V\, dx\, dy\, dz \\ &= F(\xi\bar{\eta}\zeta). \qquad (273.4) \end{aligned}$$

Thus if a function has a mirror plane through the origin, its transform also has this symmetry.

By expressing the results in terms of semi-polar coordinates, the same can be shown to be true of n-fold axes of symmetry, and the argument can be extended to cover axes of rotatory inversion. We can in fact summarize by saying that any orthogonal transformation of a function (one in which distances are preserved) results in the same operation on its transform (Sayre, 1949). Centres of symmetry, mirror planes and axes of symmetry are represented by corresponding identical symmetry elements in reciprocal space.

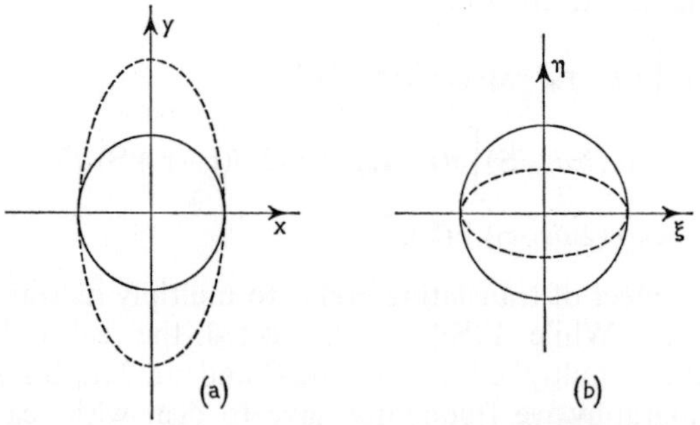

FIG. 274. When a function $\sigma(\mathbf{r})$ having circular symmetry is distorted homogeneously so that a line of constant σ becomes an ellipse (dotted line in fig. *a*), a line of constant F undergoes a reciprocal distortion to give the ellipse shown as a dotted line in fig. *b*

In equation (*273*.3) there is no reference to the axes **a**, **b**, **c** to which $\sigma(\mathbf{r})$ is referred, or to the reciprocal axes. The expression (*272*.4) for the transform of a parallelepiped is the same, whatever the shape. In this example, one parallelepiped can be distorted into any other by combinations of uniform stretching and changes in direction of the vectors **a**, **b**, **c**. Since these do not appear in the transform we need only make a corresponding change to **a***, **b***, **c*** to obtain the transform of the homogeneously deformed distribution. Thus for example if we know the transform of a uniform circle we can obtain that of an ellipse (fig. 274). This is made possible of course only by the device of referring the transform F(S) to reciprocal axes.

2.4. *The operations of projection and section.* Consider again F(S) written as in equation (*273*.3). The section of the transform by the plane $\zeta = \zeta_0$ is

$$F(\xi\eta\zeta_0) = \int \sigma_2(xy) \exp 2\pi i\,(x\xi + y\eta)\, A\, dx\, dy \qquad (274.1)$$

where

$$\sigma_2(xy) = \int \sigma(xyz) \exp 2\pi i z\zeta_0\, c\, dz \qquad (274.2)$$

and A is an area such that $Ac = V$. Thus $\sigma_2(xy)$ is the projection of $\sigma(xyz)$, weighted by the factor $\exp 2\pi iz\zeta_0$, down the **c** direction. Transforming equation (*274*.1),

$$\sigma_2(xy) = \int F(\xi\eta\zeta_0) \exp(-2\pi i(x\xi + y\eta))\, A^*\, d\xi\, d\eta \qquad (275.1)$$

$\sigma_2(xy)$ may therefore be called the generalized projection of $\sigma(xyz)$, corresponding to the section $\zeta = \zeta_0$ of the transform (section **8**.3.5). When $\zeta_0 = 0$ we obtain an ordinary projection. The operation of projection of a function therefore corresponds to taking a section through the origin of its transform by a plane perpendicular to the direction of projection.

2.5. *The operations of convolution and multiplication.* Let F_1 and F_2 be the transforms of σ_1 and σ_2 respectively. By definition, the inverse transform of the product F_1F_2 is

$$\sigma_{12}(\mathbf{r}) = \int_S F_1(S)F_2(S) \exp(-2\pi i\, \mathbf{r}\cdot\mathbf{S})\, dV^* \qquad (275.2)$$

$$= \int_S F_1(S)\left\{\int_{\mathbf{r}'} \sigma_2(\mathbf{r}') \exp 2\pi i\, \mathbf{r}'\cdot\mathbf{S}\, dV\right\} \exp(-2\pi i\, \mathbf{r}\cdot\mathbf{S})\, dV^*$$

$$= \int_{\mathbf{r}'} \sigma_2(\mathbf{r}')\left\{\int_S F_1(S) \exp(-2i\pi(\mathbf{r}-\mathbf{r}')\cdot\mathbf{S})\, dV^*\right\} dV$$

$$= \int_{\mathbf{r}'} \sigma_2(\mathbf{r}')\sigma_1(\mathbf{r}-\mathbf{r}')\, dV \qquad (275.3)$$

where dV is an element of volume at $\mathbf{r}'$. Equation (*275*.3) expresses the fact that $\sigma_{12}(\mathbf{r})$ is obtained by convolution of $\sigma_2(\mathbf{r})$ with $\sigma_1(\mathbf{r})$. Convolution of two functions occurs frequently in physics although it is not always called that specifically. For example, in considering the broadening of an X-ray reflexion we have to consider not only the ideal profile resulting from, say, the size of specimen involved, but also geometrical factors such as the angular spread of the incident beam. If the ideal profile on a photographic plate is $\sigma_1(\mathbf{r})$, and that resulting from geometrical factors alone is $\sigma_2(\mathbf{r})$, the result when both effects are present is to take each element of σ_2 and spread it out on a curve having the shape of σ_1. The addition of all such infinitesimal contributions gives the result of broadening by both effects. This operation of convolution, expressed by equation (*275*.3), is often written

$$\sigma_{12}(\mathbf{r}) = \widehat{\sigma_1(\mathbf{r})\sigma_2}(\mathbf{r}). \qquad (275.4)$$

The order in which σ_1 and σ_2 appear is immaterial. The result we have just found, in equations (*275*.2) and (*275*.3), is that the operation of convoluting two functions corresponds to multiplication of their Fourier transforms.

In the special case $\sigma_1 = \sigma_2 = \sigma$, we see from equation (*275*.2) that

$$\sigma_{11}(\mathbf{r}) = \widehat{\sigma(r)\sigma}(r) = \int_{\mathbf{r}'} \sigma(\mathbf{r}')\sigma(\mathbf{r}-\mathbf{r}')\,dV$$

has $F^2(\mathbf{S})$ as its transform. An even more important example occurs when $\sigma_1(\mathbf{r}) = \sigma(\mathbf{r})$, $\sigma_2(\mathbf{r}) = \sigma(-\mathbf{r})$, and we convolute $\sigma(\mathbf{r})$ with itself inverted in the origin. The result is

$$\mathrm{P}(\mathbf{r}) \equiv \widehat{\sigma(\mathbf{r})\sigma}(-\mathbf{r}) = \int_{\mathbf{r}'} \sigma(-\mathbf{r}')\sigma(\mathbf{r}-\mathbf{r}')\,dV$$

$$= \int_{\mathbf{r}'} \sigma(\mathbf{r}')\sigma(\mathbf{r}+\mathbf{r}')\,dV, \qquad (276.1)$$

and it follows from equations (*275*.2) and (*275*.3) that the Fourier transform of $\mathrm{P}(\mathbf{r})$ is $\mathrm{F}(\mathbf{S})\mathrm{F}(-\mathbf{S}) = |\mathrm{F}(\mathbf{S})|^2$. $\mathrm{P}(\mathbf{r})$ will of course be recognized as the Patterson function or autocorrelation function of the continuous distribution $\sigma(\mathbf{r})$, and its association with $|\mathrm{F}(\mathbf{S})|^2$, a measure of the intensity of the scattered radiation, is a result of great importance in scattering theory (section **1**.3.2).

2.6. *The operations of repetition and sampling.* We begin this section by finding the Fourier transform of a lattice of $N_1N_2N_3 = N_0$ points, the unit cell of the lattice being defined by the three vectors **a**, **b**, **c**. N_1 is the number of points in the **a** direction, etc., and we take the numbers to be odd ones so that the origin can be taken on the central lattice point. A typical point is therefore represented by $\delta(\mathbf{r} - (n_1\mathbf{a} + n_2\mathbf{b} + n_3\mathbf{c}))$, and contributes to the transform an amount $\exp 2\pi i(n_1\xi + n_2\eta + n_3\zeta)$, from equation (*273*.1), and the fact that the transform of $\delta(\mathbf{r})$ is unity. We therefore have for the Fourier transform of a lattice

$$\mathrm{F}_L(\mathbf{S}) = \sum_{-N_1/2}^{+N_1/2} \sum_{-N_2/2}^{+N_2/2} \sum_{-N_3/2}^{+N_3/2} \exp 2\pi i(n_1\xi + n_2\eta + n_3\zeta)$$

$$= \frac{\sin N_1\pi\xi}{\sin \pi\xi}\,\frac{\sin N_2\pi\eta}{\sin \pi\eta}\,\frac{\sin N_3\pi\zeta}{\sin \pi\zeta}. \qquad (276.2)$$

This function is periodic in reciprocal space, with equal peaks at every reciprocal lattice point, for which ξ, η, ζ are integers. The weight of each peak around a reciprocal-lattice point is by definition

$$\iiint_{-1/2}^{+1/2} \mathrm{F}_L(\xi\eta\zeta)\mathrm{V}^*\,d\xi\,d\eta\,d\zeta$$

which reduces to V*, or 1/V, since $\int_{-1/2}^{+1/2} \frac{\sin N_1\pi\xi}{\sin \pi\xi} = 1$, and is independent of the value of N_1. Thus as $N_0 \to \infty$, each peak becomes higher and narrower and assumes the characteristics of a delta-function whose weight is 1/V; we can thus say that the transform of an infinite lattice of points of unit weight is an infinite reciprocal lattice of points of weight 1/V.

Returning now to the lattice of finite extent, suppose that we set down the distribution $\sigma(\mathbf{r})$ (whose transform is $F(\mathbf{S})$) with its origin at each lattice point in turn. This corresponds to convoluting $\sigma(\mathbf{r})$ with the lattice; the result is the distribution in a crystal, which we write as $\rho(\mathbf{r})$. From equations (*275*.2) and (*275*.3), the transform of $\rho(\mathbf{r})$ is therefore $F_L(\mathbf{S})F(\mathbf{S})$, that is,

$$\rho(\mathbf{r}) = \int F_L(\mathbf{S})F(\mathbf{S}) \exp(-2\pi i\mathbf{r}.\mathbf{S})\, dV^* \qquad (277.1)$$

where the integral is over the whole of reciprocal space. Now as $N_0 \to \infty$, $F_L(\mathbf{S})$ varies so much more rapidly than $F(\mathbf{S})$ that in evaluating the contribution to the integral of a region near a particular reciprocal lattice point, say $\mathbf{S} = \mathbf{h}$, we can take $F(\mathbf{S}) \exp(-2\pi i\mathbf{r}\cdot\mathbf{S})$ to have a constant value, $F(\mathbf{h}) \exp(-2\pi i\mathbf{r}\cdot\mathbf{h})$. The integration of $F_L(\mathbf{S})$ over each reciprocal lattice point gives 1/V, so finally

$$\rho(\mathbf{r}) = \frac{1}{V}\sum_{\mathbf{h}} F(\mathbf{h}) \exp(-2\pi i\mathbf{r}\cdot\mathbf{h}) \qquad (277.2)$$

and the Fourier integral (*277*.1), reverts to the familiar Fourier series (*277*.2). Another way of expressing this result is that repetition of $\sigma(\mathbf{r})$ on an infinite lattice results in its transform being sampled at the points of the corresponding reciprocal lattice. The values of F at the sampling points are the structure factors. We have already met a form of this result in the introductory section **10**.1.2, where however we considered only the situation where the spacing was such that the distributions $\sigma(\mathbf{r})$ in adjacent unit cells did not overlap.

2.7. *The probability distribution of* $|F|^2$. In the transform of a centrosymmetric distribution, which is itself centrosymmetric and has no imaginary component ($B = 0$), regions corresponding to the two possible phases 0 or π are separated by lines where $A = 0$ which we may call nodal lines. In transforms $F = A + iB$, however, the phase may have any value, and only at specific points is $|F| = 0$. Just around these nodal points the phase will adopt all possible values, and, a diagram showing the phase distribution will show 'knots' concentrated at these nodal points (fig. 278). The existence of these two types of transforms accounts for the two main types of intensity distribution discussed in Chapter 3. Since a centric transform has nodal lines, and an acentric transform nodal points, there is a greater probability that a reciprocal lattice point will be near to a zero value in the former than in the latter and the centric distribution is characterised by a larger proportion of very small values of $|F(\mathbf{h})|^2$ than is the acentric distribution. If the transform is crossed by fringes arising from parallel placement of two identical distributions, the probability of small values of $|F(\mathbf{h})|^2$ is still greater (Lipson and Woolfson, 1952). Other possibilities, discussed in Chapter 3, can also be interpreted in this way.

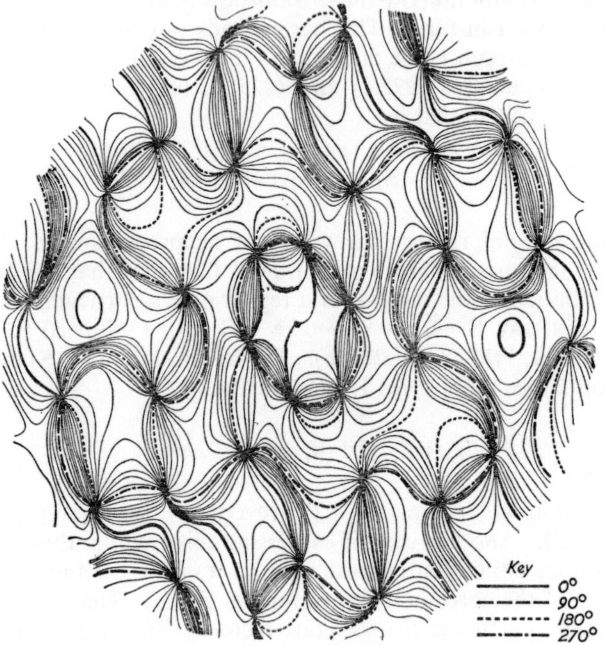

FIG. 278. Distribution of phases in a transform, showing 'knots' around nodal points. (Lipson and Taylor, 1958)

3. Fourier Transforms in Structure Analysis

3.1. *Conditions for application of transform methods.* In earlier sections we have been concerned with Fourier transforms mainly for the new point of view which they give to some of the familiar facts of crystallography. The basis of their use in structure analysis is that the transform of a rigid group of atoms can be evaluated once and for all and the contributions of this group is then given by sampling on the appropriate reciprocal lattice. This method of structure analysis was first advocated by Wrinch (1946). The unit cell of the crystal will generally contain other groups related to the first by the symmetry of the space group. How their contributions are combined is discussed in a little more detail in section **10**.3.2, since in section **10**.2.3 we considered only the effect of point-group symmetry. Certain arrangements of atoms have transforms with such characteristic features that their presence can sometimes be recognized before a detailed structure analysis is made; this applies for example to the helical structures of certain synthetic polypeptides and of deoxynucleic acid (DNA). A related feature is that if the contents of a unit cell show some periodicity, the transform will show this property. If there is approximate repetition of a group of atoms with nearly the same orientation at some fraction of a unit cell dimension, their (combined) transform will be related to the reciprocal lattice in such a way as to produce systematic strengthening and weakening of $|F(\mathbf{h})|^2$; such evidence can be used to derive crystal structures. If the repetition is unrelated to a unit-cell dimension, but occurs say within the structure of a molecule, the transform of the molecule will have a periodicity which may show up even when sampled on the reciprocal lattice (section **6**.5.2). Perhaps the most important feature of Fourier transforms for structure analysis is the fact that they can be derived by a simple physical method, described in section **10**.5, which makes use of the analogy between the diffraction of X-rays by atoms and the diffraction of light by circular apertures. The two effects are sufficiently related for almost all X-ray diffraction phenomena to be illustrated by optical diffraction.

3.2. *Some practical considerations.* We rarely wish to derive the transform of a completely general electron density distribution; we are usually concerned with spherically-symmetric atoms at specific positions, so that

$$F_N(\mathbf{S}) = \sum_1^N f_n(\mathbf{S}) \exp 2\pi i \mathbf{r}_n \cdot \mathbf{S}. \qquad (279.1)$$

Transforms may be computed in the same way as structure factors. We refer the group of N atoms to axes **a**, **b**, **c** (which are normally quite distinct from the unit-cell vectors of the crystal in which the group occurs) and imagine the group to be repeated on a lattice defined by **a**, **b**, **c**. The structure factors of this 'crystal' are then the values of the transform sampled at the points of a reciprocal lattice defined by **a***, **b***, **c*** (sections **1**.2.3 and **10**.2.6). The sampling interval chosen will depend on the computing facilities available, but as a general rule each axis should be at least three times a dimension of the group of atoms. The transform will be computed in two parts if the arrangement of atoms is non-centrosymmetric,

$$A_N(\mathbf{S}) = \sum_1^N f_n(\mathbf{S}) \cos 2\pi \mathbf{r}_n \cdot \mathbf{S}$$

$$B_N(\mathbf{S}) = \sum_1^N f_n(\mathbf{S}) \sin 2\pi \mathbf{r}_n \cdot \mathbf{S}. \qquad (279.2)$$

These can be plotted separately; sometimes it may be convenient to combine them to give $|F|=(A^2+B^2)^{1/2}$. If the group of atoms possesses symmetry it will be possible to use this to shorten the calculation; for example

$$F_N(S)=2\sum_1^{N/2} f_n(S)\exp 2\pi i(x_n\xi+z_n\zeta)\cos 2\pi y_n\eta \qquad (280.1)$$

applies when the group of atoms has a mirror plane perpendicular to the **b**-axis.

In an orthogonal transformation the group of atoms and its transform are affected in the same way. Thus if the unit cell contains only one molecule whose transform has been calculated, and if the origin of the molecule is fixed on a centre of symmetry (as for example in hexamethylbenzene Lonsdale, 1929), the only problem is to determine the molecular orientation by rotating the reciprocal lattice on the transform until the sampled values of $|F(S)|$ agree with the experimental values.

The contributions from symmetry-related groups in the same unit cell can be combined using the results given in the second part of this chapter. It is now convenient to refer the Fourier transform of a group of atoms to the reciprocal axes of the crystal under investigation, although of course it will not have been evaluated with reference to these axes as the sampling interval would be much too coarse. As the group of atoms is imagined to be rotated in the crystal, its transform rotates with it over the reciprocal lattice. Thus we continue to use $\xi\eta\zeta$ in the argument of F_N to emphasize that F_N is continuously variable but is sampled at $(hkl)=(\xi\eta\zeta)$. To take a simple example, suppose that the space group is $P2_1$ No. 4 and that the centre of the group of atoms whose transform has been calculated has coordinates x_0, 0, z_0 in the crystal. Then

$$F(hkl)=F_N(\xi\eta\zeta)\exp 2\pi i(hx_0+lz_0) + (-1)^k F_N(\xi\bar{\eta}\zeta)\exp(-2\pi i(hx_0+lz_0)). \qquad (280.2)$$

In the zero layer this simplifies to

$$F(h0l)=2F_N(\xi 0\zeta)\cos 2\pi(hx_0+lz_0). \qquad (280.3)$$

Thus the problem of specifying the positions of a group of atoms in a crystal can be reduced to three steps. First, the orientation of the group is fixed by deciding which plane through the origin of the transform constitutes the zero layer $k=0$; secondly, the azimuthal angle which then fixes the orientation completely depends upon finding where the **a*c*** net is to be drawn in this plane; and, thirdly, the position of the group in the unit cell is fixed by the wave vector of the fringe system $\cos 2\pi(hx_0+lz_0)$.

4. Examples of the Uses of Fourier Transforms

4.1. *Trial-and-error procedures.* If the Fourier transform of a molecule is known, the process of finding its orientation and position in the unit cell corresponds to finding the way in which the reciprocal lattice fits on the transform so that it 'picks out' the correct intensity for each X-ray reflexion. This process is particularly simple if the unit cell contains only one molecule; such structures are rare, but they occur more frequently in two dimensions, where a glide plane may lead to a halving of one cell dimension. For example in the space group No. 14, $P2_1/a$, the projection of the structure parallel to [010] has a unit cell of dimensions $a/2$ and b. If the structure has two molecules in the unit cell, the unit cell of the projection has only one; also its centre must lie on a centre of symmetry.

These conditions apply to the structure of naphthalene (Banerjee, 1930). The molecule is planar and therefore its transform is particularly simple; it has no variation perpendicular to the plane of the molecule except that produced by the variation in atomic scattering factor. In other words, if we treat the atoms as points, the transform could be produced from the plane section merely by translation at right-angles to this section (fig. 291(iii)). Any oblique section is therefore easily obtained. This property of transforms of plane molecules is so valuable that transform methods have been applied mainly to such molecules.

Knott (1940) first investigated the application of transform methods to this structure. The problem is to find the scale and orientation of the transform that fits best with the observed weighted reciprocal lattice, but Knott used an equivalent procedure; he found the orientation and dimension of a reciprocal lattice that would fit on the calculated transform.

His results are shown in fig. 282. The transform is represented by contours, no distinction being made between positive and negative. He then considered the sequence of $00l$ reflexions and found a line in the transform which reproduced them reasonably well; there are no large intensities but the very small intensity of 005 provides a useful clue. He then considered the $h00$ intensities; again the small value of 400 was helpful in deciding on the correct line in the transform. The two choices could then be checked by completing the reciprocal-lattice section and showing that all the other intensities are correct. By finding the inclination of the reciprocal lattice that would produce the lattice so found, the orientation of the molecules could be derived.

This method has been applied successfully to the structure of flavanthrone (Stadler, 1953), which has a plane molecule of structure shown in fig. 283. Because the atoms in the idealized molecule all lie upon points of a hexagonal lattice the transform (fig. 283) is periodic, and thus only one unit cell need be calculated (Lipson and Taylor, 1951); this is a useful simplification in dealing with compounds such as flavanthrone and naphthalene. The $h0l$ reciprocal-lattice section is shown in fig. 284(i); the large values of the structure amplitudes of the reflexions $8\ 0\ \bar{7}$, $24\ 0\ \bar{2}$ and $16\ 0\ 5$ make the fitting together of the two comparatively easy.

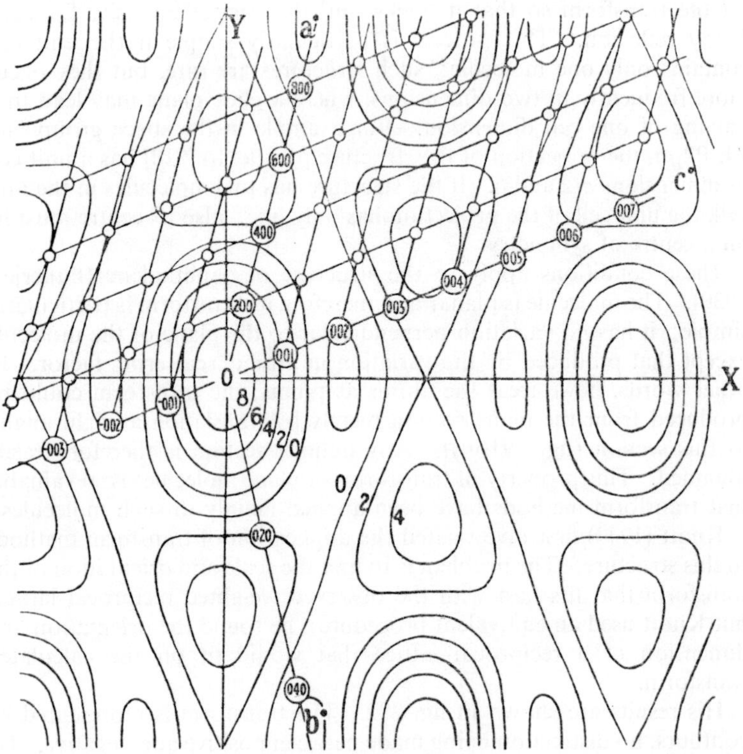

FIG. 282. Relation between the reciprocal lattice of naphthalene and the Fourier transform of the idealized molecule (Knott, 1940)

Transforms of molecules that consist mainly of parallel hexagons—such as condensed ring compounds—have one feature in common: the transforms are all based upon that of a single hexagon, which, of course, has hexagonal symmetry. Thus they all tend to have hexagonal symmetry, and if only the strong peaks of the transform are taken into account, three different orientations of the molecules are possible. These strong peaks must therefore be taken only as a guide, and the three possible orientations tried to see which gives the best agreement with the minor features of the transform.

4.2. *Structures involving combinations of transforms.* When the molecules in the unit cell do not have similar projections on to one particular plane, the simple procedure just outlined cannot be carried out. The general problem of combination of transforms will be discussed

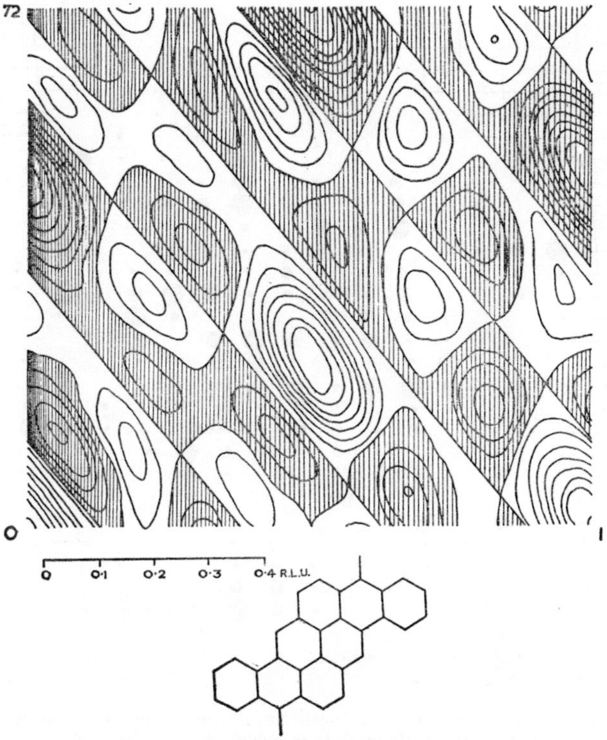

FIG. 283. Flavanthrone, $C_{28}H_{12}O_2N_2$: Fourier transform and molecular configuration (Stadler, 1953)

in the next section, but Klug (1950) has shown that, even when a projection contains four differently oriented projections, the structure can be derived from the transform of a single molecule. The substance he investigated was triphenylene, of which the idealized molecule has the structure shown in fig. 284(ii); it will be seen that the molecule has no centre of symmetry, and moreover the space group is No. 19. $P2_12_12_1$, so that the crystal also has no centre of symmetry. Nevertheless, centrosymmetrical projections on to the faces of the unit cell occur, and Klug's work was mainly concerned with the projection on the plane (001). The reality of the structure factors F(*hk*0) does not, however, greatly simplify the problem; the transform of a single molecule is complex, and the real and imaginary parts have to be calculated separately. For triphenylene, these are shown in fig. 285.

For a non-centrosymmetrical molecule no absolute significance attaches to the real and imaginary parts of the transform; their forms

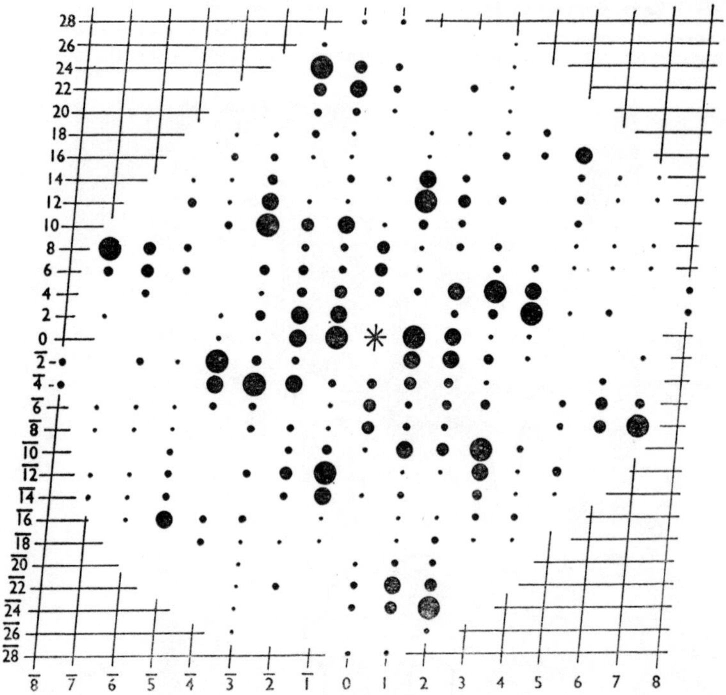

FIG. 284 (i). Weighted reciprocal lattice of flavanthrone (not on same scale as transform) (from data supplied by H. P. Stadler)

depend upon the choice of origin, and the only absolute result is that obtained by adding the squares of the corresponding amplitudes of the two parts of the transform. It should also be noted that the real and imaginary parts of the transform need have no relationship to the real and imaginary parts of the structure factors, since, in general, the origin chosen for calculating the transform is not that of the unit cell. Thus it will be seen that the problem of deciding the relative positions and orientations of the molecules in triphenylene is rather complicated.

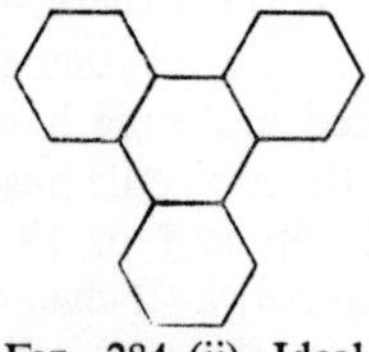

FIG. 284 (ii). Idealized form of molecule of triphenylene

Klug solved the difficulty by reducing the problem partly to one dimension; in the same way as projections on to planes may be much simpler to consider than the three-dimensional structure, so may projections on to lines be simpler still. In the space group $P2_12_12_1$, the molecules project, on to each cell edge, in pairs which are centro-

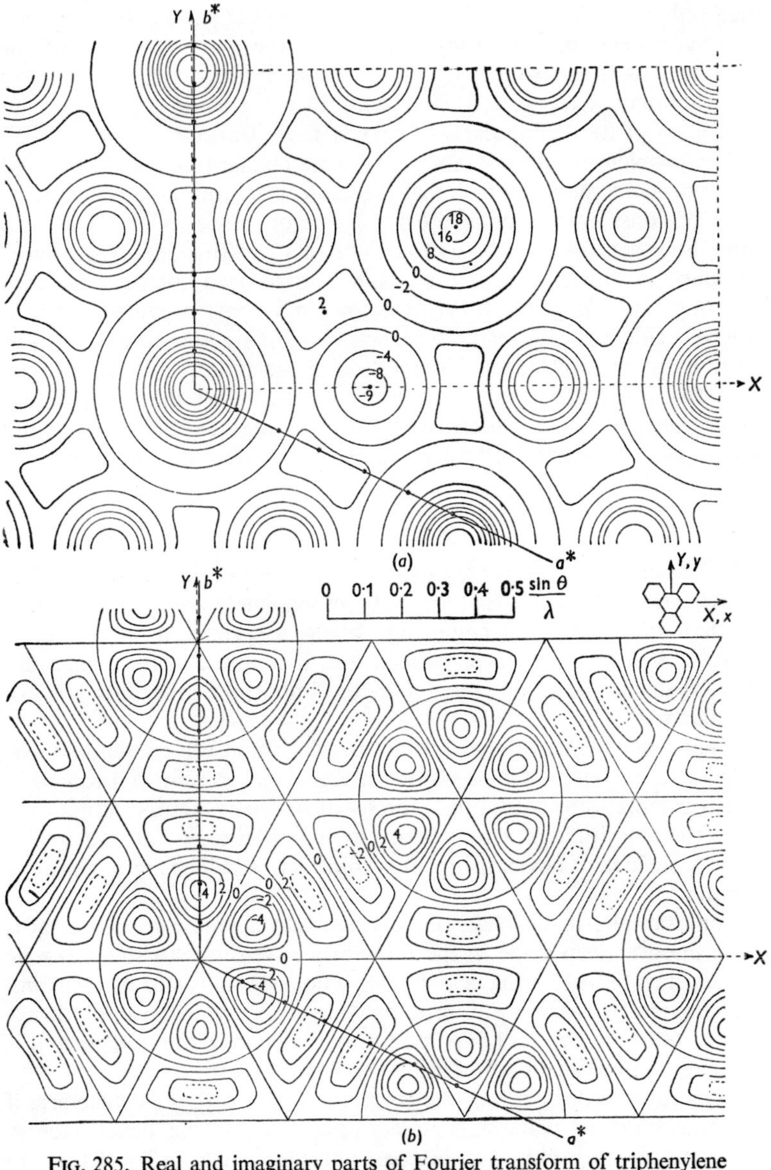

FIG. 285. Real and imaginary parts of Fourier transform of triphenylene molecule. The two straight lines which give the correct relative values of the structure amplitudes of the orders *h*00 and 0*k*0 are shown (Klug, 1950)

symmetrically related and separated by half the length of the edge (accounting for the screw-axis space-group absences). The problem then reduces to finding two radial lines in the complete transform that give agreement for the strong reflexions; a strong reflexion must be associated with a strong part of the Fourier transform, but a weak reflexion may be associated either with a weak part or with the partial cancelling of the strong parts of two or more transforms.

The problem is still not simple, because changes in orientation and in scale—corresponding to tilt of the molecule from the (001) plane—must be considered simultaneously. Some properties of the transform were, however, found to be useful. The real part (fig. 285(*a*)) is almost circularly symmetrical near the origin, and so need not be considered in fixing possible orientations; the imaginary part provided the conclusive evidence, although some help in finding the correct fit was given by prior knowledge of orientation of the molecule from magnetic data (section 6.3.2). Fig. 285 shows the two lines that Klug found to correspond most clearly with the *h*00 and 0*k*0 reflexions, and which gave a rough structure which was tested on more general reflexions.

4.3. *Recognition of correct structures.* The greatest skill in determining crystal structures—one that cannot unfortunately easily be taught—is that involved in recognizing when a proposed structure is correct. Agreement is never perfect, and therefore a correct structure may be dismissed as incorrect if a few important reflexions are not satisfactory.

Knowledge of the Fourier transform of the unit-cell contents can be helpful in arriving at a decision because the transform necessarily contains more information than the set of structure factors; it not only gives the amplitude at a particular reciprocal-lattice point, but it also gives some idea of how sensitive this value is to small changes of atomic positions.

For example, in fig. 282, one can see that a reflexion such as 801, lying upon a steep slope in the transform is sensitive to small atomic movements, but 802, lying near a peak, is not. Usually strong intensities are less sensitive than weak ones, but this general rule does not always apply: 601 is weak, but lying upon a weak region of the transform it is not likely to be greatly affected by small movements.

Therefore, in deciding on the correctness of a proposed structure, if the transform is available one can ask 'Do all the unsatisfactory reflexions lie on rapidly varying parts of the transform?' If they do there is some possibility of correcting them, and the structure is therefore probably correct. In addition, the slopes of the transform at these points should give information about the directions and amounts of the shifts required.

4.4. *Helical structures.* Although transform methods have not played an important part in determining the structures of globular proteins, in which the α-helix of Pauling, Corey and Branson (1951) is now known to occur, they have been important for the determination of the structures of fibrous or semi-crystalline materials such as poly-γ-methyl-L-glutamate (Bamford, Brown, Elliott, Hanby and Trotter (1952), Cochran and Crick (1952)) and DNA (Wilkins, Stokes and Wilson (1953), Watson and Crick (1953)), which are helical.

In other applications of transform methods, we have taken a group of N adjacent atoms as the basic scattering unit. In a helical structure, such as a polypeptide, the corresponding group is the peptide. In this instance, however, it is more profitable to regard the infinite helical chain of peptides as composed of N infinite helical chains, on each of which one atom is repeated. Each of the N helices has a different radius, and carries a different type of atom, but their other characteristics are identical. In what follows we consider the transform of one such helix.

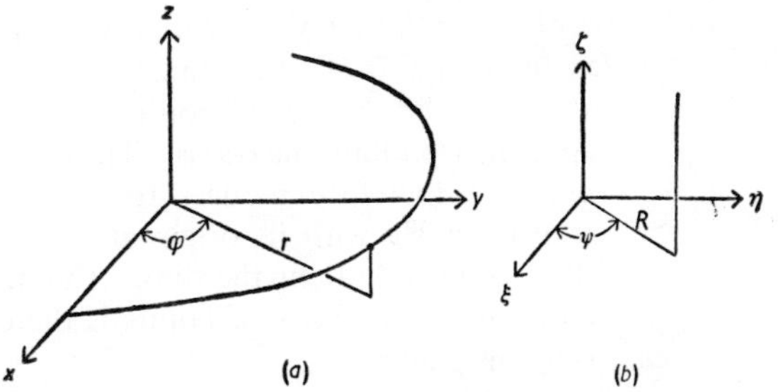

FIG. 287. (*a*) Semi-polar coordinates for specifying point on helix. (*b*) Corresponding coordinates for specifying point in reciprocal space

Consider first an infinitely long thin helical wire of radius r, with P the axial distance between successive turns. It is convenient to define a point on the helix by the semipolar coordinates (r, ϕ, z), and a point in reciprocal space by (R, ψ, ζ) (fig. 287). (In this section, therefore, z and ζ are not fractional coordinates, but distances in their respective spaces.) We note that since the distribution is periodic along the z-direction with repeat distance P, the transform is finite only on planes $\zeta = n/P$, where n is an integer. The transform, apart from unimportant constants of proportionality, is

$$F_H(R, \psi, n/P) = J_n(2\pi R r) \exp in(\psi + \pi/2) \qquad (287)$$

where $J_n(X)$ denotes the nth order Bessel function (fig. 288(i)) (Cochran, Crick and Vand (1952), Cormack (1957).) We are however interested in the transform of a helical structure in which identical atoms occur at intervals $z = p$ on the helix (fig. 288(ii)). Consider a function H which assumes the value unity on a continuous helix whose axis is vertical, and is zero elsewhere, and another function K which is zero except on a set of horizontal planes of spacing p where it assumes the value unity. The

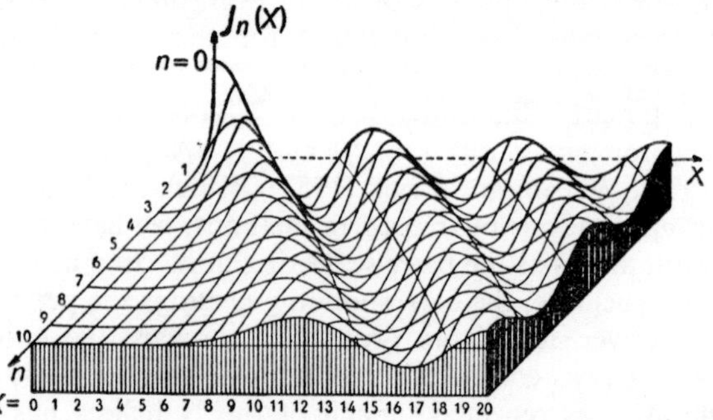

FIG. 288 (i). Perspective representation of Bessel functions of different order

product KH is then a discontinuous helix, whose transform is therefore the transform of H convoluted with that of K (section **10**.2.5). The first has already been given (equation *287*); the transform F_K is readily shown to be a lattice of points (δ-functions) with spacing $1/p$ along the ζ-axis. The process of convolution therefore reduces to setting down the transform F_K with its origin at all of the points $(0, 0, m/p)$ and taking the sum. The transform of a discontinuous helix of points is therefore finite only on planes

$$\zeta = \frac{n}{P} + \frac{m}{p} \qquad (288.1)$$

on which it assumes the value given by equation (*287*.1). Placing identical atoms at each point of the discontinuous helix merely multiplies the transform by the atomic scattering factor, f. If P/p cannot be expressed as a ratio of whole numbers, planes at height $n/P + m/p$, for all integral values of n and m, fill the whole of reciprocal space. If however it can be so expressed, the transform is confined to a set of planes (layer lines). For example, the synthetic peptide poly-γ-methyl-L-glutamate has $P = 5{\cdot}4$ Å, $p = 1{\cdot}5$ Å and $P/p = 18/5$. From equation (*288*.1) therefore

$$5P = 5n + 18m = l, \text{ say} \qquad (288.2)$$

and the transform is confined to layers for which $\zeta = l/c$ with $c = 27$ Å, corresponding to the fact that the structure has

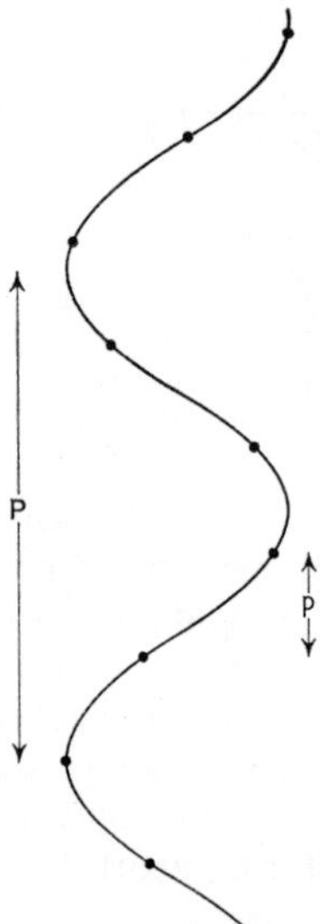

FIG. 288 (ii). Identical atoms occur at a vertical distance p on a helix of pitch P whose axis is vertical

almost an exact repeat after 27 Å. For any one value of l, the transform of a component helix of the structure is now given by

$$F(R, \psi, l/c) = \sum_n f J_n(2\pi Rr) \exp in(\psi + \pi/2), \qquad (289)$$

the sum being over all values of n which are solutions of equation (*288*.2), for example,

$$\text{for } l=0, \quad n = \ldots -36, \ -18, 0, 18, 36\ldots$$
$$\text{for } l=1, \quad n = \ldots -25, \ -7, \ +11, \ +29\ldots.$$

Thus only certain Bessel functions contribute to a particular layer. Now it is a property of Bessel functions of higher order, illustrated in fig. 288(i), that they remain very small until a certain value of $X = 2\pi Rr$ is reached, and this point recedes from the origin as the order n increases. Although there are several helices making up the structure of the polypeptide, for all of them P, p and c are the same although r is different. The maximum value of r cannot exceed about 8 Å because of the packing of the chains, and this sets a limit to the value of $2\pi Rr$ within the part of the transform covered by the observed diffraction pattern, for which $R < 0{\cdot}3$ Å^{-1} for $l \neq 0$. Thus only those layers l to which there corresponds at least one low value of n can be present in the diffraction pattern. In fact only eleven of the layer lines 0 to 28 could be seen, and these are the layers to which Bessel functions of order $n \leqslant 4$ contribute. Thus although the diffraction pattern from this material is of poor quality compared with that of a single crystal, and although neither the radii of the N discontinuous helices which make up a complete chain, nor the way in which the latter pack together, have been determined accurately, some of the important features of the structure can be established.

DNA is a polymer which has a molecular weight of millions. The repeating unit is a nucleotide consisting of a deoxyribose sugar bonded to a phosphate group and a purine or pyrimidine base. Polymerization occurs through covalent bonding between the phosphate of one nucleotide and the sugar of the next. X-ray diffraction photographs of oriented DNA fibres indicated that the molecule had a helical conformation (Wilkins, Stokes and Wilson, 1953), and Watson and Crick (1953) proposed a model for DNA in which each molecule consisted of two polynucleotide helical chains held together by hydrogen bonds between the bases, arranged so that the atomic sequence in one chain was the reverse of that in the other, with specific base pairing. A knowledge of the properties of the Fourier transform of a helical structure played a part in their deduction.

The essential features of the Watson-Crick model—a right-handed helical configuration with specific base pairing and polynucleotide chains running in opposite directions—have survived subsequent refinements of the structure based on more accurate X-ray data (Fuller, 1964).

4.5. *Future of transform methods.* The labour of computing transforms has so far militated against their general use. Since they are most useful for plane molecules, applications have been entirely confined to them, and it would thus seem that transform methods have a very limited application in the field of structure determination.

This view has to be modified, however, in the light of the discovery of methods of production of transforms by a simple physical method (Taylor and Lipson, 1964). This method makes use of the analogy between the diffraction of X-rays by atoms and the diffraction of light by holes; the two effects are sufficiently related for almost all X-ray diffraction phenomena to be illustrated by optical diffraction.

For example, the projection of the unit cell of a structure on to a plane can be represented by a set of holes in an opaque mask. The diffraction pattern of this set of holes is called the optical transform; if the holes were infinitely small, the pattern would give the intensity, $|F|^2$, of the Fourier transform of the same set of point atoms. The effect of addition of large numbers of unit cells in regular array is to introduce fringes whose intersections define the reciprocal-lattice points. Therefore, as in section **2**.4, we can regard the reciprocal lattice as sampling the optical transform, and can therefore see, at least qualitatively, which reflexions should be strong and which weak.

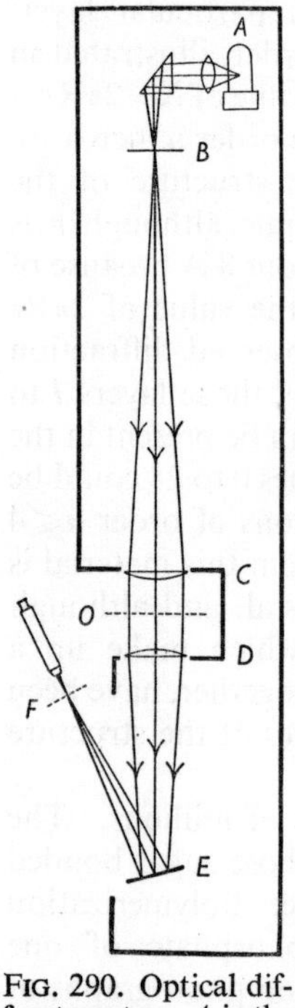

FIG. 290. Optical diffractometer. *A* is the light source, *B* is the pinhole, *C* and *D* are the lenses, and *E* is an optically flat mirror; the diffraction pattern of an object at *O* is seen in the plane *F* (Taylor, Hinde and Lipson, 1951)

5. OPTICAL TRANSFORMS

5.1. *Preparation.* Optical transforms can be derived by means of the simple optical instrument, known as the optical diffractometer, shown in fig. 290. This was originally described by Bragg (1939) and has been considerably improved by Hughes and Taylor (1953). If an object *O* is placed in the parallel light in the instrument, the optical transform is seen in the focal plane *F* of the second lens.

Normally diffraction is thought to be a phenomenon that is appreciable only for objects with a fine structure. With good lenses, properly adjusted, and a rigid mount for the instrument, the diffractometer gives detailed diffraction patterns from objects several centimetres across; the interference fringes from two holes 10 cm. apart have been observed,

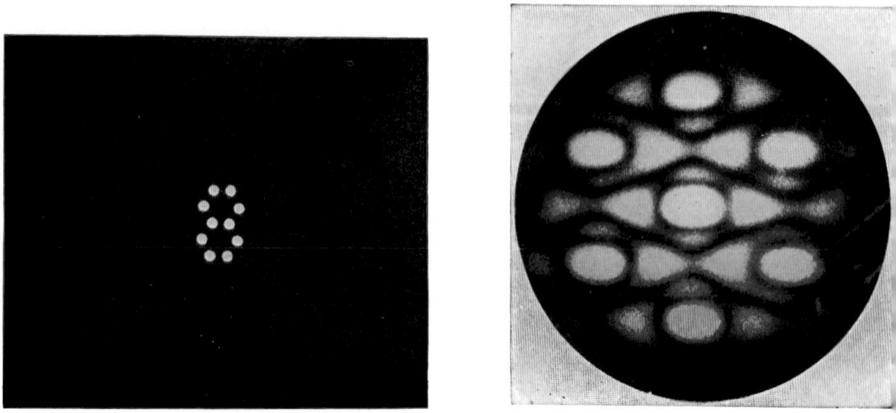

FIG. 291 (i). (*a*) Mask representing naphthalene molecule. (*b*) Diffraction pattern of mask (Lipson and Taylor, 1951)

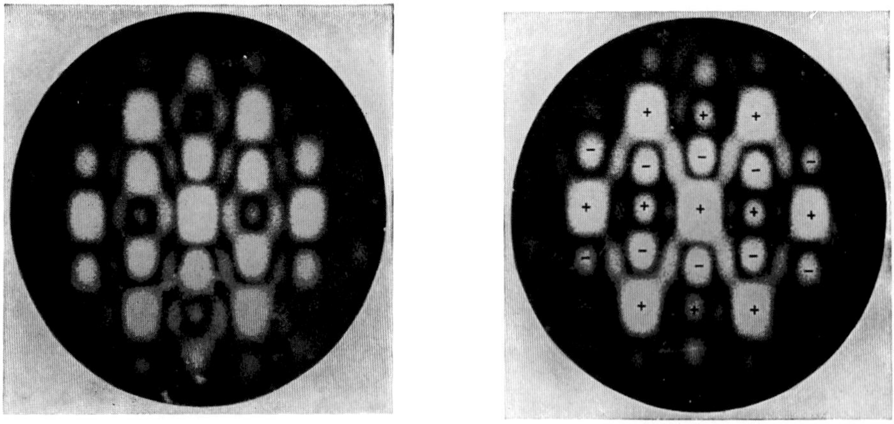

FIG. 291 (ii). Diffraction pattern of (*left*) mask representing durene molecule, (*right*) the same mask with an extra hole at the centre. Note the enhancement of the positive regions (Lipson and Taylor, 1951)

although their angular separation is only 1·2 seconds of arc. Fig. 291(i)*b* shows the optical transform of the representation of a molecule of naphthalene (fig. 291(i)*a*) and fig. 291(iii) shows the calculated transform.

As produced in the diffractometer, the transform is only about 1 mm. across, and is too small for detailed study. It can however be recorded photographically on fine-grained film and then enlarged to about 10 cm. diameter by a projection microscope. Full details of the various processes, and precautions to ensure that the scale and orientation of the transform are accurately known are described by Taylor and Lipson (1964).

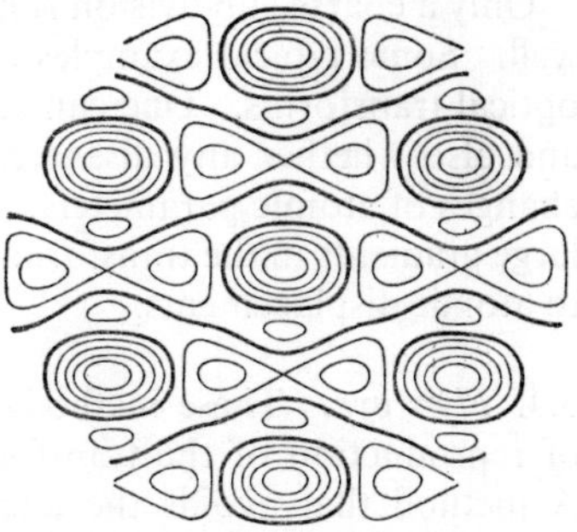

FIG. 291(iii). Calculated Fourier transform, for comparison with fig. 291(i)(*b*) (Lipson and Taylor, 1951)

In addition, the mask of diffracting holes must be accurately made; a device known as a pantograph punch has been described by Hughes and Taylor (1958) and is also described by Taylor and Lipson (1964).

5.2. *Trial-and-error methods.* To use transforms in the trial-and-error process, it is merely necessary to punch a mask representing a projection of the contents of the complete unit cell and to superpose upon this a drawing of the corresponding reciprocal-lattice section. One can see immediately which reflexions are strong and which are weak and so test the correctness of the proposed structure.

The method works best if the atoms are all similar. If they are not, some approximations must be made. For atoms such as carbon, nitrogen and oxygen, the distinction is negligible to a first approximation, and thus similar holes may be used for all atoms. For heavier atoms, such as sulphur and phosphorus, larger holes may be used, but since the scattering factor of a large hole falls off more steeply with angle than does that of a small hole (in contrast to the behaviour of atoms) the diffraction pattern will be acceptable only near to the centre. A better way of representing different atoms is to use holes of the same size for all of them, and to cover those representing lighter atoms with specially made gauzes (Harburn, 1961) which transmit amounts of light proportional to the atomic scattering factor.

5.3. *Weighted reciprocal lattice.* For quick comparison it is useful if the reciprocal lattice already has some representation upon it of the relative intensities of the reflexions. One may insert values of $|F(hkl)|$ at each reciprocal-lattice point, but more graphic representation is obtained by drawing at each point a spot whose size represents the structure factor. Experience has shown that the best quantity to represent is the unitary structure amplitude (section **9**.2.2) since this contains information up to the limits of the observed diffraction pattern; the intensities themselves fall off so rapidly that at high angles even the strong ones cannot be adequately represented.

Only a coarse subdivision is necessary; five sizes of spot will do quite well. Some typical examples are shown in fig. 292, superposed upon optical transforms. One can see clearly whether a proposal is correct, and also whether any disagreements can be easily put right by small changes of atomic parameters. As stated in section **10.4.3** reflexions on large gradients in the transform represent those which are most sensitive to atomic displacements.

5.4. *Fly's eye.* These methods are very dependent upon the accuracy of reproduction of the transform and the weighted reciprocal lattice. A method that avoids the uncertainty, although adding to the complexity and losing something of the flexibility of the procedure, is to punch a mask representing four contiguous unit cells. These then give fringes across the transform which break it up into regions representing the reciprocal-lattice points: the centre of each region gives the intensities required.

This device is an elementary form of a suggestion made by W. L. Bragg (1944), who pointed out that, if a diffraction grating could be made with a fine structure representing an atomic arrangement, its diffraction pattern would represent the set of orders of diffraction corresponding to a central section of the reciprocal lattice. Such gratings were made with a multiple pin-hole camera, and the grating was made by using this camera to form successive 'images' of a point light source; the lamp was moved to each position representing an atom, and its image recorded on a photographic plate. This device was elaborated by Bunn (1961), who used it to derive a zone of intensities for phthalocyanine (fig. 294(i)); he also used the method very effectively in the determination of the structure of sodium benzyl penicillin (Crowfoot et al., 1949).

Various improvements in the device have been suggested; in particular Bragg and Stokes (1945) have shown how to make a multiple *lens* camera. It would however seem that the device is now rendered unnecessary by the much simpler procedures using the optical diffractometer. These have been described in detail by Hanson and Lipson (1952*a*), including methods whereby different atoms may be simulated.

6. Study of Weighted Reciprocal Lattices

6.1. *Introduction.* A new physical method is of greatest importance if it leads to still further ideas, and the Fourier-transform method has certainly done so. Attempts to fit a weighted reciprocal lattice to a transform inevitably bring out certain relationships between the two, and after some time one begins to look at the reciprocal lattice with a

PLATE VII

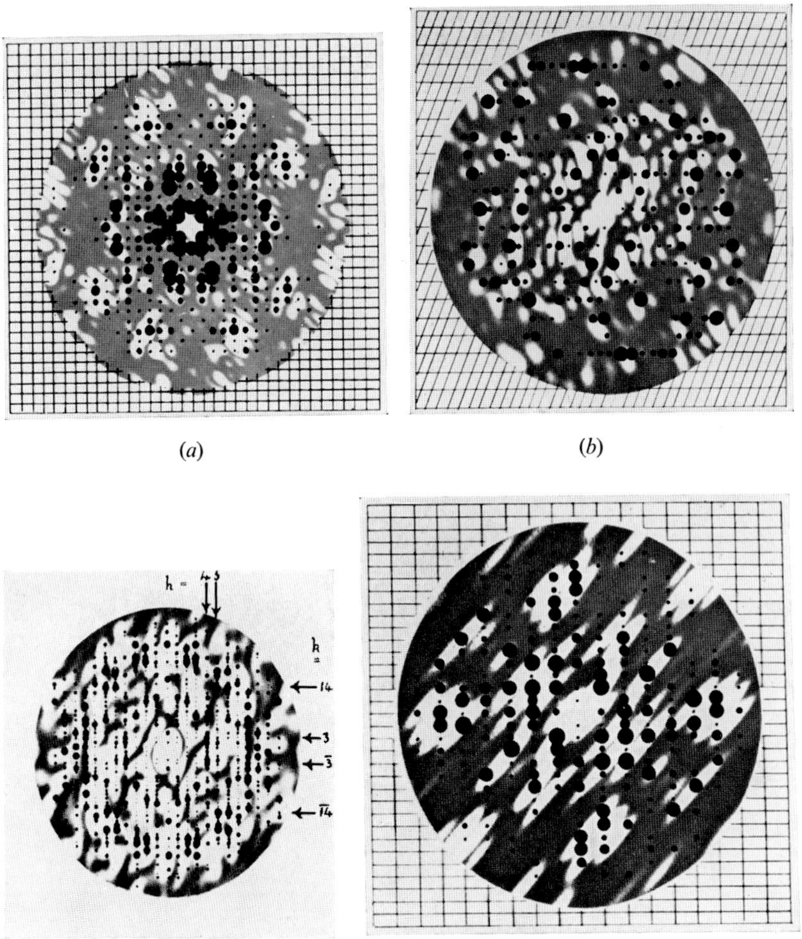

(a) (b) (c) (d)

FIG. 292. Some examples of the comparison of optical transforms and weighted reciprocal lattices. (*a*) Quinaldil. (*b*) Anhydrous citric acid. (*c*) Purpurogallin. (*d*) Benzamide

PLATE VIII

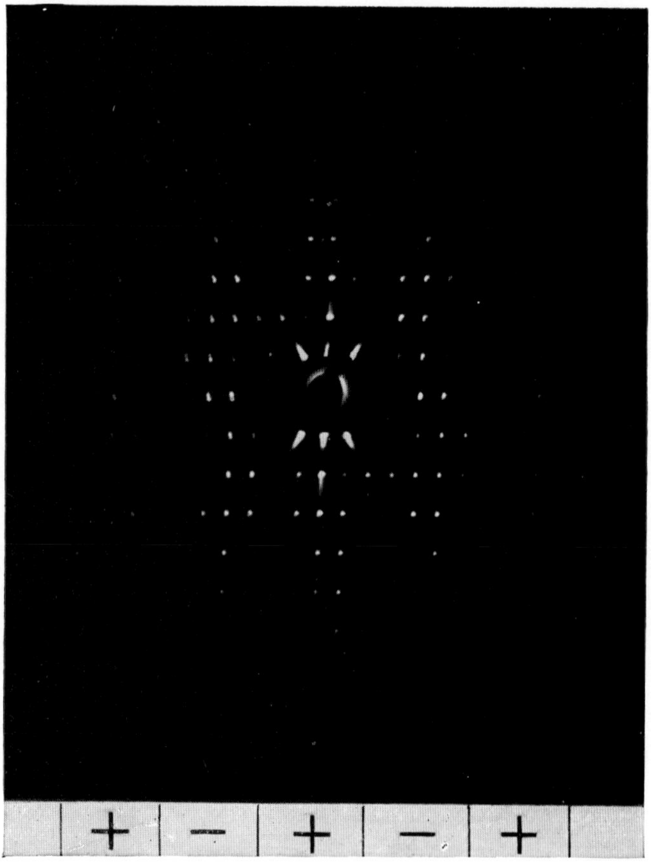

FIG. 293(i). 0*kl* precession photograph of 9-*p*-carbethoxyphenyl-9-stibiafluorene

p. 293

'reciprocal eye' so that one can see in it features of the structure. Properly developed, it may even lead to complete structural determination, but a great deal more experience needs to be gained before anything more than the fairly simple structures can be dealt with.

Obviously the method is most easily applied to planar molecules and to sections of the reciprocal lattice. But it can be applied to planar parts of non-planar molecules, and such parts can often most conveniently be recognized in the three-dimensional weighted reciprocal lattice.

6.2. *Fringes.* One feature that can be looked for in a weighted reciprocal lattice is a set of parallel equidistant fringes. These may be continuous, indicating that they are produced by some simple arrangement, or discontinuous indicating two or more units whose transforms will add or subtract at various reciprocal lattice points. They may be sharp, indicating that they are produced by a long chain, or they may be diffuse, indicating that they are produced by only two units. There may be more than one set of fringes which intersect and produce what are known as 'crossed' fringes. All these effects have been observed and have been made use of in structure determination.

Fringes due to two units have been observed in the diffraction pattern of flavanthrone (Stadler, 1953) and pyrene (Robertson and White, 1947*b*); the former compound has a molecule that can be considered as having two equal halves (fig. 293(ii)) and the latter has, in projection, two centrosymmetric molecules related by a centre of symmetry. Such fringes can be found by viewing the weighted reciprocal lattice at a glancing angle while rotating it in its own plane. It should be pointed out however that they cannot normally be clearly seen since, if the separation of the two units is about half the unit cell, each fringe will cover only one or two reciprocal lattice points.

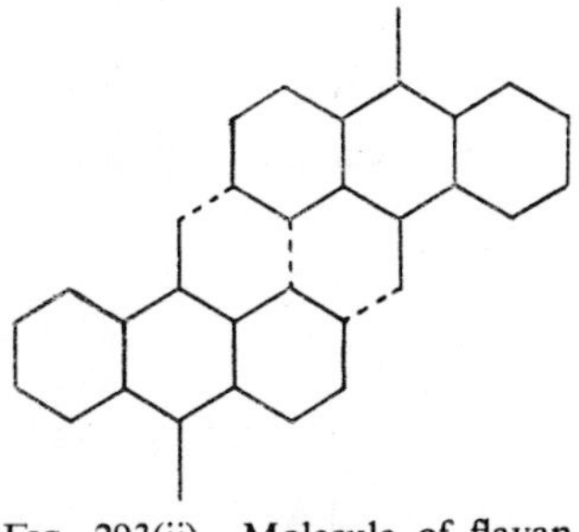

FIG. 293(ii). Molecule of flavanthrone (cf. fig. 283) considered as composed of two similar and parallel centrosymmetric parts

Fringes—Young's fringes—are also produced when there are two heavy atoms in the unit cell. These are usually quite clear, even in the X-ray photograph itself (fig. 293(i)) and so the positions of the heavy atom can be immediately deduced. So also can the signs of the structure factors; the fringes are alternately positive and negative from the centre outwards. Appreciation of this fact can save a great deal of calculation.

A more complicated example of the use of this principle is given by the compound tetraethyl diphosphine disulphide (Dutta and Woolfson, 1961). The sulphur and phosphorus atoms in projection lie on the corners of a parallelogram, and so give crossed fringes which can be easily seen (fig. 294(ii)*a*); the signs of the structure factors thus occur in a chequered pattern and so can be read off from the diagram (fig. 294(ii)*b*) (Taylor and Lipson, 1964). The Fourier synthesis showed the atoms quite clearly; only one sign was found to be wrong.

The signs of the general *hkl* reflexions could also be assigned in this

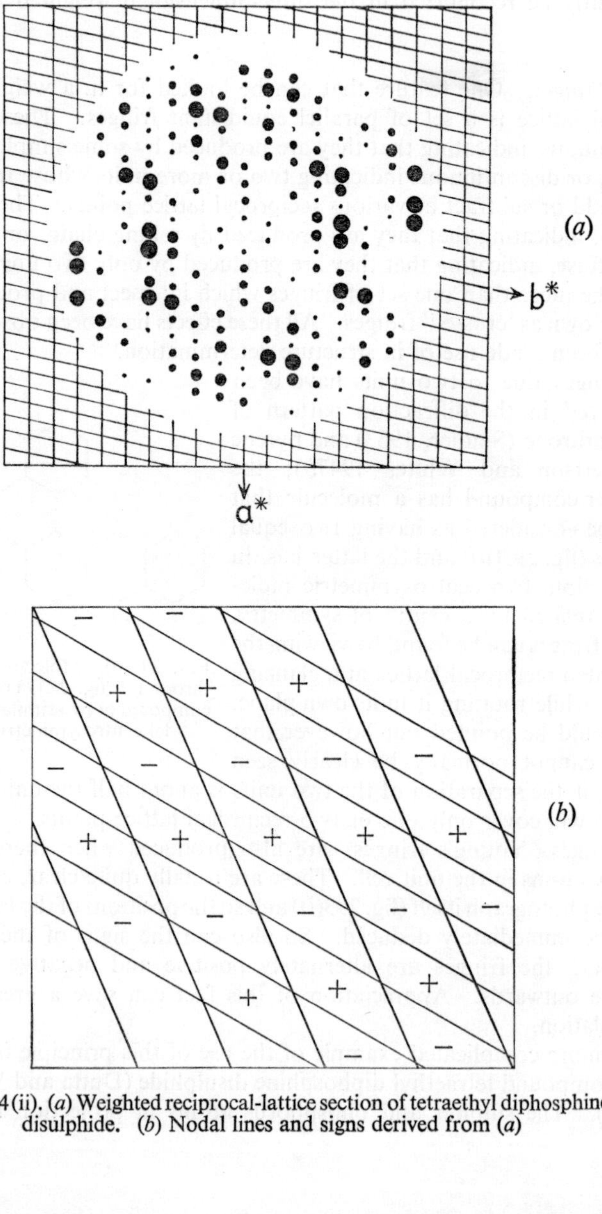

FIG. 294(ii). (*a*) Weighted reciprocal-lattice section of tetraethyl diphosphine disulphide. (*b*) Nodal lines and signs derived from (*a*)

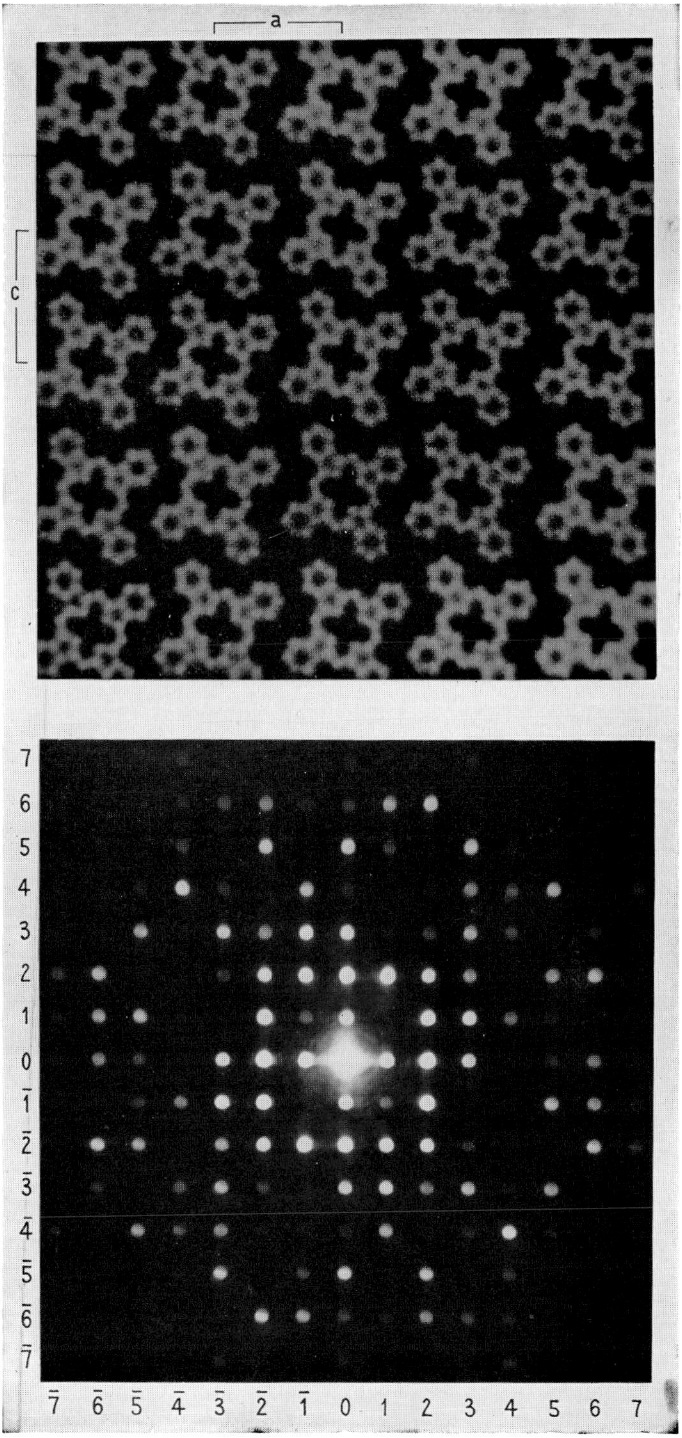

FIG. 294(i). *Above*: Pattern representing projection of phthalocyanine crystal on (010). *Below* : Optical diffraction pattern (Bunn, 1961)

p. 294

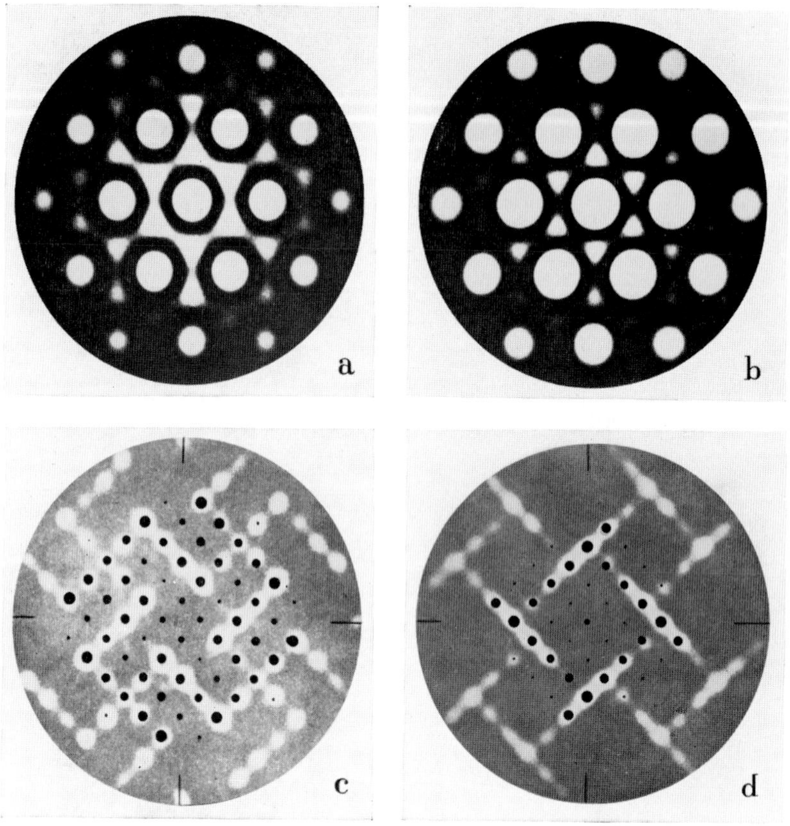

FIG. 295(i) (*a*). Transform of benzene molecule. (*b*) Transform of molecule with extra atom at centre. (*c*) and (*d*). Sections *hk*3 and *hk*6 of the weighted reciprocal lattice of pentaerythritol superimposed upon the corresponding sections of the three-dimensional transform

p. 295

way since the fringes in the three-dimensional reciprocal lattice are also quite clear.

Fringes can also arise by the presence of a regular chain of atoms in a structure; the chain behaves as a diffraction grating, and so will give spectra which are sharper the longer the chain. An example is shown in fig. 295(ii).

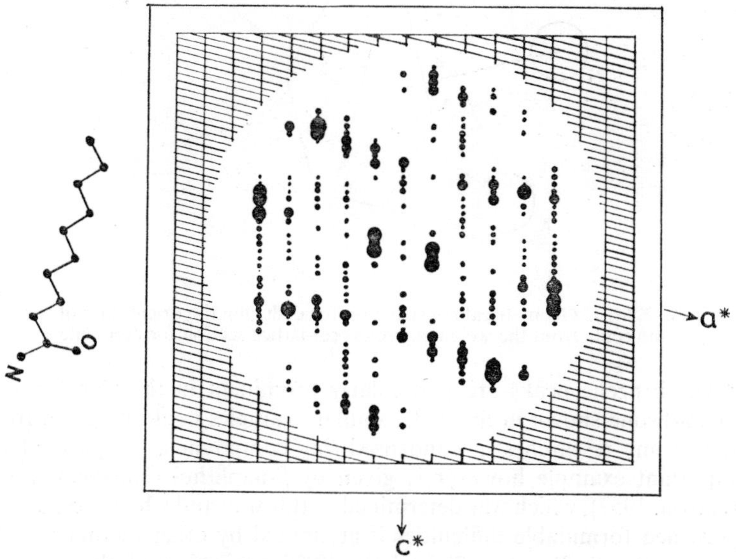

FIG. 295 (ii). Weighted reciprocal-lattice section for decanamide

6.3. *Benzene transform.* The transform of a benzene ring has six strong peaks which can be regarded as three pairs at a distance of 0·82 Å^{-1} from the origin (fig. 295(i)*a*, *b*). If a compound consists largely of benzene rings which are parallel to each other, these features of the transform should be clearly seen; they are shown in the three-dimensional reciprocal lattice of naphthalene (fig. 296(i)) for example.

An oblique section of the transform will show peaks that are at larger distances than 0·82 Å^{-1}, and these will correspond to the projection of the benzene ring on to the corresponding plane. To find these peaks it is convenient to draw a circle—called the benzene circle—of radius 0·82 Å^{-1} and to look for strong reflexions *outside* this; one or two pairs will usually be fairly close and the other or others may be at some distance away according to the obliquity of the section, that is to the tilt of the ring.

It is necessary to ensure that the three sets of peaks chosen *do* correspond to an oblique section of a hexagonal pyramid. The rule is simply that the vector distance between any two peaks must equal the vector distance of the third—unrelated—peak from the origin. If these peaks can be recognized, the simple construction shown in fig. 296(ii) gives the shape of the projected ring in the structure (Hanson, Lipson and Taylor, 1953).

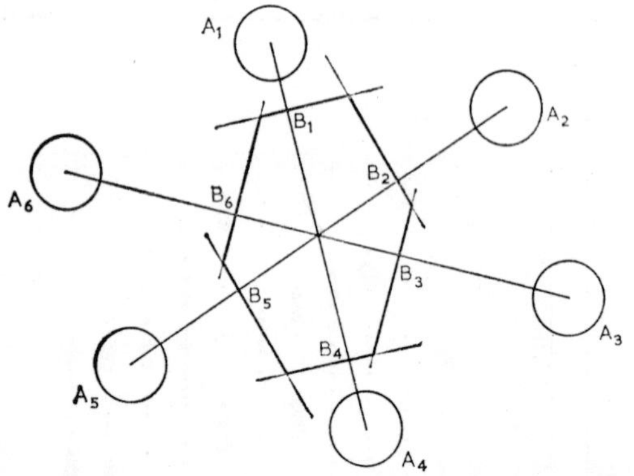

FIG. 296(ii). Geometrical construction for deducing the orientation of the molecule from the weighted reciprocal-lattice section for coronene

The benzene peaks are particularly prominent in the transform of flavanthrone shown in fig. 283; similar examples could be given from almost any researches in condensed-ring compounds. A particularly important example however is given by β-naphthol (Hargreaves and Watson, 1957), which was determined in this way and which would have presented formidable difficulties if attempted by other methods. The space group is P*a* (No. 7) and the [010] projection of the unit cell contains two unrelated molecules; fortunately their projections are so similar that the orientation of the benzene rings can be easily recognized. They are nevertheless sufficiently different for the broadening of the benzene peaks to be distinguished from the effects of tilt. The projection has no symmetry at all, and the asymmetric unit is two molecules; yet the structure was recognized immediately from its weighted reciprocal-lattice section.

The benzene-ring construction applies of course to any plane hexagonal ring of roughly the same size as benzene. In fact it also applies reasonably well to half a benzene ring—that is, a component of a conjugated chain. The construction is therefore of general importance in dealing with organic structures.

6.4. *Molecular location.* It will be noted that transform methods are particularly powerful for finding orientations of molecules; they are not so useful for finding positions because, as stated in section **10.6.2.**, such positions are given by fringe systems that may not be easy to detect. Nevertheless, information about positions *is* contained in the intensities and can be obtained in the following way.

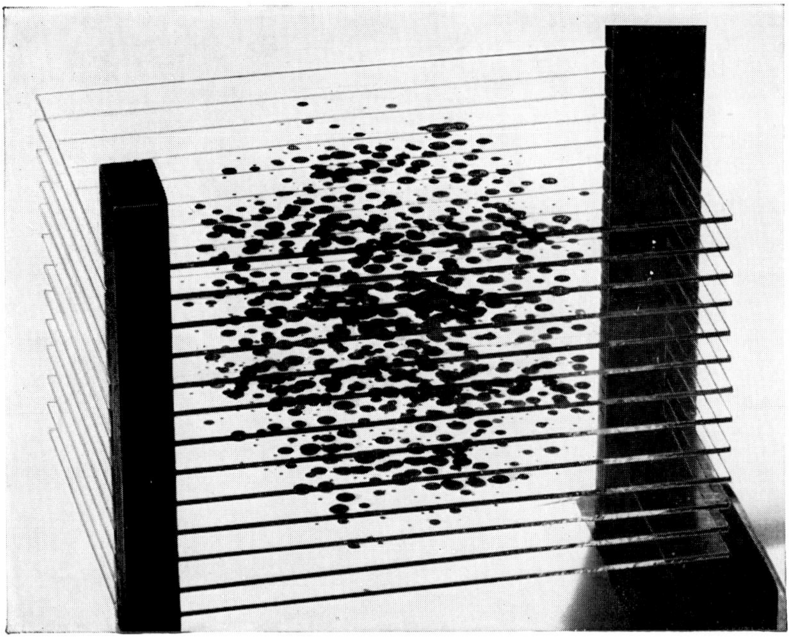

(*a*)

(*b*)

FIG. 296(i) (*a*). Photograph of a 3-dimensional weighted reciprocal lattice for naphthalene taken in a random direction. (*b*) Photograph of the same weighted reciprocal lattice taken in a direction perpendicular to the plane of the molecule

When the orientation of a molecule has been found by the methods so far described, a transform of the molecule can be superposed on the reciprocal lattice. That the orientation is correct should be confirmed by agreement with the strong intensities; they should all lie upon the strong parts of the transform. Weak reflexions may be so either because they lie upon weak parts of the transform *or* because they lie upon the nodal lines of a fringe system.

To detect the fringe system, therefore, it is necessary to consider those reflexions that lie upon the strong parts of the transform but which have small intensity. Several of these must be found, and Taylor (1954) has given the necessary theory to derive the molecular position from them. He has also considered the more complicated conditions that arise when molecules of symmetrically-related orientations are present.

A good example of the use of these methods is given by the structure of triphenylene (Klug, 1950). As shown in section **10**.4.2 the orientation of the molecule was found by transform methods, but the positions deduced gave some poor intensity agreements and also some rather unusual interatomic distances. The residual reported by Klug was reasonably low, presumably because the correct orientation itself gave some measure of agreement. Application of Taylor's method showed a minimum corresponding to the position shown by Klug (section **10**.4.2), but a much lower minimum corresponding to another position. This gave a lower residual and an acceptable set of interatomic distances.

6.5. *Relation to Patterson methods.* The methods described in the preceding sections may be called reciprocal-space methods; the operator is called upon to think in reciprocal space and then to transform his results into real space. The Patterson operation (Chapter 7) does the opposite; it converts the intensity information immediately into real space and then no transformation is necessary. Since most people find it easier to think in real space, have the reciprocal-space methods any advantage?

One advantage is that they are immediate: the intensities themselves can be examined, not merely some function of them. Thus one is not dependent upon a computer for initial deductions.

Secondly they can be more accurate. As we have seen, information is often obtainable from high-angle reflexions which may be very weak and so have little influence upon the Patterson synthesis; for this reason some enhancement of the high-angle reflexions is often artificially introduced in order to sharpen the synthesis. For weighted reciprocal lattices one can use unitary structure factors—the ultimate in enhancement.

Finally, there is the subjective pleasure of making a deduction rather than letting a machine make it!

7. Other uses of Optical Transforms

7.1. *Sign determination.* For a centrosymmetric structure the signs of the structure factors can be simply determined by the addition of a positive term to the whole transform; this enhances the positive regions and depresses the negative ones (fig. 291 (ii) (*a*), (*b*)). This positive term can be produced by adding a hole at the centre of symmetry of the diffracting mask. Pinnock and Taylor (1955) have discussed the conditions necessary for this method to be used satisfactorily.

Again what advantage has this method over computation? First, it is direct, and the operator is not dependent upon facilities for computation. Secondly, the method is self-checking; each reflexion can be considered in each half of the transform, or, in an orthogonal projection, in each quadrant. Finally, it brings out clearly which signs are doubtful, and which are best omitted in a Fourier synthesis.

From computation it may be supposed that all the F's which are small are doubtful; in fact, they may not be so and some moderately large F's, if they lie upon steep parts of the transform, may be much more uncertain.

7.2. *Three dimensions.* In order to produce sections of a three-dimensional transform, another variable must be introduced. The quantity $\exp 2\pi i(hx+ky+lz)$ may be written as $\exp 2\pi i(hx+ky) \exp 2\pi ilz$, and this latter factor can then be regarded as modifying the former by a change of phase. Thus, to produce a three-dimensional transform one can take the mask for a central section and change the phase of the light passing through each hole by the appropriate value. Thus, for the plane $l=1$, each hole will be modified by the phase corresponding to $\exp 2\pi iz$ for the particular atom. The complication is considerable but the procedure has been carried out successfully by Harburn and Taylor (1962). Some of their results are shown in fig. 295(i)(*c*), (*d*).

7.3. *Imperfect structures.* No crystal is perfect, and the study of imperfections is obviously an important branch of X-ray diffraction. Basically, the problems are much more difficult than those of crystal-structure determination, but since optical diffraction is so closely analogous to X-ray diffraction, it is probable that optical-transform methods will be able to help considerably in attempts to solve the many problems which are now presenting themselves. The subject is far too large to discuss here, but some consideration is given to it in the book by Taylor and Lipson (1964).

8. Summary

The transform approach is so different from other approaches that one is tempted to ask why it is thought worth while introducing it at all when so many other methods appear to be available. There are several answers to this question. First, it helps to fill in a gap: the most difficult problems of crystal-structure determination occur when all the atoms are of about the same weight, and it is to this sort of problem that transform methods are most easily applied. Secondly, transform theory—once the initial theorems have been accepted—provides a firm base for understanding the principles of diffraction by a crystal, and so can aid the introduction of new ideas. The acceptance of the diffraction pattern of a crystal as a single entity rather than a collection of pieces of isolated information is perhaps the best way of stating the fact. Finally, adoption of the optical method of deriving transforms lessens the dependence of the research worker on external aids and re-introduces the element of original research which the computer tends to discourage. The computer is now necessary of course, but over-use of it in the initial stages of a structure investigation can blind the research worker to the physical principles involved.

CHAPTER 11

EFFECTS OF THERMAL VIBRATION

1. Introduction

In a crystal-structure determination it is usually only the intensities of the Bragg reflexions that are utilized. In the process of Bragg reflexion the energy, and therefore the wave-length, of the reflected radiation is unchanged. The change of momentum is provided by the whole crystal. The intensity is determined by the average position of each atom, the average being over all unit cells at the same instant, or, equivalently, over a long period of time for a particular atom. Provided the force on an atom is proportional to its relative displacement (the harmonic approximation), it can be shown (see for example, James, 1957) that the probability that its centre is displaced to lie within a volume element $dx_1\, dx_2\, dx_3$ is $p(x_1x_2x_3)\, dx_1\, dx_2\, dx_3$, where

$$p(x_1x_2x_3) = ((2\pi)^{3/2}u_1u_2u_3)^{-1} \exp\left[-\left(\frac{x_1^2}{2u_1^2}+\frac{x_2^2}{2u_2^2}+\frac{x_3^2}{2u_3^2}\right)\right]. \quad (300.1)$$

In this expression u_1^2 is the mean square displacement in the x_1-direction, etc, and the axes $x_1x_2x_3$ are orthogonal. These axes in general bear no particular relation to the crystallographic axes, their direction being determined by the forces on an atom. Symmetry may however impose certain restrictions: for example if the atom lies on a two-fold axis one of the axes of the 'ellipsoid of thermal vibration' must coincide with this axis; if the atom lies on a four-fold axis the ellipsoid reduces to a spheroid with unique axis coincident with the four-fold axis, and so on. The atomic scattering factor is modified by multiplication by a factor which is just the Fourier transform of the probability distribution (Chapter 10). Thus

$$f = f_0 \exp\left[-2\pi^2(u_1^2\mathrm{H}_1^2 + u_2^2\mathrm{H}_2^2 + u_3^2\mathrm{H}_3^2)\right] \quad (300.2)$$

where $\mathrm{H}_1\mathrm{H}_2\mathrm{H}_3$ are the projections of the reciprocal-lattice vector **H** on axes parallel to the principal axes of the ellipsoid. In the early stages of a crystal-structure investigation it is a sufficiently good approximation to take the temperature factor to be isotropic (and the same for every atom of the structure), when equation (*300*.2) reduces to

$$f = f_0 \exp(-2\pi^2u^2\mathrm{H}^2) \quad \text{with } u^2 = u_1^2 = u_2^2 = u_3^2,$$

that is

$$f = f_0 \exp(-\tfrac{1}{4}\mathrm{BH}^2) \quad (300.3)$$

in the usual notation. In the course of refinement by the method of least squares (section **12**.3) parameters are obtained which specify the anisotropic temperature factor of each atom. The relation of these parameters to the directions of the axes of the ellipsoid and mean square displacements u_1^2, u_2^2, u_3^2 is discussed in the following sections, as is the interpretation of the thermal parameters in terms of rigid-body displacements and rotations for a molecular crystal.

Thermal vibration results in another scattering mechanism. A quantum of the incident radiation can exchange energy and momentum with the travelling waves which represent the normal modes of vibration of the crystal and whose energies are also quantized. In the process known as first-order scattering of X-rays the photon is scattered with emission or absorption of one quantum of lattice vibrational energy (one phonon). Higher-order processes involving two or more phonons are also possible; their relative intensities depend on the temperature of the crystal and on the scattering angle. Taken together, they are the phenomenon usually called thermal diffuse scattering. The wave-length change of X-rays in this process is very small because the energy of an X-ray photon ($\sim 10^4$ eV) is so much greater than that of a phonon ($\sim 10^{-2}$ eV). In neutron inelastic scattering, the energy (and therefore wave-length) change of the scattered neutrons is considerable, so that the technique of neutron spectroscopy can be used to study lattice vibrations. A detailed discussion of these topics would be out of place in this book; we mention them because the intensity of thermal diffuse scattering can in some instances give structural information. This topic is developed in section **11**.3.

2. Effect on Bragg Reflexions

2.1. *The anisotropic temperature factor.* When referred to the reciprocal axes of the crystal, the anistropic temperature factor takes the form

$$\exp -(b_{11}h^2 + b_{22}k^2 + b_{33}l^2 + b_{12}hk + b_{23}kl + b_{13}hl) \qquad (301.1)$$

It is the constants b_{11} etc. that are determined by the usual methods of refinement. Expression *301*.1 can conveniently be written as

$$\exp\left[-2\pi^2(\mathrm{U}_{11}^c(ha^*)^2 + (\mathrm{U}_{12}^c + \mathrm{U}_{21}^c)(ha^*kb^*) + \ldots \text{ etc.})\right] \qquad (301.2)$$

where the superscript c is used to emphasize that crystallographic axes are being used. The U_{11}^c etc. are the elements of a symmetric tensor and form a matrix

$$\mathrm{U}^c = \begin{pmatrix} \mathrm{U}_{11}^c & \mathrm{U}_{12}^c & \mathrm{U}_{13}^c \\ \mathrm{U}_{21}^c & \mathrm{U}_{22}^c & \mathrm{U}_{23}^c \\ \mathrm{U}_{31}^c & \mathrm{U}_{32}^c & \mathrm{U}_{33}^c \end{pmatrix} \qquad (301.3)$$

where, from a comparison of expressions (*301*.1) and (*301*.2),

$$\mathrm{U}_{11}^c = b_{11}/2\pi^2 a^{*2}$$
$$\mathrm{U}_{12}^c = \mathrm{U}_{21}^c = b_{12}/4\pi^2 a^* b^*, \text{ etc.} \qquad (301.4)$$

The problem now is to find an orthogonal set of coordinates in which the matrix (*301*.3) has zeros for all off-diagonal terms, thereby reducing the expression (*301*.2) to the form which appears in equation (*300*.2). While it is possible to accomplish this in one step (Waser, 1955), from a computational point of view it is simpler, if the crystallographic axes are not orthogonal, to transform first to some standard set of orthogonal axes for which we shall use the superscript *o*. The rules for accomplishing this have been given by Cruickshank et al. (1961).

We choose our standard orthogonal axes such that b^o coincides with b, a^o is the projection of a on the plane perpendicular to b and c^o is perpendicular to a^o and to b^o. Coordinates in Å then transform according to the equation

$$x^o = x \sin\gamma + z(\cos\beta - \cos\alpha\cos\gamma)/\sin\gamma$$
$$y^o = y + x\cos\gamma + z\cos\alpha$$
$$z^o = z[\sin^2\alpha - \{(\cos\beta - \cos\alpha\cos\gamma)/\sin\gamma\}^2]^{1/2}.$$

In matrix notation this becomes

$$\mathbf{x}^o = \mathbf{A}\mathbf{x} \qquad (302.1)$$

where $\mathbf{x}$ denotes the column matrix $\begin{pmatrix} x \\ y \\ z \end{pmatrix}$, etc.

Referred to the standard orthogonal axes, the anistropic temperature factor assumes the form

$$\exp[-2\pi^2(U^o_{11}(H^o_1)^2 + (U^o_{12} + U^o_{21})H^o_1H^o_2 + \ldots \text{etc.})]$$

where H^o_1, H^o_2, H^o_3 are the components of the reciprocal-lattice vector $\mathbf{H} = h\mathbf{a}^* + k\mathbf{b}^* + l\mathbf{c}^*$, referred to the standard orthogonal axes. The values of U^o_{11} etc. are given by the matrix equation

$$\mathbf{U}^o = (\mathbf{AD})\mathbf{U}^c(\mathbf{AD})' \qquad (302.2)$$

where **AD** is a matrix obtained by post-multiplication of **A** by a diagonal matrix **D** whose elements are

$$D_{11} = (\sin\alpha)/N, \quad D_{22} = (\sin\beta)/N, \quad D_{33} = (\sin\gamma)/N, \text{ with}$$
$$N^2 = 1 + 2\cos\alpha\cos\beta\cos\gamma - \cos^2\alpha - \cos^2\beta - \cos^2\gamma \qquad (302.3)$$

(Cruickshank et al., 1961). The transposed matrix (**AD**)′ is obtained from (**AD**) by interchanging rows and columns.

This intermediate step is of course unnecessary when the crystallographic axes are orthogonal. The problem of diagonalizing $\mathbf{U}^o$ is now a standard one (International Tables, Vol. II, p. 13; Waser (1955)). We set up the equations

$$u^2H^o_1 = U^o_{11}H^o_1 + U^o_{12}H^o_2 + U^o_{13}H^o_3$$
$$u^2H^o_2 = U^o_{21}H^o_1 + U^o_{22}H^o_2 + U^o_{23}H^o_3 \qquad (302.4)$$
$$u^2H^o_3 = U^o_{31}H^o_1 + U^o_{32}H^o_2 + U^o_{33}H^o_3.$$

They have a solution only when the determinant of the coefficients vanishes,

$$\begin{vmatrix} U^o_{11}-u^2 & U^o_{12} & U^o_{13} \\ U^o_{21} & U^o_{22}-u^2 & U^o_{23} \\ U^o_{31} & U^o_{32} & U^o_{33}-u^2 \end{vmatrix} = 0. \qquad (303)$$

There are three solutions to this equation, $u^2 = u_1^2$, u_2^2, u_3^2 which are the mean square displacements in the directions of the principal axes. On substituting u_1^2 for u^2 in equation (*302.4*), one obtains a solution for the components of **H**. Since the magnitude of this vector is not determined by the equations, we can introduce the normalizing condition

$$H_1^{o2} + H_2^{o2} + H_3^{o2} = 1,$$

and $(H_1^o, H_2^o, H_3^o)_1$ are then simply the direction cosines, in the standard orthogonal system, of the first principal axis. The direction cosines of the second principal axis are obtained by putting $u^2 = u_2^2$ in the equations, etc. In the language of matrix algebra, the mean square displacements along the principal axes are the eigenvalues of the matrix $\mathbf{U}^0$, and the corresponding direction cosines are the eigenvectors of the matrix.

2.2. *A numerical example.* Let us suppose we are dealing with a monoclinic crystal for which $a^* = 0{\cdot}1$, $b^* = 0{\cdot}1$, $c^* = 0{\cdot}15$ Å^{-1}, $\beta = 120°$, and that the exponent for a particular atom has been found to be

$$(21{\cdot}06h^2 + 19{\cdot}73k^2 + 85{\cdot}85l^2 + 44{\cdot}41hl) \times 10^{-4},$$
$$= 2\pi^2[(0{\cdot}01067\,(ha^*)^2 + 0{\cdot}01000\,(kb^*)^2 + 0{\cdot}01933\,(lc^*)^2 + 2 \times 0{\cdot}0075\,(ha^*\,lc^*)]$$

so that

$$U^c = \begin{pmatrix} 0{\cdot}01067 & 0 & 0{\cdot}0075 \\ 0 & 0{\cdot}01000 & 0 \\ 0{\cdot}0075 & 0 & 0{\cdot}01933 \end{pmatrix}.$$

From the absence of cross-terms involving k it is obvious that the second principal axis coincides with b, and that $u_2^2 = 0{\cdot}01$ Å^2 but we shall continue to treat the problem as a general one. From equation (*302.1*),

$$A = \begin{pmatrix} 1 & 0 & -\frac{1}{2} \\ 0 & 1 & 0 \\ 0 & 0 & \sqrt{3}/2 \end{pmatrix}$$

and from equations (*302.3*),

$$D = \begin{pmatrix} 2/\sqrt{3} & 0 & 0 \\ 0 & 1 & 0 \\ 0 & 0 & 2/\sqrt{3} \end{pmatrix}$$

and therefore using equation (*302.2*) one finds

$$\mathbf{U}^o = \begin{pmatrix} 0{\cdot}01067 & 0 & -0{\cdot}0025 \\ 0 & 0{\cdot}01000 & 0 \\ -0{\cdot}0025 & 0 & 0{\cdot}01933 \end{pmatrix}.$$

The solutions of the equation

$$\begin{vmatrix} 0{\cdot}01067 - u^2 & 0 & -0{\cdot}0025 \\ 0 & 0{\cdot}0100 - u^2 & 0 \\ -0{\cdot}0025 & 0 & 0{\cdot}01933 - u^2 \end{vmatrix} = 0$$

are readily found to be

$$u_1^2 = 0{\cdot}01, \quad u_2^2 = 0{\cdot}01, \quad u_3^2 = 0{\cdot}02\ \text{Å}^2.$$

Substituting these values in turn in the equations corresponding to equations (*302.4*) one finds

$$(H_1^o, H_2^o, H_3^o)_1 = 0{\cdot}9659,\ 0,\ 0{\cdot}2588$$
$$(H_1^o, H_2^o, H_3^o)_2 = 0,\ 1{\cdot}00,\ 0$$
$$(H_1^o, H_2^o, H_3^o)_3 = -0{\cdot}2588,\ 0,\ 0{\cdot}9659.$$

Since cos 15° = 0·9659, sin 15° = 0·2588, the relation of the axes of the ellipsoid to the standard orthogonal axes must be as shown in fig. 304.

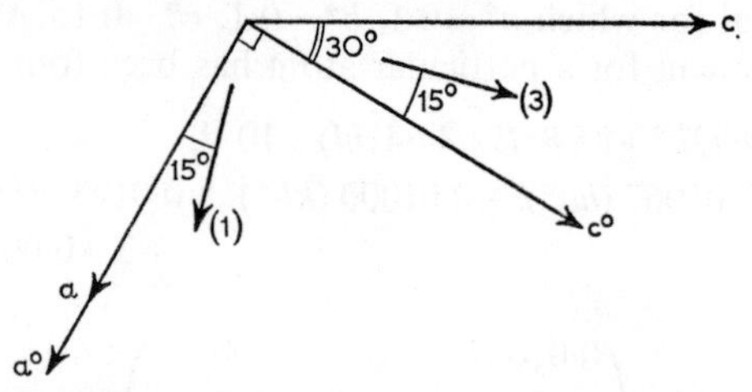

FIG. 304. Crystallographic axes (a, c), orthogonal axes (a^o, c^o) and axes of the ellipsoid of thermal vibration (1, 3) for the example worked out in the text

2.3. *Symmetry considerations.* When the temperature factor of an atom is isotropic, its contribution to the structure factor, together with that of the equivalent atoms in the unit cell, can be written

$$f_0 \exp\left(-\tfrac{1}{4}BH^2\right) \sum_{s=1}^{n} \exp 2\pi i \mathbf{H}\cdot\mathbf{r}_s. \qquad (304)$$

When the thermal vibration is not isotropic, the temperature factor cannot be taken outside the summation since the n thermal ellipsoids do not have their axes parallel to one another, but are in relative orientations determined by the space-group symmetry. The problem of the relation between the different temperature factors has been considered by Rollett and Davies (1955) and Trueblood (1956). The results can be simply presented by giving the values of b'_{11}, b'_{12} etc. for an atom at $x'y'z'$ related by a symmetry operation to a standard atom at xyz for which the constants appearing in the expression (*301*.1) are b_{11}, b_{12} etc. Translations and inversions have no effect since they do not alter the orientation of the ellipsoid. Thus both mirror planes and glide planes produce the same effect as would a two-fold axis normal to them, and screw axes have the same effect as the corresponding rotation axes. In the following tables therefore, which were obtained by Trueblood (1956) by straightforward application of vector analysis to determine the effect of different symmetry operations on the direction cosines of the principal axes of the ellipsoid with respect to the reciprocal crystallographic axes, the only operations listed are rotation axes of order 2, 3, 4 and 6. For convenience, the crystallographic axes are denoted by $\mathbf{a}_1$, $\mathbf{a}_2$, $\mathbf{a}_3$.

TABLE 305

Temperature-factor transformations for monoclinic, orthorhombic, tetragonal and cubic systems

Order of axis	Axis parallel to	b'_{11}	b'_{22}	b'_{33}	b'_{12}	b'_{13}	b'_{23}
2	$\mathbf{a}_1$	b_{11}	b_{22}	b_{33}	$-b_{12}$	$-b_{13}$	b_{23}
2	$\mathbf{a}_2$	b_{11}	b_{22}	b_{33}	$-b_{12}$	b_{13}	$-b_{23}$
2	$\mathbf{a}_3$	b_{11}	b_{22}	b_{33}	b_{12}	$-b_{13}$	$-b_{23}$
2	$\mathbf{a}_1+\mathbf{a}_2$	b_{22}	b_{11}	b_{33}	b_{12}	$-b_{23}$	$-b_{13}$
2	$\mathbf{a}_2+\mathbf{a}_3$	b_{11}	b_{33}	b_{22}	$-b_{13}$	$-b_{12}$	b_{23}
2	$\mathbf{a}_3+\mathbf{a}_1$	b_{33}	b_{22}	b_{11}	$-b_{23}$	b_{13}	$-b_{12}$
3	$\mathbf{a}_1+\mathbf{a}_2+\mathbf{a}_3$	b_{33}	b_{11}	b_{22}	b_{13}	b_{23}	b_{12}
4	$\mathbf{a}_1$	b_{11}	b_{33}	b_{22}	$-b_{13}$	b_{12}	$-b_{23}$
4	$\mathbf{a}_2$	b_{33}	b_{22}	b_{11}	b_{23}	$-b_{13}$	$-b_{12}$
4	$\mathbf{a}_3$	b_{22}	b_{11}	b_{33}	$-b_{12}$	$-b_{23}$	b_{13}

2.4. *An example.* The following illustrative example is also due to Trueblood. Let $(x''y''z'')$ be the position $(y, x-y, z)$ of space group $P6_1mc$. This is related to the standard position (xyz) by *two* successive applications of the 6_3 operation. Thus from table 306(i) we use the relations for a 6-fold axis parallel to $\mathbf{a}_3$. After the first application,

$$b'_{11}=b_{11}+b_{22}-b_{12}, \qquad b'_{12}=2b_{11}-b_{12}$$
$$b'_{22}=b_{11} \qquad b'_{13}=b_{13}-b_{23}$$
$$b'_{33}=b_{33} \qquad b'_{23}=b_{13}.$$

After the second application we have the required relations

$$\begin{aligned} b''_{11}&=b'_{11}+b'_{22}-b'_{12} &&=b_{22}\\ b''_{22}&=b'_{11} &&=b_{11}+b_{22}-b_{12}\\ b''_{33}&=b'_{33} &&=b_{33}\\ b''_{12}&=2b'_{11}-b'_{12} &&=2b_{22}-b_{12}\\ b''_{13}&=b'_{13}-b'_{23} &&=-b_{23}\\ b''_{23}&=b'_{13} &&=b_{13}-b_{23}. \end{aligned}$$

TABLE 306 (i)

Temperature-factor transformations for the hexagonal system

Order of axis	Axis parallel to	b'_{11}	b'_{22}	b'_{33}	b'_{12}	b'_{13}	b'_{23}
2	$\mathbf{a}_1$	$b_{11}+b_{22}-b_{12}$	b_{22}	b_{33}	$2b_{22}-b_{12}$	$b_{23}-b_{13}$	b_{23}
2	$\mathbf{a}_2$	b_{11}	$b_{11}+b_{22}-b_{12}$	b_{33}	$2b_{11}-b_{12}$	b_{13}	$b_{13}-b_{23}$
2	$\mathbf{a}_1+\mathbf{a}_2$	b_{22}	b_{11}	b_{33}	b_{12}	$-b_{23}$	$-b_{13}$
2	$2\mathbf{a}_1+\mathbf{a}_2$	b_{11}	$b_{11}+b_{22}-b_{12}$	b_{33}	$2b_{11}-b_{12}$	$-b_{13}$	$b_{23}-b_{13}$
2	$2\mathbf{a}_2+\mathbf{a}_1$	$b_{11}+b_{22}-b_{12}$	b_{22}	b_{33}	$2b_{22}-b_{12}$	$b_{13}-b_{23}$	$-b_{23}$
6	$\mathbf{a}_3$	$b_{11}+b_{22}-b_{12}$	b_{11}	b_{33}	$2b_{11}-b_{12}$	$b_{13}-b_{23}$	b_{13}

TABLE 306 (ii)

Temperature-factor transformations for the trigonal system with rhombohedral indexing

Order of Axis Axis parallel to:	3 $\mathbf{a}_1+\mathbf{a}_2+\mathbf{a}_3$	2 $\mathbf{a}_1-\mathbf{a}_2$	2 $\mathbf{a}_1+\mathbf{a}_2-2\mathbf{a}_2$
$b'_{11}=$	b_{33}	b_{22}	$\frac{1}{9}(4b_{11}+b_{22}+4b_{33}-2b_{12}+4b_{13}+2b_{23})$
$b'_{22}=$	b_{11}	b_{11}	$\frac{1}{9}(b_{11}+4b_{22}+4b_{33}-2b_{12}-2b_{13}+4b_{23})$
$b'_{33}=$	b_{22}	b_{33}	$\frac{1}{9}(4b_{11}+4b_{22}+b_{33}+4b_{12}-2b_{13}-2b_{23})$
$b'_{12}=$	b_{13}	b_{12}	$\frac{1}{9}(-4b_{11}-4b_{22}+8b_{33}+5b_{12}+2b_{13}+2b_{23})$
$b'_{13}=$	b_{23}	b_{23}	$\frac{1}{9}(8b_{11}-4b_{22}-4b_{33}+2b_{12}+2b_{13}+5b_{23})$
$b'_{23}=$	b_{12}	b_{13}	$\frac{1}{9}(-4b_{11}-8b_{22}-4b_{33}+2b_{12}+5b_{13}+2b_{23})$

2.5. *Thermal motion in a molecular crystal.* In a crystal such as anthracene or naphthalene the normal modes of vibration may be roughly divided into two categories. Those which involve distortion of covalent bonds without appreciable translation or rotation of a molecule have relatively high frequencies ($\sim 1000\ \text{cm}^{-1} \equiv 3 . 10^{13}$ c.p.s.) and both the frequency and pattern of movement of the atoms in such a 'molecular mode' are not very different from what they would be in an isolated molecule. 'Lattice modes' on the other hand involve translation and rotation (i.e. libration) of each molecule essentially as a rigid unit, and only force constants appropriate to the comparatively weak intermolecular bonds are operative. The frequencies of such modes are therefore low ($\sim 10^{12}$ c.p.s.). The mean square displacement of an atom resulting from the molecular modes is only a few per cent, at ordinary temperatures, of that produced by the lattice modes and it is a reasonable approximation to neglect the former contribution, the principal result of this being an overestimate of the mean square translational displacement associated with the lattice modes. This type of analysis obviously cannot be applied in all circumstances; for example in long-chain hydrocarbons the molecular modes include torsional modes of low frequency which probably make a significant contribution to the mean square displacements.

In the following discussion we assume that an orthogonal set of axes is being used, but the superscript *o* can now be omitted without risk of confusion. From the fact that the surfaces of constant probability are ellipsoids (equation (*300*.1)) it can be shown that the mean square displacement of a particular atom in the direction specified by a unit vector $\mathbf{l} = (l_1, l_2, l_3)$ is given by

$$u^2 = \sum_{i=1}^{3} \sum_{j=1}^{3} \mathrm{U}_{ij} l_i l_j \tag{307}$$

The mean square displacements resulting from rigid-body motion of the molecule can be expressed in terms of two symmetric tensors, each with six independent components, one giving the mean square displacements of the centre of the molecule and the other the mean square angular oscillations about the centre (Cruickshank, 1956). If $\mathbf{T}$ is the former tensor, the translational contribution is the same for every atom, being $\sum_{i=1}^{3} \sum_{j=1}^{3} \mathrm{T}_{ij} l_i l_j$ in the direction $\mathbf{l}$. Similarly the mean square amplitude of libration about an axis defined by the unit vector $\mathbf{t}$ is

$$\sum_{i=1}^{3} \sum_{j=1}^{3} \omega_{ij} t_i t_j,$$

where $\boldsymbol{\omega}$ is the second tensor referred to above. Let $\mathbf{r}$ denote the position of an atom with reference to the orthogonal coordinate system being used, the origin being the centre of the molecule. The mean square displacement of this atom in the direction $\mathbf{l}$, resulting from small librations, is readily shown to be

$$\sum_{i=1}^{3}\sum_{j=1}^{3} \omega_{ij}(\mathbf{l}\times\mathbf{r})_i(\mathbf{l}\times\mathbf{r})_j.$$

Combining these results, we have finally

$$\sum_{i=1}^{3}\sum_{j=1}^{3} \mathrm{U}_{ij}l_il_j = \sum_{i=1}^{3}\sum_{j=1}^{3} \{\mathrm{T}_{ij}l_il_j + \omega_{ij}(\mathbf{l}\times\mathbf{r})_i(\mathbf{l}\times\mathbf{r})_j\}. \qquad (308.1)$$

There is an equation of this type for each atom of the molecule, the tensors $\mathbf{T}$ and $\boldsymbol{\omega}$ being of course the same throughout but $\mathbf{U}$ and $\mathbf{r}$ differing from one atom to another.

It is implied in the above discussion that the coordinate system is the standard orthogonal one of earlier sections, with origin at the centre of the molecule. This is not necessarily so; it is in fact preferable to use the principal axes of the molecule since experience confirms one's physical intuition that the tensors $\mathbf{T}$ and $\boldsymbol{\omega}$ will be diagonal, or nearly so, when referred to this natural coordinate system, at least for molecules in crystals such as anthracene and naphthalene. The directions of the principal axes of naphthalene are obvious from the symmetry of the molecule (fig. 308); in general they are the axes which reduce the

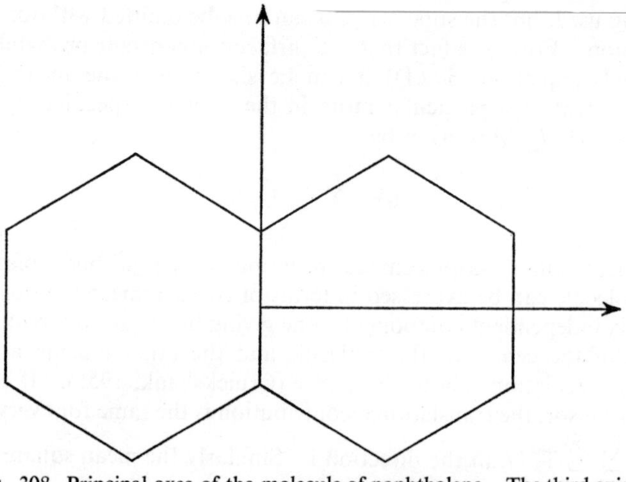

FIG. 308. Principal axes of the molecule of naphthalene. The third axis is perpendicular to the plane

moment-of-inertia tensor of the molecule to diagonal form. This topic is discussed in text-books of classical mechanics, for example Goldstein (1951). If $\mathbf{U}_1$ is the thermal vibration tensor of an atom referred to one set of orthogonal axes, and $\mathbf{U}_2$ that referred to a second set, then

$$\mathbf{U}_2 = \mathbf{A}\mathbf{U}_1\mathbf{A}' \qquad (308.2)$$

is the matrix equation for the transformation, **A** being the matrix which transforms coordinates from the first system to the second (this is a special case of equation (*302*.2)).

We have referred somewhat loosely to 'the centre of the molecule'. In naphthalene the centre of the molecule coincides with a centre of symmetry of the crystal, but in a less symmetrical molecule we might expect small angular oscillations to occur about axes through the centre of mass of the molecule. This is not necessarily correct; if the molecule is more firmly bound to its neighbours on one side than the other the 'centre of the molecule' for present purposes is moved in that direction, and coordinates specifying its position should be included in the equations (Pawley, 1963; Hirshfeld, Sandler and Schmidt, 1963).

In fact the situation can be more complicated than this, as has been pointed out by V. Schomaker (1964). The three principal axes of libration do not necessarily intersect one another, and librational and translational motions can be correlated. The mean square displacements of the atoms of a rigid molecule thus in general arise from three independent *helical* motions of the molecule about *non-intersecting* orthogonal axes, and three independent linear motions in a different orthogonal coordinate system. The number of parameters involved is twenty-one. It seems doubtful whether in practice it will be possible to detect this most general type of motion, and in what follows we assume that Cruickshank's formulation of the problem is sufficiently exact.

Returning now to equation (*308*.1), if the right-hand side is expanded using the notation $\mathbf{r} = (x, y, z)$, and coefficients of $l_i l_j$ are equated on both sides, we obtain results such as

$$\begin{aligned} \mathrm{U}_{11} &= \mathrm{T}_{11} + z^2\omega_{22} + y^2\omega_{33} - 2yz\omega_{23} \\ \mathrm{U}_{12} &= \mathrm{T}_{12} - xy\omega_{33} - z^2\omega_{12} + xz\omega_{23} + yz\omega_{13} \\ &\text{etc.} \end{aligned} \qquad (309)$$

There are six linear equations of this type for each independent atom of the molecule, so that the number of equations will generally exceed the number of unknowns, which is twelve. These should therefore be determined by the method of least squares. A general discussion of this method is given in section **12**.3, and a detailed discussion of its application in this particular instance has been given by Cruickshank (1956).

It has been pointed out by Pawley (1964) that, instead of refining the structure with six thermal parameters per independent atom and subsequently determining the twelve components of **T** and **ω**, it is possible to proceed by introducing only these twelve in the refinement (possibly plus three to define the centre of the molecule). This was done for the least-squares refinement of the structures of a number of polyhedral molecules containing boron, and in these instances the final agreement between observed and calculated structure amplitudes was as good as when thermal parameters were introduced for each independent atom, suggesting that the rigid-body approximation held good to the accuracy of the experimental data (Pawley, 1964).

2.6. *Rigid-body motion of naphthalene.* A detailed refinement of the crystal structure of naphthalene was made by Cruickshank (1957), using experimental data which Abrahams, Robertson and White (1949) measured by photographic methods at room temperature. The values of the constants b_{ij} (equation (*301*.1)) were determined in the course of this work. From these the U_{ij} for each of the five independent atoms, referred to the principal axes of the molecule (fig. 308) were determined, as described in previous sections. The thirty observational equations, corresponding to equations (*309*), were solved for twelve unknowns by the method of least squares to give the components of **T** and **ω**. The standard deviations of the latter were estimated from the residuals by the usual method (section **12**.3). The results are shown in the table.

TABLE 310

Values of T_{ij} in 10^{-2} Å^2 and of ω_{ij} in deg^2, together with their standard deviations

$$\mathbf{T} = \begin{pmatrix} 5{\cdot}01 & -0{\cdot}30 & 0{\cdot}10 \\ -0{\cdot}30 & 4{\cdot}00 & -0{\cdot}05 \\ 0{\cdot}10 & -0{\cdot}05 & 3{\cdot}44 \end{pmatrix} \qquad \boldsymbol{\omega} = \begin{pmatrix} 19{\cdot}50 & 2{\cdot}25 & 2{\cdot}56 \\ 2{\cdot}25 & 13{\cdot}95 & 0{\cdot}76 \\ 2{\cdot}56 & 0{\cdot}76 & 17{\cdot}73 \end{pmatrix}$$

$$\sigma(\mathbf{T}) = \begin{pmatrix} 0{\cdot}13 & 0{\cdot}13 & 0{\cdot}15 \\ 0{\cdot}13 & 0{\cdot}18 & 0{\cdot}18 \\ 0{\cdot}15 & 0{\cdot}18 & 0{\cdot}36 \end{pmatrix} \qquad \sigma(\boldsymbol{\omega}) = \begin{pmatrix} 6{\cdot}57 & 1{\cdot}34 & 2{\cdot}43 \\ 1{\cdot}34 & 1{\cdot}94 & 1{\cdot}44 \\ 2{\cdot}43 & 1{\cdot}44 & 1{\cdot}40 \end{pmatrix}$$

Within experimental error the principal axes of **T** and **ω** coincide with the molecular axes. The result of a theoretical calculation by Higgs (1955) suggests that the diagonal elements of **T** may be systematically overestimated by some 4 per cent as a result of the neglect of the effect of the molecular modes in this instance. The mean square angular displacements agree fairly well with estimates based on the frequencies of certain lattice modes, as determined by Raman spectroscopy. This comparison necessarily rests however on a somewhat oversimplified picture of the lattice dynamics of a molecular crystal (Cruickshank, 1958).

3. EFFECTS OF THERMAL DIFFUSE SCATTERING

3.1. *Thermal diffuse scattering by a monatomic crystal.* The problem of the diffuse scattering of X-rays was first investigated by Debye, who made the simplifying assumption that each atom when displaced is acted on by a restoring force proportional to its displacement from its equilibrium position, irrespective of the displacements of neighbouring atoms, so that atomic motions are completely uncorrelated. It can then be shown that the diffuse intensity from a crystal which contains only one atom per (primitive) unit cell, such as copper or sodium for example, is given by

$$I(S) = Nf_0^2(1 - \exp(-\tfrac{1}{2}BS^2)). \qquad (311.1)$$

In this expression, N is the number of unit cells in the crystal and $B = 8\pi^2 u^2$, as before (equation (*300*.3)). On this approximation, the diffuse intensity varies uniformly with scattering angle (James, 1957). As was shown experimentally by Laval (1941), Lonsdale (1942) and others, the intensity is in practice by no means isotropically distributed in reciprocal space; it is 'peaked' around reciprocal-lattice points, while streaks and bands of relatively high intensity often connect adjacent reciprocal-lattice points. This can be adequately explained in general terms by the theory of lattice dynamics. Since the atomic motions *are* correlated they must be expressed in terms of the normal modes of vibration of the crystal, which can be taken to be travelling waves. Each mode is characterized by a wave-vector **k**, a frequency $\nu_j(\mathbf{k})$ and a unit polarization vector $\mathbf{e}_j(\mathbf{k})$. The latter determines the direction of displacement of an atom in this particular mode of vibration, and the subscript j indicates one of three mutually perpendicular directions of polarization. The energy in each mode of vibration is quantized in units of $h\nu_j(\mathbf{k})$, the average energy $E_j(\mathbf{k})$ at temperature T being approximately $k_B T$. When a beam of X-rays is scattered by a lattice wave of wave-vector **k**, the scattered intensity is concentrated at

$$\mathbf{S} = \mathbf{H} + \mathbf{k} \qquad (311.2)$$

where, as before, **H** is any vector of the reciprocal lattice. This is the process known as first-order scattering in which the X-ray photon exchanges energy $h\nu_j(\mathbf{k})$ with the crystal. This energy is however relatively so small that the X-ray wave-length is not changed by a detectable amount. When the contributions of the modes of different polarization are combined, the intensity of scattering by this process can be shown to be given by

$$I_1(S) = Nf_0^2 \exp(-\tfrac{1}{2}BS^2) \sum_{j=1}^{3} \frac{E_j(\mathbf{k})|\mathbf{e}_j(\mathbf{k})\cdot\mathbf{S}|^2}{m\nu_j^2(\mathbf{k})} \qquad (311.3)$$

(James, 1957). In this expression **k** and **S** are related by equation (*311*.2), m is the mass of an atom, and the other symbols have already been defined. The conditions for a lattice wave to contribute relatively strongly to the first-order scattering are therefore that it should have a low frequency and its polarization should be nearly parallel to the scattering vector **S**. Waves of long wave-length, which are simply sound waves in the crystal, necessarily satisfy the condition $\nu_j(\mathbf{k}) \to 0$ as $k \to 0$ and therefore produce strong scattering for values of **S** close to **H**. Quite strong scattering can result well away from reciprocal-lattice points, but it is not possible to make detailed predictions unless the frequencies of the lattice vibrations have been calculated or measured. However we can define the 'general level' of first-order scattering as the average of $I_1(S)$ over a region of reciprocal space whose volume is somewhat greater than that of the reciprocal unit cell, but having approximately a constant value of S. It can readily be shown from equation (*311*.3) that in the temperature range where there is equipartition of energy, i.e. $E_j(\mathbf{k}) \approx k_B T$, the general level of intensity of first-order scattering is proportional to $S^2 T f_0^2 \exp(-\frac{1}{2}BS^2)$. Second- and higher-order scattering processes also occur in which two or more quanta of lattice-vibrational energy (phonons) are exchanged. The general level of intensity of second-order scattering, for instance, is proportional to $S^4 T^2 f_0^2 \exp(-\frac{1}{2}BS^2)$ and is therefore less important at moderate temperatures and scattering angles. When the intensities from the different processes are added together, the result is simply

$$\overline{I(S)} = Nf_0^2(1 - \exp(-\tfrac{1}{2}BS^2)) \qquad (312.1)$$

so that the *average* intensity is just what it would be if the atomic movements were uncorrelated, equation (*311*.1).

3.2. *Thermal diffuse scattering by a molecular crystal.* In recording the electron-diffraction pattern of a single crystal of anthracene, Charlesby, Finch and Wilman (1939) discovered a diffuse background which was clearly related to the Fourier transforms of the molecules. Similar observations have since been made using X-rays and various molecular crystals. The subject has been reviewed by Wooster (1962) and by Hoppe (1964).

We shall begin by considering thermal diffuse scattering when there is only one molecule per primitive unit cell. Hexamethylenetetramine (hexamine) provides an example. The molecular modes contribute very little to the diffuse intensity at ordinary temperatures because of their high frequencies. If in the course of displacement by the lattice modes (section 2) the molecules made translations without change of orientation, all the results of section 3.1 would apply, with $f_0(S)$ replaced by $F_0(S)$, the continuous structure factor or Fourier transform of the molecule. In particular, the general level or local average of the diffuse intensity would be given by

$$\overline{I(S)} = N|F_0(S)|^2\{1 - \exp(-\tfrac{1}{2}BS^2)\}. \qquad (312.2)$$

This result again gives I(S), the intensity without averaging, in the non-physical situation where molecular movements are uncorrelated. Nevertheless it has been found by Amoros, Canut and de Acha (1960) that the measured diffuse intensity from hexamine is in qualitative agreement with equation (*312*.2); see fig. 313. In practice of course each molecule also librates giving the six degrees of freedom of a rigid

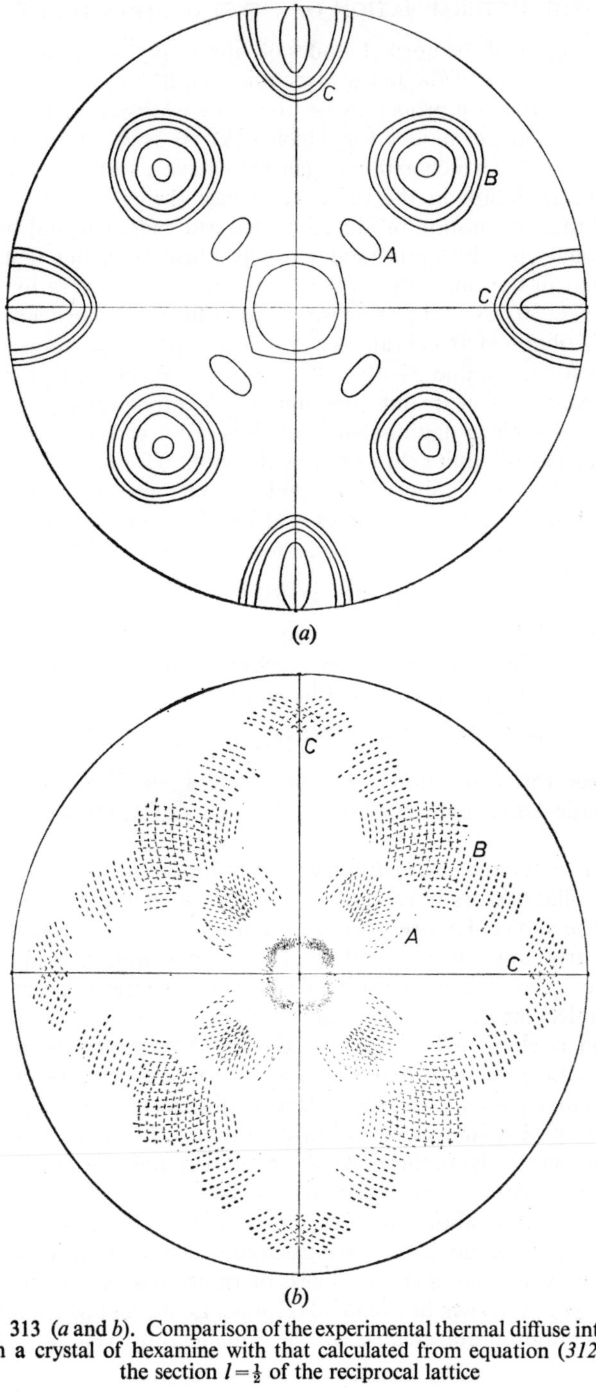

FIG. 313 (*a* and *b*). Comparison of the experimental thermal diffuse intensity from a crystal of hexamine with that calculated from equation (*312.2*), in the section $l=\frac{1}{2}$ of the reciprocal lattice body. In terms of the normal modes of vibration, this means that there are now six values of the index j (section 3.1), that is six waves having different polarization properties for the same wave-vector **k**. Three of these are 'acoustic' modes for which $\nu_j(\mathbf{k}) \to 0$ as $k \to 0$ and three are 'optic' modes for which $\nu_j(0)$ will generally have a value corresponding to that of radiation in the infra-red, hence the name. It might be expected that the motion produced by acoustic modes would be purely translational, and by optic modes purely librational, but it has been shown that in hexamine this is true only for waves of very long wavelength, i.e. $k \to 0$. An expression for the intensity of first-order scattering has been obtained (Cochran and Pawley, 1964), and numerical calculations for hexamine gave results in fair agreement with the experimental results, which are not quantitative. A corresponding calculation for a crystal such as naphthalene, which is of lower symmetry and has two molecules per unit cell, would be difficult. Hoppe (1956, 1964), as the result of a calculation which involves some approximations but is of general applicability, concludes that the diffuse intensity, at least in certain regions of reciprocal space, should be governed by

$$|F_0(S)|_A^2 + |F_0(S)|_B^2$$

where subscripts A and B refer to the two molecules. It can be shown that if the molecular motions were completely uncorrelated, and purely translational, the intensity would be given by

$$I(S) = N(|F_0(S)|_A^2 + |F_0(S)|_B^2)(1 - \exp(-\tfrac{1}{2}BS^2)) \qquad (314)$$

In practice this expression is in qualitative agreement with measurements made using single crystals of naphthalene (Amoros et al., 1960).

3.3. *Use of measurements of diffuse intensity in structure analysis.* Hoppe and his collaborators have used measurements of the diffuse intensity to give the molecular orientation in a number of structure analyses. When a structure is made up of sheets of planar molecules in the same orientation, the diffuse intensity will have strong streaks perpendicular to the molecular plane. There are two reasons for this: the Fourier transform is elongated in this direction, and there will be transverse acoustic modes of low frequency with wave-vectors perpendicular to the molecular plane, since the molecular displacements in such modes involve only weak interplanar restoring forces. The orientation of these streaks perpendicular to the molecular plane was noticed in early work on the subject (Lonsdale, 1942). If a Weissenberg photograph is taken with the crystal rotating about an axis approximately in the molecular plane, and a reciprocal-lattice layer is recorded in which the Fourier transform has a large value along certain lines, or rather bands, the appearance shown in fig. 315(i) will be obtained (Hoppe, Lenne and Morandi, 1957). Precession photographs may show the same feature even more graphically.

PLATE XII

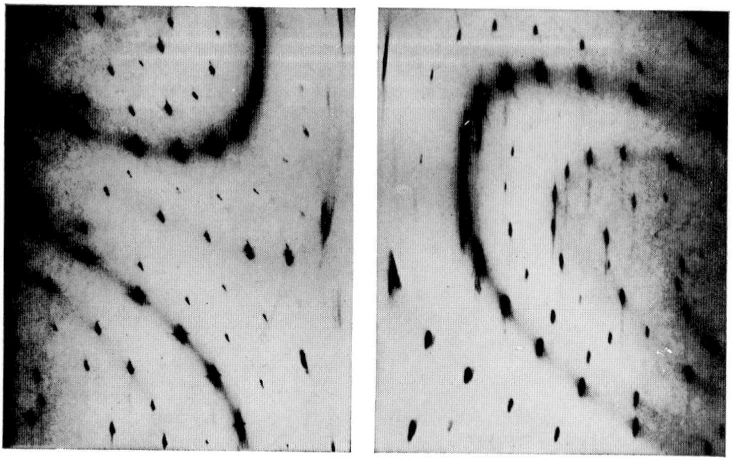

FIG. 315(i). Diffuse scattering 'streaks' on a Weissenberg photograph of cyanic acid trichloride, $C_3N_3Cl_3$ (kindly supplied by Prof. W. Hoppe)

p. 315

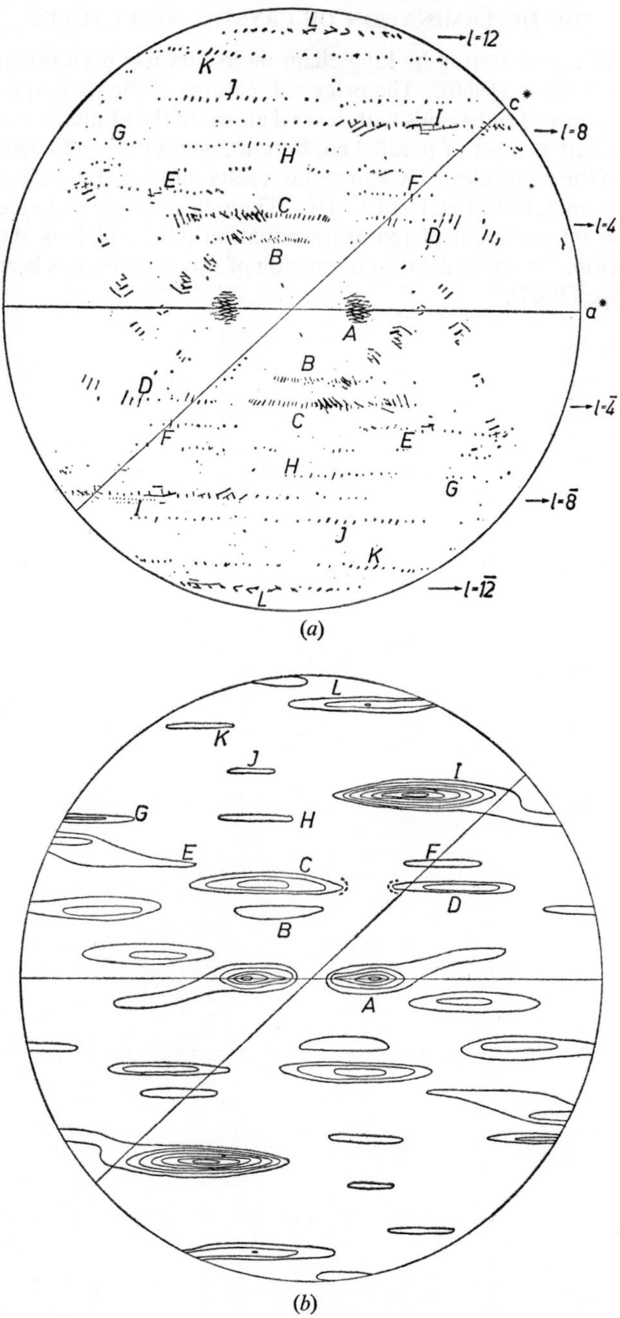

FIG. 315 (ii) (*a* and *b*). Comparison of the experimental thermal diffuse intensity from a crystal of adipic acid with that calculated from equation (*314*) in the section $l=0$ of the reciprocal lattice

The diffuse scattering by long chain molecules has been investigated by Amoros et al. (1960). The principal features of the pattern given by single crystals of fatty acids with several atoms in the aliphatic chain can be described as a set of parallel continuous sheets perpendicular to the length of the molecules. Experimental results shown in fig. 315(ii)*a* refer to adipic acid, $COOH(CH_2)_4COOH$. There is good general agreement with the intensity calculated from equation *314*, which is shown in fig. 315(ii)*b*. A more detailed discussion of this example has been given by Hoppe (1964).

CHAPTER 12

ACCURACY AND REFINEMENT

1. Introduction

In this chapter we are concerned with crystal-structure analysis at the stage where the analyst has arrived, by one method or another, at atomic coordinates which are within say 0·1 Å of the truth. Often the interest of the work lies in determining the broad features of the crystal or molecular architecture and these are already apparent at this stage. An increasing number of investigations are undertaken, however, whose object is to distinguish or identify chemical bonds which may differ in length by only a few hundredths of an Ångstrom unit. This is particularly true of work on organic compounds, where a check on theories of molecular structure is possible only when measured bond lengths can be relied on to within 0·01 Å. In such work the process of finding a structure which is essentially correct becomes merely a necessary, although sometimes a very difficult, preliminary to the task of extracting the best results from the experimental data and assessing their accuracy. This task has of course been enormously lightened by the advent of automatic computers, which have also influenced the mathematical techniques employed. In any investigation undertaken nowadays the crystallographer will be able to use a computer, and usually a computer program which he need not understand. In this situation it is still important to understand the basic physical and mathematical principles, and we have therefore thought it worth while to include in this chapter a survey of both Fourier and least-squares methods for accurate structure analysis, although the former have been largely superseded by the latter, primarily because least-squares methods are more adaptable to automatic computing. A discussion of Fourier methods, however, brings out in simpler fashion the limitations of accuracy on the final results that are imposed by random errors or systematic deficiencies in the experimental data.

While most investigations aim at the determination of accurate bond lengths and bond angles, and sometimes of the temperature-factor parameters both for their own sake and as a means of correcting coordinate parameters, the electron distribution is also of interest and Fourier synthesis must be used to determine it. In practice it has proved difficult to distinguish the comparatively small electron redistribution that takes place on chemical bonding from effects of thermal vibration, and it is only for centrosymmetric structures with few parameters that interpretable measurements of the electron density seem likely to be made.

In this chapter we shall find it convenient to use x to denote a distance in the crystal measured in the a-direction, and not as this distance expressed as a fraction of a. The accuracy with which x_j, the x-coordinate of a particular atom, can be measured depends on the accuracy with which a can be measured. There is no difficulty in measuring unit cell dimensions to 1 part in 1000, and this source of error is so small, and could so readily be reduced still further, that we can justifiably neglect it.

Fourier Methods

2.1. *Convergence of the F_0-synthesis.* The electron density is given by

$$\rho_0(\mathbf{r}) = \frac{1}{V} \sum_{H<H_m} |F_0(\mathbf{H})| \exp(-2\pi i\mathbf{H}\cdot\mathbf{r} + \alpha_c(\mathbf{H})). \qquad (318)$$

The notation serves to emphasize that the structure amplitudes are measured experimentally and are subject to at least random errors, while the phase angles are obtained from a postulated structure which approximates the true structure, and finally that the series usually does not include all terms of appreciable magnitude. For this last reason in particular, equation (*318*) cannot be used as it stands for the *final* stages of an accurate structure analysis. In the earlier stages however it may be necessary to calculate a number of successive F_0-syntheses. When the structure is centrosymmetric, it is clear that only one more Fourier synthesis is necessary when the 'model' or postulated structure from which F_c's are derived is sufficiently close to the true one that each measured $|F_0|$ can be given its correct sign. When phase angles are involved however the process of convergence requires closer investigation. We neglect random errors and series-termination errors meantime, and write the true density as

$$\rho_t = \rho_c + \Delta\rho$$

where

$$\rho_c = \frac{1}{V} \sum |F_c| \exp(i\alpha_c) \exp(-2\pi i\mathbf{H}\cdot\mathbf{r})$$

gives the density in the postulated structure. The structure amplitude corresponding to ρ_t is $|F_0|$, but the true phase angle is not known and the next stage of refinement gives

$$\rho_0 = \frac{1}{V} \sum |F_0| \exp(i\alpha_c) \exp(-2\pi i\mathbf{H}\cdot\mathbf{r}).$$

Writing

$$\Delta\rho = \frac{1}{V} \sum |\Delta F| \exp(i\phi) \exp(-2\pi i\mathbf{H}\cdot\mathbf{r})$$

where ϕ is the angle shown in fig. 319

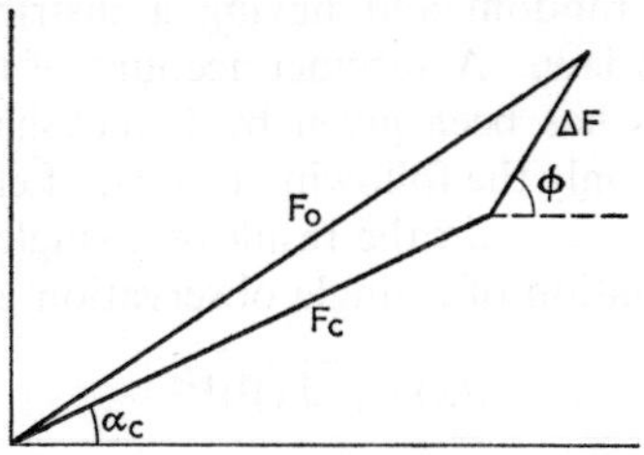

FIG. 319. Definition of structure factors referred to in the text

we see that

$$|F_0| = |F_c + \Delta F| \simeq |F_c| + |\Delta F| \cos(\phi - \alpha_c).$$

Combining these results, we find

$$\rho_0 \simeq \rho_c + \tfrac{1}{2}\Delta\rho + \frac{1}{2V}\Sigma\, |\Delta F| \exp(i\alpha_c) \exp i(\alpha_c - \phi) \exp(-2\pi i \mathbf{H}\cdot\mathbf{r}). \qquad (319)$$

If the density $\Delta\rho$ is not in any way correlated with the actual density the last term in equation (*319*) gives only a random contribution and we have approximately that

$$\rho_0 = \rho_c + \tfrac{1}{2}\Delta\rho = \tfrac{1}{2}(\rho_t + \rho_c).$$

In words, when structure amplitudes of the true structure but phase angles of a postulated structure are used in an F_0-synthesis, the result is approximately a density corresponding to the average of the two. For example, if hydrogen atoms contribute to $|F_0|$, but not to α_c, they will appear in the density given by equation (*318*) as peaks of half the correct height. If the atoms of the postulated structure are displaced by small amounts from their true positions, the maxima given by equation (*318*) (neglecting series-termination errors) will be displaced by half as much. In principle therefore, if an atomic coordinate is taken as $\mathbf{r}_j$ in calculating phase angles but the point of maximum electron density occurs at $\mathbf{r}_j + \Delta\mathbf{r}_j$ in a subsequent F_0-synthesis, the process of refinement will be speeded up by taking this atom to be at $\mathbf{r}_j + 2\Delta\mathbf{r}_j$, provided that all structure factors have general phase angles. The factor augmenting $\Delta\mathbf{r}_j$ is between one and two when certain structure factors, corresponding to centrosymmetric projections of the structure, have phase angles of 0 or π exactly (Shoemaker, Donohue, Schomaker and Corey, 1950).

2.2. *Effect of random errors.* Values of $|F_0|$ are always subject to experimental error. A discussion of the effects of certain systematic errors is postponed until a later section (**12**.4.2); in this section we shall treat the errors as random and having a distribution given by the normal or Gaussian law. A succinct account of the relevant parts of the theory of errors has been given by Cruickshank (1959). At this point we need recall only the following results. Let x_0 be the true value of a quantity, and $x = x_0 + \Delta x$ the result of a single measurement.

The standard deviation of a single observation is defined as

$$\sigma(x) = \{\overline{(\Delta x)^2}\}^{1/2}$$

where the average is taken over a large number of observations. When the true value of x is unknown, as will generally be the case, the standard deviation can be estimated from

$$\sigma(x) = \sqrt{\left[\sum_n (x - \bar{x})^2 \Big/ (n-1)\right]} \tag{320.1}$$

where $\bar{x}$ is the mean of n observations. When the distribution of errors is Gaussian, the probability that Δx exceeds $3\sigma(x)$ is only 1/1000, so that 3σ is sometimes called the maximum possible error. The only other result we require is as follows. If

$$\mathrm{X} = \sum_r \lambda_r x_r$$

then

$$\sigma(\mathrm{X}) = \left\{\sum_r (\lambda_r \sigma(x_r))^2\right\}^{1/2}. \tag{320.2}$$

We can now apply these results to the case where the electron density is given by equation (*318*), but to simplify the discussion we shall take the structure to be centrosymmetric and write the equation as

$$\rho = \frac{1}{\mathrm{V}} \sum_q \mathrm{F}_0 \cos \Theta$$

where Θ is an abbreviation for $2\pi \mathbf{H} \cdot \mathbf{r}$, and $\sum_q$ indicates that the series contains q terms whose indices correspond to all the reciprocal-lattice points contained in a sphere of radius S_0. The random error in ρ_0 is then given by

$$\Delta \rho_0 = \frac{2}{\mathrm{V}} \sum_{q/2} \Delta \mathrm{F}_0 \cos \Theta$$

where the limits of summation take account of the fact that

$$\Delta \mathrm{F}_0(\mathbf{H}) = \Delta \mathrm{F}_0(-\mathbf{H}).$$

Using the fact that $\overline{\cos^2 \Theta} = \frac{1}{2}$ we then find with the help of equation (*320.2*) that

$$\sigma(\rho_0) = \frac{2}{\mathrm{V}} \left(\sum_{q/2} \tfrac{1}{2} \sigma^2(\mathrm{F}_0)\right)^{1/2} = \frac{1}{\mathrm{V}} \left(\sum_q \sigma^2(\mathrm{F}_0)\right)^{1/2}. \tag{320.3}$$

In order to simplify this result we must make some assumption about the dependence of $\sigma(F_0)$ on the magnitude of F_0. The simplest, that $\sigma(F_0)$ is independent of $|F_0|$, is adequate for our present purpose and we then obtain

$$\sigma(\rho_0) = \left\{\frac{4\pi S_0^3}{3V}\right\}^{1/2} \sigma(F_0). \qquad (321.1)$$

To find the standard deviation of an atomic coordinate, we note that the slope of the electron density in the x-direction is

$$\frac{\partial\rho_0}{\partial x} = -\frac{2\pi}{aV}\sum_q hF_0 \sin\Theta.$$

since

$$\Theta \equiv 2\pi\left(\frac{hx}{a}+\frac{ky}{b}+\frac{lz}{c}\right).$$

An error $\Delta\left(\frac{\partial\rho_0}{\partial x}\right)_j$ in the slope at the centre of the jth atom will give a coordinate error

$$\Delta x_j = -\Delta\left(\frac{\partial\rho_0}{\partial x}\right)_j \Big/ C_j$$

where $C_j = \left(\frac{\partial^2\rho_0}{\partial x^2}\right)_j$ is the curvature of the density at the centre of this atom. We thus obtain

$$\sigma(x_j) = \frac{2\pi}{aVC_j}\left(\sum_q h^2\sigma^2(F_0)\right)^{1/2}. \qquad (321.2)$$

The formula

$$\rho(r) = Z\left(\frac{p}{\pi}\right)^{3/2} \exp(-pr^2) \qquad (321.3)$$

is often a good approximation to the electron density near the centre of an atom of atomic number Z, the numerical value of p depending somewhat on the atomic number, on the temperature factor and on the value of S_0, but typically having a value near 4·0. It is then easily shown that when the electron distribution in the atom is spherically symmetric, equation (*321*.2) leads to

$$\sigma(x_j) = \left(\frac{4\pi S_0^3}{3V}\cdot\frac{\pi^5}{5p^5}\right)^{1/2}\frac{S_0}{Z_j}\sigma(F_0). \qquad (321.4)$$

For a centrosymmetric projection of area A the results corresponding to equations (*321*.1) and (*321*.4) are

$$\sigma(\rho_0) = \left(\frac{\pi S_0^2}{A}\right)^{1/2} \sigma(F_0) \qquad (321.5)$$

and

$$\sigma(x_j) = \left(\frac{\pi S_0^2}{A} \cdot \frac{\pi^4}{4p^4}\right)^{1/2} \frac{S_0}{Z_j} \sigma(F_0). \tag{322}$$

It is perhaps an unexpected result that $\sigma(\rho_0)$ is independent of the particular point of the unit cell considered, so that the standard deviation of the electron density at the centre of an atom is no greater than at a point where the expected value of the electron density is zero. (An exception occurs for special points such as the origin, for which the assumption $\overline{\cos^2 \Theta} = \frac{1}{2}$ has to be replaced by $\cos^2 \Theta = 1$.) When the crystal contains atoms of different atomic number, the standard deviation of the coordinate of a particular atom is approximately inversely proportional to its atomic number. There is no reason to expect a greater standard deviation in, say, the x-direction than in any other, unless the atom has an anisotropic temperature factor. For the same accuracy of measurement of structure factors, a three-dimensional synthesis gives more accurate atomic coordinates than a two-dimensional one.

In order to find the order of magnitude of the standard deviations likely to occur in practice we may apply the above formulae to the case of dibenzyl, for which we find from data published by Robertson (1935*b*), Jeffrey (1947) and Cruickshank (1949) that $V = 540$ Å^3, $A = 78$ Å^2 for the projection on (001), $p = 3{\cdot}35$ Å^{-2} and $S_0 = 1{\cdot}07$ Å^{-1}. A comparison of independent measurements made by Robertson and Jeffrey gives $\sigma(F_0) = 0{\cdot}8$, assuming $\sigma(F_0)$ independent of $|F_0|$. Application of the above formulae then gives the following results.

TABLE 322

$\sigma(\rho_0)$, and $\sigma(x_j)$ for carbon atoms in dibenzyl

3-dimensional synthesis	2-dimensional synthesis
$\sigma(\rho_0) = 0{\cdot}08e/$Å^3	$\sigma(\rho_0) = 0{\cdot}17e/$Å^2
$\sigma(x_j) = 5{\cdot}3 \,.\, 10^{-3}$Å	$\sigma(x_j) = 1{\cdot}3 \,.\, 10^{-2}$Å

Formulae may be derived for the situation where $\sigma(F_0) = K|F_0|$; when applied to the above example with $K = 0{\cdot}10$ they lead to numerical results very similar to those given in the table. Although these figures apply to a particular example similar ones will be found in other cases where the same method of intensity measurement—visual comparison with a scale—is used, and subject to a number of qualifications we may conclude that the standard deviation of an atomic coordinate from a three-dimensional synthesis is about $5 \,.\, 10^{-3}$Å, while the standard deviation of the electron density is about $0{\cdot}1e$ Å^{-3}. (An important qualification is of course that we are assuming that systematic errors, such as those associated with the termination of the series, can be corrected.) A more accurate method of intensity measurement, such as the use of a counter-diffractometer, would reduce these figures by a factor of at least three.

In this discussion it has been assumed that in the final stages of refinement atomic scattering factors are known with sufficient accuracy to give correctly the signs of all structure factors. In practice the magnitudes of coefficients inserted with incorrect signs are unlikely to be much greater than the value of $\sigma(F_0)$; for such terms the net result is equivalent to an increase in the value of $\sigma(F_0)$ for small F_0's. Except in the most accurate measurements of electron density the effect is not important. In the case of a non-centrosymmetric synthesis, the phase angles are calculated from a postulated structure and will always be in error even when the scattering factors of atoms in the real and postulated structures are identical. The reason for this is that the random errors of the coefficients cause errors in the derived atomic coordinates and these in turn cause errors in calculated phase angles. The net result, as was shown by Cruickshank (1950), is that the standard deviation of a coordinate derived from a non-centrosymmetric synthesis is twice that of one derived from an otherwise identical centrosymmetric synthesis. It is clear that errors in assumed atomic scattering factors, or, more precisely, in their ratios, will also cause errors in phase angles. Considerations similar to those set out in section **12**.2.1 suggest that although the electron density will be affected, the influence on atomic coordinates will be very small. The effect of deficiencies in the model structure is overestimated by putting $\sigma(F_0) = |F_0 - F_c|$ in equations (*320*.3) and (*321*.2), a procedure discussed later (section **12**.2.5).

2.3. *Effect of series termination.* The way in which an electron distribution expressed in the form of a Fourier series is changed by the termination of the series when its coefficients are still appreciable can be seen from the following considerations. To any three-dimensional distribution $\rho(\mathbf{r})$ there corresponds a function

$$F(\mathbf{S}) = \int_V \rho(\mathbf{r}) \exp\,[2\pi i\mathbf{r}\cdot\mathbf{S}]dV, \qquad (323.1)$$

which is the Fourier transform (section **1**.3.3) of $\rho(\mathbf{r})$ and possesses the property expressed in the equation

$$\rho(\mathbf{r}) = \int_{V^*} F(\mathbf{S}) \exp\,[-2\pi i\mathbf{r}\cdot\mathbf{S}]dV^*. \qquad (323.2)$$

Volume elements in space and in reciprocal space are represented by dV and dV^* respectively, and each integral is taken over the whole of the appropriate space. As has already been pointed out, $F(\mathbf{S})$ may be regarded as a generalized structure factor which is a continuous function in reciprocal space. When the distribution $\rho(\mathbf{r})$ is repeated at regular intervals by the translations of an infinite lattice, $F(\mathbf{S})$ is observable only at the points of a corresponding reciprocal lattice, and the Fourier integral (*323*.2) is replaced by a Fourier series. Provided that the translations of the direct lattice are sufficiently great to contain the distribution $\rho(\mathbf{r})$ within one unit cell, repetition on a lattice will have no effect on $\rho(\mathbf{r})$, and it may still be calculated from (*323*.2); $\rho(\mathbf{r})$ might represent a single atom, for instance. The termination of the Fourier series will have the same effect on $\rho(\mathbf{r})$ as integrating (*323*.2) over the region $S < S_0$, giving instead of $\rho(\mathbf{r})$ the modified distribution

$$\rho'(\mathbf{r}) = \int_{\text{sphere } S<S_0} F(S) \exp[-2\pi i \mathbf{r}\cdot\mathbf{S}]dV^*$$

$$= \int_{V^*} t(S)F(S) \exp[-2\pi i \mathbf{r}\cdot\mathbf{S}]dV^*,$$

where

$$t(S) = 1 \text{ for } S < S_0,$$
$$= 0 \text{ for } S > S_0.$$

But by equation (*323*.1),

$$F(S) = \int_V \rho(\mathbf{r}+\mathbf{R}) \exp[2\pi i(\mathbf{r}+\mathbf{R})\cdot\mathbf{S}]dV.$$

It follows that

$$\rho'(\mathbf{r}) = \int_{V^*} t(S) \left\{\int_V \rho(\mathbf{r}+\mathbf{R}) \exp[2\pi i(\mathbf{r}+\mathbf{R})\cdot\mathbf{S}]dV\right\} \exp[-2\pi i \mathbf{r}\cdot\mathbf{S}]dV^*,$$

or, changing the order of integration,

$$\rho'(\mathbf{r}) = \int_V \rho(\mathbf{r}+\mathbf{R}) \left\{\int_{V^*} t(S) \exp[2\pi i \mathbf{R}\cdot\mathbf{S}]dV^*\right\}dV. \qquad (324)$$

The expression within brackets on the right-hand side of equation (*324*) will be recognized as the Fourier transform of $t(S)$, and can be shown to be a function of R only, given by

$$T_3(R) = \frac{4}{3}\pi S_0^3 \cdot \frac{3(\sin 2\pi S_0 R - 2\pi S_0 R \cos 2\pi S_0 R)}{(2\pi S_0 R)^3}.$$

Hence, finally, the relation between $\rho'(\mathbf{r})$ and $\rho(\mathbf{r})$ is

$$\rho'(\mathbf{r}) = \int_V \rho(\mathbf{r}+\mathbf{R})T_3(R)dV.$$

Expressed in terms of Cartesian coordinates, with x, y, z and u, v, w the components in the a, b, c directions of $\mathbf{r}$ and R respectively,

$$\rho'(xyz) = \int_V \rho(x+u, y+v, z+w)T_3(R)du dv dw,$$

where

$$\mathbf{R} = \mathbf{u}+\mathbf{v}+\mathbf{w}.$$

In the same way it may be shown that in the corresponding two- and one-dimensional cases,

$$\rho'(xy) = \int_A \rho(x+u,\, y+v)\mathrm{T}_2(\mathrm{R})\,du\,dv,$$

where

$$\mathbf{R} = \mathbf{u} + \mathbf{v}$$

and

$$\rho'(x) = \int_V \rho(x+u)\mathrm{T}_1(u)\,du.$$

T_2 is the two-dimensional Fourier transform of a function which is unity inside a circle of radius S_0, and is zero elsewhere, being given by

$$\mathrm{T}_2(\mathrm{R}) = \pi \mathrm{S}_0^2 \frac{2\mathrm{J}_1(2\pi \mathrm{S}_0 \mathrm{R})}{2\pi \mathrm{S}_0 \mathrm{R}},$$

while

$$\mathrm{T}_1(\mathrm{R}) = 2\mathrm{S}_0 \frac{\sin 2\pi \mathrm{S}_0 \mathrm{R}}{2\pi \mathrm{S}_0 \mathrm{R}}$$

is the transform of a function which is unity from $S = -S_0$ to $+S_0$, but zero elsewhere.

What these results mean physically can be illustrated by considering the expression for $\rho'(x)$. Given the distribution $\rho(x)$ of fig. 325, the value

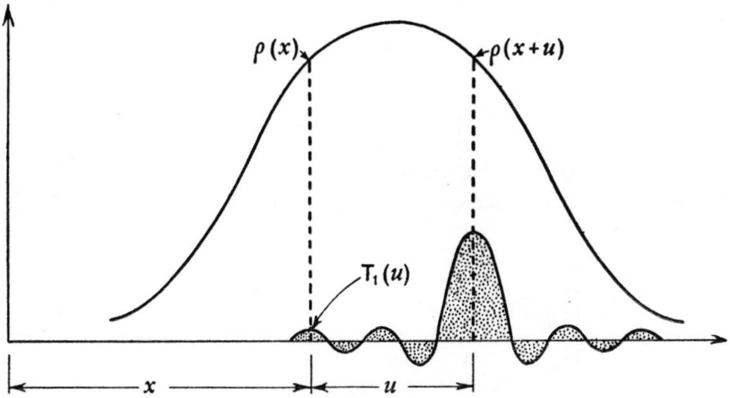

FIG. 325. When a one-dimensional Fourier series is terminated, the corresponding electron density in a line element *du* is spread out through multiplication by $\mathrm{T}_1(u) = \dfrac{\sin 2\pi \mathrm{S}_0 u}{\pi u}$

of $\rho'(x)$ is obtained by summing contributions from all points $x+u$, the contribution from a line element du at $x+u$ being $\rho(x+u)\mathrm{T}_1(u)du$. The electrons in every line element are spread out into the curve shown in fig. 325, and the net result is obtained by superposing all such curves. The distribution ρ' bears the same relation to ρ as an image in a microscope of limited resolving power bears to the object, in the two-dimensional case. Similarly, in three dimensions, the electrons in every volume element $du\,dv\,dw$ at distance R from (xyz) are spread out through multiplication by $\mathrm{T}_3(\mathrm{R})$ and contribute to $\rho'(xyz)$ an amount $\rho(x+u,\, y+v,\, z+w)\mathrm{T}_3(\mathrm{R})\,du\,dv\,dw$.

The termination of the Fourier series may be said to 'scramble' the electron density; the scrambling is least when the functions T are 'sharpest'. The degree of sharpness depends only on the range of the series, that is, on the value of S_0.

We can now make use of these results to find the modified electron density corresponding to a spherically-symmetric atom whose density is $\rho(r)$. A rough, but convenient, approximation is to treat the atom as if all its electrons were concentrated at its centre. It is then clear from the treatment given above that $\rho'(r)$ is directly proportional to $T(r)$. This approximation has been used by Bragg and West (1930) and by James (1948) to estimate the effect of series termination on two- and three-dimensional syntheses respectively. Although the approximation appears to be a crude one, the results obtained from it are not unsatisfactory. An exact result can be obtained for any spherically-symmetric atom by a method suggested by Cruickshank (1949). For an atom,

$$\rho(r) = \int_0^\infty 4\pi S^2 f(S) \frac{\sin 2\pi r S}{2\pi r S} \, dS,$$

where $f(S)$ is the atomic scattering factor. Correspondingly,

$$\rho'(r) = \int_0^{S_0} 4\pi S^2 f(S) \frac{\sin 2\pi r S}{2\pi r S} \, dS,$$

and is also spherically symmetric.

Suppose the area under the f-curve of an atom (fig. 326) to be divided

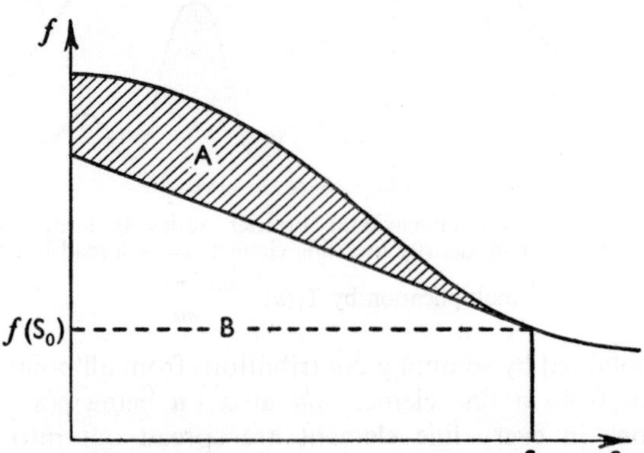

FIG. 326. Division of the area under the f-curve into two parts A and B by a straight line which is a tangent to the curve at $S = S_0$

into two parts, A and B, by a line $f_e(S) = a + bS$ which is a tangent to the f-curve at $S = S_0$ so that $f_0 \equiv f(S_0) = a + bS_0$, $f_0^1 \equiv \left(\frac{df}{dS}\right)_{S=S_0} = b$;

ρ' can then be considered as the sum of ρ'_A and ρ'_B, where

$$\rho'_B(r) = \int_0^{S_0} (a+bS)\, 4\pi S^2 \frac{\sin 2\pi r S}{2\pi r S}\, dS$$

$$= \cos 2\pi S_0 r \left(\frac{-S_0 f_0}{\pi r^2} + \frac{f_0^1}{2\pi^3 r^4} \right) - \frac{f_0^1}{2\pi^3 r^4} + \sin 2\pi S_0 r \left(\frac{f_0 + S_0 f_0^1}{2\pi^2 r^3} \right)$$

and $$\rho'_A(r) = \int_0^{S_0} (f - f_e)\, 4\pi S^2 \frac{\sin 2\pi r S}{2\pi r S}\, dS,$$

which can be evaluated numerically. Cruickshank's calculations show that in a particular example ρ'_A falls to zero, without assuming negative values, in a distance of about 2 Å. In the unit cell of a crystal it would therefore overlap only nearest-neighbour atoms. Although the exact form of ρ'_A will depend on the form of the f-curve and the value of S_0, this result is likely to be generally true. There remains the effect of $\rho'_B(r)$, which is approximately periodic with wave-length $1/S_0$, and amplitude decreasing with r. For large values of r,

$$\rho'_B(r) = -\frac{S_0 f_0}{\pi r^2} \cos 2\pi S_0 r.$$

This is also essentially the result given by the point-atom approximation, when the constant scattering factor of the point atom is taken as f_0, the scattering factor of the actual atom for $S = S_0$. The same method, applied to a two-dimensional example, for which

$$\rho'(r) = \int_0^{S_0} 2\pi S f(S) J_0(2\pi r S)\, dS,$$

leads to

$$\rho'_B(r) = \frac{aS_0}{r} J_1(2\pi S_0 r) + \frac{b}{4\pi^2 r^3} \int_0^{2\pi S_0 r} x^2 J_0(x)\, dx.$$

The maxima and minima of $\rho'_B(r)$, as defined above, are quite closely fitted by those of $\dfrac{J_1(2\pi S_0 r)}{2\pi S_0 r}$, which is proportional to the modified density corresponding to a point atom, so that again the point-atom approximation gives a reasonable result except for small values of r.

When the electron distribution consists of a group of spherically-symmetric atoms, the modified density given by a terminated Fourier series also consists of a group of spherically-symmetric distributions centred around the *same* points, so that it is not immediately obvious why the atomic coordinates given by a terminated series are inaccurate. The reason is that while $\rho(r)$ for an individual atom will generally decrease to zero in a distance less than that between the centres of neighbouring atoms, this will not be true of $\rho'(r)$, and the point of maximum (modified) electron density of one atom will be slightly displaced by the superposition of the modified densities of all others; $\rho'_A(r)$ of a given atom will at most overlap nearest neighbours only, but $\rho'_B(r)$ will overlap all others, although its effect diminishes with increasing separation of the atomic centres.

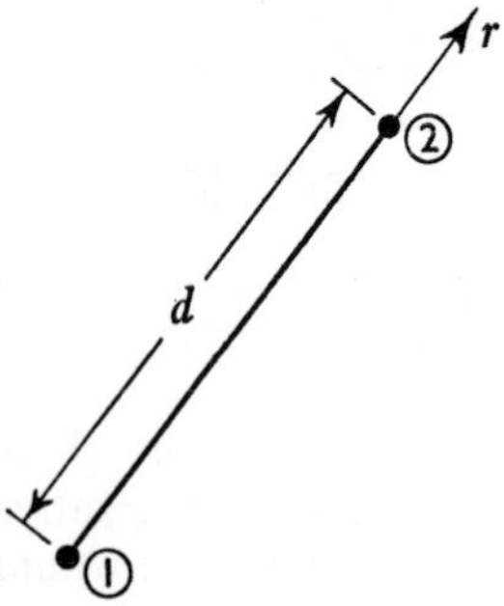

FIG. 328

If two atoms 1 and 2 (fig. 328) are situated a distance d apart, the effect of the first is to displace the point of maximum electron density of the second by

$$\Delta d = \frac{-\left(\dfrac{\partial \rho'_1}{\partial r}\right)_{r=d}}{C_2}.$$

ρ'_1 and ρ'_2 are the modified electron densities of the first and second atom respectively, and C_2 is the value of $\dfrac{\partial^2 \rho'_2}{\partial r^2}$ at the centre of the second atom. For values of r greater than about 2 Å we can take $\rho' = \rho'_B$, and consequently

$$(\Delta d)_{\max} = \frac{2S_0^2 f_{01}}{C_2 r^2},$$

where f_{01} is the scattering factor of the first atom at $S = S_0$. The above results enable us to make an estimate of the importance of series-termination errors in practice. We see that the effect of one atom on the coordinates of another decreases rapidly with increasing separation of the atoms concerned, and that the coordinates of atoms of low atomic number in a structure are most affected by series termination, just as they are most affected by random errors in the coefficients. The presence in a structure of one atom of high atomic number will result in particularly large series-termination errors in the coordinates of other atoms, especially those which lie near the heavy atom. Series-termination errors are about the same in two-dimensional as in three-dimensional syntheses.

Taking dibenzyl as an example where the atoms are all of the same atomic number, but each peak is disturbed by the ripples from two or three others, the effect of terminating the series at $S_0 = 1{\cdot}07$ Å^{-1}, where $f_0 = 0{\cdot}32$ and $f_{01} = 1{\cdot}16$ for all atoms, would be to shorten a bond of length 1·54 Å by about 0·025 Å, while a benzene ring of side 1·385 Å would appear with each bond shortened by 0·01 Å. In dibenzyl, the combined effect of all other atoms is to change the maximum (modified) density in an atom of the benzene ring from 5·70 e/Å^3 to 6·00 e/Å^3. A reinvestigation of the crystal structure of β-isoprene sulphone by Jeffrey (1951) showed that in this compound the mean coordinate error due to series termination was 0·02 Å, and the maximum 0·06 Å. These comparatively large errors are to be attributed mainly to the presence of a sulphur atom in the molecule:—

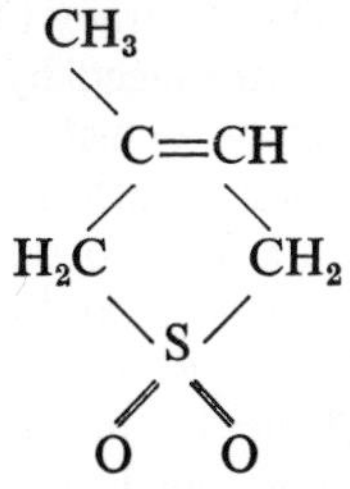

The standard deviation of the coordinate of a carbon atom, due to random errors of measurement, was only 0·016 Å, which emphasizes the relative importance of series-termination errors. The discussion of series-termination errors, given above, is important from a theoretical view, but fortunately simpler methods are available by means of which these systematic errors can be at least partially corrected. A well-known one is that first used by Bragg and West (1930). This consists of the introduction of a converging factor $\phi(S)$, which is chosen so as to reduce the coefficients at $S = S_0$ to very small values. The modified density in a particular atom, as it appears when the coefficients $\phi(S)F_0$ replace the coefficients F_0 in the Fourier series, is related to the unmodified density by the equation.

$$\rho'(\mathbf{r}) = \int_V \rho(\mathbf{r} + \mathbf{R})\psi(R)dV,$$

where $\psi(R)$ is the Fourier transform of $\phi(S)$. The form of the converging factor is usually taken to be

$$\phi(S) = \exp[-\alpha S^2];$$

its effect is then to modify the electron density in exactly the same way as it is modified by the temperature movement of the atoms, so that ϕ is usually referred to as an artificial temperature factor. By choosing a sufficiently large value of α ($\sim$2 in practice), series-termination errors may be eliminated in the sense that each atom is no longer the centre of a modified density which extends over large distances. The overlapping of an atom by its nearest neighbours, to which reference has already been made, is however increased by the introduction of a converging factor, and a correction for this must be made, although it can scarcely be called a series-termination correction.

A particularly simple method for the correction of atomic coordinates for the effect of series termination was suggested by Booth (1946, 1947). Corresponding to the F_0 synthesis, an F_c synthesis is made using structure factors calculated from the coordinates given by the F_0 synthesis, and assumed values of atomic scattering factors. The points of maximum electron density of the F_c synthesis will deviate by small amounts from the coordinates used to calculate the coefficients. These deviations, with reversed signs, are the corrections to the atomic coordinates. The accuracy of this method of correction, assuming that no errors are introduced by the method used to locate the points of maximum electron density, depends essentially on the accuracy of the assumed atomic scattering factors, a point we shall discuss later. This method makes no correction to the electron density, but a way in which this can be done and coordinates corrected at the same time, was suggested by van Reijen (1942). This method consists in including, as Fourier coefficients, the values of F_c where experiment has not supplied the corresponding F_0's. This gives for the electron density

$$\rho = \frac{1}{V} \sum_{q} F_0 \cos \Theta + \frac{1}{V} \sum_{Q-q} F_c \cos \Theta,$$

where the notation indicates that q coefficients have been measured experimentally, and of the remainder all but $Q-q$ are of negligible magnitude. This result may be rewritten as

$$\rho = \frac{1}{V} \sum_{q} (F_0 - F_c) \cos \Theta + \frac{1}{V} \sum_{Q} F_c \cos \Theta,$$

or

$$\rho = \frac{1}{V} \sum_{q} (F_0 - F_c) \cos \Theta + \rho_c',$$

where ρ_c' is the electron distribution on which the calculated structure factors are based. Provided the actual and assumed atomic scattering factors coincide in the range $S > S_0$, this method will lead, apart from the effects of random errors in the F_0's, to the correct atomic coordinates and electron distribution, when a sufficient number of successive syntheses have been calculated.

2.4. *Electron density in crystals of simple structure*. The work of Witte, Wolfel and their collaborators on the electron distribution in, for example, NaCl, LiF, CaF_2 and Al (Witte and Wolfel, 1958) provides examples of the use of Fourier methods, and in particular of the method of correction for series-termination errors which was mentioned at the end of section **12**.2.3.

Careful measurements of seventy-five independent structure amplitudes for sodium chloride were made, using both single crystal and powdered specimens for some reflexions, and with corrections for absorption, extinction etc. (Witte and Wolfel, 1955). The density calculated with this range of observations ($(\sin \theta)/\lambda \leqslant 1{\cdot}256$ Å^{-1}) showed marked series-termination errors. The coefficients of the Fourier series were then extended to $(\sin \theta)/\lambda = 2{\cdot}4$ Å^{-1} by adding in calculated structure factors, based on the theoretical scattering factors given by Vierwoll and Ogrim (1949). The resulting electron distribution

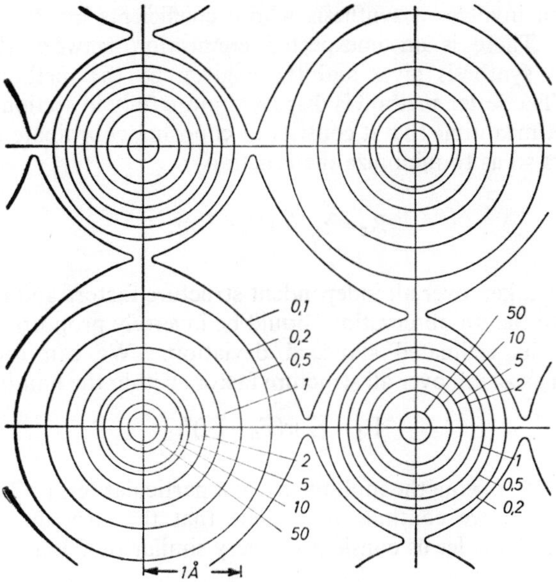

FIG. 331. A section through the electron density in the plane $x=0$ for sodium chloride

is shown in (fig. 331). An alternative and less laborious method of evaluating the density consisted in adding the difference density

$$D=\frac{1}{V}\sum_{q}(F_0-F_c)\cos\Theta$$

to the calculated density

$$\rho_c=\frac{1}{V}\sum_{Q}F_c\cos\Theta$$

The latter was not evaluated as a Fourier series however but by the method of Hosemann and Bagchi (1953), which consists in approximating each atomic scattering factor by the sum of two Gaussian terms. The contribution of each atom to the calculated density can then readily be evaluated since it is the Fourier transform of the atomic scattering factor and therefore also given by the sum of two Gaussian terms (section **10**.2.1). Although the F_c's based on empirical Gaussian scattering factors were not identical with those given by the scattering factors of Viervoll and Ogrim, the density obtained by these two methods was almost identical in the interesting region 'between the atoms'. This follows from the fact that ρ_c is relatively small in this region.

2.5. *Difference synthesis.* At the end of section **12**.2.3 and again in section **12**.2.4 we found that one method of correcting for series termination involves a synthesis whose coefficients are the values of $(F_0 - F_c)$. There is an unexpected connection between the results which this synthesis gives and those given by the method of least squares. The latter method is discussed more fully in section **12**.3; we note in the meantime that it consists in choosing coordinate and other parameters so as to minimize the function

$$R_1 = \sum_{i=1}^{s} W_i(F_0 - F_c)_i^2.$$

The sum is taken over all independent structure factors and the weight W_i given to the ith observation should be inversely proportional to the square of its estimated standard deviation. We can rewrite this expression as a sum over all structure factors within the limiting sphere,

$$R_1 = \sum_q w(F_0 - F_c)^2,$$

where $tw = W$, t being the multiplicity of a particular term. To simplify the discussion, we continue to assume that the structure is centrosymmetric. Now let us consider the very similar function

$$\phi_j = \sum_q \frac{1}{f_j}(F_0 - F_c)^2$$

where f_j is, as before, the scattering factor of the jth atom, including the appropriate temperature factor. The coordinates (x_j, y_j, z_j) which minimize ϕ_j satisfy the conditions

$$\frac{\partial \phi_j}{\partial x_j} = \frac{\partial \phi_j}{\partial y_j} = \frac{\partial \phi_j}{\partial z_j} = 0,$$

that is

$$\sum_q \frac{1}{f_j}(F_0 - F_c)\frac{\partial F_c}{\partial x_j} = \ldots = 0, \text{ etc.}$$

Now for a centrosymmetric structure

$$F_c = 2\sum_{j=1}^{N/2} f_j \cos \Theta_j$$

$$\therefore \frac{\partial F_c}{\partial x_j} = -\frac{4\pi h}{a} f_j \sin \Theta_j$$

and the condition $\frac{\partial \phi_j}{\partial x_j} = 0$ becomes

$$-\frac{4\pi}{a}\sum_q h(F_0 - F_c) \sin \Theta_j = 0. \qquad (332)$$

However the function

$$D = \rho_0 - \rho_c = \frac{1}{V}\sum_q (F_0 - F_c) \cos \Theta$$

has a slope in the x-direction at the point (x_j, y_j, z_j) of

$$\left(\frac{\partial \mathrm{D}}{\partial x}\right)_j = -\frac{2\pi}{a\mathrm{V}}\sum_q h(\mathrm{F}_0 - \mathrm{F}_c)\sin \Theta_j.$$

Comparison with equation (*332*) shows that the condition for ϕ_j to be a minimum with respect to the coordinates of the jth atom is that $\frac{\partial \mathrm{D}}{\partial x}, \frac{\partial \mathrm{D}}{\partial y}$ and $\frac{\partial \mathrm{D}}{\partial z}$ should all vanish at the centre of this atom. We notice that in principle a different function has to be minimized for each different kind of atom in the structure, but since the f-curves of all atoms are somewhat similar (section **4**.2.5) the coordinates will not deviate far from those that would be obtained on minimizing

$$\phi = \sum_q \frac{1}{\hat{f}}(\mathrm{F}_0 - \mathrm{F}_c)^2.$$

In principle the best atomic coordinates are not those which result in zero slope in the difference synthesis at atomic centres, and which therefore minimize ϕ, but are those which result in a minimization of

$$\mathrm{R}_1 = \sum_q w(\mathrm{F}_0 - \mathrm{F}_c)^2$$

with w correctly chosen for each observation. But just as ϕ is associated with D, so is R_1 associated with the function

$$\mathrm{D}' = \frac{1}{\mathrm{V}}\sum_q w\hat{f}(\mathrm{F}_0 - \mathrm{F}_c)\cos \Theta$$

for when R_1 is a minimum, D′ has zero slope at atomic centres. In practice however the improvement in the standard deviation of atomic coordinates which results from introducing appropriate weights can be more conveniently accomplished by the method of least squares; the point in favour of the difference synthesis with unweighted coefficients $(\mathrm{F}_0 - \mathrm{F}_c)$ is that it may show significant detail in the electron density which would be obscured by the series-termination ripples in an F_0-synthesis.

Just as the atomic coordinates which minimize ϕ are those which make $\left(\frac{\partial \mathrm{D}}{\partial x}\right)_j$ etc. $=0$, so the condition $\frac{\partial \phi}{\partial \mathrm{B}_j} = 0$, where B_j is the isotropic temperature factor of the jth atom, corresponds to $\left(\frac{\partial^2 \mathrm{D}}{\partial r^2}\right)_j = 0$, where r is the distance measured from the centre of the atom in any direction. In general six parameters are required to define the anisotropic temperature factor of an atom (section **11**.2.1); correct choice of all six in the sense of minimizing ϕ can be shown to correspond to the six conditions

$$\left(\frac{\partial^2 D}{\partial x^2}\right)_j = \left(\frac{\partial^2 D}{\partial y^2}\right)_j = \left(\frac{\partial^2 D}{\partial z^2}\right)_j = \left(\frac{\partial^2 D}{\partial x\,\partial y}\right)_j = \left(\frac{\partial^2 D}{\partial y\,\partial z}\right)_j = \left(\frac{\partial^2 D}{\partial z\,\partial x}\right)_j = 0$$

(Cochran 1951*a*, Cruickshank 1956).

The standard deviation of the difference density can be estimated using equation (*320*.3) with $\sigma(F_0) = |F_0 - F_c|$. The standard deviation of an atomic coordinate can be estimated in the same way, using equation (*321*.2) (Cruickshank, 1949). This procedure is likely to overestimate the standard deviations. An alternative procedure, which consists for example in setting $\sigma(D) = (\overline{D^2})^{1/2}$, the average being taken over all points where the electron density is expected to be zero, is likely to lead to an underestimate.

When the structure is not centrosymmetric the standard deviations given by equations (*320*.3) and (*321*.2), or by the corresponding equations with $\sigma(F_0) = ||F_0| - |F_c||$, must be increased by a factor two. The reason for this follows from the discussion given in sections **12**.2.1 and **12**.2.2. The result which applies when certain projections are centrosymmetric although the structure is non-centrosymmetric has been given by Cruickshank (International Tables, Vol. II).

2.6. *Example of the use of the difference synthesis.* A reinvestigation of the crystal structure of adenine hydrochloride (Cochran 1951*b*) provides an example of the use of the difference synthesis for refinement of coordinate and temperature factor parameters, and location of hydrogen atoms. The projection of this crystal structure on (010) can be referred to a unit cell of dimensions $a = 8{\cdot}77$ Å, $c = 9{\cdot}73$ Å and $\beta = 114°\ 15'$, containing two molecules. Coordinates were first obtained from photographically-recorded X-ray intensities, by means of an F_0-

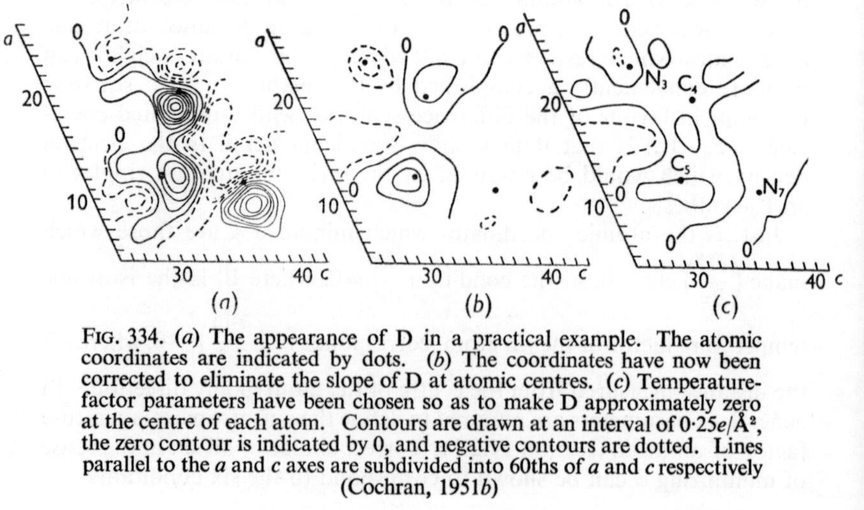

FIG. 334. (*a*) The appearance of D in a practical example. The atomic coordinates are indicated by dots. (*b*) The coordinates have now been corrected to eliminate the slope of D at atomic centres. (*c*) Temperature-factor parameters have been chosen so as to make D approximately zero at the centre of each atom. Contours are drawn at an interval of $0{\cdot}25e/Å^2$, the zero contour is indicated by 0, and negative contours are dotted. Lines parallel to the *a* and *c* axes are subdivided into 60ths of *a* and *c* respectively (Cochran, 1951*b*)

synthesis. More accurate coefficients were subsequently obtained, and an $(F_0 - F_c)$ synthesis calculated. The variation of D in the neighbourhood of certain atoms of the organic molecule is shown in fig. 334*a*. The assumed coordinates are indicated by dots, and all of them fall in regions where D has a large slope. The correction to a coordinate can be found as follows. We assume that in the neighbourhood of an atomic centre ρ_0 and ρ_c coincide in shape, but the points at which they reach a maximum differ by $(\Delta x_j, 0, 0)$.

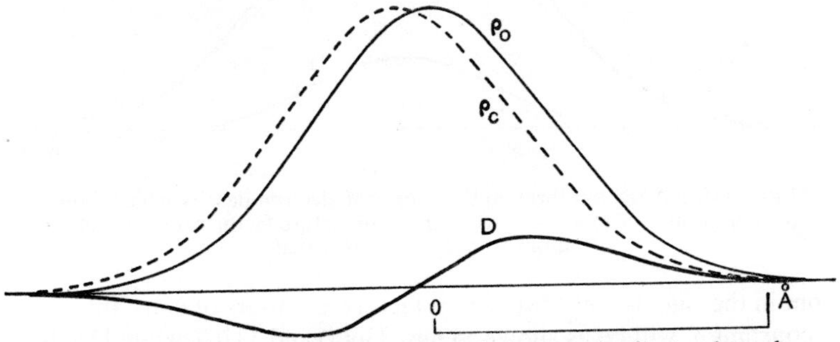

FIG. 335. A section through the projected electron density to show the appearance of $D = \rho_0 - \rho_c$ when an atomic coordinate differs by 0·1 Å from its correct value. The diagram represents an idealised situation in that the Fourier series from which the curves were obtained was not terminated, and the coefficients were free from experimental errors. This is true also of figs. 336 (i), (ii) and 337 (i)

Simple geometrical considerations (see fig. 335) then show that

$$\delta x_j = -\left(\frac{\partial D}{\partial x}\right)_j \Big/ \left(\frac{\partial^2 \rho_0}{\partial x^2}\right)_j. \qquad (335)$$

In practice the approximation

$$\left(\frac{\partial^2 \rho_0}{\partial x^2}\right)_j = -2p(\rho_0)_j$$

was used, and the correction made was

$$\delta r_j = \left(\frac{\partial D}{\partial r}\right)_j \Big/ 2p(\rho_0)_j$$

where r denotes a distance measured in the direction in which D increases most rapidly. Fig. 334*b* shows the fourth $(F_0 - F_c)$ synthesis of a series, for the projection of adenine hydrochloride, the coordinates having now been corrected.

If the isotropic temperature factor B_j of an atom, defined by the equation

$$f_j = (f_0)_j \exp\left(-\tfrac{1}{4} B_j H^2\right)$$

has been overestimated in magnitude, ρ_c in the neighbourhood of the *j*th atom centre will be more diffuse than ρ_0, and D will exhibit the variation shown in fig. 336 (i). If the thermal vibration is in fact anisotropic (Chapter 11), but an isotropic scattering factor is assumed for this

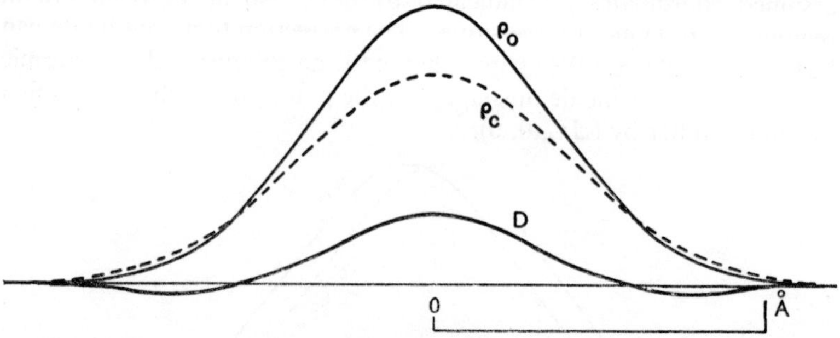

FIG. 336(i). A section through the projected electron density which shows the appearance of $D = \rho_0 - \rho_c$ when the temperature factor parameter of an atom is incorrectly estimated

atom in the calculation of structure factors, contours of constant ρ_0 and of constant ρ_c will be as shown in figs. 336(ii) and 337(i), while D will be as shown in fig. 337 (ii). More quantitative relations have been given by

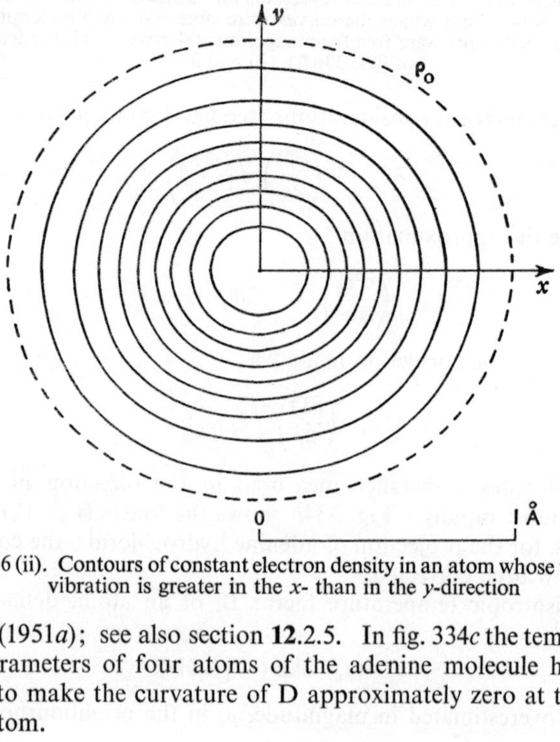

FIG. 336 (ii). Contours of constant electron density in an atom whose thermal vibration is greater in the *x*- than in the *y*-direction

Cochran (1951*a*); see also section **12**.2.5. In fig. 334*c* the temperature-factor parameters of four atoms of the adenine molecule have been adjusted to make the curvature of D approximately zero at the centre of each atom.

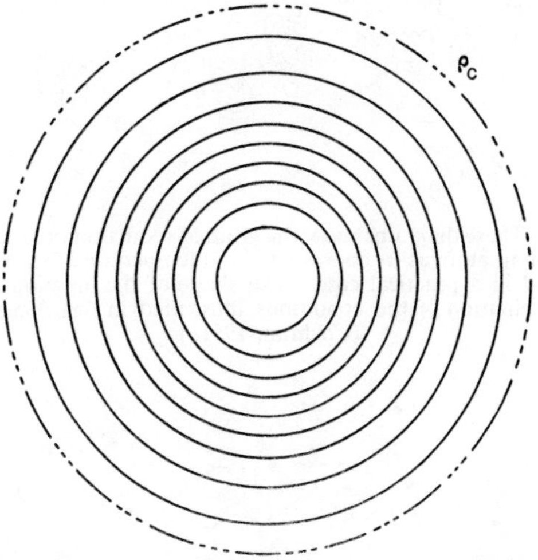

FIG. 337 (i). Contours of constant electron density in an atom which has a corresponding isotropic thermal vibration. The contours may be taken to represent density increments of $1e/\text{Å}^2$. The $0{\cdot}5e/\text{Å}^2$ contour is dotted

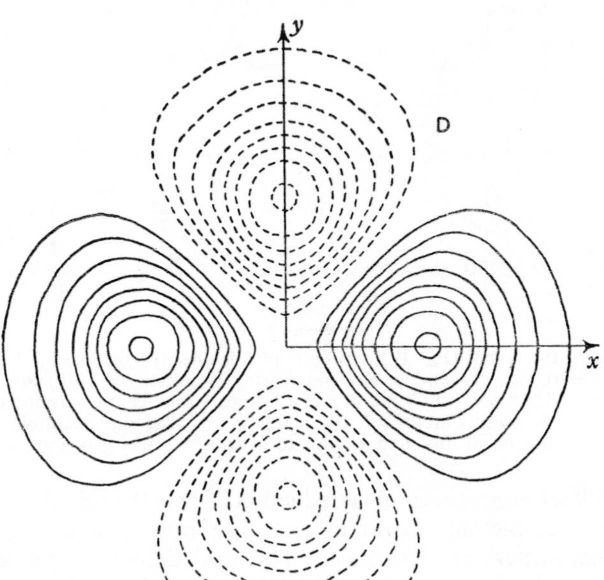

FIG. 337 (ii). The difference of the electron densities shown in 336 (ii) and 337 (i). The contours represent density increments of $0{\cdot}05e/\text{Å}^2$. Contours are dotted where the function is negative

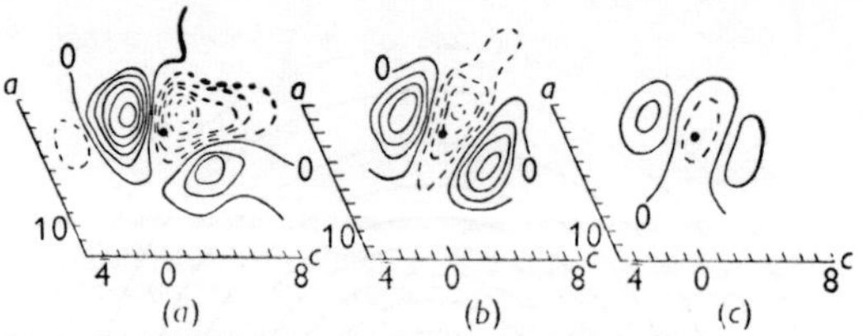

FIG. 338 (i). These diagrams show the gradual reduction of D in the neighbourhood of an atom as its coordinates and temperature factor parameters are corrected in a practical case. The shape of the function in (*a*) arises from a combination of the conditions illustrated in figs. 335 and 337 (ii) (Cochran, 1951*b*)

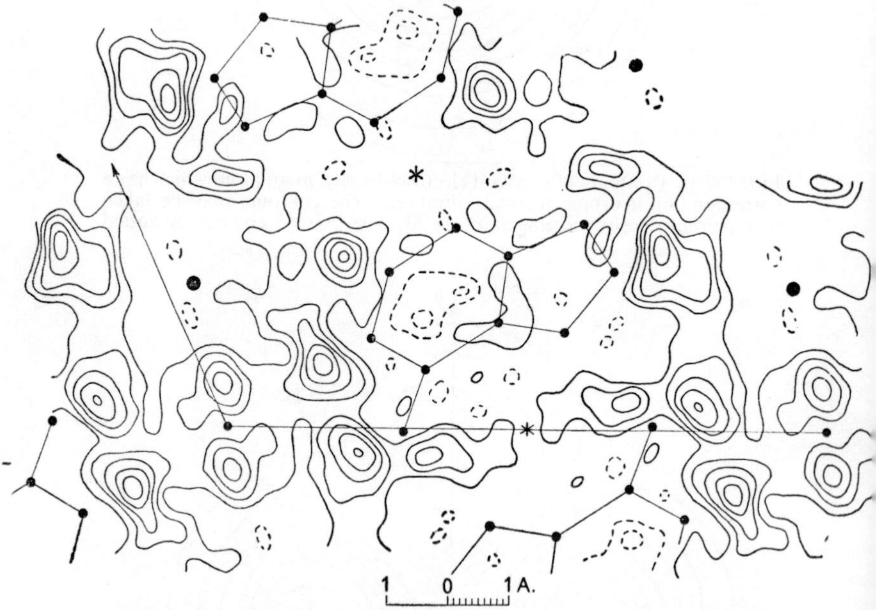

FIG. 338 (ii). Final ($F_0 - F_c$) synthesis of adenine hydrochloride, showing the difference between the electron density projected on (010) and that calculated for isolated Cl, O, N and C atoms whose centres are indicated by dots. Contours are at 0·2, 0·4, ..., 1·0e/Å². The significant electron-density maxima in this map are due to hydrogen atoms (Cochran, 1951*b*)

Fig. 338 (i) shows the gradual reduction of D in the neighbourhood of the centre of the chlorine atom as the coordinates and temperature-factor parameters are corrected. The final difference synthesis (the seventh) is shown in fig. 338 (ii). All the significant electron-density maxima can be interpreted as hydrogen atoms.

2.7. *Cruickshank's modified Fourier method.* While the difference-synthesis method automatically corrects for series-termination errors, its use in the way illustrated in section **12**.2.6 is not suitable for automatic computing because of the amount of output and the fact that the difference density must be inspected at the end of each cycle of refinement. Furthermore equation (*335*) for coordinate refinement, and corresponding equations for temperature-factor parameters, are approximate in that they are based on the assumption that changes made to a parameter of one atom will not affect the difference density near other atoms. This assumption is valid when atoms are well resolved and when the phase angles for a non-centrosymmetric structure are not dominated by one atom or a few atoms. A Fourier method has been developed by Cruickshank which overcomes some of these difficulties.

In the general non-centrosymmetric case, we can write equation (*318*) as

$$\rho_0 = \frac{1}{V} \sum_q |F_0| \cos(\Theta - \alpha) \qquad (339.1)$$

and correspondingly

$$D = \frac{1}{V} \sum_q (|F_0| - |F_c|) \cos(\Theta - \alpha).$$

Cruickshank (1952) has shown that the criterion that finally $\left(\frac{\partial D}{\partial x}\right)_j$ is to be zero, on making a Taylor expansion as far as first-order terms in the corrections $\delta x_{j'}$ to *every* independent coordinate parameter, leads to a simultaneous equation in these corrections,

$$\sum_{j'=1}^{n} \{C_{j'j}(xx)\, \delta x_{j'} + C_{j'j}(yx)\, \delta y_{j'} + C_{j'j}(zx)\, \delta z_{j'}\} = \left(\frac{\partial D}{\partial x}\right)_j \qquad (339.2)$$

where, for example,

$$C_{j'j}(yx) = \frac{2\pi}{aV} \sum_q h \frac{\partial |F_c|}{\partial y_{j'}} \sin(\Theta_j - \alpha). \qquad (339.3)$$

Analogous equations follow from the conditions that finally

$$\left(\frac{\partial D}{\partial y}\right)_j = \left(\frac{\partial D}{\partial z}\right)_j = 0,$$

so that a set of $3n$ simultaneous equations in the $3n$ coordinate corrections is obtained. These equations are identical with the normal equations of the method of least squares (section **12**.3), but with each $|F_0|$ given the weight $w = 1/f_j$.

When the structure is centrosymmetric, it can be shown that equation (*339*.3) becomes

$$C_{j'j}(yx) = \frac{\partial}{\partial y_{j'}} \left(\frac{\partial \rho_{j'}}{\partial x}\right)_j$$

where $\rho_{j'}$ is the calculated density (with the same series termination as equation (*339*.1)) for the j'th atom and its symmetry-related equivalents. If the atoms are all well resolved, as is usually the case in three-dimensional analyses, coefficients $C_{j'j}$ are very small for $j' \neq j$. Neglecting them is the block-diagonal approximation in the method of least squares (section **12**.3.1). Finally if the axes are also orthogonal equation (*339*.2) becomes

$$C_{jj}(xx)\delta x_j = \left(\frac{\partial D}{\partial x}\right)_j \qquad (340.1)$$

which is equation (*335*), and is the diagonal approximation in the method of least squares.

A convenient summary of the equations, showing the simplifications that can be made in different circumstances, has been given in International Tables, II, p. 329. The method has been used for many structure refinements (see for example Ahmed and Cruickshank (1953) and Truter (1954)). However it does not give results which cannot be obtained by the method of least squares, and when it is modified so as to give an appropriate weight to each observation it becomes identical with the latter method.

3. Method of Least Squares

3.1. *Brief outline.* As we have already mentioned, the method of least squares, as applied to structure refinement, consists in systematically varying the atomic parameters so as to minimize the quantity

$$R_1 = \sum_{i=1}^{s} W_i(|F_0| - |F_c|)_i^2 \qquad (340.2)$$

where the sum is taken over all independent structure amplitudes, and W is the weight alloted to an observation. Each weight W is to be taken as the inverse of the square of the standard deviation of the corresponding observation, and may be estimated from the agreement of independent measurements or from the way the measurement was made. Usually in crystallography only relative weights can be estimated, and it is often assumed that $\sigma(F_0)$ depends only on $|F_0|$. In the first application of the method to structure analysis, Hughes (1941) took $W \propto |F_0|^{-2}$. Cruickshank et al. (1961) suggest that

$$W \propto (a + |F_0| + c|F_0|^2)^{-1},$$

where a and c are about $2F_{\min}$ and $2/F_{\max}$ respectively. A test that a correct weighting scheme has been used can be made towards the end of a structure refinement; if structure amplitudes are put into groups in some systematic way, for example according to $|F_0|$ or according to position in reciprocal space or any other factor which might be supposed to influence the standard deviation, the average value of $W(|F_0| - |F_c|)^2$ in each group should be approximately the same.

The method of least squares is well adapted to automatic computing; observations can be weighted so as to reduce the standard deviations of the parameters deduced, and these standard deviations can readily be evaluated in the course of the calculation. This method has therefore largely replaced Fourier methods for accurate determination of bond lengths and angles. It does not however give the electron density and it may therefore be worth while, at the end of a least-squares refinement process, to calculate the difference density and to inspect it for significant features.

3.2. *Procedure for linear equations.* The basis of the method of least squares can most easily be understood by first considering the situation where the parameters $p_1, \ldots, p_m$ are linearly related to the observations $g_1, \ldots, g_s$, thus:

$$\begin{array}{c|l} & \xrightarrow{j=1 \text{ to } m} \\ i=1 & a_{11}p_1 + a_{12}p_2 + \ldots + a_{1m}p_m = g_1 \\ \text{to } s \downarrow & a_{21}p_1 + a_{22}p_2 + \ldots + a_{2m}p_m = g_2 \\ & \cdots\cdots\cdots\cdots\cdots\cdots\cdots\cdots \\ & a_{s1}p_1 + a_{s2}p_2 + \ldots + a_{sm}p_m = g_s. \end{array} \qquad (341.1)$$

We shall assume that the a's are not subject to error, and the problem is to find the values of $p_1, \ldots, p_m$ which minimize

$$R_1 = \sum_{i=1}^{s} W_i \Delta_i^2.$$

The residual Δ_i is given by

$$\Delta_i = g_i - \sum_{j=1}^{m} a_{ij} p_j \qquad (341.2)$$

that is, it is the difference between the 'observed' and the 'calculated' value of g_i.

The unweighted observational equations (*341*.1) can be written more succinctly as

$$\mathbf{ap} = \mathbf{g} \qquad (341.3)$$

where $\mathbf{p}$ and $\mathbf{g}$ are column matrices having m and s elements respectively, and $\mathbf{a}$ is a rectangular matrix of order $m \times s$. (A refresher course in matrix algebra is given in International Tables, Vol. II, p. 11.)

The weighted observational equations are defined as the equations obtained by multiplying both sides of the ith observational equation by $\sqrt{W_i}$, thus

$$\sqrt{W_i} \sum_{j=1}^{m} a_{ij} p_j = \sqrt{W_i} g_i \qquad (341.4)$$

which we shall write in matrix notation as

$$\mathbf{Ap} = \mathbf{G} \qquad (341.5)$$

so that $A_{ij} = \sqrt{W_i} a_{ij}$ and $G_i = \sqrt{W_i} g_i$.

The conditions for R_1 to be a minimum are the equations $\partial R_1/\partial p_{j'} = 0$ for $j' = 1, \ldots, m$, that is,

$$\sum_{i=1}^{s} W_i \Delta_i \frac{\partial \Delta_i}{\partial p_{j'}} = 0.$$

However from equation (*341*.2), $\partial \Delta_i/\partial p_{j'} = -a_{ij'}$, so that

$$\sum_{i=1}^{s} W_i a_{ij'} \left(g_i - \sum_{j=1}^{m} a_{ij} p_j \right) = 0.$$

Rewriting this equation, we obtain

$$\sum_{j=1}^{m} \left\{ \sum_{i=1}^{s} W_i a_{ij'} a_{ij} p_j \right\} = \sum_{i=1}^{s} W_i a_{ij'} g_i. \qquad (342.1)$$

There are m such equations corresponding to the m possible values of j'. They are the 'normal' equations for the 'best' values of the parameters $p_1, \ldots, p_m$. If we write the normal equations (*342*.1) as

$$\mathbf{Mp} = \mathbf{E} \qquad (342.2)$$

inspection of equation (*342*.1) and comparison with equations (*341*.4) and (*341*.5) will show that

$$\mathbf{M} = \mathbf{A'A} \quad \text{and} \quad \mathbf{E} = \mathbf{A'G}$$

where $\mathbf{A'}$ is obtained from $\mathbf{A}$ by interchanging rows and columns. The solution of the equations (*342*.1) in matrix notation is

$$\mathbf{p} = \mathbf{NE} \qquad (342.3)$$

where $\mathbf{N}$ is the matrix inverse to $\mathbf{M}$, i.e. $\mathbf{N} = \mathbf{M}^{-1}$.

The standard deviation of any parameter p_j can now be obtained as follows (International Tables, Vol. II, p. 92; Whittaker and Robinson, 1944). Suppose, as will often be the case, that only the relative weights of the observations are known, and set

$$W_i = \sigma^2/\sigma^2(g_i) \qquad (342.4)$$

where $\sigma^2 = 1$ if the absolute weights *are* known. Then the standard deviation of p_j is given by

$$\sigma^2(p_j) = N_{jj}\sigma^2 \qquad (342.5)$$

where N_{jj} is the jth diagonal element of the matrix $\mathbf{N}$. Furthermore σ^2 can now be estimated from

$$\sigma^2 = \frac{\sum_{i=1}^{s} W_i \Delta_i^2}{(s-m)} \qquad (342.6)$$

Expressing the equations in matrix notation enables them to be written down economically and also indicates how computer programming may be simplified by making use of sub-programs already available for matrix algebra.

A situation can arise where the method of least squares leads to two (or more) parameters with standard deviations which are much greater than those of the other parameters. To take a simple example, suppose there are only two parameters to be determined, the normal equations being

$$\begin{aligned} M_{11}p_1 + M_{12}p_2 &= E_1 \\ M_{21}p_1 + M_{22}p_2 &= E_2 \end{aligned} \qquad (343.1)$$

with $M_{21} = M_{12}$ since **M** is always symmetric. If the elements of **M** also satisfy approximately the relation

$$\frac{M_{12}}{M_{11}} \approx \frac{M_{22}}{M_{21}} \qquad (343.2)$$

it is clear that both p_1 and p_2 will have large standard deviations, however accurate the original observations, for any variation Δp_2 in p_2 can be almost compensated in *both* equations (*343*.1) by a change $-(M_{12}/M_{11})\Delta p_2$ in p_1. When the relation (*343*.2) is exactly satisfied, p_1 and p_2 cannot be separately determined from the observations which have been made, although the linear combination $p_1 + (M_{12}/M_{11})p_2$ *can* be determined.

The parameters p_1 and p_2 are then said to be 'completely correlated', and their standard deviations given by equation (*342*.5) become infinite. This follows from the fact that each element of **N** is inversely proportional to the determinant of **M**, and the latter is zero when the condition (*343*.2) is exactly satisfied.

In the general case where several parameters are involved, correlation between them can most readily be detected by evaluating the correlation matrix **λ**. The elements of this matrix are defined by

$$\lambda_{jj'} = \frac{N_{jj'}}{\sqrt{(N_{jj}N_{j'j'})}} \qquad (343.3)$$

It follows that diagonal elements λ_{jj} are all equal to unity. A value for $\lambda_{jj'}$ approaching unity shows that p_j and $p_{j'}$ are correlated (and will have large standard deviations), $\lambda_{jj'} = 1$ shows that p_j and $p_{j'}$ are completely correlated and cannot be separately determined. Any degree of correlation between two parameters need not prevent the others being accurately determined, although in practice a very small value of the determinant of **M** may lead to difficulties of numerical calculation, and make it advisable to recast the equations so as to involve a linear combination of the strongly correlated parameters. Even when the correlation is not sufficiently great for this difficulty to arise, it can be useful to introduce new parameters which are linear combinations of the correlated parameters, in such a way that some of the new parameters have quite small standard deviations. This point has been discussed by Diamond (1958) in the context of a particular problem, but Diamond's method is in fact quite general.

3.3. *Numerical example.* According to Whittaker and Robinson (1944), the following example was used by Gauss to illustrate the method of least squares. We shall however use matrix notation. There are four observational equations ($s=4$) for three parameters ($m=3$). They are

$$\begin{aligned} p_1 - p_2 + 2p_3 &= 3 \\ 3p_1 + 2p_2 - 5p_3 &= 5 \\ 4p_1 + p_2 + 4p_3 &= 21 \\ -2p_1 + 6p_2 + 6p_3 &= 28. \end{aligned} \qquad (344)$$

The standard deviations of the observations are not known, but it is known that the fourth observation has twice as great a standard deviation as the other three. We therefore take $W_1 = W_2 = W_3 = 1$, $W_4 = \frac{1}{4}$, (section **12**.3.1) and the weighted observational equations are now obtained by replacing the fourth equation by $-p_1 + 3p_2 + 3p_3 = 14$, so that

$$\mathbf{A} = \begin{pmatrix} 1 & -1 & 2 \\ 3 & 2 & -5 \\ 4 & 1 & 4 \\ -1 & 3 & 3 \end{pmatrix}, \qquad \mathbf{G} = \begin{pmatrix} 3 \\ 5 \\ 21 \\ 14 \end{pmatrix}$$

$$\therefore \mathbf{M} = \mathbf{A'A} = \begin{pmatrix} 27 & 6 & 0 \\ 6 & 15 & 1 \\ 0 & 1 & 54 \end{pmatrix}, \quad \text{(section 12.3.2)}$$

and

$$\mathbf{E} = \mathbf{A'G} = \begin{pmatrix} 88 \\ 70 \\ 107 \end{pmatrix}$$

At this stage we have the normal equations in matrix form. N_{11} is now given as the cofactor of M_{11}, $\begin{vmatrix} 15 & 1 \\ 1 & 54 \end{vmatrix} = 809$, divided by the determinant of **M**, which is 19899. The other elements of **N** are obtained similarly, so that

$$\mathbf{N} = \begin{pmatrix} 809 & -324 & 6 \\ -324 & 1458 & -27 \\ 6 & -27 & 369 \end{pmatrix} \div 19899.$$

Premultiplying **E** by **N**, we obtain

$$p_1 = 2{\cdot}470, \quad p_2 = 3{\cdot}551, \quad p_3 = 1{\cdot}916$$

as the least-squares solution. Substituting this solution in the observational equations (*344*) we then obtain

$$\Delta_1 = +0{\cdot}249, \quad \Delta_2 = +0{\cdot}067, \quad \Delta_3 = -0{\cdot}095, \quad \Delta_4 = -0{\cdot}141$$

and therefore
$$\sigma^2 = \frac{\sum_{i=1}^{4} W_i \Delta_i^2}{(s-m)} = 0{\cdot}0804.$$

Using equation (*342.5*) we now have

$$\sigma^2(p_1) = 0{\cdot}0804 \times \frac{809}{19899}, \text{ etc.,}$$

and therefore $\sigma(p_1) = 0{\cdot}057$, $\sigma(p_2) = 0{\cdot}077$, $\sigma(p_3) = 0{\cdot}039$.

3.4. *Application to structure refinement.* The quantity to be minimized in structure analysis is

$$R_1 = \sum_{i=1}^{s} W_i(|F_0| - |F_c|)_i^2.$$

Provided that approximate values of the parameters are known, the *i*th weighted observational equation can be written as a linear equation for the *corrections* to the parameters, thus

$$\sqrt{W_i} \sum_{j=1}^{m} \frac{\partial |F_c|_i}{\partial p_j} \delta p_j = \sqrt{W_i}(|F_0| - |F_c|)_i. \qquad (345)$$

The normal equations are then set up and solved for the corrections δp_j in the same way as before, thus giving improved values for the parameters. Since however the equations (*345*) are approximate only, values of $|F_c|$ and of $\partial|F_c|/\partial p_j$ must now be recalculated to give a set of equations (*345*) with new coefficients, which are solved for a further set of corrections. The process is repeated until each correction δp_j becomes small compared with its standard deviation. The value of a residual Δ_i is therefore the final value of $(|F_0| - |F_c|)_i$, and the residuals can be used to calculate each $\sigma(\delta p_j)$, (which is of course equal to $\sigma(p_j)$) at the end of the refinement process, using the equation

$$\sigma^2(p_j) = N_{jj} \frac{\sum_{i=1}^{s} W_i \Delta_i^2.}{(s-m)}$$

As before, N_{jj} is the *j*th diagonal element of the matrix $\mathbf{N} = \mathbf{M}^{-1}$, and $\mathbf{M}$ is formed from the coefficients in the weighted observational equations (*345*) in the way described in section **12**.3.2.

When the structure has N atoms in the asymmetric unit, and general anisotropic temperature factors are involved, the matrix $\mathbf{M}$ is of order $9N \times 9N$. Operations involving this matrix can be very time-consuming, and some simplification is clearly desirable. If the structure is centrosymmetric and the atoms well-resolved from one another, small changes in the parameters of one atom do not affect the difference density in the neighbourhood of other atoms. The close connection between Fourier and least-squares methods can be used to show that the corresponding result is that elements of the matrix **M** which involve the parameters of different atoms can be neglected. An example of such an element is

$$\sum_{i=1}^{s} W_i \frac{\partial|F_c|_i}{\partial p_j} \frac{\partial|F_c|_i}{\partial p_{j'}}$$

where $p_j = x_1$ and $p_{j'} = x_2$ are the x-coordinates of well-resolved atoms. Elements involving parameters of the same atom, for example $p_j = x_1$, $p_{j'} = y_1$ can be neglected if the axes are orthogonal or nearly so, and the 'interaction' between coordinate and temperature factor parameters can also be neglected. Each parameter correction is then given by a single equation,

$$M_{jj}\delta p_j = E_j.$$

For a coordinate correction for example this is

$$\delta x_j \sum_{i=1}^{s} W_i \left(\frac{\partial|F_c|}{\partial x_j}\right)^2 = \sum_{i=1}^{s} W_i \frac{\partial|F_c|_i}{\partial x_j} (|F_0| - |F_c|)_i \ ,$$

which is in fact identical with equation (*340*.1) of section **12**.2.7 when the weights W_i are chosen appropriately. The standard deviation $\sigma(p_j)$ can readily be calculated using equations (*342*.5) and (*342*.6) and the fact that now $N_{jj} = (M_{jj})^{-1}$. This method is known as the diagonal approximation since all off-diagonal elements of **M** are neglected.

Even when the axes are not orthogonal, and anisotropic temperature factors are involved, it can be assumed that there is no interaction between parameters of different atoms (except in an unresolved projection) and that coordinate and temperature-factor parameters of the same atom do not interact. The matrix **M** is then composed of N 3×3 and N 6×6 submatrices, where N is the number of atoms in the asymmetric unit. Each submatrix corresponds to a set of three or of six simultaneous equations for the corrections to the coordinates or temperature factors respectively of one atom, and can be treated independently of the others, so that the problem of forming and inverting **M** is reduced to that of forming and inverting separately N matrices of order 3 and N of order 6. This is the block-diagonal approximation (Cruickshank et al., 1961). Standard deviations involve a diagonal element of a matrix which is the inverse of the appropriate submatrix. The block-diagonal approximation breaks down when atoms are unresolved in a Fourier synthesis. It has also been shown by Srinivasan (1961) that when the structure is non-centrosymmetric but contains a centrosymmetric group of atoms, there may be 'inverse overlap' of atoms related by the pseudo centre of symmetry. Off-diagonal elements such as

$$\sum_{i=1}^{s} W_i \frac{\partial|F_c|_i}{\partial x_1} \frac{\partial|F_c|_i}{\partial x_2}$$

cannot be neglected if atoms 1 and 2 are related in this way. A somewhat similar situation is discussed later in section **12**.3.6. Computer programs involving the full matrix have sometimes been used (Cruickshank et al., 1961; Busing and Levy, 1961).

3.5. *Some practical details.* In practice values of $|F_0|$ are rarely on an absolute scale. The quantity to be minimized is then

$$R_1 = \sum_{i=1}^{s} W_i(|F_0| - b|F_c|)_i^2 \qquad (347.1)$$

and the scaling factor b is treated as an additional parameter. It should be applied to $|F_c|$, as in the above equation, so that the observations being fitted do not change in the course of the refinement, but provided that b is not very different from unity, application of the scaling factor to $|F_0|$ can have no worse effect than a slowing of the process of convergence. Some investigators prefer to minimize the quantity

$$R_1' = R_1 \div \sum_{i=1}^{s} W_i|F_0|_i^2. \qquad (347.2)$$

It has the advantage that $\sqrt{R_1'}$ is about equal to the conventional R-factor. A minor difficulty is that the parameter b is correlated with the temperature-factor parameters of all the atoms, the reason being that a small decrease in b has nearly the same effect as a small increase in the over-all temperature factor. This difficulty can be overcome as follows. During each major cycle of refinement the scaling factor b is kept fixed, and there is no parameter representing the over-all temperature factor. This is followed by a minor refinement cycle involving only the scaling factor and an over-all isotropic temperature factor, applied to the current values of $|F_c|$, and therefore small. The correction found for the former is applied; that found for the latter is ignored since the necessary changes will be made to the temperature-factor parameters of individual atoms by the next major refinement cycle. An alternative method has been described by Cruickshank et al. (1961).

It is a fact of experience that the parameter corrections given by the method of least squares may be too large so that the solution tends to oscillate. This can be prevented by multiplying each δp_j by a 'fudge factor', commonly between 0·5 and 0·8. As the name indicates, the reason or reasons why such a factor is required in a particular instance are usually not known; some of the points involved have been analysed by Sparks (1961).

Generally speaking, the calculation of the derivatives $\partial|F_c|/\partial p_j$ does not present any special difficulty.

With $F = A + iB$ and $|F| = A \cos \alpha + B \sin \alpha$ we note that we may write

$$A = \sum A_j$$

where A_j is the contribution to A of an atom and the symmetry-related equivalent atoms. It then follows that

$$\frac{\partial|F|}{\partial p_j}=\frac{\partial A_j}{\partial p_j}\cos\alpha+\frac{\partial B_j}{\partial p_j}\sin\alpha.$$

For example, when the space group is $P2_1$, we have

$$A_j=A_{j1}+A_{j2}$$
$$=(f_0)_j\left\{T_{j1}\cos 2\pi\left(\frac{hx}{a}+\frac{ky}{b}+\frac{lz}{c}\right)_j+(-1)^k T_{j2}\cos 2\pi\left(-\frac{hx}{a}+\frac{ky}{b}-\frac{lz}{c}\right)_j\right\}$$

where the anisotropic temperature factors are *not* the same for symmetry related atoms, and are given by

$$T_{j1}=\exp-(b_{11}h^2+b_{22}k^2+b_{33}l^2+b_{12}hk+b_{13}hl+b_{23}kl)_j$$
$$T_{j2}=\exp-(b_{11}h^2+b_{22}k^2+b_{33}l^2-b_{12}hk+b_{13}hl-b_{23}kl)_j$$

(see table 305, Chapter 11.).

Differentials such as $\frac{\partial A_j}{\partial x_j}, \frac{\partial (b_{12})_j}{\partial A_j}$ etc., can now be written down without difficulty. A more general discussion has been given by Cruickshank et al. (1961).

3.6. *Some examples of refinement by least squares.* Examples of what may be called 'straightforward' application of least squares, and the results obtained for the atomic parameters, with their standard deviations, are given in Chapter 13, where the accuracy of different techniques is discussed. The examples given in this section represent more unusual applications of the method.

Crystals of the low-temperature phase of perchloric acid monohydrate are monoclinic with $\beta=98°$, and the unit-cell dimensions do not differ from those of the orthorhombic phase (which is stable at room temperature) by more than 4 per cent (Nordman, 1962). The space group of the orthorhombic phase is *Pnma*, No. 62 which contains the symmetry elements $2_1/n$ of the monoclinic phase. Nordman was able to refine the monoclinic structure directly, using the atomic coordinates of the orthorhombic structure as starting parameters. Structure amplitudes of 250 low-angle reflexions were used initially with isotropic temperature factors, and all off-diagonal terms of the matrix **M** were neglected. After several cycles of refinement an essentially correct structure was obtained, the position of the chlorine atom having changed by 0·5 Å and those of the five oxygen atoms by 0·9, 0·9, 0·4, 0·3 and 0·2 Å respectively. These shifts are relatively so large that this investigation should perhaps be counted as a rare instance of structure determination by the method of least squares. At this stage, with all observed structure amplitudes now included, the value of R_1' (equation *347.2*) was 0·0145, and was reduced to 0·0062 by a few additional cycles employing anisotropic temperature factors.

The hydrogen atoms could now be located as resolved peaks in a difference synthesis, and their contributions, with isotropic temperature factors, were included in F_c. The final value of R_1' after making an empirical correction for the effect of extinction on a few particularly large structure amplitudes, was 0·0036, the corresponding value of R being 0·052. Standard deviations were estimated in an unusual way which while interesting must also have been time-consuming. The 811 independent structure amplitudes were divided into six equal sets with the same distribution in $(\sin\theta)/\lambda$, but otherwise selected at random. Each such set was used separately in four cycles of least-squares refinement, enough to ensure complete convergence of the process, so that six essentially independent values were obtained for each positional and thermal parameter, of which there are 66 in all. An estimate of the standard deviation of a parameter could now be obtained from the deviations of six individual parameters from their mean, using the result

$$\sigma(\bar{p}) = \sqrt{\frac{\sum\limits_{i=1}^{n}(p_i - \bar{p})^2}{n(n-1)}}, \text{ with } n=6.$$

The space group of tetragonal barium titanate is P4*mm*, No. 99. The unit cell has

$$a = 3{\cdot}9945, \quad c = 4{\cdot}0335 \text{ Å}$$

and contains one formula unit of $BaTiO_3$. The fractional atomic coordinates are as follows:

Ba in 0, 0, 0, taken as origin
Ti in $\frac{1}{2}, \frac{1}{2}, \frac{1}{2} + Z(Ti)$
O_1 in $\frac{1}{2}, \frac{1}{2}, Z(O_1)$
$2O_2$ in $0, \frac{1}{2}, \frac{1}{2} + Z(O_2)$ and $\frac{1}{2}, 0, \frac{1}{2} + Z(O_2)$.

The values of Z are not expected to exceed 0·1 Å, since the structure is cubic above 120° C and $c - a$ is comparatively small at room temperature. Ba, Ti and O_1 lie on four-fold axes and have therefore two thermal parameters each while O_2 atoms lie on two-fold axes and may therefore have three thermal parameters. The total number of coordinate and thermal parameters is thus twelve. The accurate structure is of considerable interest since the material is ferroelectric. Accurate measurements of 99 independent *h0l* structure amplitudes were made by Evans (1961) using X-rays.

The structure was refined by the method of least squares, and when individual isotropic temperature factors were used the results shown under E1 in Table 351 were obtained. The standard deviations are estimated from results given in the original paper. When however anisotropic temperature factors were introduced, anomalous results were obtained. Large values of Z were indicated for certain atoms; some temperature factors became impossibly large while others became negative. The standard deviations are shown under E2 of Table 351; they are based on the inversion of the full matrix and some of them are ten times larger than appear under E1. The correlation matrix (section

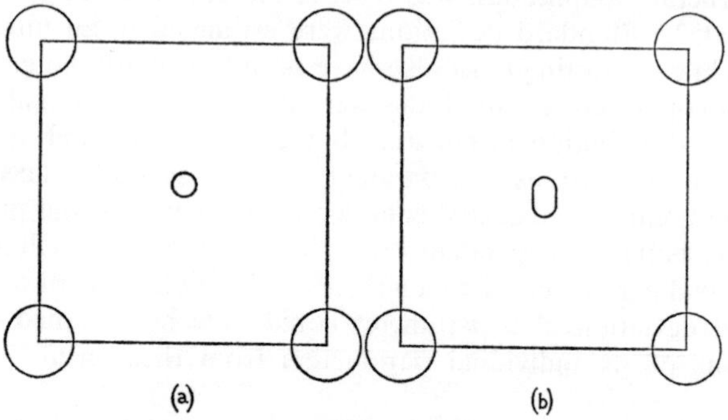

FIG. 350 (i). A schematic representation of the Ba and Ti atomic positions in $BaTiO_3$. In fig. *a* Ti is displaced from the centre of the cell, in fig. *b* this atom vibrates anisotropically about the undisplaced site

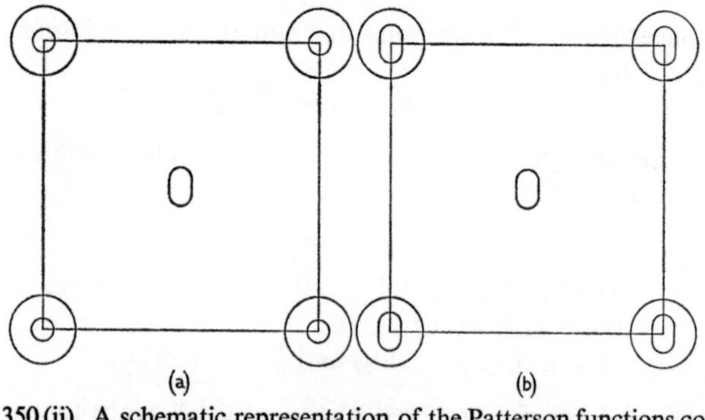

FIG. 350 (ii). A schematic representation of the Patterson functions corresponding to figs. 350 (i)*a* and *b*. They differ only in the shape of the relatively weak Ti–Ti peak at the origin

12.3.2) was evaluated by Geller (1961), and was found to have off-diagonal elements of 0·99 in two instances (involving Z(Ti) and B_{33}(Ti), and B_{11}(Ti) and $B_{22}(O_2)$ respectively); other off-diagonal elements exceeded 0·8.

The difficulty in obtaining accurate values for certain parameters of $BaTiO_3$ can be demonstrated in another way. Consider the two structures shown in figs. 350 (i)*a* and 350 (i)*b*, representing Ba and Ti atoms only. In 350(i)*a* the Ti atom is displaced from the symmetrical position, in 350 (i)*b* it has an anisotropic temperature factor. The corresponding

Patterson functions are shown schematically in figs. 350 (ii)*a* and 350 (ii)*b*; the shapes of the peaks corresponding to Ba–Ti vectors would in practice be indistinguishable, and the two Patterson functions really differ only in the shapes of their Ti–Ti peaks, at the origin. Since the Ti–Ti peak has a relatively small weight, the intensities corresponding to structures 350 (i)*a* and 350 (i)*b* can differ by only relatively small amounts. Such considerations can always be used to decide when parameters will be correlated.

When parameters are strongly correlated, only new information can lead to much more accurate parameters. The structure amplitudes for neutron diffraction have been measured for tetragonal $BaTiO_3$ by Frazer, Danner and Pepinsky (1955). When these data are used parameters are less strongly correlated, simply because the Patterson function is less dominated by vectors involving Ba.

It is however physically reasonable to assume that in tetragonal $BaTiO_3$, which is so nearly cubic, the atoms have isotropic temperature factors, and $B(O_1) = B(O_2)$. The results obtained by Frazer, Danner and Pepinsky, assuming isotropic temperature factors, are shown under FDP in Table 351, and are physically reasonable.

TABLE 351

Parameters of the structure of tetragonal $BaTiO_3$

	El		E2	FDP
	p	$\sigma(p)$	$\sigma(p)$	p
Z(Ti)	0·015	0·0012	0·018	0·014
$Z(O_1)$	−0·024	0·0062	0·017	−0·023
$Z(O_2)$	−0·020	0·0035	0·097	−0·014
B_{11} B_{33} } Ba	0·29	0·013	0·05 0·07	0·273
B_{11} B_{33} } Ti	0·39	0·055	0·051 0·63	0·152
B_{11} B_{22} } O_1	0·88	0·45	0·65 0·87	0·334
B_{11} B_{22} B_{33} } O_2	0·49	0·23	0·24 1·48 1·02	0·267

4. Interpretation of Results

4.1. *Possible systematic errors of interpretation.* The most important single source of error in early attempts to measure bond lengths and angles accurately by X-ray methods was the termination of the Fourier series. We have already seen how this source of error can be eliminated by difference synthesis or least-squares refinement procedures. Even if the scattering factors of the atoms of the 'calculated' structure are not correct, the fact that the scale factor and individual isotropic temperature factors are adjustable parameters will serve to bring the 'observed' and 'calculated' scattering factors more nearly into coincidence, particularly at the upper end of the range of $(\sin\theta)/\lambda$. Considerations set out in section **12**.2.3 suggest that residual series-termination errors will mostly affect the coordinates derived for near neighbours of an atom whose scattering factor is still in error after such adjustments have been made. They will scarcely affect the coordinates of the atom itself, although the thermal parameter deduced will be incorrect.

Situations may arise in which the electron distribution associated with covalent bonding can be 'explained away' by adjustment of coordinate and temperature-factor parameters fro mtheir correct values. What is probably an extreme case has been described by Dawson (1964), who evaluated the structure factors for an 'observed' centrosymmetric structure consisting of two nitrogen atoms with sp^3 hybrid orbitals, each therefore having a markedly anisotropic electron distribution but an isotropic temperature factor. The structure was then refined by the method of least squares, the calculated structure factors being based on isotropic atoms with anisotropic temperature factors. A low R-factor was obtained, with temperature-factor parameters which were of course incorrect and, what is more striking, atomic coordinates which were in error by about 0·02 Å. This is a warning against the overoptimism that can be engendered by standard deviations as low as 0·002 Å! The systematic errors that can arise from our lack of knowledge of the bonding electron distribution can be avoided completely by using neutron-diffraction techniques (Chapter 13), and in principle a combination of X-ray and neutron measurements can be used to show unambiguously the effect of covalent bonding, although as yet little progress has been made in this direction in practice. To some extent the influence of the bonding electrons can be reduced by giving zero weight to X-ray structure amplitudes whose value of $(\sin\theta)/\lambda$ is below a certain value.

The apparent parameters of hydrogen atoms are particularly affected by bonding. In many crystal structure analyses by X-ray methods, CH, OH and NH bond lengths have been found to be significantly shorter than the values given by spectroscopic methods. While the standard deviation of a coordinate, usually at least 0·05 Å for a hydrogen atom, means that little reliance can be placed on individual values, Sundaralingam and Jensen (1965) for example have shown conclusively that in three different organic compounds the mean CH bond length is about 0·1 Å less than the spectroscopic value. While the point of maximum electron density must coincide with the proton, so that in principle X-ray measurements of sufficient accuracy and range in $(\sin\theta)/\lambda$ must always give a correct result, the usual refinement techniques lead to a coordinate parameter which minimizes $(\rho_0 - \rho_c)^2$, or some related function, in the region of the hydrogen atom, and an apparent shortening of the bond is therefore to be expected, which might depend to some extent on the refinement technique employed. There is also a pronounced tendency for the apparent temperature factor of a hydrogen atom to be less than that of the atom to which it is bonded. This is not the case when neutron-diffraction data are used; for example in the investigation of 4, 4′-dichlorodiphenyl sulphone by Bacon and Curry (1960) the average value of B for protons was found to be 1·8 Å² greater than that of the adjacent carbon nuclei.

While it is likely that the value of B for electrons in the vicinity of the proton will be intermediate between that of the proton and that of the neighbouring atom (bearing in mind that the concept of a B-value for such electrons can be only an approximate one), the major cause of the

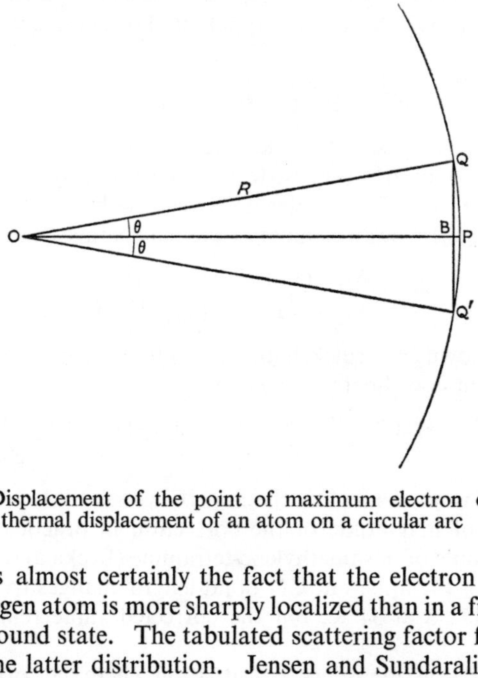

FIG. 353. Displacement of the point of maximum electron density by thermal displacement of an atom on a circular arc

discrepancy is almost certainly the fact that the electron density in a bonded hydrogen atom is more sharply localized than in a free hydrogen atom in its ground state. The tabulated scattering factor for hydrogen is based on the latter distribution. Jensen and Sundaralingam (1964) have shown that

$$f(\text{bonded}) = f(\text{free}) \exp(2{\cdot}5(\sin\theta/\lambda)^2)$$

is probably closer to the truth, for a hydrogen atom bonded to carbon.

Angular oscillation of a molecule can lead to an apparent decrease in interatomic distances within the molecule. Consider an atom whose equilibrium position is P (fig. 353). If only translational oscillations are made, the point of maximum density will remain at P. If however the molecule makes small oscillations about O so that the atom is displaced along the arc Q′PQ, a positional error is introduced. Suppose the atom spends half the time at Q and half at Q′. The average density will be a maximum at B, and the atom will appear too close to O by an amount

$$\Delta = \mathrm{PB} = \mathrm{R}(1-\cos\theta) \simeq \tfrac{1}{2}\mathrm{R}\theta^2.$$

If in the course of oscillation the mean square displacement along the arc is s^2, we therefore expect Δ to be roughly equal to $s^2/2\mathrm{R}$. Cruickshank (1956) has investigated the situation in which the atom has a density in the absence of angular oscillations given by

$$\rho(r) \propto \exp(-r^2/2q^2)$$

so that q is a measure of the peak width.

Mean square displacements s^2 and t^2 as a result of angular oscillations about two axes through O which are mutually perpendicular, and perpendicular to OP, lead to an apparent shortening given by

$$\Delta = \frac{1}{2\mathrm{R}}\left\{\frac{s^2}{1+s^2/q^2} + \frac{t^2}{1+t^2/q^2}\right\}.$$

In a more general situation, let xyz be the coordinates in Å of an atom relative to an arbitrary cartesian coordinate system in which the angular oscillation of the molecule is defined by a matrix $\boldsymbol{\omega}$ (section 11.2.5). Let $(\omega_{ij})^{-1}$ be an element of the matrix inverse to $\boldsymbol{\omega}$, and define

$$\mathrm{A}_{11} = (y^2+z^2)/q^2 + (\omega_{11})^{-1}$$
$$\mathrm{A}_{12} = -xy/q^2 + (\omega_{12})^{-1} \quad \text{etc.}$$

It has been shown by Cruickshank (1961) that the corrections required to the apparent coordinates are given by

$$\Delta_x = \tfrac{1}{2}\{x(\mathrm{A}_{22})^{-1} + x(\mathrm{A}_{33})^{-1} - y(\mathrm{A}_{12})^{-1} - z(\mathrm{A}_{13})^{-1}\} \quad \text{etc.}$$

where $(\mathrm{A}_{jj})^{-1}$ is an element of the matrix inverse to $\mathbf{A}$.

The order of magnitude of the correction in practice may be seen from the example of hexamethylene-tetramine (Becka and Cruickshank, 1961) in which the apparent CN bond-length changes from 1·464 Å at 298°K, to 1·474 Å at 34°K, but the corrected value remains constant at 1·477 Å.

The above discussion refers to a situation where the correlation in the displacements of different atoms is known, since they are assumed part of a rigid unit. When this is not the case, only upper and lower limits to the correction required can be estimated (Busing and Levy, 1964).

The need for such corrections can be almost eliminated by making measurements at a low temperature. Random errors are generally also reduced in this way, since the number of accidentally absent reflections is decreased, and the range of $(\sin\theta)/\lambda$ over which measurements can be made is increased, see for example the work of Hirshfeld, Sandler and Schmidt (1963).

4.2. *Systematic errors in the data.* The sources of error which we discussed in the last section are still present when the experimental data are free from error. As we noted in section **12**.2.2, purely random errors in the structure amplitudes lead to a random error in the electron density with about the same standard deviation everywhere in the unit cell. Correlated errors in the structure amplitudes can however change the shape of electron-density maxima in a systematic way. The use of a specimen of elliptic cross-section, without correction for absorption, can lead to a peak shape very similar to that produced by anisotropic thermal vibration (Jellinek, 1958). Any systematic error of measurement which depends on $(\sin\theta)/\lambda$ only, such as that resulting from absorption in a spherical specimen, will be largely taken up in the overall isotropic temperature factor. The latter is therefore often unreliable.

Errors resulting from secondary extinction usually need not be important for the determination of bond lengths and angles in a fairly complicated crystal structure, since the comparatively few structure amplitudes affected can be given reduced or even zero weights. For the accurate measurement of electron density, experimental methods of eliminating secondary extinction should be used. These comprise the use of radiations of different wave-lengths, of very small specimens, or of powdered specimens. This topic however lies outside the scope of our book. The possibility of double Bragg reflexion (section **2**.4.4) should also be remembered when accurate measurements are being made.

4.3. *Bond lengths and significance levels.* The standard deviation of the length l_{12} of a bond between two atoms is given by the relation

$$\sigma^2(l_{12}) = \sigma^2(x_1) + \sigma^2(x_2)$$

where x_1 and x_2 are the atomic coordinates measured in the direction of the bond. If the atoms are related by a mirror plane, or a centre of symmetry,

$$\sigma(l_{12}) = 2\sigma(x_1)$$

and other amendments must be made to deal, for example, with atoms in special positions.

If β is the angle formed at atom 2 between bonds l_{12} and l_{23}, the errors in the coordinates of the three atoms being independent of one another, then

$$\sigma^2(\beta) = \frac{\sigma^2(x_1)}{l_{12}^2} + \frac{l_{13}^2}{l_{12}^2 l_{23}^2}\,\sigma^2(x_2) + \frac{\sigma^2(x_3)}{l_{23}^2}\,.$$

In this expression x_1 and x_3 are measured in directions perpendicular to l_{12} and l_{23} respectively, and x_2 is measured in the direction of the centre of the circle passing through the three atoms (Darlow, 1960).

The importance of applying proper significance tests before drawing conclusions from a comparison of two measurements, both of which are subject to error, has been emphasized by Cruickshank, who considers the following example. A bond length l_1, standard deviation $\sigma(l_1)$, is determined as greater than a bond length l_2, standard deviation $\sigma(l_2)$, by an amount $\delta l = l_1 - l_2$. Is there a real difference between l_1 and l_2 or not? Cruickshank suggests the adoption of the following numerical significance levels, where P is the probability that the first bond could be at least δl greater than the second by chance, and

$$\sigma^2 = \sigma^2(l_1) + \sigma^2(l_2).$$

If $P \geqslant 5\%$, $\delta l \leqslant 1{\cdot}645\sigma$, the difference is not significant.
If $5\% > P > 1\%$, $2{\cdot}327\sigma > \delta l > 1{\cdot}645\sigma$, the difference is possibly significant.
If $1\% > P > 0{\cdot}1\%$, $3{\cdot}090\sigma > \delta l > 2{\cdot}327\sigma$, the difference is significant.
For instance, when all atoms concerned have $\sigma(x) = 1{\cdot}5 \times 10^{-2}$Å, a bond-length difference of 5×10^{-2}Å is only possibly significant. Fortunately it is now standard practice in X-ray crystallography to estimate the standard deviations of results, and to use numerically specified levels of significance in comparing them.

4.4. *Summary.* The usual object of the X-ray analysis of a crystal is the measurement of the lengths of the bonds between certain atoms of the crystal; less frequently it is the measurement, with some accuracy, of the electron distribution in the crystal. Of these two problems the first is the more easily solved, because atoms in crystals are so nearly spherically symmetric, and their atomic scattering factors are known with reasonable accuracy. When so much is known in advance about the 'shape' of the atoms in the crystal concerned, accurate atomic coordinates and temperature factors can be derived from an accurate set of experimental measurements which is incomplete in that structure factors which cannot be measured because of the experimental arrangement, or whose magnitudes lie outside a certain range of values, are excluded. This is not true of measurement of the electron density, for which a complete set of intensity measurements is required, at least in the range where the atomic scattering factors concerned are not accurately known.

For a centrosymmetric structure, the 'best' atomic parameters (coordinates and temperature factors) are, according to the theory of errors, those which minimize the quantity

$$R_1 = \sum_q w(F_0 - F_c)^2$$

where the weight w allotted to each observation depends on its standard deviation. If a particular structure factor has not been measured at all, or if the measurement is for some reason considered to be very inaccurate, the weight w is set equal to zero.

Starting from approximate values, atomic parameters may be varied systematically, so as to minimize R_1 by a number of methods which, although apparently different, are in fact closely related. For example if we choose atomic parameters so that the function

$$D' = \frac{1}{V} \sum_q (F_0 - F_c) w\hat{f} \cos \Theta$$

has zero first and second derivatives at the centres of atoms, the function R_1 is minimized. The form of D′ at any stage of the approximation to the final coordinates can be used to minimize R_1 systematically. In practice however the standard method of least squares is better adapted to automatic computing, and to the estimation of the standard deviations of the results obtained. In the final stages of the refinement process it may however be advisable to evaluate the difference density

$$D = \frac{1}{V} \sum_q (F_0 - F_c) \cos \Theta$$

and inspect it for physically significant features. The possibility of systematic errors of measurement or of interpretation, particularly those resulting from anisotropic thermal vibration and electron redistribution, should not be overlooked.

CHAPTER 13

NEUTRON DIFFRACTION AND ELECTRON DIFFRACTION

1. Basic Principles

1.1. *Introduction.* In this chapter we survey briefly two other diffraction techniques which have been used for structure determination. We do not intend to try to give a complete account of the physics of neutron or of electron diffraction, and we mention experimental techniques only to the extent required to show the limitations of a particular method. The reader who wishes to learn more should consult the text books *Neutron Diffraction* (Bacon, 1962) and *Structure Analysis by Electron Diffraction* (Vainshtein, 1964*a*). There are also review articles by Bacon (1964), Vainshtein (1964*b*) and Cowley and Rees (1958). Neither technique will replace X-ray diffraction as the most convenient means of crystal structure determination; on the other hand the use of neutrons in particular has given structural information that could have been obtained only with great difficulty using X-rays, or not at all. In other fields such as the study of lattice vibrations by inelastic scattering, neutron methods are much superior to X-ray methods but this topic is outside the scope of this book.

1.2. *Nuclear scattering of neutrons.* When a plane-polarized X-ray beam of unit amplitude is scattered by an atom, the amplitude of the scattered beam at unit distance is given by

$$A_x = -\sin\phi \frac{e^2}{mc^2} f \qquad (358)$$

where ϕ is the angle between the scattered beam and the direction of polarization of the incident beam. (We neglect here the possibility of anomalous scattering, Chapter 14.) The scattering is therefore not isotropic, by reason of the presence both of the atomic scattering factor f and the factor $\sin\phi$ (James, 1957). In similar circumstances the amplitude of a scattered beam of neutrons whose wave-length is in the range useful for structure analysis is $-b$ where b is the bound scattering length if the scattering nucleus is not free to recoil. The scattering is isotropic because the radius of the nucleus is much smaller than neutron wave-lengths (1 to 2 Å, say), and there is no polarization factor.

This expression applies strictly only to a nucleus with zero spin. When the scattering nucleus has a spin, it has in effect two distinct scattering lengths, b_+ and b_-, which may be quite different. A weighted mean of b_+ and b_- then replaces b to give the amplitude of the coherently scattered radiation—that is, of the radiation which has a definite phase relationship to that of the incident beam. When b_+ and b_- are numerically different, neutrons are also scattered incoherently. In scattering by a crystal there is a further source of incoherent scattering in that different isotopes of an element generally have different scattering lengths. The coherent intensity from a crystal is of course concentrated at reciprocal-lattice points, while the incoherent intensity is not, so that in neutron diffraction the background of incoherent scattering is generally unimportant, and the coherent contribution from each element depends on an appropriately weighted mean, $\bar{b}$. Bacon (1962) tabulates the measured values of $\bar{b}$ for each element. The scattering length of an element is practically independent of neutron wave-length; among the elements it increases slowly but is subject to irregular fluctuations with increasing mass number. For most elements $\bar{b}$ is found to be positive, but for a few such as H, Ti, Mn it is negative; all values lie between about $\pm 1{\cdot}0 \times 10^{-12}$ cm. For example the value for hydrogen is $\bar{b} = -0{\cdot}38$, for oxygen $+0{\cdot}58$ and for lead $+0{\cdot}96 \times 10^{-12}$ cm.

Apart from the absence of a polarization factor, the intensity of reflection of neutrons from a crystal is governed by the same physical principles as apply in X-ray diffraction. The structure factor, for example, is given by

$$F_n(\mathbf{H}) = \sum_{j=1}^{N} \bar{b}_j \exp\left(-\tfrac{1}{4}B_j H^2\right) \exp 2\pi i \mathbf{H}.\mathbf{r}_j \qquad (359)$$

and we note the appearance of a Debye-Waller temperature factor (which may in fact be anisotropic, Chapter 11) exactly as for X-rays. The quantities $\bar{b}$ and $\dfrac{e^2 f}{mc^2}$ are of the same order of magnitude ($\sim 10^{-12}$ cm.) for many atoms so that X-rays and neutrons are scattered about equally strongly by a crystal. Extinction effects, leading to systematic errors in the measured intensities of strong reflexions, are somewhat more liable to occur in neutron measurements since specimens of at least a few cubic millimetres in volume are used to offset the comparatively low intensity of neutron beams, even from a high-flux reactor. True absorption of neutrons is negligible in most materials.

1.3. *Magnetic scattering of neutrons.* Most structural investigations made by neutron diffraction involve nuclear scattering, which we have just considered. There is however a second means of interaction of neutrons with certain atoms which have a magnetic moment. To simplify the discussion we shall assume in what follows that the magnetic moment of an atom arises from the spin of its unpaired electrons (with no contribution from their orbital motion) as is the case for atoms belonging to the first transition series, in a crystalline environment.

Somewhat different results apply for atoms of the rare-earth series, where orbital motion contributes to the magnetic moment (Bacon, 1962).

In an ideal paramagnetic material the moments of individual atoms are randomly oriented and uncorrelated, and the scattering is therefore incoherent. It was shown by Halpern and Johnson (1939) that the scattered intensity per atom, at unit distance, is given by

$$A_m^2 = \tfrac{2}{3}\mathscr{S}(\mathscr{S}+1)\left(\frac{e^2\gamma}{mc^2}\right)^2 f_m^2(S) \qquad (360)$$

In this expression, $\mathscr{S}$ is the spin quantum number ($\frac{5}{2}$ for Mn^{++} for example), γ is the magnetic moment of the neutron in nuclear magnetons (numerically $\gamma = -1{\cdot}91$) and f_m is the magnetic scattering factor. Just as f (equation *358*) is the Fourier transform of the electron density in an atom, f_m is the transform of the density of electrons responsible for the magnetic scattering of neutrons, normalized to correspond to one electron. From their measurements of the incoherent scattering by MnF_2, Shull, Strauser and Wollan (1951) were able to determine f_m as a function of $S = (2 \sin \theta)/\lambda$, (fig. 360), and hence were able to deduce the distribution of electrons in the $3d$ shell of Mn^{++}.

In a ferromagnetic material the individual magnetic moments within a single domain (which may comprise the whole crystal) are aligned parallel to one another. In an antiferromagnetic material all the atoms

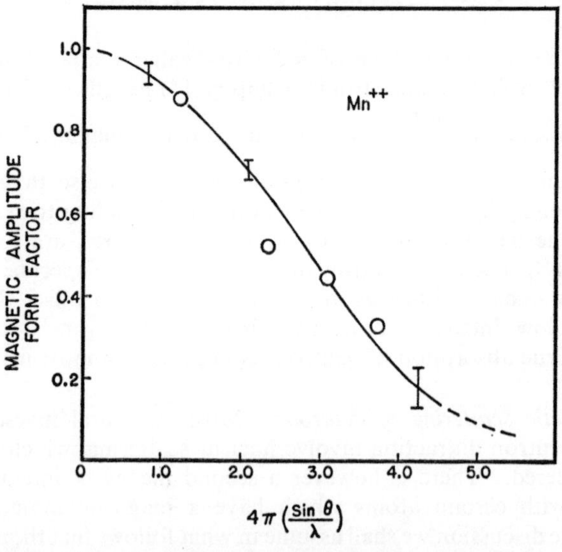

FIG. 360. Magnetic amplitude form factor for Mn^{++} ions. The curve is that obtained from paramagnetic diffuse scattering with estimated error as shown. The points represent values of the form factor obtained from the low-temperature antiferromagnetic reflexions of MnO

of one sub-lattice have their moments parallel to a particular direction, and those on another sub-lattice have equal moments oppositely directed. In a ferrimagnetic crystal, the oppositely directed moments are unequal. The existence of a well-defined moment on each atom means that neutrons are scattered coherently. Still confining our attention to atoms for which only the moment associated with electron spin is effective, we find that the magnetic scattering length of an atom is given by

$$p(\mathrm{S}) = \left(\frac{e^2\gamma}{mc^2}\right) \mathcal{S} f_m(\mathrm{S}). \qquad (361.1)$$

This quantity, for small values of S, is typically of the same order of magnitude as a nuclear scattering length, b.

When a neutron beam from a reactor is incident on a suitable magnetized monochromating crystal, it is possible for the reflected beam to consist entirely of neutrons with their spins aligned in one direction. Such a neutron beam is said to be polarized; the beam reflected from the (220) plane of a magnetized single crystal of magnetite (Fe_3O_4) is an example. Let $\hat{\boldsymbol{\lambda}}$ be a unit vector in the direction of polarization of a monochromatic beam of neutrons which is incident on a ferromagnetic or an antiferromagnetic specimen. The intensity of the scattered beam at unit distance from a single atom is determined by both nuclear and magnetic interactions and is given by

$$|\mathrm{A}_{n,m}|^2 = b^2 + 2bp\,\mathbf{q}\cdot\hat{\boldsymbol{\lambda}} + p^2q^2 \qquad (361.2)$$

(Halpern and Johnson, 1939). The situation considered is of course somewhat artificial in that an isolated atom has no moment in a defined direction. The situation is defined in fig. 362; $-\mathbf{q}$ is the projection of a unit vector in the direction of the magnetic moment on to a plane perpendicular to the scattering vector **S**. This plane is the Bragg reflecting plane, when the atom is in a crystal.

When the incident neutrons are not polarized the cross-term in equation (*361*.2) involving $\hat{\boldsymbol{\lambda}}$ averages to zero, and the intensities of nuclear and magnetic origin are additive. The extension of this result to apply to the reflexion of unpolarized neutrons by a crystal, is that the relevant structure factor F(**H**) is given by

$$|\mathrm{F}|^2 = |\mathrm{F}_n|^2 + q^2|\mathrm{F}_m|^2 \qquad (361.3)$$

where F_n was defined by equation (*359*.1) and

$$\mathrm{F}_m(\mathbf{H}) = \sum_{j=1}^{N} p_j \exp\left(-\tfrac{1}{4}\mathrm{B}_j\mathrm{H}^2\right) \exp 2\pi i\mathbf{H}\cdot\mathbf{r}_j \qquad (361.4)$$

In an antiferromagnetic or ferrimagnetic crystal both +ve and −ve values of p occur. It must be remembered that the sum is to be taken over all atoms in the ‘magnetic unit cell’ which may differ from the

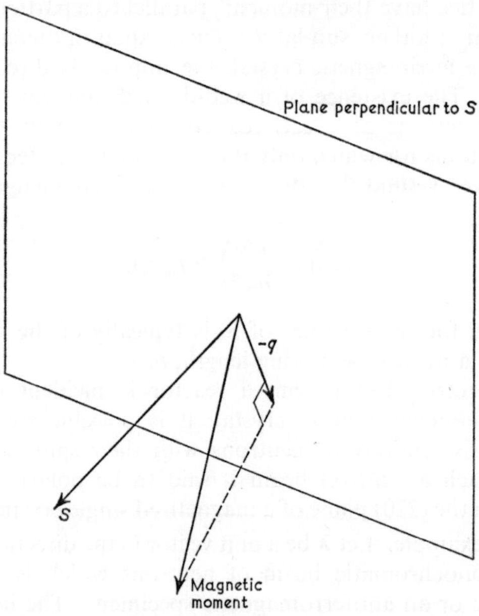

FIG. 362. The vector **q** is such that $-\mathbf{q}$ is the projection of a unit vector in the direction of the magnetic moment on to a plane perpendicular to the scattering vector **S**

'chemical unit cell' since, for example, alternate atoms of the same element may have oppositely directed spins. Certain reflexions may therefore result entirely from magnetic scattering, others from the sum of nuclear and magnetic scattering. In a ferromagnet, the latter contribution to (*361*.3) can be varied by changing the direction of magnetization. When the latter is parallel to S, $q^2=0$ and when it is perpendicular to S, $q^2=1$, for example. For a material which has domains magnetized in different directions, an appropriate average of q^2 must be used in equation (*361*.3). The contribution of the magnetic scattering is not appreciable at comparatively high values of S, since the second term of equation (*361*.3) involves f_m^2.

When a polarized incident beam of neutrons is used there is coherence between nuclear and magnetic scattering, enabling more accurate measurements of F_m to be made. It can be deduced from equation (*361*.2) that in a ferromagnet with one atom in each primitive unit cell, for example, and with magnetization perpendicular to the reciprocal-lattice vector **H**,

$$|F|^2=(b\pm p)^2 \exp\left(-\tfrac{1}{2}BH^2\right), \qquad (362)$$

the plus and minus signs applying respectively when the neutron spin is parallel and antiparallel to the magnetization. This expression is relatively sensitive to small values of p, so the range of measurement of

magnetic scattering can be extended (Nathans, Shull, Shirane and Andresen, 1959).

We also see from equation (*362*) how in principle a polarized beam of neutrons can be obtained. An unpolarized beam can be regarded as composed of two independent components with spin parallel and antiparallel respectively to the magnetization of a ferromagnetic crystal on which it falls. If the reflecting plane of this monochromator is such that $b=p$, only one component of the incident beam will be reflected, and it will be completely polarized. This condition is almost exactly satisfied for the (220) plane of magnetite.

1.4. *Electron diffraction.* As in earlier sections, we consider an electron beam of unit amplitude to fall on an atom. The amplitude of the scattered beam at unit distance is $+f_e$ where

$$f_e(\mathrm{S}) = \frac{me}{2\pi\hbar^2}\int 4\pi r^2\phi(r)\frac{\sin 2\pi r\mathrm{S}}{2\pi r\mathrm{S}}\,dr. \qquad (363.1)$$

Apart from the constant factor $me/2\pi\hbar^2$, f_e is the Fourier transform of the potential distribution $\phi(r)$ in the atom. As before, **S** is the scattering vector and $\hbar$ is Planck's constant divided by 2π. It can be shown that f_e of equation (*363.*1) is related to f, the atomic scattering factor for X-rays, by the result

$$f_e(\mathrm{S}) = \frac{me^2}{2\pi^2\hbar^2}\frac{(\mathrm{Z}-f(\mathrm{S}))}{\mathrm{S}^2} \qquad (363.2)$$

where Z is the atomic number. When use is made of the Thomas-Fermi statistical method to calculate the electron distribution in atoms, it is found that $f_e(0)\propto \mathrm{Z}^{1/3}$. However more accurate calculations using the Hartree-Fock method (Vainshtein, 1953) have shown that this result is correct only on the average; abrupt jumps in $f_e(0)$ occur after closed electron shells have been formed at $\mathrm{Z}=2$, 10, 18 etc. and in the ranges $\mathrm{Z}=3$ to 10, 11 to 18 etc., $f_e(0)$ actually decreases with increasing Z. For values of S greater than about 0·8 Å^{-1}, $f_e(\mathrm{S})$ increases fairly uniformly with Z. Fig. 364 shows some theoretical results obtained by Vainshtein (1953). One general result of these considerations is that the potential near the centre of an atom increases with Z more slowly than does the electron density. 'Light' atoms are therefore relatively more prominent in a map of the potential distribution than in a map of the electron distribution; hydrogen atoms in particular are more readily detected and the potential should be quite sensitive to their state of ionization.

As in X-ray or neutron diffraction, the reflected intensity from a small crystal depends on $|\mathrm{F}_e|^2$, where

$$\mathrm{F}_e(\mathbf{H}) = \sum_{j=1}^{N}(f_e)_j \exp\left(-\tfrac{1}{4}\mathrm{B}_j\mathrm{H}^2\right)\exp 2\pi i\mathbf{H}\cdot\mathbf{r}_j. \qquad (363.3)$$

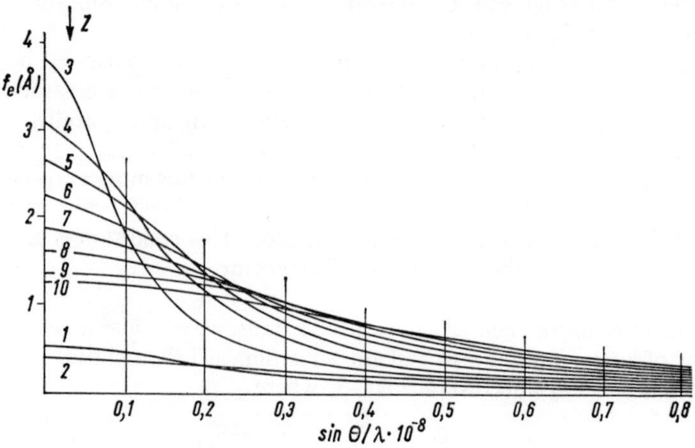

FIG. 364 *f*-curves for electron diffraction, for atoms of atomic number 1 to 10

We have seen that the quantities $(e^2/mc^2)f$ (X-rays), b and p (neutrons), are all of order 10^{-12} cm. The quantity f_e is however much larger in the range in which measurements are usually made, being about 10^{-8} cm., although it decreases comparatively rapidly with S. The interaction of electrons with a crystal is therefore so strong that the simple kinematic theory of diffraction breaks down for a crystal more than about 100 Å thick (Blackman, 1939; Horstmann and Meyer, 1962). Unless an exceedingly thin crystal is used, the measured intensities can be related to values of $|F_e|^2$ only after somewhat uncertain corrections for multiple reflexion have been made. When polycrystalline specimens are used, extra rings and diffuse bands can appear, and with single crystals the appearance of forbidden reflexions may result, (fig. 365(i)). In practice Pinsker, Vainshtein and their collaborators (see Vainshtein, 1964*a*) have used thin layers of polycrystalline or partially oriented material. Difficulties then arise from the overlapping of reflexions. Cowley, Moodie, Rees and their collaborators (see Cowley and Rees, 1958) have used very thin single crystals. Their investigations have been largely confined to materials such as mica for which very thin flakes can be obtained, and electron beams only a few microns in diameter have been used since such thin crystals are invariably bent or otherwise distorted over regions of greater diameter. For a very thin crystal, the intensity in reciprocal space is drawn out from each reciprocal lattice point along lines parallel to the short dimension of the crystal (Wilson, 1962). The wave-length used in electron diffraction is usually about 0·05 Å and so the radius of the reflecting sphere is relatively very large; even when the specimen is held stationary this sphere will intercept several 'reciprocal lattice streaks', as shown in cross-section in fig. 365(ii). The pattern

FIG. 365(i). Cross-grating pattern from single-crystal of dicetyl showing effects attributable to secondary scattering. The odd orders on both axes are forbidden on space-group grounds, but appear in the pattern as a result of secondary scattering

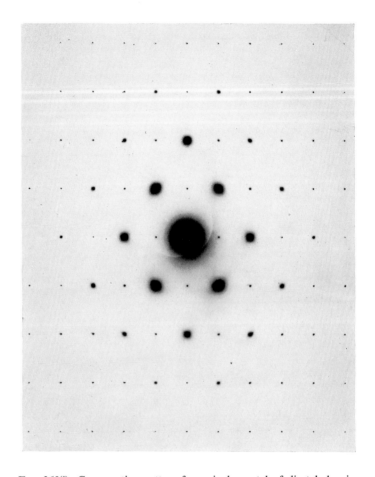

produced is then a 'cross-grating' pattern (fig. 365 (i)). The intensities give in principle the structure amplitudes for a projection of the potential distribution on a plane perpendicular to the short dimension of the specimen. It is generally true however that structure amplitudes obtained by electron diffraction are liable to be less accurate than those obtained by X-ray or neutron diffraction.

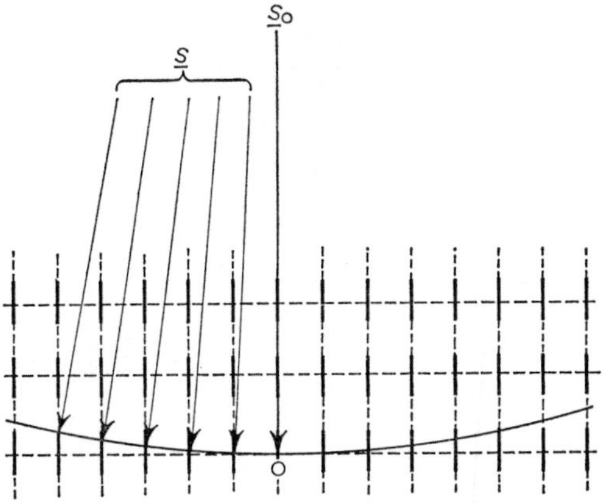

FIG. 365 (ii). Reciprocal-lattice construction for diffraction by a thin crystal plate. Electron beam parallel to short dimension of crystal

2. Fourier Methods in Neutron and Electron Diffraction

2.1. *Nuclear density.* It will be obvious by analogy with the result which holds for X-ray diffraction that nuclear density is given by

$$\rho_n(\mathbf{r}) = \frac{1}{V}\sum_{\mathbf{H}} F_n(\mathbf{H}) \exp(-2\pi i\mathbf{H}\cdot\mathbf{r}) \qquad (365)$$

where F_n was defined by equation (*359*). So far, most investigations have involved a calculation of the density in projection because of the slowness of data collection, but with the development of automatic diffractometers this situation is certain to change. Atoms with a positive value of $\bar{b}$ are represented by positive peaks in a nuclear density map, atoms such as hydrogen for which $\bar{b}$ is negative are represented by negative peaks.

The density in projection represents a point as seen in a microscope of limited resolution. If S_0 is the value of 2 sin θ/λ within which the Fourier coefficients lie, and $\bar{b}$ the appropriate scattering length, the density at distance r from the centre will be proportional to

$$\bar{b}\,\frac{J_1(2\pi r S_0)}{\pi r S_0}$$

To take account of thermal motion, this must be convoluted with a Gaussian distribution (section **10**.2.5). Numerical calculations made by Bacon and Pease (1955) gave the theoretical density of superimposed

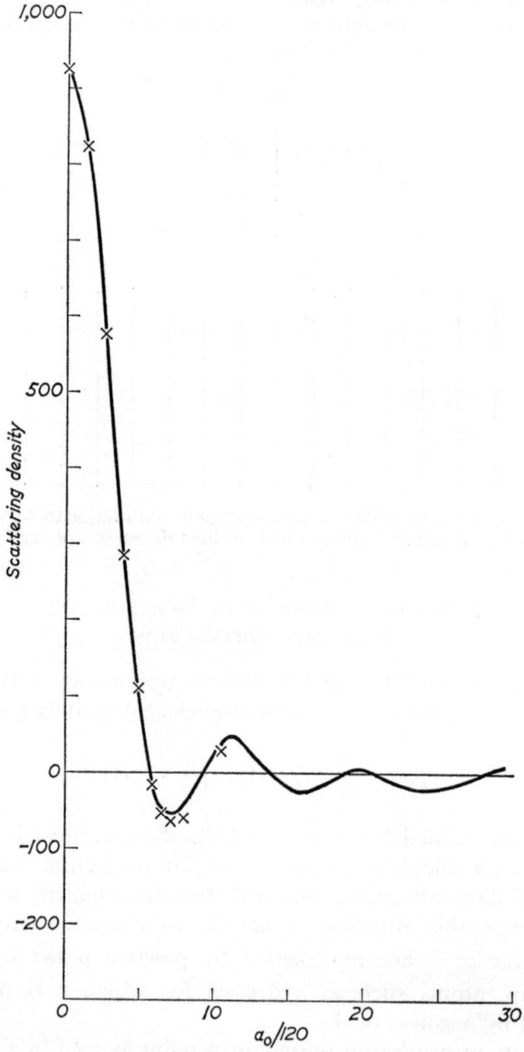

FIG. 366. The calculated nuclear density (with allowance for thermal vibration and series termination) in a projection of superimposed K and P atoms in KH_2PO_4

potassium and phosphorus atoms in a projection of KH_2PO_4. Results are shown in fig. 366. The diffraction ripples are more pronounced than in an electron-density map. Contrary to what has been often asserted, this does not mean that the coordinates of other atoms need be in error, provided that proper allowance is made for series termination, by calculating the difference density or using least-squares refinement techniques (section **12**.3).

The phase problem has not as yet been a serious handicap in neutron diffraction because most structures investigated had already been determined by an X-ray investigation. Where certain features of a structure remained doubtful—for example the positions of hydrogen atoms in ice or in the ammonium halides—the number of possibilities to be tested by trial calculation of structure factors was a manageable one. In principle the use of a novel form of isomorphous replacement (section **8**.3.3) is possible in a neutron-diffraction study, by replacing one isotope by another of different scattering length. The replacement of hydrogen by deuterium provides an obvious example; in most compounds of interest there are however too many hydrogens capable of being replaced simultaneously. In an investigation of the structure of pentaerythritol, Hvoslef (1958) found it useful to make a comparison of neutron intensities for $C(CH_2OH)_4$ and $C(CH_2OD)_4$.

2.2 *Spin density.* The density of magnetic electrons is proportional to

$$\sum_{\mathbf{H}} F_m(\mathbf{H}) \exp(-2\pi i \mathbf{H}\cdot\mathbf{r}).$$

Strictly speaking, it is the difference between the density of electrons with spin 'up' and spin 'down' that is given by this equation. From the definitions of the magnetic scattering length p in terms of electron spin (equation *361*.1) and of the magnetic structure factor F_m (equation *361*.4), the spin density $\sigma(\mathbf{r})$ in units of electron spin per unit volume is given by

$$\frac{e^2\gamma}{mc^2}\sigma(\mathbf{r}) = \frac{1}{V}\sum_{\mathbf{H}} F_m(\mathbf{H}) \exp(-2\pi i \mathbf{H}\cdot\mathbf{r}). \qquad (367)$$

Since a spin of $\frac{1}{2}$ corresponds to a magnetic moment of 1 Bohr magneton (μ_B) the result is often expressed in Bohr magnetons per unit volume, μ_B Å^{-3} being a convenient unit. The absolute scale of the measured values of $|F_m(\mathbf{H})|$ can be obtained by a comparison of magnetic and nuclear structure amplitudes, since the latter can usually be calculated quite accurately from the known values of $\bar{b}$ once the nuclear coordinates have been determined. The constant term $F_m(0)$ in the Fourier series must be chosen so as to give the correct total moment, as determined by magnetic measurements. In an antiferromagnetic structure for example $F_m(0)$ is obviously zero.

The discussion given in section **14**.1.3 applies only to ferromagnetic and simple ferrimagnetic and antiferromagnetic structures in which electron spins are parallel or antiparallel to a particular direction. Much more complicated arrangements have been found in practice, including spin spirals and sinusoidal modulation of spin. These give rise to interesting diffraction patterns. Fourier methods have not been used in their interpretation and a detailed discussion of their investigation and significance would take us too far into the physics of magnetism. The subject has been reviewed by Nathans and Pickart (1963).

2.3. *Distribution of potential.* The potential $\phi(\mathbf{r})$ in a crystal is given by

$$\frac{me}{2\pi\hbar^2}\phi(\mathbf{r}) = \frac{1}{V}\sum_{\mathbf{H}} F_e(\mathbf{H}) \exp(-2\pi i \mathbf{H}\cdot\mathbf{r}). \qquad (368)$$

The constant $2\pi\hbar^2/me$ appears in this expression because it is involved in the conventional definition of $f_e(S)$ (equation *363*.1). This is not in line with the conventional definition of the atomic scattering factor for X-rays, $f(S)$, which does not involve the analogous constant e^2/mc^2, and Cowley and Rees (1958) have in fact advocated a change of notation for electron diffraction. In practice, constants of proportionality in equation (*368*) can be ignored since the scale of the measured $|F_e(\mathbf{H})|$, and the value of $F_e(0)$, are determined by comparison with calculated values of $|F_e(\mathbf{H})|$. This of course involves theoretical values of f_e, and the assumption that the potential in the crystal is a superposition of that of the isolated atoms. In this and other respects the procedure is the same as is used in X-ray analysis. The phase problem is unchanged, for example. Despite the short wave-length generally used in electron diffraction, series-termination effects may not always be unimportant, because of the limited angular range of recording.

3. Examples of Structure Analysis by Neutron and Electron Diffraction

3.1. *The structure of benzene by neutron diffraction.* The space group of crystalline benzene is P*bca* (No. 61) and there are four molecules per unit cell. The centre of a molecule coincides with a crystallographic centre of symmetry and there are therefore three carbon and three hydrogen atoms in the asymmetric unit. Cox, Cruickshank and Smith (1958) made an accurate structure determination at $-3°$ C, using three-dimensional X-ray data, while Bacon, Curry and Wilson (1964) have used neutron measurements at $-55°$ C and at $-135°$ C. The structure amplitudes corresponding to projections along [001], [010], [100] and [101] were utilized in the neutron investigation. At the lower temperature 184 structure amplitudes were measured using a neutron wave-length of 1·08 Å; at the higher temperature a smaller number, 113, could be detected and measured. These numbers may be compared with the number of structure amplitudes measured in the X-ray investigation, which was 284, and with the number of parameters, which is 55 (three positional and six thermal parameters per independent atom, plus a scale factor). The signs of the structure factors were calculated using the positions of carbon atoms determined by Cox et al. (1958) and with hydrogen-atom positions determined for a C—H bond length of 1·08 Å. The coordinate and anisotropic thermal parameters were then determined by the method of least squares (section **12**.3), with appropriate weighting of each measured $F_n(\mathbf{H})$. A small change with temperature in the orientation of each molecule relative to the crystallographic axes was detected and measured. Fig. 369 shows projections

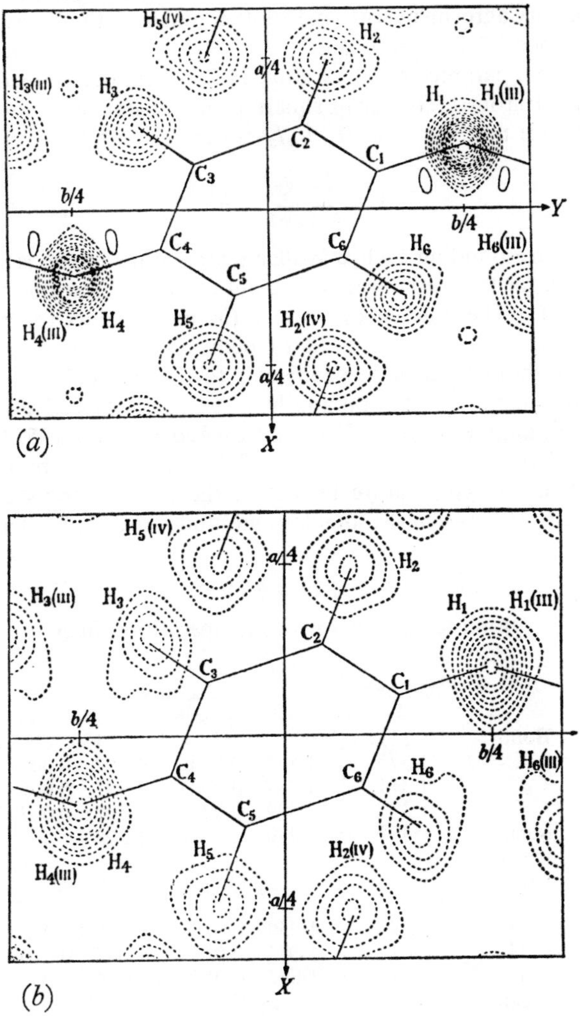

FIG. 369. Projections of the hydrogen atoms in benzene on the (001) plane, by neutron diffraction. In figs. *a* and *b* the crystal is at 138° K and 218° K respectively

of the hydrogen atoms on the (001) plane, obtained by Fourier synthesis of structure factors from which the contributions of the carbon atoms have been subtracted (section **12**.2.5). The contours all enclose negative densities since the scattering length of hydrogen, *b*, is negative (section **13**.1.2). The greater diffuseness of the density at the higher temperature is apparent on comparing figs. 369*a* and *b*. The final bond lengths are shown in table 370, the correction for thermal motion having been made on the assumption that each molecule vibrates as a rigid unit (section **11**.2.5). Values obtained at the two different temperatures are in satisfactory agreement with one another and with the X-ray value for the C—C bond.

Six thermal parameters U_{ij} (section **11**.2.1) were determined for each independent atom. The mean square displacement of an atom in the direction of a unit vector $\mathbf{l}=(l_1, l_2, l_3)$ is then given by

$$u^2 = \sum_{i=1}^{3} \sum_{j=1}^{3} U_{ij} l_i l_j$$

and the corresponding Debye-Waller temperature factor is $B = 8\pi^2 u^2$. Values of B for tangential, radial and out-of-plane directions are shown in table 371. The differences between the mean values for radial and tangential motions can be used to deduce the r.m.s. amplitude of oscillation about an axis perpendicular to the molecular plane. The temperature factors of carbon and hydrogen give respectively 4·9° and 4·4° for this amplitude at −55° C, and 2·5 and 3·4° at −135° C. These values are consistent with the value of 7·9° determined by Cox et al. (1958) from the temperature factors of the carbon atoms at −3° C. The agreement between the angular amplitudes deduced independently

TABLE 370

Bond lengths at various temperatures, in Å

	X-Rays	Neutrons	
Bond	−3° C	−55° C	−135° C
C_1C_2	1·379	1·394 ±0·010	1·392 ±0·007
C_2C_3	1·374	1·387 ±0·009	1·397 ±0·007
C_3C_4	1·379	1·389 ±0·009	1·391 ±0·007
Mean	1·377	1·390	1·393
Corrected value	1·392	1·398	1·398
C_1H_1	—	1·059 ±0·015	1·095 ±0·008
C_2H_2	—	1·085 ±0·017	1·087 ±0·010
C_3H_3	—	1·072 ±0·016	1·076 ±0·009
Mean	—	1·072	1·086
Corrected value	—	1·077	1·090

from the carbon and hydrogen mean temperature factors shows that the assumption of rigid-body motion is a reasonable one.

It is worth recalling at this point that the value of B for a hydrogen atom, as determined by an X-ray investigation, is not only subject to a comparatively large standard deviation but is liable to be systematically too small (section **12**.4.1).

TABLE 371

Values of B in tangential, radial and out-of-plane (⊥) directions. σ is the standard deviation of an individual value

Temp.	Atom	tang.	rad.	⊥	Atom	tang.	rad.	⊥
−135° C	C_1	2·2	1·7	1·8	H_1	3·4	2·6	4·6
	C_2	2·0	1·6	2·2	H_2	4·1	1·7	7·1
	C_3	2·1	2·1	2·3	H_3	4·1	2·2	4·9
	Mean C	2·1	1·8	2·1	Mean H	3·9	2·2	5·5
	σ	0·1	0·1	0·1	σ	0·3	0·3	0·3
	C_1	4·2	3·3	3·2	H_1	9·0	3·1	7·2
−55° C	C_2	4·3	2·9	4·2	H_2	7·6	5·5	7·4
	C_3	4·0	3·2	3·7	H_3	6·5	5·9	6·3
	Mean C	4·2	3·1	3·7	Mean H	7·7	4·8	7·0
	σ	0·2	0·2	0·2	σ	0·6	0·5	0·7
−3° C	Mean C	7·4	4·5	4·8				

3.2. *The structures of UO_2 and of UO_{2+x}.* X-ray powder photographs of UO_2 are consistent with the fluorite-type structure (fig. 371), space group F*m*3*m* (No. 225), but direct evidence for the positions of the oxygen atoms is lacking since the ratio of atomic scattering factors is greater than 11·5, which is the ratio of the atomic numbers. However the appropriate neutron scattering lengths have a ratio of 1·47, and a neutron investigation by Willis (1963) has confirmed the structure shown in fig. 371. Three-dimensional structure amplitudes were

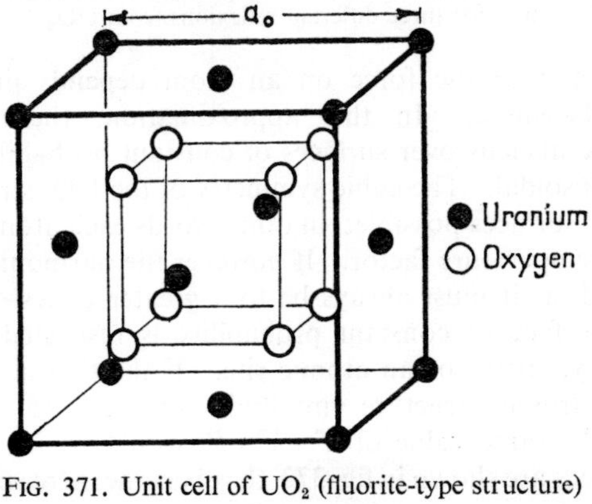

FIG. 371. Unit cell of UO_2 (fluorite-type structure)

carefully measured using single crystals prepared by three different techniques—from the melt, from the vapour and from solution. The results from different crystals showed the influence of secondary extinction in varying degrees, and intensities were corrected for this effect. A least-squares analysis of the data, which consisted of about 20 independent structure amplitudes, led to the results

$$\bar{b}_U/\bar{b}_O = 1{\cdot}474 \pm 0{\cdot}01, \quad B_U = 0{\cdot}31 \pm 0{\cdot}04\text{Å}^2, \quad B_O = 0{\cdot}49 \pm 0{\cdot}06\text{Å}^2$$

for the ratio of scattering lengths and the temperature factors at room temperature. A similar study was made of the isomorphous compound ThO_2.

Measurements were also made on single crystals at temperatures up to 1100° C. It was discovered that the results were inconsistent with the usual theory of thermal vibration, which involves the harmonic

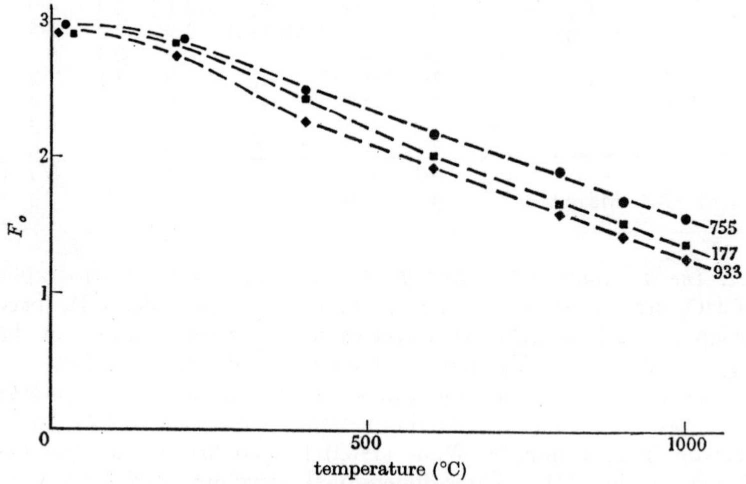

FIG. 372. Measured values of structure amplitudes as functions of temperature for three different reflexions from UO_2

approximation, that the force on an atom depends linearly on its relative displacement. In this approximation, thermal vibration distributes the nucleus over surfaces of constant probability which are in general ellipsoidal. The cubic symmetry of the UO_2 structure makes only spherical surfaces possible; in other words each atom should have an isotropic temperature factor. If however the harmonic approximation is invalid, as it must always be to a greater or lesser degree, the shape of a surface of constant probability is restricted only by the point-group symmetry of an atomic site. If the thermal vibration in UO_2 were isotropic, structure amplitudes such as 755, 177, and 933 which have the same value of $h^2+k^2+l^2$, would be identical. Their measured values are shown in fig. 372, they become increasingly different as the temperature increases. This can be explained if it is assumed that each oxygen atom can move more easily towards each of four equidistant interstitial holes in the structure than in the opposite directions, in which four equidistant uranium atoms lie (fig. 373). This

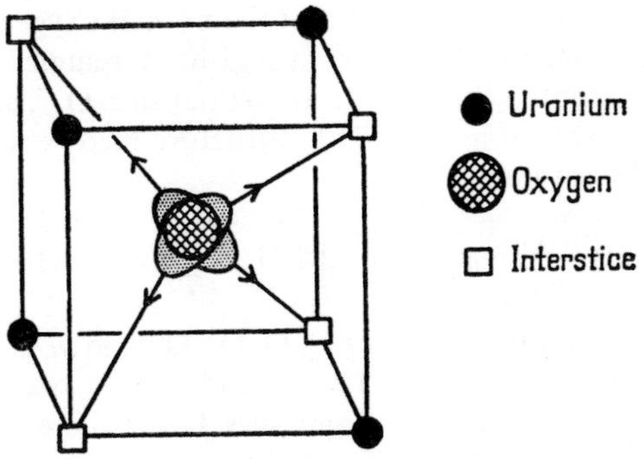

FIG. 373. Diagram showing extension of the oxygen atom under the influence of thermal vibration

is physically very plausible. The precise shape of the non-spherical surfaces was not determined by the limited data available, but satisfactory agreement between observed and calculated structure factors was obtained by putting one quarter of an oxygen atom in each of four positions, such as $(\frac{1}{4}+\delta, \frac{1}{4}+\delta, \frac{1}{4}+\delta)$, $(\frac{1}{4}-\delta, \frac{1}{4}-\delta, \frac{1}{4}+\delta)$, $(\frac{1}{4}+\delta, \frac{1}{4}-\delta, \frac{1}{4}-\delta)$, $(\frac{1}{4}-\delta, \frac{1}{4}+\delta, \frac{1}{4}-\delta)$ instead of one in the site $(\frac{1}{4}, \frac{1}{4}, \frac{1}{4})$. Each fractional oxygen had the same isotropic temperature factor. The results obtained by a least-squares analysis of the data at 1000° C were as follows:

B_U	B_O	δ	R-factor
1·07 ± 0·05 Å²	1·26 ± 0·10 Å²	0·016 ± 0·001	3·3%

This statistical distribution of the oxygen atoms is almost certainly not to be interpreted literally as a static random distribution over new sites; it represents an approximation to the effect of anisotropic anharmonic thermal vibration. Values of δ determined from the experimental data increase uniformly with increasing temperature, the value at room temperature being scarcely measurable. The vibration of U atoms is isotropic at all temperatures, as might be expected from their more symmetrical environment. Anisotropic thermal vibration as a consequence of anharmonicity has also been detected for the fluorine atoms in CaF_2 (Willis, 1965).

At temperatures below 1800° C, UO_2 can be oxidized to the non-stoichiometric compound UO_{2+x}. Three-dimensional structure factors were measured for a single crystal of composition $UO_{2\cdot12}$ at 800° C, with careful checks for the effects of secondary extinction and double

Bragg reflexion (Willis, 1964). The space group was found still to be F*m*3*m*, and projections of the difference density, calculated with signs of structure factors appropriate to UO_2 and with the uranium and normal oxygen atoms subtracted out, showed that there was partial occupation of *two* sites, O′ and O″ and their symmetry-related equivalents, by interstitial oxygens, and that the normal oxygen sites were not fully occupied. (Before this work it had been assumed that the additional oxygen atoms went into the interstitial sites O‴, such as $(\frac{1}{2}, \frac{1}{2}, \frac{1}{2})$ etc., which are shown in fig. 373.) Structure factors should therefore be fitted by the formula

$$F(\mathbf{H}) = \sum_{j=1}^{4} m_j \bar{b}_j \exp\left(-\tfrac{1}{4}B_j H^2\right)\left\{\sum_t \exp 2\pi i \mathbf{H}\cdot\mathbf{r}_t\right\} \qquad (374)$$

The first sum is over the four sites U, O, O′, O″ and m_j is the occupation number of a particular site. The second sum is over all equivalent positions of the space group. For every U-site there are two O-sites, twenty-four O′-sites and sixteen O″-sites (see fig. 374). Although

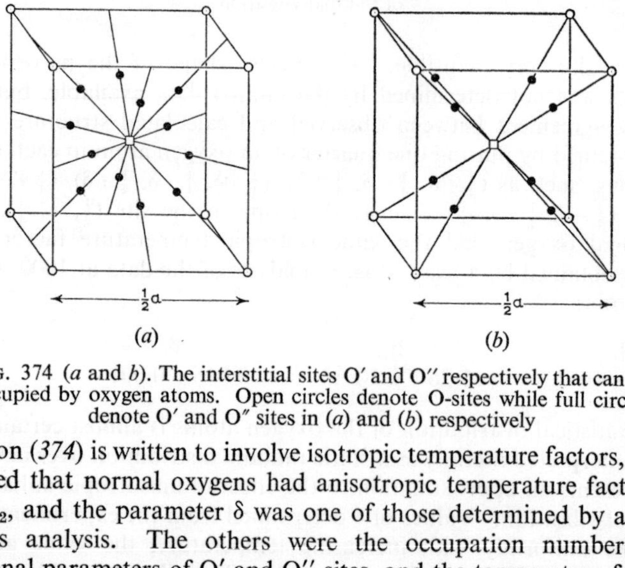

FIG. 374 (*a* and *b*). The interstitial sites O′ and O″ respectively that can be occupied by oxygen atoms. Open circles denote O-sites while full circles denote O′ and O″ sites in (*a*) and (*b*) respectively

equation (*374*) is written to involve isotropic temperature factors, it was assumed that normal oxygens had anisotropic temperature factors as in UO_2, and the parameter δ was one of those determined by a least-squares analysis. The others were the occupation numbers, the positional parameters of O′ and O″ sites, and the temperature factors. The results are shown in table 375.

Within the limits of error there are no oxygen atoms in O‴ sites, and the formula $UO_{2\cdot12}$ can be written as $UO_{1\cdot87}\,O'_{0\cdot08}\,O''_{0\cdot16}$. It should be emphasized that equation (*374*) refers to the statistical unit cell; the comparatively large values of B for O′ and O″ probably indicate that in fact atoms in different unit cells have somewhat different values of *v* and *w*—another aspect of the fact that measurement of Bragg intensities cannot distinguish static and dynamic effects. It is unlikely that

TABLE 375

Atom	Coordinates x	y	z	Contribution to 2·12 oxygens	B in Å²
U	0	0	0	—	1·18 ±0·02
O	$\frac{1}{4}$	$\frac{1}{4}$	$\frac{1}{4}$	1·87 ±0·02	1·45 ±0·04
O′	$\frac{1}{2}$	v	v	0·08 ±0·04	1·8 ±1·4
O″	w	w	w	0·16 ±0·06	2·0 ±1·6
O‴	$\frac{1}{2}$	$\frac{1}{2}$	$\frac{1}{2}$	−0·02 ±0·02	2·0 (fixed)

$v=0{\cdot}38 \pm 0{\cdot}01$, $w=0{\cdot}41 \pm 0{\cdot}01$.

vacancies and extra atoms occur completely at random as this would sometimes have the effect of bringing atoms much too close together. Willis has suggested that when two extra oxygen atoms enter the structure at adjacent O′ sites, the two closest atoms on O-sites are ejected to O″-sites. This would give a composition $UO_{1\cdot 88}\,O'_{0\cdot 12}\,O''_{0\cdot 12}$, in fair agreement with observation, and there are then no impossibly short interatomic distances.

3.3. *Spin density in Mn_2Sb.* The crystal structure of the ferrimagnetic intermetallic compound Mn_2Sb is tetragonal and contains non-equivalent manganese atoms. Mn(I) atoms are located at (0, 0, 0) and ($\frac{1}{2}$, $\frac{1}{2}$, 0), Mn(II) atoms at (0, $\frac{1}{2}$, z_1), ($\frac{1}{2}$, 0, $\bar{z}_1$). The (non-magnetic) antimony atoms are located at (0, $\frac{1}{2}$, z_2), ($\frac{1}{2}$, 0, $\bar{z}_2$), the space group being P4/*nmm* (No. 129). The magnetic structure was determined by Wilkinson, Gingrich and Shull (1957), who showed that Mn atoms of type I and II have oppositely directed unequal moments. The net moment of two manganese atoms, from magnetic measurements, is 1·18 μ_B, which serves to determine $F_m(0)$. Values of $F_m(\mathbf{H})$ for two zones of reflexions out to $\sin\theta/\lambda \approx 0{\cdot}8$ Å^{-1} were determined by Alperin, Brown and Nathans (1963) using the technique of polarized neutrons. In this instance the intensity is determined by $(F_n+F_m)^2$ when the incident neutrons are polarized in one direction, $(F_n-F_m)^2$ when their polarization is reversed (cf. equation (*362*)). The atomic coordinates and Debye-Waller temperature factors were accurately determined by a separate X-ray investigation which was made because small single crystals of good quality were available, giving reflexions over a considerably greater range than the crystals used for the neutron investigation. Values of F_n could then be calculated from the known values of $\bar{b}$ for manganese and antimony, and hence values of F_m were obtained on an absolute scale. The space group is centrosymmetric. The spin density in projection on (110) and on (001) was calculated (equation (*367*), modified to apply to a projection). Fig. 376 shows the spin density for

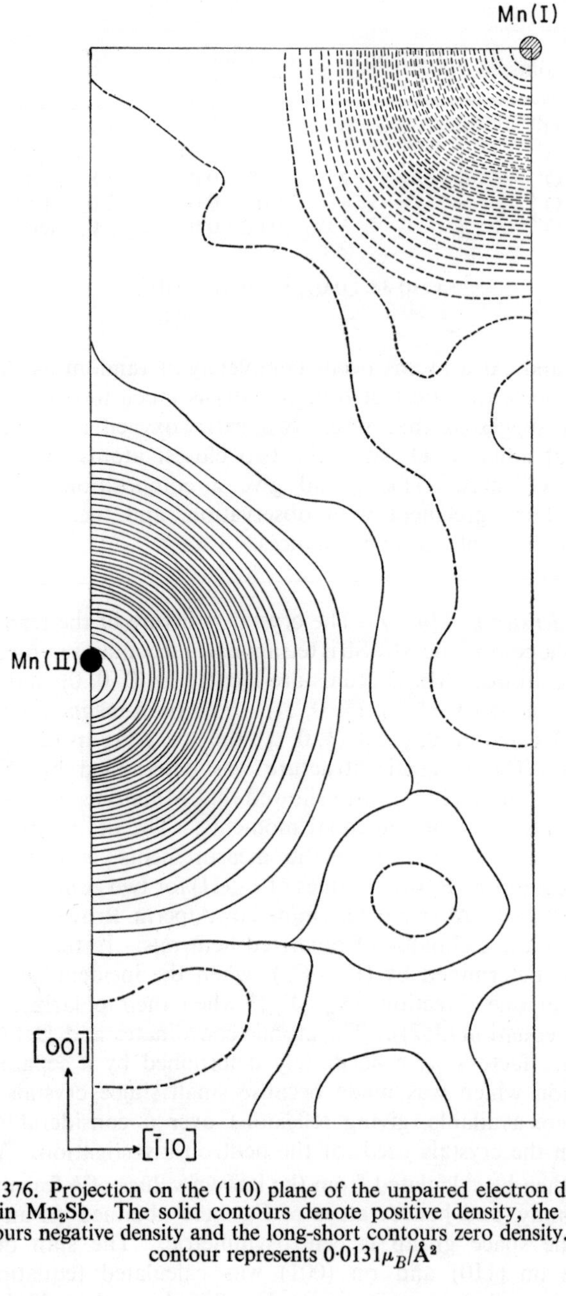

FIG. 376. Projection on the (110) plane of the unpaired electron distribution in Mn_2Sb. The solid contours denote positive density, the dashed contours negative density and the long-short contours zero density. Each contour represents $0{\cdot}0131\mu_B/\text{Å}^2$

the asymmetric unit projected on (110). The standard deviation of this density was estimated to be about one contour interval. The most interesting feature of the map is the displacement of the Mn (II) spin density from the nucleus by 0·025 ± 0·010 Å in the direction of the nearest antimony atom. The projection on (001) showed a similar feature. This may indicate that the interaction between the ferromagnetically aligned Mn (II) atoms takes place through the neighbouring antimony atoms.

The presentation of the results in the form of a map of the 'difference density' (section **12**.2.5) is a useful way of showing the effect of covalent bonding on the outer electron distribution. An example is provided by the work of Pickart and Nathans (1961) on ordered Fe_3Al.

3.4. *Potential distribution in diketopiperazine.* The study of diketopiperazine by Vainshtein (1955) is one of the most complete structure analyses made by electron diffraction. From arc patterns produced by polycrystalline material with a high degree of preferred orientation the intensities of about 280 reflexions were measured. In some 25 instances two arcs overlapped, and the measured intensity was apportioned in the

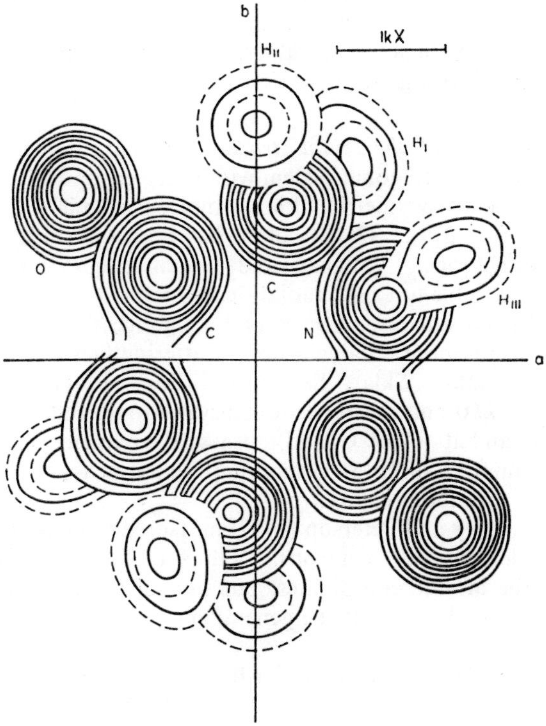

FIG. 377. Three-dimensional potential distribution in diketopiperazine, derived by means of electron diffraction (after Vainshtein)

ratio of the calculated intensities. The 0*k*0 reflexions were not recorded as the *b*-axis was the axis of preferred orientation, and estimated intensities were used. The derived structure amplitudes $F_e(\mathbf{H})$ were estimated to have standard deviations of perhaps 15 per cent. The signs of the structure factors were calculated in the usual way, using the atomic coordinates which Corey (1938) obtained from an X-ray investigation. Projected sections of the three-dimensional potential, and sections through it, were calculated. Fig. 377 shows a composite map made up of parallel sections through the atomic centres. The two hydrogen atoms covalently bonded to a carbon atom showed maximum potentials of 33 and 32 V; that bonded to a nitrogen atom showed a maximum of 36 V, corresponding to a reduced electron density, as might be expected from the formation of a N—H---O bond. The standard deviation of a bond length not involving hydrogen was estimated to be 0·012 Å; however the values deviate by amounts ranging from 0·019 to 0·055 Å from those found by Degeilh and Marsh (1959) in a subsequent X-ray investigation using 1144 measured reflexions. There can be no doubt that the X-ray measurements in this instance led to more accurate C—C and C—N bond lengths. On the other hand, the lengths of C—H and N—H bonds derived from the X-ray investigation are consistently about 0·15 Å shorter than those obtained by Vainshtein, which agree well with accepted values. Similar discrepancies have been found in other investigations (section **12**.4.1).

3.5. *Investigations of the crytal structure of urea.* Urea, $CO(NH_2)_2$, crystallizes in the tetragonal system with space group $P\bar{4}2_1m$ (No. 113), which is not centrosymmetric. Planar molecules lie in (110) and $(\bar{1}10)$ type planes (fig. 379). The structure has been the subject of several X-ray investigations. Vaughan and Donohue (1952) measured all intensities accessible to Cu K_α radiation and refined the structure by the method of least squares. Caron and Donohue (1964) repeated the refinement using more reliable atomic scattering factors, but the same experimental data. Sklar, Senko and Post (1961) measured the intensities of *hk*0 and *h*0*l* reflections using Mo K_α radiation, at room temperature and at −140° C, and repeated the refinement with the new data. The number of *h*0*l* structure amplitudes measured at the lower temperature was about eighty.

Worsham, Levy and Peterson (1957) measured the intensities of over fifty *h*0*l* reflexions with neutrons. Values of F(*h*0*l*) are sufficient to determine the atomic coordinates, but not all the parameters of the thermal motion. If we write the general anisotropic temperature factor as

$$\exp -\tfrac{1}{4}(B_{11}H_1^2+B_{22}H_2^2+B_{33}H_3^2+B_{12}H_1H_2+B_{23}H_2H_3+B_{31}H_3H_1),$$

where (H_1, H_2, H_3) are the components of a reciprocal lattice vector $\mathbf{H}$, then B_{11} etc. are closely analogous to B which appears in the expression for the isotropic temperature factor. The symmetry relations between the B_{ij} of the atoms in urea has been given by Worsham, Levy and Peterson (1957). The subject is discussed more generally in Chapter 11. We need only note here that there are three independent temperature parameters for C and O, and four for N and H. The *h0l* data allow the determination of two of these for C and O, and three for N and H.

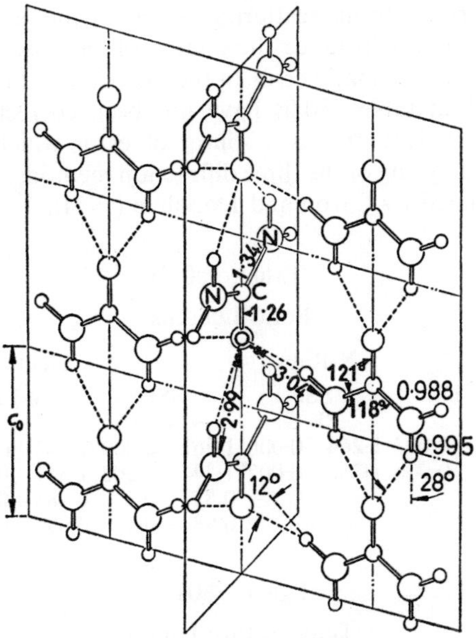

FIG. 379. The structure of urea, showing how the planar molecules lie in two sets of orthogonal planes

The structure has been the subject of an electron-diffraction investigation by Lobachev and Vainshtein (1961) who measured the intensities of over sixty *h0l* reflections. Projections of the potential on the (010) plane were calculated, and bond lengths and angles derived. The anisotropy of thermal vibration was apparent in the potential distribution, but quantitative deductions were not attempted.

Table 380 (i) shows bond lengths and their standard deviations from five separate investigations. Temperature factors are given in table 380 (ii). The standard deviations of the results have been arrived at from the agreement between observed and calculated structure factors, as described in Chapter 12. It is apparent from the tables that the agreement between results obtained by different techniques is generally satisfactory. Results involving hydrogen atoms are of course not reliably determined by the X-ray investigations. There are significant differences between the values of B_{33} at room temperature deduced from X-ray and from neutron measurements respectively. Real differences between temperature parameters determined by different techniques can of course occur because the outer electrons of an atom may not move rigidly with the nucleus. We have already noted that a similar effect may operate in the case of hydrogen atoms (Chapter 12). For other atoms in urea however such an effect is not adequate to account for the discrepancies. Apparent differences could result from the use of incorrect atomic scattering factors or the neglect of bonding electrons, but in this instance the source of the discrepancy is more likely to be some systematic error in the experimental data. The bond lengths quoted in table 380 (i) have not been corrected for thermal motion (Chapter 12); this is a source of error which will affect the results obtained by any of the three diffraction methods. The correction has been estimated by Caron and Donohue (1964).

TABLE 380 (i)

Bond Lengths

	X-Rays			Neutrons	Electrons
	CD	SSP 20° C	SSP −140° C	WLP	LV
C—O	1·268 ± 0·007	1·264 ± 0·006	1·262 ± 0·003	1·243 ± 0·006	1·28 ± 0·02
C—N	1·326 ± 0·006	1·336 ± 0·007	1·341 ± 0·003	1·351 ± 0·007	1·35 ± 0·02
N—H(1)			0·83 ± 0·1	0·988 ± 0·02	1·07 ± 0·06
N—H(2)			0·98 ± 0·1	0·995 ± 0·01	1·05 ± 0·06

TABLE 380 (ii)

Temperature Factors

		X-Rays			Neutrons
		CD	SSP 20° C	SSP −140° C	WLP
N	B_{11}	5·86 ± 0·17	5·2 ± 0·16	2·57 ± 0·07	4·86 ± 0·20
	B_{33}	1·74 ± 0·17	1·8 ± 0·09	0·98 ± 0·03	1·39 ± 0·09
	B_{13}	−0·43 ± 0·21	0·08 ± 0·09	0·05 ± 0·04	0·14 ± 0·24
C	B_{11}	2·85 ± 0·14	2·75 ± 0·14	1·34 ± 0·07	2·35 ± 0·24
	B_{33}	1·87 ± 0·21	1·56 ± 0·16	0·88 ± 0·04	0·85 ± 0·14
O	B_{11}	4·15 ± 0·16	3·65 ± 0·16	1·63 ± 0·06	3·74 ± 0·34
	B_{33}	1·38 ± 0·15	1·68 ± 0·08	0·78 ± 0·03	0·80 ± 0·12
H(1)	B_{11}				6·33 ± 0·64
	B_{33}	2·60 ± 1·40 (isotropic)			3·54 ± 0·43
	B_{13}				0·68 ± 0·92
H(2)	B_{11}				6·72 ± 0·53
	B_{33}	1·00 ± 1 10 (isotropic)			1·82 ± 0·18
	B_{13}				−0·45 ± 0·69

4. SUMMARY

Neutron crystallography has given much information which could not have been obtained in any other way. Atoms which could be distinguished only with difficulty using X-rays can often be readily distinguished by their very different scattering lengths for neutrons. The positions of light atoms, such as hydrogen in an organic molecule, can only be roughly determined using X-rays; by the use of neutrons they can be located almost as precisely as the other atoms. Measurements of the same percentage accuracy and covering the same range may lead to results of slightly greater accuracy with neutrons than with X-rays since scattering lengths are likely to be more accurately known than atomic scattering factors, and these are involved in the elimination of series-termination errors. Atomic coordinates and temperature factors are more directly related to neutron than to X-ray intensities, since even when the atomic scattering factors of isolated atoms are accurately known, there must be a redistribution of electrons in the bonds. On the other hand the electron distribution is of considerable interest in itself, and cannot be studied by neutron methods unless atoms with a magnetic moment are involved, in which case very interesting results can be obtained. At the present time structural studies made using the two techniques have led to results of apparently about the same accuracy; but there are some unexplained discrepancies. The chief drawbacks of neutron crystallography are purely practical ones, namely the small number of neutron sources available and their relative weakness which would necessitate the use of larger single crystals than are often available.

Electron diffraction has given results of considerable interest for their own sake; as a means of structure analysis it is, at least at the present time, inferior to the other two diffraction techniques because of the many difficulties which stand in the way of making accurate intensity measurements.

CHAPTER 14

ANOMALOUS SCATTERING AND STRUCTURE DETERMINATION

1. General Discussion

1.1. *Elementary theory.* The theory of anomalous scattering, and its relation to the absorption and refraction of X-rays has been fully dealt with in Vol. II of this series (James, 1957). There is an analogy between the quantum-mechanical theory of X-ray scattering and the classical theory of scattering, and a brief discussion of the latter will serve to illustrate those features of the former which are important for crystal-structure analysis. The equation of motion of a classical electron in a periodic field $E_0 \exp(i\omega t)$ is

$$\frac{d^2x}{dt^2}+k\frac{dx}{dt}+\omega_s^2x=\frac{e}{m}E_0\exp(i\omega t) \qquad (382.1)$$

where k is a damping constant and ω_s is the resonant (circular) frequency of the bound electron. The electron makes a forced oscillation of frequency ω, giving rise to an oscillating dipole moment

$$M=ex=\frac{e^2}{m}\frac{E_0\exp(i\omega t)}{\omega_s^2-\omega^2+ik\omega}. \qquad (382.2)$$

This oscillating dipole is the source of a scattered electromagnetic wave which at distance R in the plane perpendicular to x has an electric field

$$E_s=\frac{e^2}{Rmc^2}\frac{\omega^2E_0\exp i\omega(t-R/c)}{\omega_s^2-\omega^2+ik\omega} \qquad (382.3)$$

(James, 1957). The result for a free electron is obtained by putting $\omega_s=0$, $k=0$, and we see from equation (*382*.3) that a free electron scatters 180° out of phase with the primary wave. Taking the free electron as our unit, therefore, the scattering factor of a bound, damped electron is given by

$$f=\omega^2/(\omega^2-\omega_s^2-ik\omega). \qquad (382.4)$$

For normally used X-ray wave-lengths only the most tightly bound electrons in an atom have resonance frequencies ω_s approaching or exceeding ω, so that for the atomic scattering factor only the contributions of the innermost electrons differ appreciably from their normal values calculated on the assumption that ω_s and k are zero. The atomic scattering factor may therefore be written

$$f=f_0+\Delta f'+i\Delta f'' \qquad (382.5)$$

where f_0 is the Fourier transform of the electron distribution. The correcting terms are often small enough to be ignored, as they have been in other chapters of the book, but particularly when the frequency of the primary radiation is just above that corresponding to an absorption edge of the scattering atom, the term $\Delta f''$ can lead to important effects. Values of $\Delta f'$ and $\Delta f''$ for various elements and wave-lengths have been calculated by Dauben and Templeton (1955). A more extensive table is given in International Tables, Vol. III (1962). To a fairly good approximation $\Delta f'$ and $\Delta f''$ may be taken to be independent of scattering angle, since the most tightly bound electrons occupy only a small volume around the nucleus.

It can be seen from equation *382*.4 that the imaginary term $\Delta f''$ is always positive; that is, the phase of the scattered radiation is advanced relative to that from a normally-scattering atom. This is a physical result; another way of expressing it is that if an atom A which scatters anomalously and a normal atom N are to scatter *in phase*, N must be displaced a small distance relative to A in the direction of the scattering vector S (fig. 383), so as to *decrease* the path length between source $\mathscr{S}$

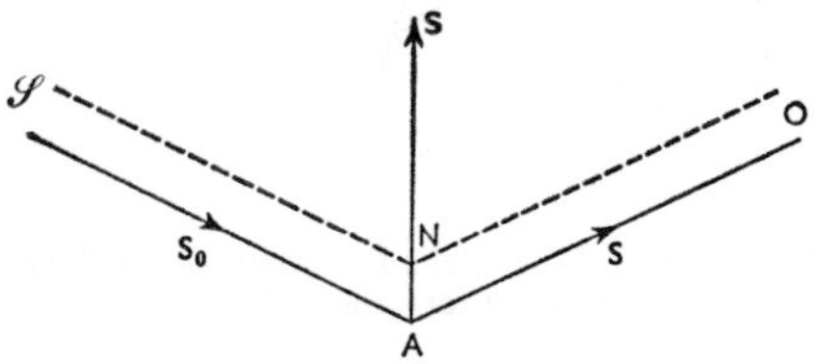

FIG. 383. Illustrates the condition for normal (N) and anomalous (A) scatterers to be in phase

and point of observation O. In this book we use complex exponentials with a sign convention such that an electron at **r** contributes exp $(2\pi i\mathbf{r}\cdot\mathbf{S})$ to the scattered amplitude (section **1**.2.6); it follows that the scattering factor of an atom which scatters anomalously should appear in the form $f = f' + if''$, with $f'' > 0$, and equation (*382*.4) agrees with this. If however we had used the convention that an electron at **r** contributes exp $(-2\pi i\,\mathbf{r}\cdot\mathbf{S})$, it would be necessary to write the scattering factor of an atom which scatters anomalously as $f = f' - if''$, with $f'' > 0$. This is a fruitful source of confusion, arising from the fact that advancement of phase or increase of time is usually represented by counter-clockwise rotation on a rotating-vector diagram (as in this book), but the opposite convention is possible and admixture can lead to errors.

Anomalous scattering leads to the breakdown of Friedel's law for crystals in which the atoms are not related by a centre of symmetry. This is seen as follows:

$$\begin{aligned} F(\mathbf{H}) &= \sum_j (f_j' + if_j'') \exp(2\pi i\mathbf{H}\cdot\mathbf{r}_j) \\ F(-\mathbf{H}) &= \sum_j (f_j' + if_j'') \exp(-2\pi i\mathbf{H}\cdot\mathbf{r}_j) \neq F^*(\mathbf{H}), \end{aligned} \qquad (383)$$

from which it follows that $|F(\mathbf{H})|^2 \neq |F(-\mathbf{H})|^2$. This is illustrated in fig. 384 for a crystal with two atoms per unit cell, one of which scatters anomalously.

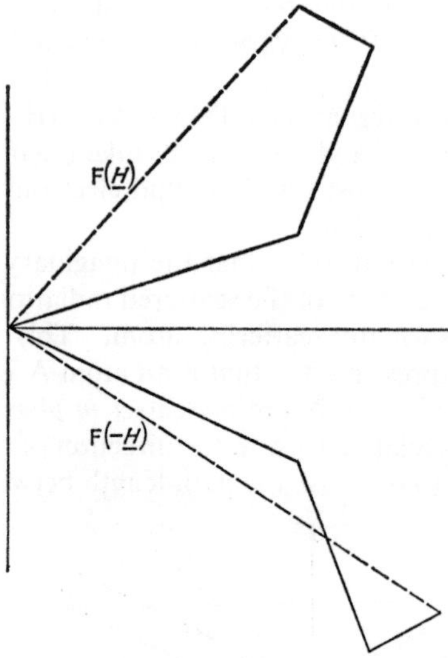

FIG. 384. The breakdown of Friedel's law when one of two atoms in the unit cell scatters anomalously

Anomalous scattering can therefore be used as a test for centrosymmetry, and also as a means of acquiring additional structural information, as a means of distinguishing enantiomorphic structures, and to some extent for direct structure analysis.

1.2. *Anomalous scattering by ZnS.* A classic experiment on anomalous scattering was made by Coster, Knol and Prins (1930). Opposite octahedral faces on a natural crystal of cubic zinc sulphide differ in appearance: one face is shinier and better developed than the other; the former becomes positively charged when the crystal is compressed in the [111] direction and is conventionally taken to be a (111) face; the opposite less well developed face is then $(\overline{1}\overline{1}\overline{1})$. The sequence of atomic planes in ZnS is shown in fig. 385 (i); that face B is in fact (111) was shown by the experiment, in which Au $L\alpha_1$ ($\lambda = 1{\cdot}274$ Å) and Au $L\alpha_2$ ($\lambda = 1{\cdot}285$ Å) radiations were used. The zinc atom has an absorption edge at 1·281 Å, and it was calculated that while for Au $L\alpha_2$ radiation, sulphur and zinc would scatter in phase if coincident, for Au $L\alpha_1$ the relative phase of the scattering by zinc would be advanced by $10\frac{1}{2}°$. In first-order reflexion from face A, the spatial separation of the layers advances by 90° the relative phase of the scattering by zinc, giving a nett phase difference of $90+10\frac{1}{2}=100\frac{1}{2}°$, while in reflexion from face B the relative phase of the scattering by zinc is advanced by $-90+10\frac{1}{2}=-79\frac{1}{2}°$. This smaller phase difference results in stronger reflexion of Au $L\alpha_1$ radiation from face B than from face A. In the experiment the intensity of the Au $L\alpha_2$ reflexions served as a standard to eliminate effects of varying surface roughness etc., and it was found that the (111) face corresponds to B. The result is important for the theory of piezoelectricity.

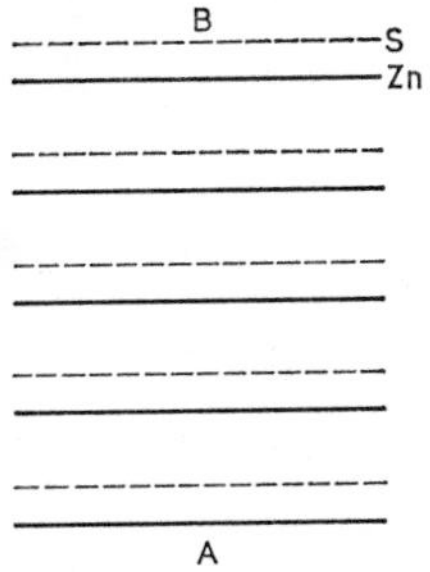

FIG. 385 (1). Sequence of planes in the [111] direction in zinc blende, ZnS

1.3. *Configurations in enantiomorphs.* It was first pointed out by Bijvoet (1949) that anomalous scattering can be used to determine the absolute configuration of molecules, that is, to distinguish optical isomers. The investigation of ZnS is sometimes erroneously cited as an example, but this structure is its own enantiomorph. In the experiment described in the previous section, a structural feature was related to morphological and piezoelectric properties of the crystal. A crystal used for a determination of absolute configuration need not have recognizable faces, but one must know whether the molecules have the D or the L-configuration, as determined by the direction of rotation of the plane of polarized light by the substance in solution. Naturally-occurring amino acids have the L-configuration, and according to the standard Fischer convention used by chemists, L-alanine would be represented as in fig. 385 (ii). That this is in fact the correct choice was discovered by

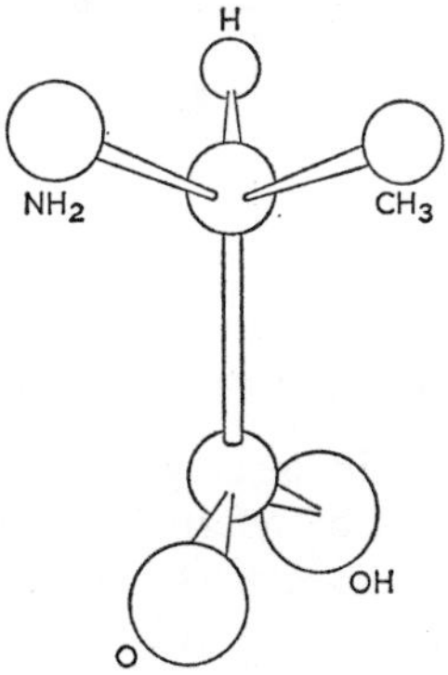

FIG. 385 (ii). A molecule of L-alanine, in the correct configuration. (Hydrogen atoms not all shown)

the investigation of Na Rb tartrate (Peerdeman, van Bommel and Bijvoet, 1951) and of the hydrobromide of D-isoleucine (Trommel and Bijvoet, 1954), using anomalous scattering techniques.

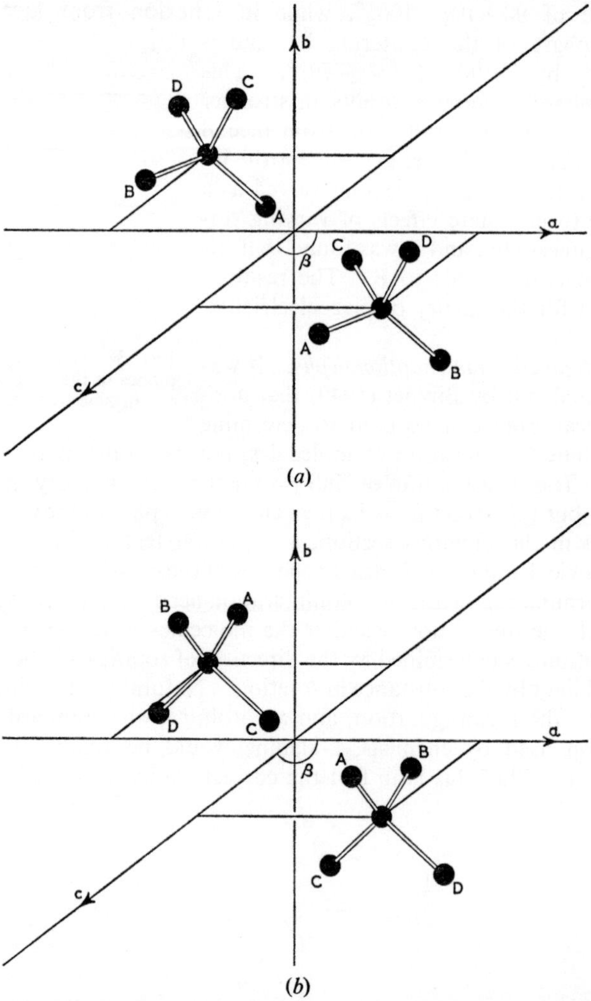

FIG. 386. Two enantiomorphic structures in the space group P2

If a substance crystallizes in space group P1 with one asymmetric molecule per unit cell, it can be referred to a right-handed system of axes having the interaxial angles α, β, γ greater than 90°. The reciprocal axes then give a right-handed system with α^*, β^*, γ^* less than 90°. This suffices to distinguish the reciprocal lattice points hkl and $\bar{h}\bar{k}\bar{l}$. Intensities can then be calculated assuming a particular configuration for the molecule and the results compared with observation. Suppose however that the space group is P2, and that the two possible enantiomorphic structures are as shown in fig. 386*a* and fig. 386*b*. They are referred to the same right-handed system of axes, with $\beta > 90°$, and could not be distinguished unless at least one atom of the asymmetric unit scatters anomalously. The a^* and c^* axes must then enclose $\beta^* < 90°$, and when these have been chosen the direction of positive b^* is uniquely defined as giving a right-handed system. While this serves to distinguish the points hkl and $\bar{h}\,\bar{k}\,\bar{l}$, it does not distinguish between hkl and $\bar{h}\,k\,\bar{l}$. This is however of no importance since $F(hkl) = F(\bar{h}\,k\,\bar{l})$ by symmetry.

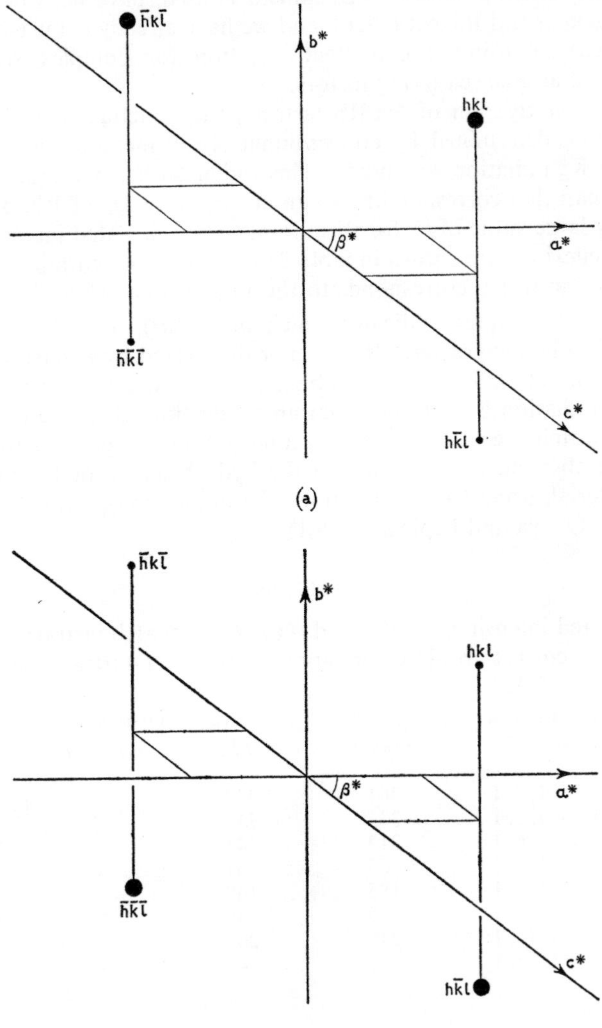

FIG. 387. Schematic representation of the weighted reciprocal lattices of the two structures shown in fig. 386

The patterns of intensities corresponding to the structures shown in figs. 386*a* and 386*b* are represented diagrammatically in figs. 387*a* and 387*b* respectively. Just as there is no rotation which will bring the two structures into coincidence, there is no rotation which will bring the two weighted reciprocal lattices into coincidence, and one intensity pattern corresponds to one particular enantiomorph. Precautions which should be taken in practice to avoid mistakes in indexing, particularly when a Weissenberg camera is used, have been described by Peerdeman and Bijvoet (1956), and we have already emphasised the importance of using a consistent notation for complex structure factors and atomic scattering factors.

In the investigation of Na Rb tartrate, the structure of which had earlier been determined by conventional X-ray methods, monochromatic Zr K_α radiation was used. This radiation has a frequency just greater than that corresponding to an absorption edge of Rb, giving a relatively large value of f'' for this atom. The calculated intensities of certain reflexions are shown in table 388, using a configuration for the L-tartrate ion which corresponds to the Fischer one, while the symbol in the fourth column indicates which of $|F(hkl)|$ and $|F(\bar{h}\bar{k}\bar{l})|$ was observed to be the greater. It was later discovered by Peterson (1955) that measurable effects can be obtained when the frequency of the incident radiation is quite far from an absorption edge of an element such as bromine, and it has become almost common practice to determine the absolute configuration of the hydrobromide or hydroiodide of a material, using Cu K_α radiation. Examples are given in a review article by Okaya and Pepinsky (1961).

TABLE 388

Calculated intensities $\mathscr{I}(hkl)$ and $\mathscr{I}(\bar{h}\bar{k}\bar{l})$ for NaRb tartrate, using the correct absolute configuration for the L-tartrate ion

Indices hkl	Calculated . . . $\mathscr{I}(hkl)$	intensities $\mathscr{I}(\bar{h}\bar{k}\bar{l})$	Observation hkl $\bar{h}\bar{k}\bar{l}$
1, 4, 1	361	377	?
1, 5, 1	337	313	?
1, 6, 1	313	241	>
1, 7, 1	65	241	<
1, 8, 1	185	148	>
1, 9, 1	65	46	>
1, 10, 1	248	208	>
1, 11, 1	27	41	<

In the case of α-quartz, determination of the absolute configuration means establishing whether the space group of a given crystal is $P3_12$ or $P3_22$. The specimen used by de Vries (1958) in an anomalous scattering experiment rotated the plane of polarized light in a clockwise direction (for an observer looking in the direction in which the light is travelling, usually described as laevorotation) and was found to contain right-handed spirals in its structure, in agreement with a prediction of Wooster (1953).

The absolute configurations of several ferroelectric crystals have been determined by Pepinsky and his collaborators (see Okaya and Pepinsky, 1961). A biasing electric field can be used to switch the spontaneous polarization of a crystal such as $BaTiO_3$, thus converting *hkl* to $\bar{h}\bar{k}\bar{l}$ and facilitating the experimental measurements. It was found that in this material the positive direction of spontaneous polarization is the direction of displacement of the titanium ion. This particular investigation is in the same category as the experiment on ZnS (section **14**.1.2); it relates a structural feature to a physical property and does not distinguish two enantiomorphs, since the structure of tetragonal $BaTiO_3$ is its own enantiomorph.

2. Use of Anomalous Scattering for Direct Structure Analysis

2.1. *Patterson methods.* It was pointed out by Okaya, Saito and Pepinsky (1955) that when a crystal contains one or a few atoms per unit cell which scatter anomalously, the problem of interpreting the Patterson function is greatly simplified, provided reliable measurements of $|F(\mathbf{H})|^2 - |F(-\mathbf{H})|^2$ can be made. The Patterson function is given by

$$P(\mathbf{r}) = \frac{1}{V}\sum_{\mathbf{H}} |F(\mathbf{H})|^2 \exp(-2\pi i\mathbf{H}\cdot\mathbf{r}) \qquad (389.1)$$

and is the result of convoluting $\rho(\mathbf{r})$ with $\rho^*(-\mathbf{r})$. Both $\rho(\mathbf{r})$ and $P(\mathbf{r})$ now have imaginary components, and we write

$$P(\mathbf{r}) = P^e(\mathbf{r}) - iP^o(\mathbf{r}). \qquad (389.2)$$

The minus sign in equation (*389*.2) is arbitrary, and follows the convention of Okaya and Pepinsky (1961). Thus

$$P^e(\mathbf{r}) = \frac{1}{V}\sum_{\mathbf{H}} |F(\mathbf{H})|^2 \cos 2\pi\mathbf{H}\cdot\mathbf{r},$$

and (*389*.3)

$$P^o(\mathbf{r}) = \frac{1}{V}\sum_{\mathbf{H}} |F(\mathbf{H})|^2 \sin 2\pi\mathbf{H}\cdot\mathbf{r}$$

the superscripts indicating that these real functions have even and odd symmetry respectively. It is the odd Patterson function which has interesting properties.

From the formula for the structure factor

$$F(\mathbf{H}) = \sum_j (f_j' + if_j'') \exp(2\pi i\mathbf{H}\cdot\mathbf{r}_j)$$

one finds

$$|F(\mathbf{H})|^2 = \sum_{j,k} (G_{jk} - iH_{jk}) \exp 2\pi i\mathbf{H}\cdot(\mathbf{r}_j - \mathbf{r}_k) \qquad (390.1)$$

where the quantities G_{jk} and H_{jk}, which are functions of $|\mathbf{H}|$, are given by

$$\begin{aligned} G_{jk} &= f_j' f_k' + f_j'' f_k'' \\ H_{jk} &= f_j' f_k'' - f_k' f_j''. \end{aligned} \qquad (390.2)$$

They therefore satisfy $G_{jk} = G_{kj}$ and $H_{jk} = -H_{kj}$, so that the right-hand side of equation (*390*.1) is entirely real. Substituting from equation (*390*.1) in equation (*389*.1),

$$P(\mathbf{r}) = \frac{1}{V}\sum_{\mathbf{H}}\left\{\sum_{j,k} (G_{jk} - iH_{jk}) \exp(-2\pi i\mathbf{H}\cdot[\mathbf{r} - (\mathbf{r}_j - \mathbf{r}_k)])\right\} \qquad (390.3)$$

Comparison with equation (*389*.2) leads to

$$P^o(\mathbf{r}) = \frac{I}{V}\sum_{\mathbf{H}}\left\{\sum_{j,k} H_{jk} \exp(-2\pi i\mathbf{H}\cdot[\mathbf{r} - (\mathbf{r}_j - \mathbf{r}_k)])\right\} \qquad (390.4)$$

This can be written

$$P^o(\mathbf{r}) = \sum_{j,k} P^o_{jk}(\mathbf{r} - (\mathbf{r}_j - \mathbf{r}_k)) \qquad (390.5)$$

where

$$P^o_{jk}(\mathbf{r}) = \frac{1}{V}\sum_{\mathbf{H}} H_{jk} \exp(-2\pi i\mathbf{H}\cdot\mathbf{r}). \qquad (390.6)$$

The reasoning is in fact the same as was given at the beginning of Chapter 7. The significance of these results is the following. The odd Patterson function can be calculated directly from the measured intensities, using equation (*389*.3). This equation can be rewritten as

$$P^o(\mathbf{r}) = \frac{1}{V}\sum_{\mathbf{H}}{}' \{|F(\mathbf{H})|^2 - |F(-\mathbf{H})|^2\} \sin 2\pi\mathbf{H}\cdot\mathbf{r} \qquad (390.7)$$

where the prime indicates that the sum is over half the reciprocal-lattice points. Accurate measurements of the differences between intensities which would be equal in the absence of anomalous scattering are therefore required. From equations (*390*.5) and (*390*.6) however, we see that $P^o(\mathbf{r})$ consists of a superposition of spherically-symmetric peaks at points which represent vector distances between atoms. The peak at $\mathbf{r}_j - \mathbf{r}_k$, $P^o_{jk}(\mathbf{r} - (\mathbf{r}_j - \mathbf{r}_k))$, is the Fourier transform of $H_{jk} = f_j' f_k'' - f_k' f_j''$, set down at $(\mathbf{r}_j - \mathbf{r}_k)$. Thus the peak is positive if $(\mathbf{r}_j - \mathbf{r}_k)$ is a vector from an 'anomalous' atom k to a 'normal' atom j, negative if the peak corresponds to a vector in the opposite direction, and zero if the vector

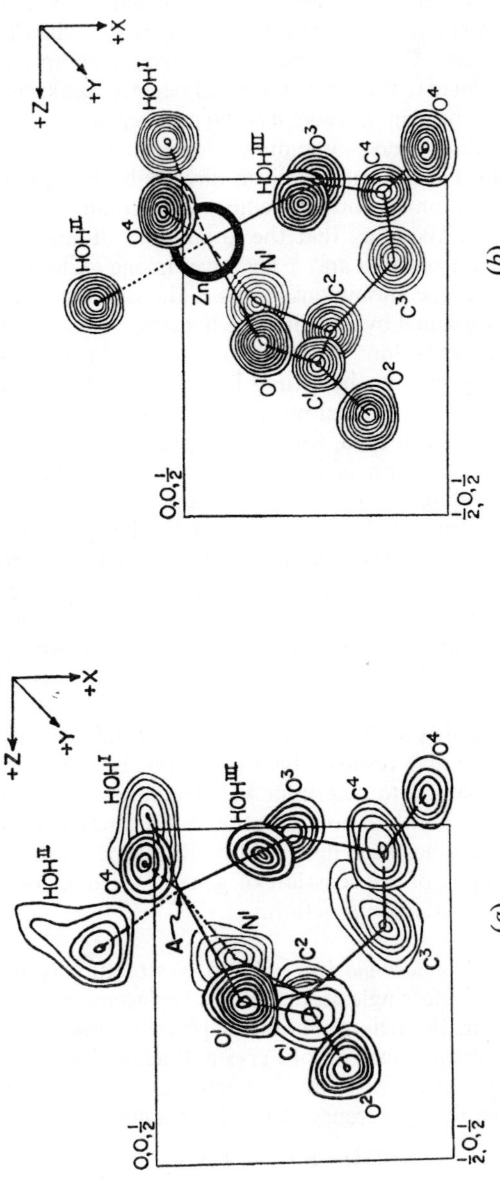

FIG. 391. The structure of cobaltous aspartate trihydrate as derived from the sum function obtained by adding the Patterson function $\mathbf{P}^0(\mathbf{r})$ with origin in the positions of each of the four cobalt atoms in turn. Fig. *b* shows for comparison the electron density in the isomorphous zinc compound

is between normal atoms, since these three possibilities correspond to $f_k''>0, f_j''=0$; $f_k''=0, f_j''>0$ and $f_k''=f_j''=0$ respectively. Thus while the ordinary Patterson function comprises N^2 peaks when there are N atoms per unit cell, the odd Patterson function comprises $n(N-n)$ positive peaks, related to the same number of negative peaks by a centre of anti-symmetry at the origin, where n is the number of anomalous atoms per unit cell. Thus if there is one molecule per unit cell containing one anomalous atom, the structure is given directly by $P^o(\mathbf{r})$, including the absolute configuration of the molecule. One could scarcely ask for more! Generally, assuming that the anomalous atoms are identical, $P^o(\mathbf{r})$ will contain a positive and a negative 'image' (Chapter 7) of the structure in each of the anomalous atoms. The structure can therefore, in principle, be obtained by ignoring the negative peaks and evaluating one of the superposition functions described in Chapter 7—for example the sum function—by setting $P^o(\mathbf{r})$ down with its origin at the positions of each of the anomalous atoms in turn.

This method has been used, for example, to determine the structure and absolute configuration of cobaltous aspartate trihydrate (Doyne, Pepinsky and Watanabe, 1957; Okaya and Pepinsky, 1961). The positions of the four cobalt atoms, related by the symmetry of space group $P2_12_12_1$, were determined by inspection of the function $P^e(\mathbf{r})$, which has the same properties as an ordinary Patterson function. The function corresponding to setting the origin of $P^o(\mathbf{r})$ at each of these four positions and taking the sum is shown in fig. 391*a*. In fig. 391*b* the electron density in the isomorphous zinc derivative is shown for comparison.

While the method is an interesting one, it will only be rather exceptionally that it will give results which could not be obtained by using the heavy-atom method to determine the structure, and the method of Bijvoet to give the absolute configuration. An alternative method of interpreting the data has been described by Ramachandran and Raman (1959), in the course of a discussion of general methods of deriving a structure from its Patterson function.

2.2. *General phase determination.* When a structure is not centrosymmetric, use of the single isomorphous-replacement method leads to an ambiguity in the determination of phase angles (section **8**.4.6). Let $F(\mathbf{H})$ be a structure factor of one crystal (haemoglobin for example) and $F_1(\mathbf{H})$ a structure factor of an isomorphous crystal (a derivative of haemoglobin containing mercury atoms for example), and write

$$f(\mathbf{H}) = F_1(\mathbf{H}) - F(\mathbf{H})$$

for the contribution of the replaceable atoms. In practice only $f(\mathbf{H})$, $|F(\mathbf{H})|$ and $|F_1(\mathbf{H})|$ are known. In fig. 393 (i) we draw a circle of radius $|F(\mathbf{H})|$ about the origin, and a circle of radius $|F_1(\mathbf{H})|$ about the point R, the vector **OR** representing $-f(\mathbf{H})$ (section **8**.4.6). The circles

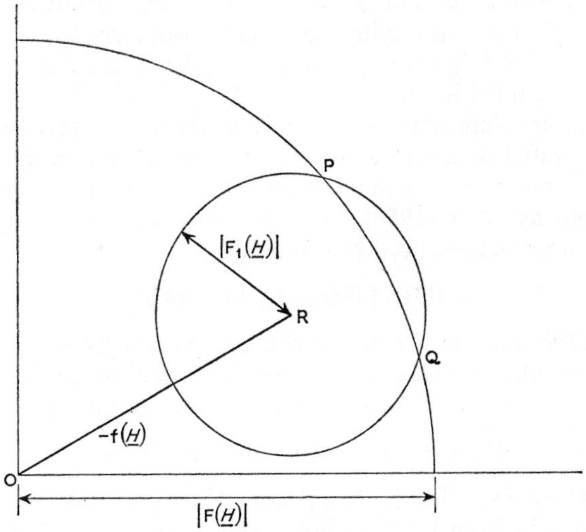

FIG. 393 (i). Illustrates the ambiguity in determination of the phase of F(**H**) using the method of single isomorphous replacement, as discussed in the text

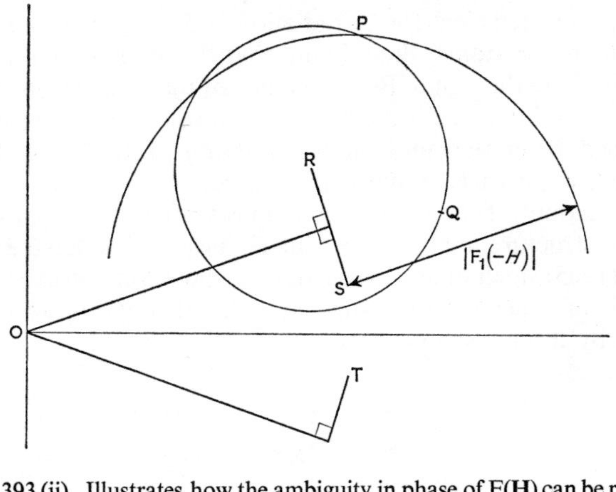

FIG. 393 (ii). Illustrates how the ambiguity in phase of F(**H**) can be resolved when the replaceable atoms scatter anomalously (see text).

intersect in the points P and Q, and therefore either **OP** or **OQ** may represent F(**H**). It was pointed out by Bijvoet (1954) that the ambiguity can be resolved if the replaceable atoms in one member of the isomorphous pair scatter anomalously. In fig. 393 (ii) we redraw **OR**, resolved into two components at right angles to indicate that the replaceable atoms are scattering anomalously, and on the same diagram we draw **OT** to represent $-f(-\mathbf{H})$, while **OS** represents $-f^*(-\mathbf{H})$. With S as centre a circle of radius $|F_1(-\mathbf{H})|$ is now drawn. This circle passes through P but not through Q, so that **OP** is the correct solution for F(**H**). In effect we are using the double isomorphous-replacement method (section **8**.4.7), with $F_1(-\mathbf{H})$ playing the same role as a structure amplitude of a third isomorphous crystal.

In protein structure analysis it sometimes happens that the replaceable atoms are related by a centre of symmetry not present in the structure as a whole, as was the case in an investigation of the (100) projection of haemoglobin by Blow (1958). The above analysis is still applicable, but a graphical method need not be used.

Write
$$F_1(\mathbf{H}) - F(\mathbf{H}) = (f'_m + if''_m)M(\mathbf{H})$$

where M(**H**) is the sum $\sum \exp 2\pi i\mathbf{r}\cdot\mathbf{H}$ taken over the known coordinates of the replaceable mercury atoms, and is entirely real since these are related by a centre of symmetry. A line or two of algebra then gives

$$|F_1(\mathbf{H})|^2 - |F_1(-\mathbf{H})|^2 = 4f''_m M(\mathbf{H})B(\mathbf{H}),$$

where $F(\mathbf{H}) = A(\mathbf{H}) + iB(\mathbf{H})$. In principle therefore B(**H**) is determined by the deviation from Friedel's law. The result need only be used to give the sign of B(**H**), since in this situation this is the only ambiguity.

For Cr K_α radiation the value of f''_m for a mercury atom is as high as 15 electrons. In practice, because of numerous difficulties including a high absorption coefficient for Cr radiation and appreciable anomalous scattering by other atoms, Blow found that the method could only be used as a check on the sign of B(**H**) obtained by the double isomorphous-replacement method. In a separate experiment, additional evidence was obtained from the anomalous scattering of the iron atoms in haemoglobin when Cu K_α radiation was used.

A fuller account of the use of anomalous scattering for phase determination in structure analysis, particularly of proteins, has been given by North (1965), including a discussion of the effects of experimental errors, lack of exact isomorphism, etc. Another useful account has been given by Ramaseshan (1964).

REFERENCES AND NAME INDEX

Abrahams, S. C. & Robertson, J. M., 1948. Acta Cryst. **1,** 252 - - 135
Abrahams, S. C., Robertson, J. M. & White, J. G., 1949. Acta Cryst. **2,** 238 310
Acha, A. de, 1960. *See* Amoros, J. L. - - - 312, 314, 316
Ahmed, F. R. & Cruickshank, D. W. J., 1953. Acta Cryst. **6,** 385 - 340
Alperin, H. A., Brown, P. J. & Nathans, R., 1963. J. App. Phys. **34,** 1201 - 375
Amoros, J. L., Canut, M. L. & Acha, A. de, 1960. Z. Krist. **114,** 39 - - 312, 314, 316
Andresen, A., 1959. *See* Nathans, R. - - - - 363
Anzenhofer, K. & Hoppe, W., 1962. Phys. Verh. Mosbach **13,** 119 235, 248, 263
Arndt, U. W. & Phillips, D. C., 1961. Acta Cryst. **14,** 807 - - 231
Avrami, M., 1938. Phys. Rev., **54,** 300 - - - - 234

Bacon, G. E., 1962. *Neutron Diffraction.* Oxford: Clarendon Press 358, 359, 360
Bacon, G. E., 1964. *Advances in Structure Research by Diffraction Methods,* **1,** 1 - - - - - - - 358
Bacon, G. E. & Curry, N. A., 1960. Acta Cryst. **13,** 10 - - 353
Bacon, G. E., Curry, N. A. & Wilson, S. A., 1964. Proc. Roy. Soc. A. **279,** 98 368
Bacon, G. E. & Pease, R. S., 1955. Proc. Roy. Soc. A. **230,** 359 - - 366
Bagchi, S. N., 1953. *See* Hosemann, R. - - - - 331
Bagchi, S. N., 1954. *See* Hosemann, R. - - - - 164
Bagchi, S. N., 1962. *See* Hosemann, R. - - - - 164
Bamford, C. H., Brown, L., Elliott, A., Hanby, W. E. & Trotter, I. F., 1952. Nature **169,** 357 - - - - - - 287
Banerjee, K., 1930. Nature **125,** 456 - - - - 281
Banerjee, K., 1933. Proc. Roy. Soc. A. **141,** 188 - - 234, 248
Barth, T. F. W. & Posnjak, E., 1932. Z. Krist. **82,** 325 - - 42
Becka, L. N. & Cruickshank, D. W. J., 1961. Acta Cryst. **14,** 1092 - 354
Beevers, C. A., 1939. Proc. Phys. Soc. **51,** 660 - - - 96
Beevers, C. A., 1952. Acta Cryst. **5,** 670 - - - - 97
Beevers, C. A. & Ehrlich, H. W., 1959. Z. Krist. **112,** 414 - - 178
Beevers, C. A. & Lipson, H., 1932. Z. Krist. **82,** 297 - - - 28
Beevers, C. A. & Lipson, H., 1934. Proc. Roy. Soc. A. **146,** 570 - - 92, 121, 138, 172, 206, 207
Beevers, C. A. & Lipson, H., 1935. Proc. Roy. Soc. A. **148,** 664 - 209. 211
Beevers, C. A. & Lipson, H., 1938. Proc. Phys. Soc. **50,** 275 - 80, 82
Beevers, C. A., McDonald, T. R. R., Robertson, J. H. & Stern, F., 1952. Acta Cryst. **5,** 689 - - - - - - 181
Beevers, C. A. & Robertson, J. H., 1950. Acta Cryst. **3,** 164 - 154, 157
Beevers, C. A. & Schwartz, C. M., 1935. Z. Krist. **91,** 157 - 113, 195
Beevers, C. A., 1936. *See* Lipson, H. - - - - 96
Beevers, C. A., 1950. *See* Robertson, J. H. - - - 202, 206
Beevers, C. A., 1951. *See* Robertson, J. H. - - - - 178
Beevers, C. A., 1950. *See* Stern, F. - - - - 176
Bell, I. P., 1951. *See* Vand, V. - - - - - 130

Bernal, J. D., 1926. Proc. Roy. Soc.A. **113,** 117 - - - 31

Bernal, J. D. & Megaw, H. D., 1935. Proc. Roy. Soc. A. **151,** 384 - 113

Bijvoet, J. M., 1949. Proc. Acad. Sci. Amst. **52**, 313 - - - 385

Bijvoet, J. M., 1954. Nature **173,** 888 - - - - 393

Bijvoet, J. M., 1948. *See* Bokhoven, C. - - - 202, 215, 224

Bijvoet, J. M., 1949. *See* Bokhoven, C. - - - 202, 215, 224

Bijvoet, J. M., 1951. *See* Bokhoven, C. - - 202, 215, 224, 230, 231

Bijvoet, J. M., 1938. *See* MacGillavry, C. H. - - - 40

Bijvoet, J. M., 1951. *See* Peerdeman, A. F. - - - - 385

Bijvoet, J. M., 1956. *See* Peerdeman, A. F. - - - - 388

Bijvoet, J. M., 1954. *See* Trommel, J. - - - - 385

Binnie, W. P., 1948. *See* Morrison, J. D. - - - - 103

Blackman, M., 1939. Proc. Roy. Soc. A. **173,** 68 - - - 364

Blow, D. M., 1958. Proc. Roy. Soc. A. **247,** 302 - - 189, 192, 394

Blow, D. M. & Crick, F. H. C., 1959. Acta Cryst. **12,** 754 - 231, 232

Bodo, G., Dintzis, H. M., Kendrew, J. C. & Wyckoff, H. W., 1959. Proc. Roy. Soc. A. **253,** 70 - - - - - - - 189

Bokhoven, C., Schoone, J. C. & Bijvoet, J. M., 1948. Kon. Ned. Akad. Wet. **51,** No. 8 - - - - - - - 202, 215, 224

Bokhoven, C., Schoone, J. C. & Bijvoet, J. M., 1949. Kon. Ned. Akad. Wet. **52,** No. 2 - - - - - - - 202, 215, 224

Bokhoven, C., Schoone, J. C. & Bijvoet, J. M., 1951. Acta Cryst. **4,** 275 - - 202, 215, 224, 230, 231

Bommel, A. J. van, 1951. *See* Peerdeman, A. F. - - - 385

Booth, A. D., 1945a. Nature **156,** 51 - - - - 194

Booth, A. D., 1945b. Phil. Mag. **36,** 609 - - - - 141

Booth, A. D., 1945c. Trans. Faraday Soc. **41,** 434 - - 87, 88

Booth, A. D., 1946. Proc. Roy. Soc. A. **188,** 77 - - - 329

Booth, A. D., 1947. Proc. Roy. Soc. A. **190,** 482 - - - 329

Bosanquet, C. H., 1922. *See* Bragg, W. L. - - - - 194

Boyes-Watson, J. & Perutz, M. F., 1943. Nature **151,** 714 - - 201

Bradley, A. J., 1935. Z. Krist. **91,** 302 - - - - 141

Bradley, A. J. & Lu, S. S., 1937. Z. Krist. **96,** 20 - 29, 72, 123, 124

Bradley, A. J. & Thewlis, J., 1926. Proc. Roy. Soc. A. **144,** 340 - 29, 126

Bragg, W. L., 1913. Proc. Camb. Phil. Soc. **17,** 43 - - - 4

Bragg, W. L., 1924. Proc. Roy. Soc. A. **105,** 370; **106,** 346 - - 119

Bragg, W. L., 1929a. Proc. Roy. Soc. A. **123,** 537 - - - 85

Bragg, W. L., 1929b. Z. Krist. **70,** 483 - - - - 105

Bragg, W. L., 1930. Z. Krist. **74,** 237 - - - - 119

Bragg, W. L., 1939. Nature **143,** 678 - - - 20, 107, 290

Bragg, W. L., 1944. Nature **154,** 69 - - - 20, 292

Bragg, W. L., 1958. Acta Cryst. **11,** 70 - - - - 189

Bragg, W. L., James, R. W. & Bosanquet, C. H., 1922. Phil. Mag. **44,** 433 194

Bragg, W. L. & Lipson, H., 1936. Z. Krist. **95,** 323 - 45, 77, 78, 79, 80

Bragg, W. L. & Lipson, H., 1943. J. Sci. Inst. **20,** 110 - - 107

Bragg, W. L. & Stokes, A. R., 1945. Nature **156,** 332 - - - 292

Bragg, W. L. & West, J., 1926. Proc. Roy. Soc. A. **111,** 691 - - 116

Bragg, W. L. & West, J., 1928. Z. Krist. **69,** 120 - - - 131

Bragg, W. L. & West, J., 1930. Phil. Mag. **10,** 823 - 94, 200, 326, 329

Bragg, W. L., 1928. *See* Warren, B. E. - - - - 131

Branson, H. R., 1951. *See* Pauling, L. - - - - 287
Brown, C. J. & Corbridge, D. E. C., 1948. Nature **162**, 72 - 122, 123
Brown, C. J., Peiser, H. S. & Turner-Jones, A., 1949. Acta Cryst. **2**, 167 - 122
Brown, L., 1952. *See* Bamford, C. H. - - - - 287
Brown, P. J., 1963. *See* Alperin, H. A. - - - - 375
Buerger, M. J., 1931. Amer. Min. **16**, 861 - - - - 125
Buerger, M. J., 1946. J. App. Phys. **17**, 579 - - 46, 150, 151, 153
Buerger, M. J., 1950a. Acta Cryst. **3**, 465 - - - 46, 148, 150
Buerger, M. J., 1950b. Acta Cryst. **3**, 87 - - - 154, 155
Buerger, M. J., 1950c, d. Proc. Nat. Acad. Sci. **36**, 376; **36**, 738 - 161
Buerger, M. J., 1950e. Proc. Nat. Acad. Sci. **36**, 324 - - - 46
Buerger, M. J., 1951. Acta Cryst. **4**, 531 - - - 107, 154, 155
Buerger, M. J., 1959. *Vector Space*. New York: J. Wiley & Sons - - 148, 150, 153, 155, 157, 161
Bujosa, A., 1961. *See* Cruickshank, D. W. J. - 302, 340, 346, 347, 348
Bunn, C. W., 1961. *Chemical Crystallography*. Oxford: O.U.P. - - 81, 115, 120, 122, 216, 292
Bunn, C. W. & Garner, E. V., 1942. J. Chem. Soc. 654 - - 116
Bunn, C. W., 1949. *See* Crowfoot, D. - 137, 199, 212, 216, 217, 292
Busing, W. R. & Levy, H. A., 1961. *Computing Methods and the Phase Problem in X-ray Crystal Analysis*. Oxford: Pergamon - - - 347
Busing, W. R. & Levy, H. A., 1964. Acta Cryst. **17**, 142 - - 354

Canut, M. L., 1960. *See* Amoros, J. L. - - - 312, 314, 316
Carlisle, C. H. & Crowfoot, D., 1945. Proc. Roy. Soc. A. **184**, 64 171, 206
Caron, A. & Donohue, J., 1964. Acta Cryst. **17**, 544 - - 378, 380
Charlesby, A., Finch, G. I. & Wilman, H., 1939. Proc. Phys. Soc. **51**, 479 - 312
Chrobak, L., 1937. Z. Krist. **96**, 503 - - - - 80
Clastre, J. & Gay, R., 1950a. C. R. Acad. Sci. Paris **230**, 1976 - 154, 157
Clastre, J. & Gay, R., 1950b. J. Phys. Radium **11**, 75 - - 154, 157
Cochran, W., 1951a. Acta Cryst. **4**, 408 - - - 334, 336
Cochran, W., 1951b. Acta. Cryst. **4**, 81 - - - 334, 338
Cochran, W., 1951c. Acta Cryst. **4**, 376 - - - - 182
Cochran, W., 1952. Acta Cryst. **5**, 65 - - - - 234
Cochran, W., 1954. Acta Cryst. **7**, 581 - - - - 259
Cochran, W., 1955. Acta Cryst. **8**, 473 - - - - 266
Cochran, W., 1958. Acta Cryst. **11**, 579 - - - 164, 170
Cochran, W. & Crick, F. H. C., 1952. Nature **169**, 234 - - 287
Cochran, W., Crick, F. H. C. & Vand, V., 1952. Acta Cryst. **5**, 581 - 287
Cochran, W. & Douglas, A. S., 1955. Proc. Roy. Soc. A. **227**, 486 - 258
Cochran, W. & Douglas, A. S., 1957. Proc. Roy. Soc. A. **243**, 281 - 261
Cochran, W. & Pawley, G. S., 1964. Proc. Roy. Soc. A. **280**, 1 - - 314
Cochran, W. & Penfold, B. R., 1952. Acta Cryst. **5**, 644 - - 250
Cochran, W. & Woolfson, M. M., 1954. Acta Cryst. **7**, 450 - 259, 260
Cochran, W. & Woolfson, M. M., 1955. Acta Cryst. **8**, 1 - 248, 249
Cochran, W., 1964. *See* Tollin, P. - - - - - 182
Collin, R. L., 1955. Acta Cryst. **8**, 499 - - - 57, 61
Collin, R. L. & Lipscomb, W. N., 1949. Acta Cryst. **2**, 104 - - 32
Corbridge, D. E. C., 1948. *See* Brown, C. J. - - 122, 123
Corey, R. B., 1938. J. Am. Chem. Soc. **70**, 1568 - - - 378

Corey, R. B., 1950. *See* Shoemaker, D.P. - - - 185, 187, 319
Corey, R. B., 1951. *See* Pauling, L. - - - - 287
Cork, J. M., 1927. Phil. Mag. **4,** 688 - - - 114, 208, 209
Cormack, A. M., 1957. Acta Cryst. **10,** 354 - - - - 287
Coster, D., Knol, K. S. & Prins, J., 1930. Z. Physik. **63,** 345 - - 384
Cowley, J. M. & Rees, A. L. G., 1958. Rep. Prog. Phys. **21,** 165 358, 368
Cox, E. G., Cruickshank, D. W. J. & Smith, J. A. S., 1958. Proc. Roy. Soc. A. **247,** 1 - - - - 368, 369
Cox, E. G. Gillott, R. J. J. H. & Jeffrey, G. A., 1949. Acta Cryst. **2,** 356 - 127
Crick, F. H. C., 1952. *See* Cochran, W. - - - - 287
Crick, F. H. C., 1953. *See* Watson, J. D. - - - 287, 289
Crick, F. H. C., 1959. *See* Blow, D.M. - - - 231, 232
Crookes, D. A., 1947. Nature **160,** 17 - - - - 122
Crowfoot, D., Bunn, C. W., Rogers-Low, B. W. & Turner-Jones, A., 1949. *The X-ray Crystallographic Investigation of the Structure of Penicillin.* Oxford: O.U.P. - 137, 195, 199, 208, 212, 216, 217, 292, 340, 346, 347, 348
Crowfoot, D. & Dunitz, J. D., 1948. Nature **162,** 608 - - - 206
Crowfoot, D., 1945. *See* Carlisle, C. H. - - - 171, 206
Cruickshank, D. W. J., 1949. Acta Cryst. **2,** 65 - - 322, 326, 334
Cruickshank, D. W. J., 1950. Acta Cryst. **3,** 10 - - - 323
Cruickshank, D. W. J., 1952. Acta Cryst. **5,** 511 - - - 339
Cruickshank, D. W. J., 1956. Acta Cryst. **9,** 747, 754 - 307, 309, 334, 354
Cruickshank, D. W. J., 1957. Acta Cryst. **10,** 504 - - - 310
Cruickshank, D. W. J., 1958. Rev. Mod. Phys. **30,** 163 - - 310
Cruickshank, D. W. J., 1959. International Tables, Vol. 2 - 320, 334
Cruickshank, D. W. J., 1961. Acta Cryst. **14,** 896 - - - 354
Cruickshank, D. W. J., Pilling, D. E., Bujosa, A., Lovell, F. M. & Truter, M. R., 1961. *Computing Methods in the Phase Problem.* Oxford: Pergamon Press - - - - 302, 340, 346, 347, 348
Cruickshank, D. W. J., 1953. *See* Ahmed, F. R. - - - 340
Cruickshank, D. W. J., 1961. *See* Becka, L. N. - - - 354
Cruickshank, D. W. J., 1958. *See* Cox, E. G. - - 368, 369
Cullis, A. F., Dintzis, H. M. & Perutz, M. F., 1957. Conference on Haemoglobin. Nat. Acad. Sci., N.R.C. Pub. 557, p. 50. Washington - 222
Curry, N. A., 1960. *See* Bacon, G. E. - - - - 353
Curry, N. A., 1964. *See* Bacon, G. E. - - - - 368

Danner, H. R., 1955. *See* Frazer, B. C. - - - - 351
Darlow, S. F., 1960. Acta Cryst. **13,** 683 - - - - 355
Dauben, C. H. & Templeton, D. H., 1955. Acta Cryst. **8,** 841 - - 383
Davies, D. R., 1955. *See* Rollett, R. S. - - - - 304
Dawson, B., 1964. Acta Cryst. **17,** 990 - - - - 352
Debye, P. & Mencke, H., 1931. Ergebn. tech. Röntgenk. **2,** 1 - - 144
Degeilh, R. & Marsh, R. E., 1959. Acta Cryst. **12,** 1007 - - 378
Diamond, R., 1958. Acta Cryst. **11,** 129 - - - - 344
Diamond, R., 1963. Acta Cryst. **16,** 627 - - - 235, 243
Dintzis, H. M., 1957. *See* Cullis, A. F. - - - - 222
Dintzis, H. M., 1959. *See* Bodo, G. - - - - 189
Donnay, J. D. H., 1939. Amer. Min. **24,** 184 - - - 121
Donnay, J. D. H., & Harker, D., 1937. Amer. Min. **22,** 446 - - 121

Donohue, J. & Trueblood, K. N., 1956. Acta Cryst. **9,** 960 - - 135
Donohue, J., 1964. *See* Caron, A. - - - 378, 380
Donohue, J., 1950. *See* Shoemaker, D. P. - - - 185, 187, 319
Donohue, J., 1952. *See* Vaughan, P. A. - - - - 378
Douglas, A. S., 1955. *See* Cochran, W. - - - - 258
Douglas, A. S., 1957. *See* Cochran, W. - - - - 261
Doyne, T., Pepinsky, R. & Watanabe, T., 1957. Acta Cryst. **10,** 438 - 392
Duane, W., 1925. Proc. Nat. Acad. Sci. **11,** 489 - - - 194
Dunitz, J. D. & Robertson, J. M., 1947. J. Chem. Soc. 1145 - - 142
Dunitz, J. D., 1948. *See* Crowfoot, D. - - - - 206
Dutta, S. N. & Woolfson, M. M., 1961. Acta Cryst. **14,** 178 - - 293
Dyer, H. B., 1951a. Acta Cryst. **4,** 42 - - - 173, 174
Dyer, H. B., 1951b. Ph. D. thesis, University of Cambridge - 172, 188, 219

Edwards, O. S. & Lipson, H., 1942. Proc. Roy. Soc. A. **180,** 268 - 41
Ehrlich, H. W., 1959. *See* Beevers, C. A. - - - - 178
Eiland, P. F., 1957. *See* Vand, V. - - - - 72
Eller, G. von, 1955a. Bull. Soc. Franc. Miner. Crist. **78,** 275 - - 106
Eller, G. von, 1955b. Acta Cryst. **8,** 641 - - - - 242
Eller, G. von, 1960. Acta Cryst. **13,** 628 - - - - 242
Eller, G. von, 1961. Acta Cryst. **14,** 958 - - - - 242
Eller, G. von, 1962. Acta Cryst. **15,** 590 - - - - 242
Eller-Pandraud, H. von, 1960. Acta Cryst. **13,** 936 - - - 106
Elliott, A., 1952. *See* Bamford, C. H. - - - - 287
Emde, F., 1933. *See* Jahnke, E. - - - - - 50
Evans, H. T., 1961. Acta Cryst. **14,** 1019 - - - - 349
Ewald, P. P., 1921. Z. Krist. **56,** 129 - - - - 31

Finch, G. I., 1939. *See* Charlesby, A. - - - - 312
Forsyth, J. B. & Wells, M., 1959. Acta Cryst. **12,** 412 - - - 72
Foster, F. & Hargreaves, A., 1963a. Acta Cryst. **16,** 1124 - - 58
Foster, F. & Hargreaves, A., 1963b. Acta Cryst. **16,** 1133 - 58, 62
Fowweather, F. & Hargreaves, A., 1950. Acta Cryst. **3,** 81 51, 115, 119, 202
Frazer, B. C., Danner, H. R. & Pepinsky, R., 1955. Phys. Rev. **100,** 745 - 351
Fricke, R. & Havestadt, L., 1928. Z. Anorg. Chem. **170,** 35 - - 28
Fridrichsons, J. & Mathieson, A. McL., 1962. Acta Cryst. **15,** 1065 - 182
Fuller, W., 1964. Science Progress, **52,** 26 - - - - 290
Furberg, S., 1950. Acta Cryst. **3,** 325 - - - - 142

Garner, E. V., 1942. *See* Bunn, C. W. - - - - 116
Garrido, J., 1950a. C. R. Acad. Sci. Paris **230,** 1878 - - - 154
Garrido, J., 1950b. C. R. Acad. Sci. Paris **231,** 297 - - - 154
Gay, R., 1950a. *See* Clastre, J. - - - - 154, 157
Gay, R., 1950b. *See* Clastre, J. - - - - 154, 157
Geller, S., 1961. Acta Cryst. **14,** 1026 - - - - 350
Gillis, J., 1948. Acta Cryst. **1,** 76 - - - - - 244
Gillott, R. J. J. H., 1949. *See* Cox, E. G. - - - - 127
Gingrich, N. S., 1934. *See* Warren, B. E. - - - - 144
Gingrich, N. S., 1957. *See* Wilkinson, M. K. - - - 375
Goedkoop, J. A., 1950. Acta Cryst. **3,** 374 - - - 150, 234, 248

Goldschmidt, V. M., 1929. Geochemische Verteilungsgesetze der Elemente, P. VII. - - - - - - - 110
Goldstein, H., 1951. *Classical Mechanics.* Cambridge, Mass.: Addison-Wesley - - - - - - - 308
Goodwin, T. H. & Hardy, R., 1938. Phil. Mag. **25,** 1096 - - 89
Grant, D. F., Howells, R. G. & Rogers, D., 1957. Acta Cryst. **10,** 489 - 252
Green, P. M., Ingram, V. M. & Perutz, M. F., 1954. Proc. Roy. Soc. A. **225,** 287 - - - - - - - 189
Groth, P., 1908. *Chemische Kristallographie* 2. Leipzig: Engelmann - 138

Halpern, O. & Johnson, M. H., 1939. Phys. Rev. **55,** 898 - 360, 361
Hanby, W. E., 1952. *See* Bambord, C. H. - - - - 287
Hanson, A. W., 1962. Acta Cryst. **16,** 939 - - - - 226
Hanson, A. W. & Lipson, H., 1952a. Acta Cryst. **5,** 145 - - 292
Hanson, A. W. & Lipson, H., 1952b. Acta Cryst. **5,** 362 - 108, 200
Hanson, A. W., Lipson, H. & Taylor, C. A., 1953. Proc. Roy. Soc. A. **218,** 371 - - - - - - - 296
Hanson, A. W., Taylor, C. A. & Lipson, H., 1951. Nature **168,** 160 - 108
Harburn, G., 1961. Ph.D. thesis, Manchester - - - 291
Harburn, G. & Taylor, C. A., 1962. Nature **194,** 764 - - 108, 298
Hardy, R., 1938. *See* Goodwin, T. H. - - - - 89
Hargreaves, A., 1946. Nature **158,** 620 - - - - 212
Hargreaves, A., 1955. Acta Cryst. **8,** 12 - - - - 57
Hargreaves, A., 1956. Acta Cryst. **9,** 191 - - - 57, 61
Hargreaves, A. & Watson, H. C., 1957. Acta Cryst. **10,** 368 - - 296
Hargreaves, A., 1963a. *See* Foster, F. - - - - 58
Hargreaves, A., 1963b. *See* Foster, F. - - - 58, 62
Hargreaves, A., 1950. *See* Fowweather, F. - 51, 115, 119, 202
Harker, D., 1936. J. Chem. Phys. **4,** 381 - - - 151, 175, 176
Harker, D., 1948. Amer. Min. **33,** 764 - - - - 131
Harker, D., 1956. Acta Cryst. **9,** 1 - - - 189, 230, 231
Harker, D. & Kasper, J. S., 1948. Acta Cryst. **1,** 70 - - 74, 234
Harker, D., 1937. *See* Donnay, J. D. H. - - - - 121
Harker, D., 1950. *See* Kasper, J. S. - - - - 134
Hartshorne, N. H. & Stuart, A., 1950. *Crystals and The Polarizing Microscope.* London: Arnold - - - - 28, 120
Hauptman, H. & Karle, J., 1953. Solution of the Phase Problem, I. The Centrosymmetric Crystal. *A.C.A. Monograph,* No. 3, Wilmington: The Letter Shop - - - - - - - 57, 258
Hauptman, H. & Karle, J., 1957. Acta Cryst. **10,** 267 - - - 260
Hauptman, H. & Karle, J., 1959. Acta Cryst. **12,** 404 - - - 260
Hauptman, H. & Karle, J., 1962. Acta Cryst. **15,** 547 - - 235, 248, 262
Hauptman, H., 1950. *See* Karle, J. - - - 150, 234, 241
Hauptman, H., 1953. *See* Karle, J. - - - 57, 234
Hauptman, H., 1956. *See* Karle, J. - - - - 266
Hauptman, H., 1957. *See* Karle, J. - - - 248, 266
Hauptman, H., 1958. *See* Karle, J. - - - - 266
Havestadt, L., 1928. *See* Fricke, R. - - - - 28
Havighurst, R. J., 1925. Proc. Nat. Acad. Sci. **11,** 502 - - - 194
Hemily, P., 1952. C.r. Acad. Sci. Paris **234,** 2085 - - 179, 180, 181

Henry, N. F. M., Lipson, H. & Wooster, W. A., 1951. *Interpretation of X-ray Diffraction Photographs.* London: Macmillan - - - 119
Herbstein, F. H. & Schoening, F. R. L., 1957. Acta Cryst. **10,** 657 - 64
Herglotz, G., 1911. Ber. sachs. Ges. (Akad.) Wiss. **63,** 501 - - 241
Higgs, P. W., 1955. Acta Cryst. **8,** 99 - - - - 310
Hilton, H., 1906. *Mathematical Crystallography.* Oxford: O.U.P. - 27
Hinde, R. M., 1951. *See* Taylor, C. A. - - - - 290
Hirshfeld, F. L., Sandler, S. & Schmidt, G. M. J., 1963. J. Chem. Soc. 2108 - - 309, 354
Hodgkin, D. C., Kamper, J., Lindsey, J., MacKay, M., Pickworth, J., Robertson, J. H., Shoemaker, C. B., White, J. G., Prosen, R. J. & Trueblood, K. N., 1957. Proc. Roy. Soc. A. **242,** 228 - - 227
Hoppe, W., 1956. Z. Krist. **107,** 406, 434 - - - - 314
Hoppe, W., 1957. Z. Electrochem. **61,** 1076 - - - - 182
Hoppe, W., 1964. Advances in Structure Research by Diffraction Methods **1,** 90 - - - - - - 312, 314, 316
Hoppe, W., Lenne, H. U. & Morandi, G., 1957. Z. Krist. **108,** 321 - 314
Hoppe, W., 1962. *See* Anzenhofer, K. - - - 235, 248, 263
Horstmann, M. & Meyer, G., 1962. Acta Cryst. **15,** 271 - - 364
Hosemann, R. & Bagchi, S. N., 1953. Nature **171,** 785 - - 331
Hosemann, R. & Bagchi, S. N., 1954. Acta Cryst. **7,** 237 - - 164
Hosemann, R. & Bagchi, S. N., 1962. *Direct Analysis of Diffraction by Matter.* Amsterdam: North-Holland Publishing Co. - - 164
Howells, E. R., Phillips, D. C. & Rogers, D., 1949. Research **2,** 338 - 51
Howells, E. R., Phillips, D. C. & Rogers, D., 1950. Acta Cryst. **3,** 210 - 50, 65
Howells, R. G., 1957. *See* Grant, D. F. - - - - 252
Huggins, M. L., 1944. J. Chem. Phys. **12,** 520 - - - 105
Hughes, E. W., 1941. J. Am. Chem. Soc., **63,** 1737 - - 120, 340
Hughes, E. W. & Moore, W. J., 1949. J. Am. Chem. Soc. **71,** 2618 184, 185
Hughes, J. W., Phillips, D. C., Rogers, D. & Wilson, A. J. C., 1949. Acta Cryst. **2,** 420 - - - - - - 114
Hughes, W. & Taylor, C. A., 1953. J. Sci. Inst. **30,** 105 - 108, 290
Hughes, W. & Taylor, C. A., 1958. J. Sci. Inst. **35,** 261 - 114, 291
Hvoslef, J., 1958. Acta Cryst. **11,** 383 - - - - 367

Ingram, V. M., 1954. *See* Green, P. M. - - - - 189

Jackson, W. W. & West, J., 1930. Z. Krist **76,** 211 - - - 122
Jackson, W. W., 1928. *See* Taylor, W. H. - - - 111, 120
Jacobson, R. A., Wunderlich, J. A. & Lipscomb, W. N., 1961. Acta Cryst. **14,** 598 - - - - - - 169, 181
Jaeger, F. M., Terpstra, P. & Westenbrink, H. G. K., 1927. Z. Krist. **66,** 195 141
Jahnke, E. & Emde, F., 1933. *Funktionen Tafeln mit Formerln und Kurven.* Leipzig: Teubner - - - - - - 50
James, R. W., 1948. Acta Cryst. **1,** 132 - - - - 326
James, R. W., 1957. *The Crystalline State*, Vol. II. London: Bell - - 300, 311, 358, 382
James, R. W., 1922. *See* Bragg, W. L. - - - - 194
Jeffrey, G. A., 1945. Proc. Roy. Soc. A. **183,** 388 - - 103, 104
Jeffrey, G. A., 1947. Proc. Roy. Soc. A. **188,** 222 - - - 322

Jeffrey, G. A., 1951. Acta Cryst. **4,** 58 - - - - 328
Jeffrey, G. A., 1949. *See* Cox, E. G. - - - - 127
Jellinek, F., 1958. Acta Cryst. **11,** 677 - - - - 355
Jenkins, F. A. & White, H. E., 1950. *Fundamentals of Optics.* New York: McGraw-Hill - - - - - - 17
Jensen, A. T., 1940. Kgl. D. Vid. Selsk mat. fys. Medd. **17,** No. 9 - 112
Jensen, A. T., 1948. *Krystallinske Salthydrater.* Copenhagen: Arnold Busck 112, 114
Jensen, L. H. & Sundaralingam, M., 1964. *Science,* **145,** 1185 - - 353
Johnson, M. H., 1939. *See* Halpern, O. - - - 360, 361
Jordahl, O. M., 1934. Phys. Rev. **45,** 87 - - - - 121

Kamper, J., 1957. *See* Hodgkin, D. C. - - - - 227
Karle, J. & Hauptman, H., 1950. Acta Cryst. **3,** 181 - - 150, 234, 241
Karle, J. & Hauptman, H., 1953. Acta Cryst. **6,** 131 - - 57, 234
Karle, J. & Hauptman, H., 1956. Acta Cryst. **9,** 635 - - - 266
Karle, J. & Hauptman, H., 1957. Acta Cryst. **10,** 515 - - 164, 248, 266
Karle, J. & Hauptman, H., 1958. Acta Cryst. **11,** 264 - - - 266
Karle, I. L. & Karle, J., 1964. Acta Cryst. **17,** 835 - - - 266
Karle, J., 1953. *See* Hauptman, H. - - - 57, 258
Karle, J., 1957. *See* Hauptman, H. - - - - 260
Karle, J., 1959. *See* Hauptman, H. - - - - 260
Karle, J., 1962. *See* Hauptman, H. - - - 235, 248, 262
Karle, J., 1964. *See* Karle, I. L. - - - - - 266
Kartha, G., 1964. *See* Norton, D. A. - - - - 225
Kasper, J. S., Lucht, C. M. & Harker, D., 1950. Acta Cryst. **3,** 436 - 134
Kasper, J. S., 1948. *See* Harker, D. - - - 74, 234
Kästner, F., 1931. Z. Krist. **77,** 353 - - - - 43
Kendrew, J. C., 1959. *See* Bodo, G. - - - - 189
Kitaygorodsky, A. I., 1961. *Theory of crystal-structure analysis.* New York Consultants Bureau - - - - - - 113, 242
Klug, A., 1950. Acta Cryst. **3,** 176 - - - 283, 285, 297
Klug, A., 1958. Acta Cryst. **11,** 515 - - - 57, 248
Knol, K. S., 1930. See Coster, D. - - - - 384
Knott, G., 1940. Proc. Phys. Soc. **52,** 229 - - - 281, 282
Kraut, J. & Reed, H. J., 1962. Acta Cryst. **15,** 747 - - - 179
Krishnan, K. S. & Mookherji, A., 1936. Phys. Rev. **50,** 860 - - 121
Krishnan, K. S. & Mookherji, A., 1937. Nature **140,** 896 - - 121
Krishnan, K. S. & Mookherji, A., 1938. Phys. Rev. **54,** 533, 841 - 121
Krishnan, K. S., 1936. *See* Lonsdale, K. - - - - 121

Laval, J., 1941. Bull. Soc. Franc. Mineral **64,** 1 - - - 311
Lenne, H. U., 1957. *See* Hoppe W. - - - - 314
Levy, H. A., 1961. *See* Busing, W. R. - - - - 347
Levy, H. A., 1964. *See* Busing, W. R. - - - - 354
Levy, H. A., 1957. *See* Worsham, J. E. - - - 378, 379
Lindsey, J., 1957. *See* Hodgkin, D. C. - - - - 227
Lipscomb, W. N., 1949. Acta Cryst. **2,** 193 - - - - 201
Lipscomb, W. N., 1949. *See* Collin, R. L. - - - - 32
Lipscomb, W. N., 1961. *See* Jacobson, R. A. - - 169, 181
Lipson, H., 1935. Nature **135,** 912 - - - - 209

Morandi, G., 1957. *See* Hoppe, W. - - - - 314
Morrison, J. D., Binnie, W. P. & Robertson, J. M., 1948. Nature **162,** 889 - 103

Nakatsu, K., 1963. *See* Nordman, K. - - - - 182
Naray-Szabo, I. & Sasvari, K., 1938. Z. Krist. **99,** 27 - - - - 70
Nathans, R. & Pickart, S. J., 1963. *Magnetism.* Ed. by G. T. Rado & H. Suhl. New York & London: Vol. 3. Acad. Press - - - 368
Nathans, R., Shull, C. G., Shirane, G. & Andresen, A., 1959. J. Phys. Chem. Solids, **10,** 138 - - - - - 363
Nathans, R., 1963. *See* Alperin, H. A. - - - - 375
Nathans, R., 1961. *See* Pickart, S. J. - - - - 377
Nitta, I., 1952. *See* Okaya, Y. - - - - - 244
Nordman, C. E., 1962. Acta Cryst. **15,** 18 - - - - 348
Nordman, C. E. & Nakatsu, K., 1963. J. Am. Chem. Soc. **85,** 353 - 182
North, A. C. T., 1965. Acta Cryst. **18,** 212 - - - - 394
Norton, D. A., Kartha, G. & Lu, C. T., 1964. Acta Cryst. **17,** 77 - 225
Nowacki, W., 1942. Helv. Chim. Acta. **25,** 863 - - - 195

Ogrim, O., 1949. *See* Vierwoll, H. - - - - 330, 331
Okaya, Y. & Nitta, I., 1952. Acta Cryst. **5,** 564 - - - 244
Okaya, Y. & Pepinsky, R., 1961. *Computing Methods and the Phase Problem in X-ray Crystal Analysis.* Oxford: Pergamon Press - - 388, 389, 392
Okaya, Y., Saito, Y. & Pepinsky, R., 1955. Phys. Rev. **98,** 1857 - - 389
Ott, H., 1927. Z. Krist. **66,** 136 - - - - - 234

Palin, D. E. & Powell, H. M., 1947. J. Chem. Soc. 208 - - 216
Palin, D. E. & Powell, H. M., 1948. J. Chem. Soc. 571 - - 216
Pant, A. K., 1965. Acta Cryst. **19,** 440 - - - 41
Patterson, A. L., 1934. Phys. Rev. **46,** 372 - - - 144
Patterson, A. L., 1935a. Z. Krist. **90,** 517 - 12, 144, 149, 166, 171, 172
Patterson, A. L., 1935b. Z. Krist. **90,** 543 - - 45, 147
Patterson, A. L., 1944. Phys. Rev. **65,** 195 - - - 139, 162
Patterson, A. L., 1952. *Computing Methods and the Phase Problem in X-ray Crystal Analysis.* State College, Pennsylvania: X-ray Crystal Analysis Laboratory - - - - - - - 149
Pauling, L., 1929. J. Am. Chem. Soc. **51,** 1010 - - - 117
Pauling, L., Corey, R. B. & Branson, H. R., 1951. Proc. Nat. Acad. Sci. Washington **37,** 205 - - - - - 287
Pauling, L. & Shappell, M. D., 1930. Z. Krist. **75,** 128 - - 162
Pawley, G. S., 1963. Acta Cryst. **16,** 1204 - - - - 309
Pawley, G. S., 1964. Acta Cryst. **17,** 457 - - - 309, 310
Pawley, G. S., 1964. *See* Cochran, W. - - - - 314
Pease, R. S., 1955. *See* Bacon, G. E. - - - - 366
Peerdeman, A. F. & Bijvoet, J. M., 1956. Acta Cryst. **9,** 1012 - - 388
Peerdeman, A. F., van Bommel, A. J. & Bijvoet, J. M., 1951. Proc. Acad. Sci. Amst. **54,** 16 - - - - - - 385
Peiser, H. S., 1949. *See* Brown, C. J. - - - - 122
Penfold, B. R., 1952. *See* Cochran, W. - - - - 250
Pepinsky, R., 1947. J. App. Phys. **18,** 601 - - - - 106
Pepinsky, R., 1957. *See* Doyne, T. - - - - 392

Pepinsky, R., 1955. *See* Frazer, B. C. - - - - 351
Pepinsky, R., 1955. *See* Okaya, Y. - - - - 389
Pepinsky, R., 1961. *See* Okaya, Y. - - - 388, 389, 392
Pepinsky, R., 1953. *See* Vand, V. - - - - - 260
Pepinsky, R., 1956. *See* Vand, V. - - - - - 258
Pepinsky, R., 1957. *See* Vand, V. - - - - - 72
Perutz, M. F., 1956. Acta Cryst. **9,** 867 - - - 189, 192
Perutz, M. F., & Weiss, O., 1946. J. Chem. Soc. 438 - - - 202
Perutz, M. F., 1943. *See* Boyes-Watson, J. - - - - 201
Perutz, M. F., 1957. *See* Cullis, A. F. - - - - 222
Perutz, M. F., 1954. *See* Green, D. M. - - - - 189
Peterson, S. W., 1955. Nature **176,** 395 - - - - 388
Peterson, S. W., 1957. *See* Worsham, J. E. - - - 378, 379
Phillips, D. C., 1950. Research **3,** 573 - - - - 128
Phillips, D. C., Rogers, D. & Wilson, A. J. C., 1950. Acta Cryst. **3,** 398 - 142
Phillips, D. C., 1961. *See* Arndt, U. W. - - - - 231
Phillips, D. C., 1949. *See* Howells, E. R. - - - - 51
Phillips, D. C., 1950. *See* Howells, E. R. - - - 50, 65
Phillips, D. C., 1949. *See* Hughes, J. W. - - - - 114
Phillips, F. C., 1946. *Introduction to Crystallography*. London: Longmans Green - - - - - - 23, 27, 28, 118
Phragmen, G., 1925. *See* Westgren, A. - - - - 126
Pickart, S. J. & Nathans, R., 1961. Phys. Rev. **123,** 1163 - - 377
Pickart, S. J., 1963. *See* Nathans, R. - - - - 368
Pickworth, J., 1957. *See* Hodgkin, D. C. - - - - 227
Pilling, D. E., 1961. *See* Cruickshank, D. W. J. - 302, 340, 346, 347, 348
Pinnock, P. R. & Taylor, C. A., 1955. Acta Cryst. **8,** 687 - - 298
Posnjak, E., 1932. *See* Barth, T. F. W. - - - - 42
Post, B., 1961. *See* Sklar, N. - - - - - 378
Powell, H. M., 1957. *See* Palin, D. E. - - - - 216
Powell, H. M., 1948. *See* Palin, D. E. - - - - 216
Prins, J., 1930. *See* Coster, D. - - - - - 384
Prins, J., 1927. *See* Zernicke, F. - - - - - 144
Prosen, R. J., 1957. *See* Hodgkin, D. C. - - - - 227

Ramachandran, G. N., 1964. *Advanced Methods of Crystallography*. London: Academic Press - - - - - 198
Ramachandran, G. N. & Raman, S., 1959. Acta Cryst. **12,** 957 - - 392
Raman, S., 1959. *See* Ramachandran, G. N. - - - 392
Ramaseshan, G., 1964. *Advanced Methods of Crystallography*. London: Academic Press - - - - - - 394
Reed, H. J., 1962. *See* Kraut, J. - - - - - 179
Rees, A. L. G., 1958. *See* Cowley, J. M. - - - 358, 368
Reijen, van L. L., 1942. Physica, IX, **5,** 461 - - - - 330
Renninger, M., 1937. Z. Krist. **97,** 107 - - - - 30
Robertson, J. H., 1951. Acta Cryst. **4,** 63 - - - - 178
Robertson, J. H. & Beevers, C. A., 1950. Nature **165,** 690 - 202, 206
Robertson, J. H. & Beevers, C. A., 1951. Acta Cryst. **4,** 270 - - 178
Robertson, J. H., 1950. *See* Beevers, C. A. - - - 154, 157
Robertson, J. H., 1952. *See* Beevers, C. A. - - - - 181

Robertson, J. H., 1957. *See* Hodgkin, D. C. - - - - 227
Robertson, J. M., 1933. Proc. Roy. Soc. A. **141,** 594; **142,** 659 - 115, 197
Robertson, J. M., 1935a. J. Chem. Soc. 615 - - - 119
Robertson, J. M., 1935b. Proc. Roy. Soc. A. **150,** 348 - - 322
Robertson, J. M., 1935c. Proc. Roy. Soc. A. **150,** 106 - - - 74
Robertson, J. M., 1937. Phys. Soc. Rep. Prog. Phys. **4,** 332 - - 194
Robertson, J. M., 1945. Nature **155,** 645 - - - - 140
Robertson, J. M. & White, J. G., 1945. J. Chem. Soc., 607 - 135, 136
Robertson, J. M. & White, J. G., 1947a. J. Chem. Soc. 358 - - 63
Robertson, J. M. & White, J. G., 1947b. Proc. Roy. Soc. A. **190,** 329 - 293
Robertson, J. M. & Woodward, I., 1937a. Proc. Roy. Soc. A. **154,** 187 - 115
Robertson, J. M. & Woodward, I., 1937b. J. Chem. Soc. 219 - - 214
Robertson, J. M. & Woodward, I., 1940. J. Chem. Soc. 36 - 202, 203, 205
Robertson, J. M., 1948. *See* Abrahams, S. C. - - - 135
Robertson, J. M., 1949. *See* Abrahams, S. C. - - - 310
Robertson, J. M., 1947. *See* Dunitz, J. D. - - - - 142
Robertson, J. M., 1948. *See* Morrison, J. D. - - - 103
Robinson, G., 1944. *See* Whittaker, E. - - - 342, 344
Robinson, R. & Stephen, A. M., 1948. Nature **162,** 177 - - 215
Rogers, D., 1950. Acta Cryst. **3,** 455 - - - - 48
Rogers, D., Stanley, E. & Wilson, A. J. C., 1955. Acta Cryst. **8,** 383 - 65
Rogers, D. & Wilson, A. J. C., 1953. Acta Cryst. **6,** 439 - - 64
Rogers, D., 1957. *See* Grant, D. F. - - - - 252
Rogers, D., 1949. *See* Howells, E. R. - - - - 51
Rogers, D., 1950. *See* Howells, E. R. - - - 50, 65
Rogers, D., 1949. *See* Hughes, J. W. - - - - 114
Rogers, D., 1950. *See* Phillips, D. C. - - - - 142
Rogers-Low, B. W., 1949. *See* Crowfoot, D. 137, 199, 212, 216, 217, 292
Rollett, R. S. & Davies, D. R., 1955. Acta Cryst. **8,** 125 - - 304
Rossmann, M., 1960. Acta Cryst. **13,** 221 - - - - 189
Rumanova, I. M., 1954. Doklady Acad. Nauk., U.S.S.R. **98,** 399 - 252

Saito, Y., 1955. *See* Okaya, Y. - - - - - - 389
Sandler, S., 1963. *See* Hirshfeld, F. L. - - - - 309, 354
Sayre, D. M., 1949. M.Sc. thesis, Alabama Polytechnic Institute - 274
Sayre, D. M., 1951. Acta Cryst. **4,** 362 - - - - 101
Sayre, D. M., 1952. Acta Cryst. **5,** 60 - - - 234, 245, 246
Schmidt, G. M. J., 1963. *See* Hirshfeld, F. L. - - 309, 354
Schoening, F. R. L., 1957. *See* Herbstein, F. H. - - - 64
Schomaker, V., 1964. Private communication - - - 309
Schomaker, V., 1950. *See* Shoemaker, D. P. - - - 185, 187, 319
Schoone, J. C., 1948. *See* Bokhoven, C. - - - 202, 215, 224
Schoone, J. C., 1949. *See* Bokhoven, C. - - - 202, 215, 224
Schoone, J. C., 1951. *See* Bokhoven, C. - - 202, 215, 224, 230, 231
Schwartz, C. M., 1935. *See* Beevers, C. A. - - 113, 195
Senko, M. E., 1961. *See* Sklar, N. - - - - - 378
Shappell, M. D., 1930. *See* Pauling, L. - - - - 162
Shirane, G., 1959. *See* Nathans, R. - - - - - 363
Shoemaker, C. B., 1957. *See* Hodgkin, D. C. - - - 227

Westgren, A. & Phragmen, G., 1925. Phil. Mag. **50,** 311 - - 126
White, H. E., 1950. *See* Jenkins, F. A. - - - - 17
White, J. G., 1949. *See* Abrahams, S. C. - - - - 310
White, J. G., 1957. *See* Hodgkin, D. C. - - - - 227
White, J. G., 1945. *See* Robertson, J. M. - - - 135, 136
White, J. G., 1947a. *See* Robertson, J. M. - - - - 63
White, J. G., 1947b. *See* Robertson, J. M. - - - - 293
Whittaker, E. & Robinson, G., 1944. *The Calculus of Observation.* London:
Blackie & Son - - - - - 342, 344
Wilde, J. H. de, 1938. *See* MacGillavry, C. H. - - - 40
Wilkins, M. H. F., Stokes, A. R. & Wilson, H. R., 1953. Nature **171,** 738 287, 289
Wilkinson, M. K., Gingrich, N. S. & Shull, C. G., 1957. J. Phys. Chem.
Solids **2,** 289 - - - - - - 375
Williams, G., 1940. *See* Wood, R. G. - - - - 120
Willis, B. T. M., 1963. Proc. Roy. Soc. A. **274,** 122 and 134 - - 371
Willis, B. T. M., 1964. Journal de Physique **25,** 431 - - - 374
Willis, B. T. M., 1965. Acta Cryst. **18,** 75 - - - - 373
Wilman, H., 1939. *See* Charlesby, H. - - - - 312
Wilson, A. J. C., 1942. Nature **150,** 152 - - - - 73
Wilson, A. J. C., 1949. Acta Cryst. **2,** 318 - - - 48, 49, 62
Wilson, A. J. C., 1950a. Acta Cryst. **3,** 258 - - - 48, 53
Wilson, A. J. C., 1950b. Acta Cryst. **3,** 397 - - - 142
Wilson, A. J. C., 1951. Research **4,** 141 - - - 49, 58
Wilson, A. J. C., 1956. Acta Cryst. **9,** 143 - - - - 64
Wilson, A. J. C., 1962. *X-ray Optics.* London: Methuen - - 364
Wilson, A. J. C., 1949. *See* Hughes, J. W. - - - - 114
Wilson, A. J. C., 1950. *See* Phillips, D. C. - - - - 142
Wilson, A. J. C., 1953. *See* Rogers, D. - - - - 64
Wilson, H. R., 1953. *See* Wilkins, M. H. F. - - 287, 289
Wilson, S. A., 1964. *See* Bacon, G. E. - - - - 368
Witte, H. & Wolfel, E., 1955. Z. Phys. Chem. **3,** 296 - - - 330
Witte, H. & Wolfel, E., 1958. Rev. Mod. Phys. **30,** 51 - - 105, 330
Wolfel, E., 1955. *See* Witte, H. - - - - - 330
Wolfel, E., 1958. *See* Witte, H. - - - - 105, 330
Wollan, E. O., 1951. *See* Shull, C. G. - - - - 360
Wood, R. G. & McCale, C. H., 1940. J. Sci. Instr. **17,** 225 - - 119
Wood, R. G. & Williams, G., 1940. Proc. Roy. Soc. A. **177,** 144 120
Woodward, I., 1937a. *See* Robertson, J. M. - - - 115
Woodward, I., 1937b. *See* Robertson, J. M. - - - - 214
Woodward, I., 1940. *See* Robertson, J. M. - - - 202, 203, 205
Woolfson, M. M., 1953. Acta Cryst. **6,** 838 - - - - 63
Woolfson, M. M., 1954. Acta Cryst. **7,** 61 - - - 201, 253
Woolfson, M. M., 1956. Acta Cryst. **9,** 804 - - - - 203
Woolfson, M. M., 1957. Acta Cryst. **10,** 116 - - - 253
Woolfson, M. M., 1958a. Acta Cryst. **11,** 4 - - - 246, 256
Woolfson, M. M., 1958b. Acta Cryst. **11,** 277 - - - 246
Woolfson, M. M., 1958c. Acta Cryst. **11,** 393 - - - 261
Woolfson, M. M., 1960. Computing Methods: Glasgow Conference - 255
Woolfson, M. M., 1961. *Direct Methods in Crystallography.* Oxford: O.U.P.
- - 234 247

Woolfson, M. M., 1954. *See* Cochran, W. - - - 259, 260
Woolfson, M. M., 1955. *See* Cochran, W. - - - - 249
Woolfson, M. M., 1961. *See* Dutta, S. N. - - - - 293
Woolfson, M. M., 1952. *See* Lipson, H. - - - 62, 278
Woolfson, M. M., 1963. *See* Main, P. - - - 235, 248, 264
Wooster, W. A., 1938. *Crystal Physics.* Cambridge: C.U.P. - - 119
Wooster, W. A., 1953. Rep. Prog. Phys. **16,** 62 - - - 389
Wooster, W. A., 1962. *Diffuse X-ray reflexions from crystals.* Oxford: O.U.P. - - - - - - - - 312
Wooster, W. A., 1951. *See* Henry, N. F. M. - - - 119
Worsham, J. E., Levy, H. A. & Peterson, S. W., 1957. Acta Cryst. **10,** 319 - - 378, 379
Wrinch, D. M., 1939. Phil. Mag. **27,** 98 - - - 14, 154, 162
Wrinch, D. M., 1946. *Fourier Transforms and Structure Factors.* Cambridge, Mass.: A.S.X.R.E.D. - - - - - - 278
Wunderlich, J. A., 1961. *See* Jacobson, R. A. - - 169, 181
Wyckoff, H. W., 1959. *See* Bodo, G. - - - - 189

Zachariasen, W. H., 1952. Acta Cryst. **5,** 68 - - - 234, 249
Zernicke, F. & Prins, J., 1927. Z. Phys. **41,** 184 - - - 144

SUBJECT INDEX